A-level Mathematics

A-level Mathematics

F. G. J. Norton

HLT Publications

HLT PUBLICATIONS
200 Greyhound Road, London W14 9RY

First published 1994

ISBN 0 7510 0248 8

British Library Cataloguing-in-Publication.

A CIP Catalogue record for this book is available from the British Library.

Photoset by Parker Typesetting Service, Leicester
Printed and bound in Great Britain.

Preface

The A-level Mathematics examination now contains many syllabus alternatives and different modules. This book will be found suitable for candidates offering the Common Core Pure Mathematics, together with either extra Pure Mathematics or Mechanics or some elementary Probability and Statistics. There is a detailed list of contents so that readers can find the different topics easily, and they should select those that are required for their examinations.

Recent years have seen a welcome increase in the number of candidates taking A-level Mathematics. Many of these come from a wider educational background than previously, and care is taken to make at first only realistic demands on the algebra of the readers. In particular, topics like inequalities, quadratic equations, indices and logarithms, elementary probability and statistics, which can easily fall between GCSE and A-level courses, are introduced carefully, and little prior knowledge is demanded of the reader. Notes are given at the beginning of each chapter, to illustrate the contents of that chapter and to remind the reader afterwards of the more important results of that chapter.

Many of the questions towards the end of each chapter are very similar to those set in current A-level papers but questions from past papers have not been used, so that candidates can attempt past papers set by their Boards, for practice, and will not find that they have already answered some of the questions in them.

F.G.J.N.

Contents

1 Functions 1

Definition 3
Inverse function 4
Inverse trig functions 6
Composite functions 7
Even and odd functions 8
Periodic functions 9

2 The quadratic function 13

Solving a quadratic equation 15
Completing the square 15
Finding a formula 15
The roots of a quadratic equation 16
Maximum and minimum values of a quadratic function 16
Solution of two simultaneous equations: one linear, one quadratic 17
Symmetric functions of the roots of a quadratic equation 18

3 The factor theorem, indices and logarithms 23

The factor theorem 25
Repeated factors 26
Indices 26
Summary of the laws of indices 27
Logarithms 27
Changing the base of logarithms 28
Rationalising the denominator 29
Equations containing surds 30
Use of logarithms to determine the relation between two variables 30

4 Induction 35

Induction 37

41 **5 Series**

44 Arithmetic series
44 Sum of an arithmetic series
45 Geometric series
45 Sum of a geometric series
45 Sum to infinity
47 Convergent series
48 Binomial series
49 Expansion when x is large
49 Use of the binomial theorem to find approximations
50 Logarithmic series
51 Exponential and trigonometric series

55 **6 Partial fractions**

57 Equations and identities
58 Partial fractions
62 Applications of partial fractions

67 **7 Inequalities and curve sketching**

70 Inequalities
73 Curve sketching
73 Polynomials of the form $y=a(x-b)(x-c)(x-d)$
74 Some common curves
75 Translations
75 Transformations
76 Summary
78 The graph of $y=(x-b)/(x-a)$
79 The curve $y=ax/(x^2+a^2)$
80 Curves described by the products of functions

83 **8 Arrangements and selections**

85 Arranging n objects in a straight line
85 Arranging r objects chosen from n
85 Arranging n objects, r of which are identical
86 Selecting r objects from n different objects
86 Selecting any number of objects from n
87 Relations between the binomial coefficients

9 Structure 89

Binary operations 91
Closure 91
Commutative operations 91
Associative operations 92
Identity element 92
Inverse element 92
Group: definition 93
Order of an element, order of a group 93
Cyclic groups, generators 94
Isomorphic groups 94
Group of symmetries, group of permutations 95

10 Plane Cartesian coordinates: the straight line and circle 99

The distance between two points 101
The midpoint of the line joining two points 101
The point dividing a line-segment in the ratio $\lambda : \mu$ 102
The centroid of a triangle 102
Equation of a straight line 103
The straight line with given gradient m 104
The straight line in intercept form 104
Parallel and perpendicular lines 104
The angle between two straight lines 105
The equation of a circle 105
Equation of the tangent at (x',y') 106

11 Parabola and rectangular hyperbola 109

Definition of a parabola 111
Translation of axes 111
Tangent with given gradient m 112
Tangent at the point (x',y') 112
Normal to a parabola 113
Rectangular hyperbola: definition 113
Symmetry of the rectangular hyperbola 114
Asymptotes of a rectangular hyperbola 115
The equation of a rectangular hyperbola, given the asymptotes 116
The tangent at (x',y') 116
The equation of the normal 116

119 **12 Ellipse and hyperbola**

122 Ellipse and hyperbola: definitions
122 The equation of an ellipse
122 The equation of a hyperbola
123 Symmetry of an ellipse
123 Sum of the focal distances of an ellipse
123 Equation of the tangent at (x',y')
124 Equation of the normal at (x',y')
124 Tangent to an ellipse with given gradient m
125 Hyperbolae: foci, directrices and asymptotes
126 Equations of tangent and of normal

129 **13 Parametric forms**

131 Circle
131 Equation of the tangent
132 Parabola
132 Equation of the tangent
133 Equation of the normal
134 Equation of a chord
134 The rectangular hyperbola $x=ct$, $y=c/t$
135 Equation of the tangent
135 Equation of the normal
137 The ellipse
137 Equation of tangent and of normal
138 The semi-cubical parabola

141 **14 Polar coordinates**

143 Polar coordinates: pole and axis
144 The curve $r=a(1+\cos\theta)$
144 The curve $r^2=a^2\cos 2\theta$
144 The straight line $r=p\,\mathrm{cosec}\,(\theta-\alpha)$
145 The circle $r=2a\cos\theta$
146 The spirals $r=a\theta$, $r=ae^{k\theta}$
147 The area of a sector

149 **15 Trigonometry I**

152 Definition of the trigonometric functions
154 General solution of the equation $\sin\theta=\sin\alpha$
154 General solution of the equation $\cos\theta=\cos\alpha$
154 General solution of the equation $\tan\theta=\tan\alpha$
156 Radian measure

The sine formula 157
The cosine formula 158

16 Trigonometry II 161

Sums and products formulae 163
Double angle formulae 164
Identities 166
Half angle formulae 168

17 Complex numbers 171

Introduction 173
Complex conjugate 173
Operations on complex numbers 173
Equality of complex numbers 174
Representation in an Argand diagram 175
Product and quotient of two complex numbers 176
Powers of complex numbers 176
Loci 177
Algebraic method 180

18 Matrices 183

Matrices 186
Transpose 186
Determinant of a 2×2 matrix 186
Inverse of a 2×2 matrix 187
Geometrical transformation in a plane 187
Transformation of a straight line 189
Mapping a straight line onto itself 190
Determinant of a 3×3 matrix 191
Minors and cofactors 192
Adjoint of a matrix 192
Inverse of a 3×3 matrix 193

19 Vectors 195

Vectors 198
Magnitude and direction of a vector 199
Parallel vectors and equal vectors 200
Addition and subtraction of vectors 201
Section theorem 203
Geometrical theorems 205
Equation of a straight line 207

210 The scalar product
210 Parallel and perpendicular vectors
211 The angle between two vectors
211 Equation of a straight line
212 Equation of a plane perpendicular to a given vector **n**
213 Equation of a plane through three points
214 Alternative method

219 **20 Differentiation**

221 The gradient of a curve
222 Notation
223 Other derivatives
223 Composite functions
224 Products and quotients
225 Limit of $(\sin x)/x$ as $x \to 0$
225 Derivative of $\sin x$
226 Derivative of $\tan x$
226 Derivative of $\sec x$
226 Derivative of $\sin 2x$
227 Derivative of logarithmic functions
227 Derivative of exponential functions
228 Derivative of a function given implicitly
230 Parametric relations

235 **21 Applications of differential calculus**

238 Maxima and minima
240 Use of second derivative
240 Summary
241 Maximum and minimum values
241 Rates of change
242 Small increments

245 **22 Integration**

248 Integration
248 Notation
249 Trigonometric integrals
249 Logarithmic integrals
250 Partial fractions
250 Inverse trigonometric integrals
251 Integrals requiring substitution
252 Integration by parts
254 Areas of regions

Summary 257
Volume of solid of revolution 259
Summary 260
Mean value 261

23 Differential equations 267

Differential equations 269
Exponential functions 269
Separable variables 270
Equations requiring substitution 271
Second-order differential equations 273
Trigonometric functions 274
Second-order differential equations with a constant 275

24 Numerical methods 279

Approximations to integrals: trapezium rule 282
Simpson's rule 282
Maclaurin's theorem 285
Taylor's theorem 286
Newton–Raphson method for finding successive approximations to a root of an equation 286
Other iterative methods 288

25 Displacement, velocity, acceleration 293

Displacement and distance 295
Velocity and speed 295
Acceleration 295
Constant acceleration formulae 295
Graphical illustrations 296
Variable acceleration 298
Force as a function of displacement 299
Displacement as a function of velocity 300
Power 301

26 Use of vector notation 305

Displacement, velocity, acceleration 307
Relative velocity 308
Forces 309
Application of scalar product 309
Momentum and impulse 310
Kinetic energy 310
Work and power 310

315 **27 Direct impact**

318 Newton's experimental law

321 **28 Projectiles**

323 Time of flight
323 Range on a horizontal plane
323 Maximum range on a horizontal plane
324 Greatest height
326 Impact with a vertical wall
326 Range on an inclined plane
327 Particle bouncing on an inclined plane
329 Equation of the trajectory
329 Direction of motion

333 **29 Motion in a circle**

336 Accleration towards the centre
336 Use of parameters
337 Motion in a horizontal circle
339 Motion in a vertical circle

343 **30 Elasticity**

345 Hooke's law
345 Energy in a stretched spring
345 Springs and strings
345 Further examples

349 **31 Friction**

351 Laws of friction

357 **32 Composition and resolution of forces, moments of a force**

360 Addition of forces
360 Composition of forces
361 Moment of a force
362 Rigid bodies in equilibrium

33 Centre of mass 365

Centre of gravity 368
Centre of mass 368
Centroid 368
Centre of mass of a rod 369
Use of symmetry 371

34 Probability 375

Definition 377
Mutually exclusive events 377
Independent events 377
Dependent events 377
Addition law 378
Application of Venn diagrams 379
Conditional probability 379
Product law 380
Use of tree diagrams 381
Binomial distribution 383
Geometric distribution 384

35 Statistics 387

Some definitions 389
Frequency 389
Summary 391
Working zero 392
Measures of spread, dispersion 393
Grouped data 395
Continuous variable 396
Cumulative frequency curve 398
Median and quartiles 399
Upper boundary 399

Answers 401

Index 437

Functions 1

Definition 3

Inverse function 4

Inverse trig functions 6

Composite functions 7

Even and odd functions 8

Periodic functions 9

Notes

A **function** maps one element in a set (the domain) into one and only one element in another set (the range).

The **composite function** fg means 'first find the image under g, then the image of that under f',
e.g. if f: $x \rightarrow \sin x$ and g: $x \rightarrow 2x$,
fg: $x \rightarrow \sin 2x$ and gf: $x \rightarrow 2 \sin x$
The alternative notation $f \circ g$ is sometimes used.

The **inverse** of fg is $(g^{-1})(f^{-1})$, usually written $g^{-1}f^{-1}$

An **even** function f is such that $f(x) = f(-x)$; its graph is symmetrical about Oy. Examples of even functions are

$$f{:}x \rightarrow x^2, \qquad f{:}x \rightarrow \cos x, \qquad f{:}x \rightarrow e^{-x^2}$$

An **odd** function f is such that $f(x) = -f(x)$; its graph is symmetrical about the origin. Examples of odd functions are

$$f{:}x \rightarrow x, \qquad f{:}x \rightarrow \sin x \qquad f{:}x \rightarrow 1/x$$

A **periodic** function f is such that $f(x) \equiv f(x+a)$. If a is the smallest number for which this is true, the function f is said to have period a. Examples of periodic functions are

$$f{:}x \rightarrow \sin x, \text{ period } 2\pi, \text{ since } \sin x \equiv \sin(x+2\pi) \equiv \sin(x+4\pi) \ldots$$
$$f{:}x \rightarrow \tan x, \text{ period } \pi, \text{ since } \tan x \equiv \tan(x+\pi) \equiv \tan(x+2\pi) \ldots$$

Definition

A function maps any one element x in a set (usually called the domain, D) into one and only one element (usually denoted by y, the image of x) in another set (called the range).* A function may map one element in the domain into one and

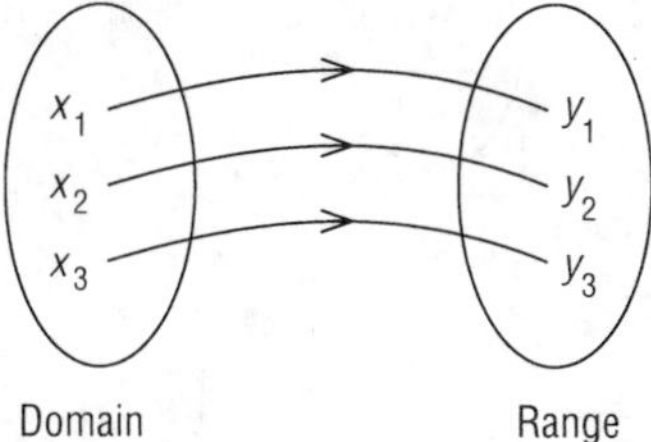

Figure 1.1

only one element in the range; this is a one-to-one mapping. Alternatively, a function may map several elements in the domain into one element in the range; this is a many-to-one mapping. For example, the function that maps every element in the domain into its reciprocal is written f:$x \rightarrow 1/x$ or $y=1/x$. This function maps 2 into $\frac{1}{2}$, $\frac{1}{4}$ into 4, $-\frac{1}{3}$ into -3, etc., and is an example of a one-to-one function. The function which maps every element in the domain into its square is written f:$x \rightarrow x^2$, or $y=x^2$, and maps both 1 and -1 into 1, both 2 and -2 into 4, etc., and is an example of a many-to-one function.

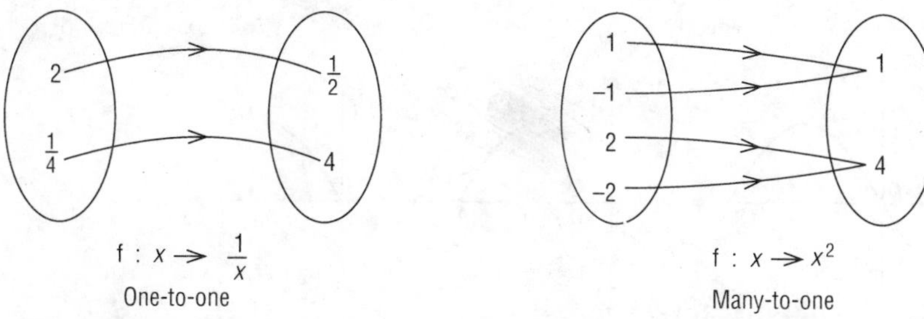

Figure 1.2

Whether a function is one-to-one or many-to-one may depend on the domain over which the function is defined. If the sine function f:$x \rightarrow \sin x°$ is defined over the domain $\mathbb{R}$, the set of all real numbers, then 30, 150, 390 . . ., -210 all map into $\frac{1}{2}$, and it is a many-to-one function. But if the domain is restricted to $\{x: 0 \leqslant x \leqslant 90\}$, then only 30 maps into $\frac{1}{2}$, and the function is one-to-one. This set $\{x: 0 \leqslant x \leqslant 90\}$ is not the only set for which the function is one-to-one. When the domain is $\{x: 90 \leqslant x \leqslant 180\}$ the function is still one-to-one, with range $\{y: 0 \leqslant y \leqslant 1\}$;

*It is now generally agreed that the terms 'function' and 'mapping' mean exactly the same.

when the domain is $\{x: 0 \leqslant x \leqslant 30\}$ the function is again one-to-one, but the range is now $\{y: 0 \leqslant y \leqslant \frac{1}{2}\}$.

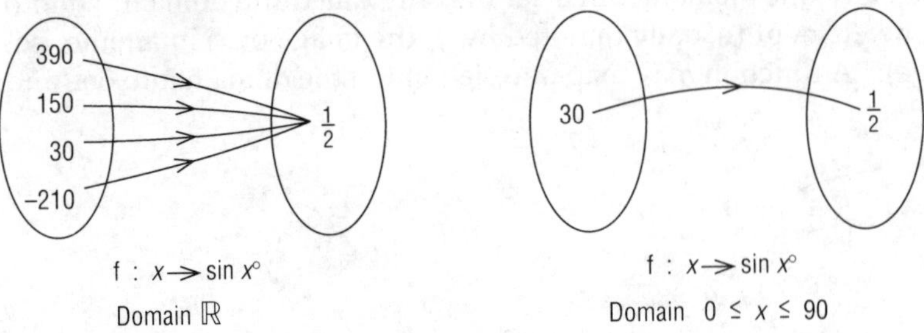

Figure 1.3

This can be seen easily from the graph of the sine function over different domains (Figure 1.4).

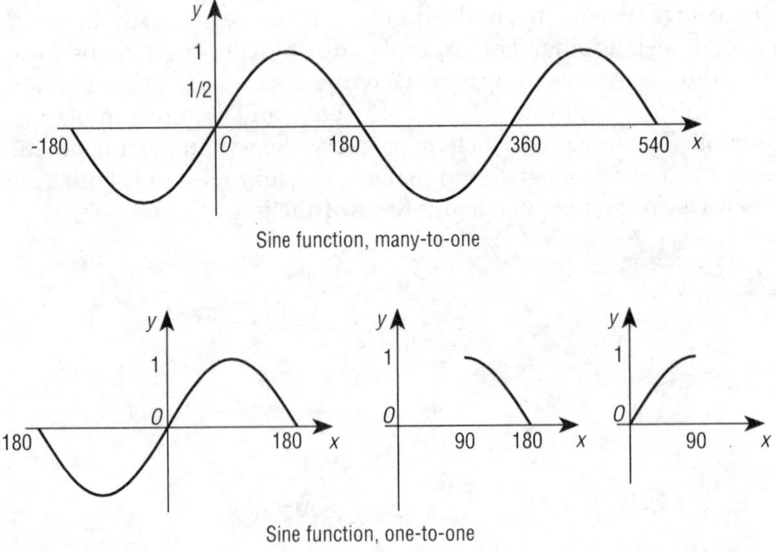

Figure 1.4

Inverse function

If a function f maps an element x in the domain into an element y in the range, the function that maps y back into x is called the inverse function, written f^{-1}. Since there must be a unique image under a function, only one-to-one functions have inverses. We can deduce from a graph whether there is an inverse function, for we can see whether or not one and only one value of x corresponds to any one value of y. Thus for $y=1/x$, a one-to-one function, there is always an inverse function; for $y=x^2$, if the domain is $\mathbb{R}$, the function is many-to-one, so there is not an inverse function, but if the domain is $\mathbb{R}^+$, the set of positive numbers, the function is one-to-one, and there is an inverse function, written $f^{-1}:x \rightarrow \sqrt{x}$.

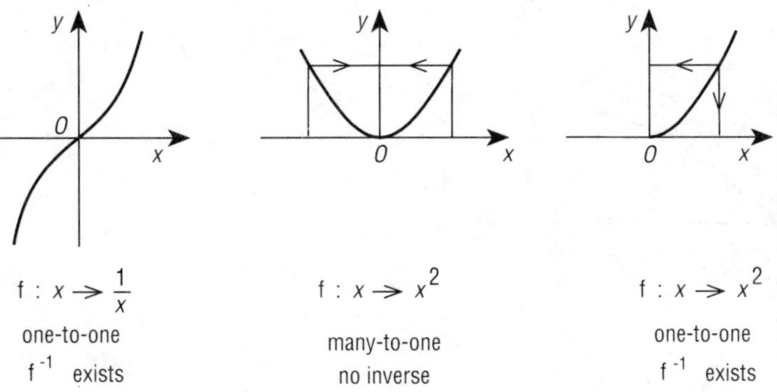

Figure 1.5

The use of the letter y to denote an element in the range enables the relation to be written in the form $y=f(x)$, and does enable us to find the inverse function easily. Thus if $y=1/x$, $x=1/y$, so that if $f:x \rightarrow 1/x$, $f^{-1}:y \rightarrow 1/y$. Again if $f:x \rightarrow 2x+3$ write $y=2x+3$ whence $y-3=2x$, $x=\frac{1}{2}(y-3)$ and the inverse function is written $f^{-1}:y \rightarrow \frac{1}{2}(y-3)$ or $f^{-1}:x \rightarrow \frac{1}{2}(x-3)$.

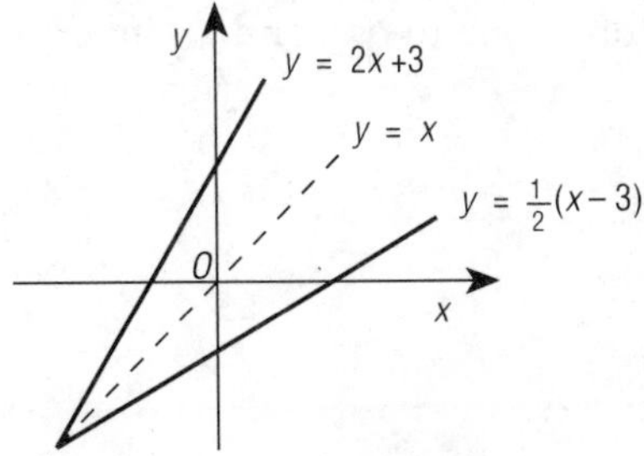

Figure 1.6

The inverse function, when graphed, is always the reflection of the original function in the line $y=x$. This is obvious with simple functions like $y=1/x$ and $y=x^2$; Figure 1.6 illustrates this relation when the function is $y=2x+3$.

Inverse trig functions

The inverse of the sine function, sin x, is now usually written arcsin x (or sometimes invsin x), to prevent confusion between $\sin^{-1}$ and $1/\sin x$, though $\sin^{-1}$ is often seen on calculators. A similar notation is used for the other trig functions.

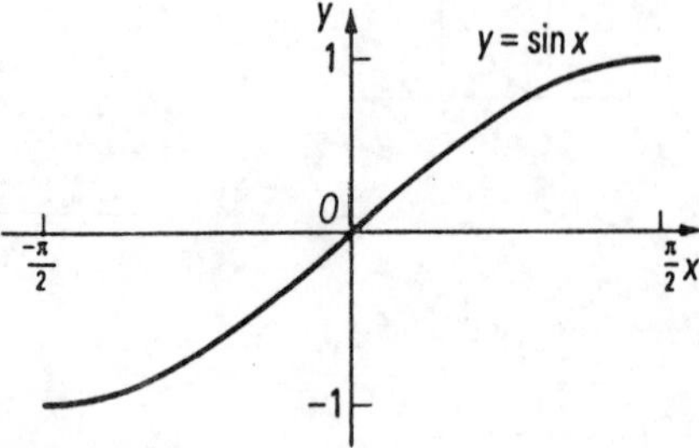

Figure 1.7

We can see from Figure 1.7 that if the domain is $\{x:-\pi/2 \leqslant x \leqslant \pi/2\}$ and the range the set $\{y:-1 \leqslant y \leqslant 1\}$, then the function $f:x \to \sin x$ has an inverse. The values for x in this case are called the **principal values**. One can see the restrictions on the domain that are built into any calculator; use of, for example, the invsin button produces one and only one image because the domain is restricted by the calculator.

Considering the function $f:x \to \cos x$, Figure 1.8 shows that if the domain is $0 \leqslant x \leqslant \pi$ and the range $-1 \leqslant y \leqslant 1$, then the function is one-to-one and an inverse function exists.

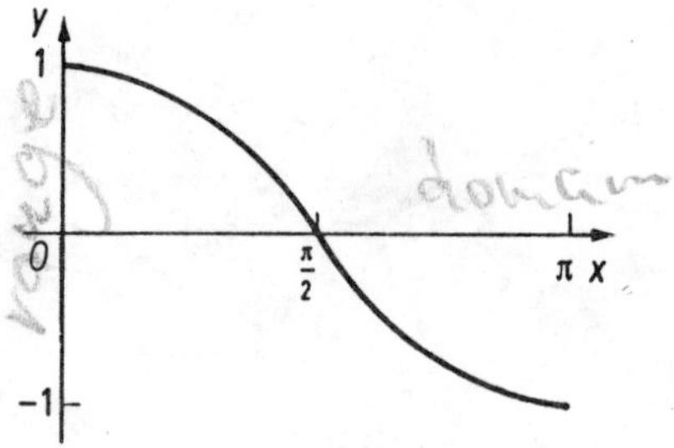

Figure 1.8

Exercise 1.1

1 Find the image of each of the elements $\{-2, -1, 1, 2\}$ under the given functions:

(a) $f:x \to 3x$, (b) $f:x \to x-3$, (c) $f:x \to 1-x$, (d) $f:x \to 1/x$, (e) $f:x \to 1/x^2$,

(f) $f{:}x \to x^2$, (g) $f{:}x \to 1-x^2$, (h) $f{:}x \to 2^x$, (i) $f{:}x \to \sin(90x)°$,
(j) $f{:}x \to \cos(90x)°$.

2 Which of the functions defined in Q.1 are one-to-one?

3 Find the inverse function of each of the one-to-one functions in Q.1.

4 Given that the domain D is the set of positive integers, show by a sketch that $f{:}x \to 1+x^2$ is a one-to-one mapping, and give the inverse function f^{-1}.

5 If the domain is the universal set, what is the range of $f{:}x \to \sin x°$? If the domain of x is $0 \leqslant x \leqslant 30$, what is now the range?

Composite functions

If we apply first a function $f{:}x \to f(x)$, then a function $g{:}y \to g(y)$, they form a composite function. This is usually written gf, but the

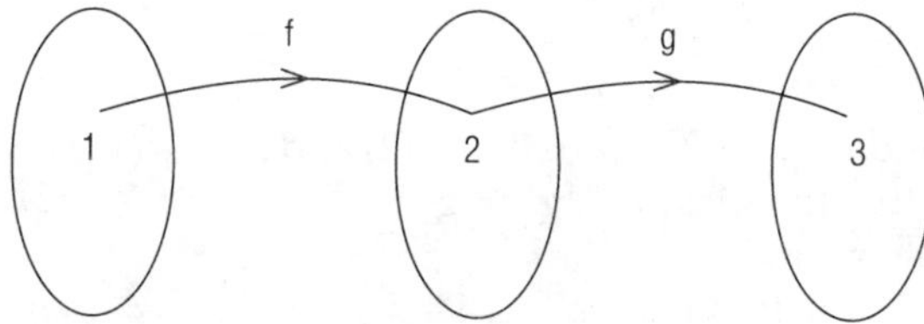

Figure 1.9

notations g.f, g∘f and g[f(x)] are sometimes used. For example, if $f{:}x \to 2x$ and $g{:}x \to 5-x$, then f(1)=2 and gf(1)=5−2=3.

Notice that for these functions, fg(1)=f(4)=8, which is not equal to gf(1). In general, fg(x) ≠ gf(x). When finding the inverse of a composite function, we also have to note the order in which the functions are operating.

Example. If $f{:}x \to 2x$ and $g{:}x \to x-3$, find
(a) gf(3) and fg(3)
(b) $g^{-1}f^{-1}(3)$ and $f^{-1}g^{-1}(3)$
(c) $g^{-1}f^{-1}(0)$ and $f^{-1}g^{-1}(0)$

(a) f maps 3 into 6, then g maps 6 into 3, so that gf(3)=g(6)=3. But g maps 3 into 0 and f maps 0 into 0, so fg(3)=f(0)=0.

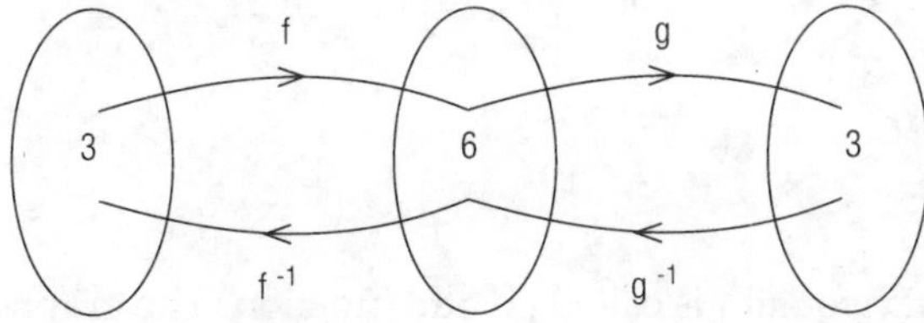

Figure 1.10

(b) Since $f:x \to 2x$, $f^{-1}:x \to \frac{1}{2}x$; since $g:x \to x-3$, $g^{-1}:x \to x+3$
so $g^{-1}f^{-1}(3)=g^{-1}(3/2)=9/2$,
and $f^{-1}g^{-1}(3)=f^{-1}(6)=3$.

(c) $g^{-1}f^{-1}(0)=g^{-1}(0)=3$,
and $f^{-1}g^{-1}(0)=f^{-1}(3)=3/2$.

Notice that gf maps 3 into 3 and $f^{-1}g^{-1}$ maps 3 back into 3, whereas fg maps 3 into 0 and $g^{-1}f^{-1}$ maps 0 back into 3.

NB. gf(x) means 'first find the image of x under f, then the image of f(x) under g'.

The composite function gf can be written as a single function h, for
since $f:x \to 2x$ and $g:x \to x-3$, $gf(x)=g(2x)=2x-3$,
$h:x \to 2x-3$
Similarly, $fg(x)=f(x-3)=2(x-3)$,
so H=fg is such that $H:x \to 2(x-3)$

Exercise 1.2

1 If $f:x \to 3x$ and $g: \to x+2$, find
(a) gf(2) and fg(2), (b) $g^{-1}f^{-1}(8)$ and $f^{-1}g^{-1}(8)$, (c) $g^{-1}f^{-1}(12)$ and $f^{-1}g^{-1}(12)$.

2 If $f:x \to x^2$ and $g:x \to 1/x$, show that fg=gf and $f^{-1}g^{-1}=g^{-1}f^{-1}$.

3 If $f:x \to 2x$, $g:x \to x+3$ and $h:x \to x^2$, find
(a) hgf(2) and fgh(2), (b) $f^{-1}g^{-1}h^{-1}(49)$ if domain is $\mathbb{R}^+$.

4 If $f:x \to x+2$ and $g:x \to x^2$, find as a single mapping
(a) fg, (b) gf.

5 If $f:x \to x^2$ and $g:x \to 3x-2$, find the one value of f for which $gf(x)=fg(x)$.

Even and odd functions

If f(x) denotes the image under f of x, a function f such that $f(-x)=f(x)$ for all x is called an **even** function. The graph of an even function is symmetrical about the line $x=0$. Examples of even functions are $f:x \to 1-x^2$; $f:x \to \cos x$; $f:x \to e^{-x^2}$ (Figure 1.11).

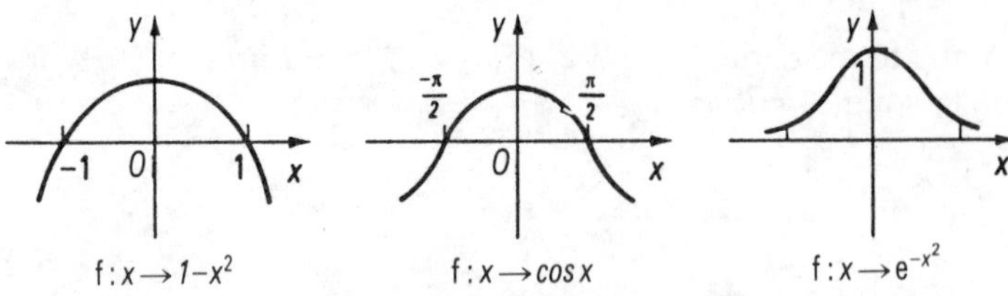

Figure 1.11

A function f such that $f(-x)=-f(x)$ for all x is called an **odd** function. The graph of an odd function is symmetrical about the origin. Examples of odd functions are $f:x \to x$; $f:x \to x^3$ and $f:x \to \sin x$ (Figure 1.12).

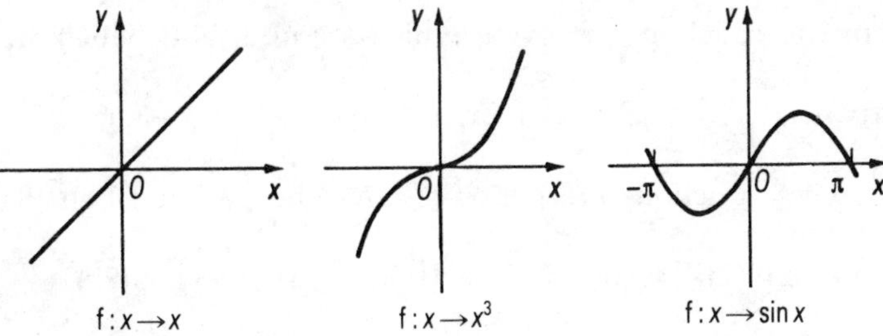

Figure 1.12

Periodic functions

A function f such that f:$x+a$)=f(x) for **all** x is said to be periodic, period a. The most important periodic functions are f:$x \to \sin x$ and f:$x \to \cos x$ (period 2π), f:$x \to \tan x$ (period π). Figure 1.13 shows two other period functions.

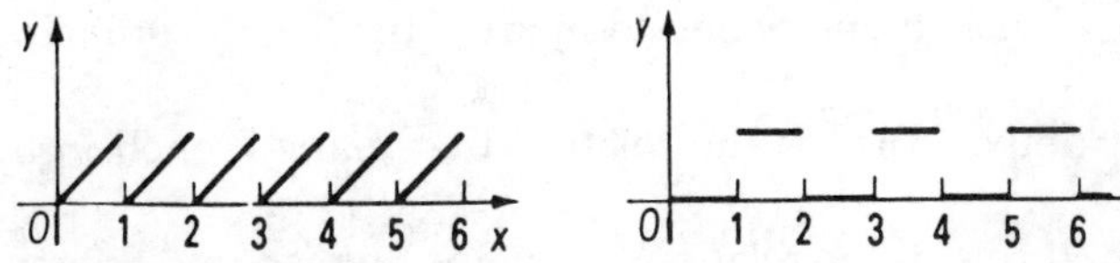

Figure 1.13

Example. Find whether the function f:$x \to \sin(x^2)$ is even or odd, and whether or not it is periodic.

Since $f(-x)=\sin(-x^2)=\sin(x^2)=f(x)$, the function f is even, although the sin function is odd.

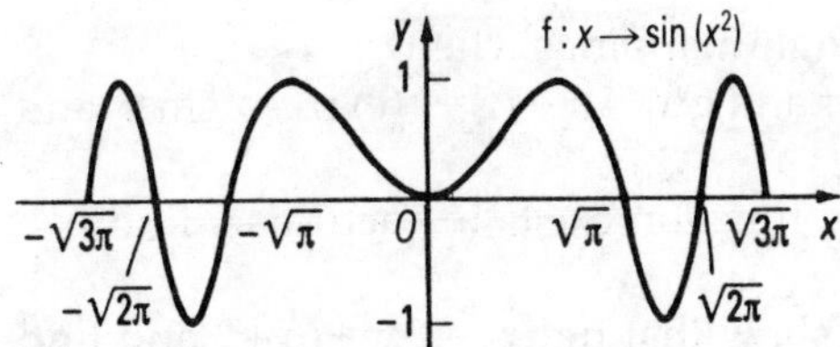

Figure 1.14

To see whether the function is periodic, we know the sin function is periodic, period 2π, but unequal intervals of x are required to give equal intervals of x^2, so this function is not periodic. These properties are illustrated in Figure 1.14.

Exercise 1.3

1 Which of the following functions are even, which are odd, and which are neither?
(a) $f:x \to 2x^2$, (b) $f:x \to 2/x$, (c) $f:x \to \sin 2x$, (d) $f:x \to \sin(x+30)°$,
(e) $f:x \to \cos \frac{1}{2}x$.

2 Which of the following functions are periodic? Give the period when the function is periodic.
(a) $f:x \to x+1$, (b) $f:x \to \sin(2x)°$, (c) $f:x \to \cos(\frac{1}{2}x)°$, (d) $f:x \to \tan(2x)°$,
(e) $f:x \to \sin(x+30)°$.

Miscellaneous exercise 1.4

1 The table below is part of that issued by The Post Office in 1991 to show the relation between the mass of a packet in grammes and the postal charge for first-class post in pence.

Not over	60 g	24p
60 g but not over	100 g	36p
100 g but not over	150 g	45p
150 g but not over	200 g	54p

(a) Is the relation many-to-one, one-to-one or one-to-many? (b) Give the domain x and the range y.

2 (a) If the domain is 'un, deux, trois', is the relation that maps French into English a function?
(b) If the domain is 'one, two, three', is the relation that maps English into French a function?

3 If the domain and range are both $\mathbb{R}^+$, which of the following functions are one-to-one?
(a) $f:x \to x^3$, (b) $f:x \to x^4$, (c) $f:x \to (x-1)^2$, (d) $f:x \to (\sin x°)^2$,
(e) $f:x \to 1/x^2$.

4 Give a possible domain and range so that each of the following functions has an inverse:
(a) $f:x \to (x-1)^2$, (b) $f:x \to (x+2)^2$, (c) $f:x \to \sin 2x°$, (d) $f:x \to (\sin x°)^2$,
(e) $f:x \to 1/x^2$.

5 If h=fg and H=gf, write h and H as single mappings when
(a) $f:x \to 3x$ and $g:x \to x+2$, (b) $f:x \to x^2$ and $g:x \to x+1$, (c) $f:x \to \sin x°$ and $g:x \to x^2$.

6 If the domain is such that the inverse function exists in each case, find h^{-1} and H^{-1} for each pair of functions in Q.5.

7 If $f:x \to x+1$, $g:x \to x^2$ and $h:x \to 3x$, show that $hgf:x \to 3x^2+6x+3$ and find fgh.

8 Find functions as in Q.7 such that $fgh:x \to \dfrac{1}{(x+2)^2}$.

9 If $f:x \to 2x$ and $g:x \to x^2$ and $h:x \to 3x+1$, find the two values of x for which $gf(x)=h(x)$.

10 Functions f and g are defined over the domain $1 \leqslant x \leqslant 5$, where $f:x \to x^2$ and $g:x \to \frac{1}{(x+2)}$.
(a) Find the range of each function.
(b) Write fg and gf each as a single function.
(c) Find the domain of each of fg and gf.
(d) Find the inverse functions f^{-1} and g^{-1}.

Revision exercise 1.5

NB. The notation $\sin x°$ indicates that x is a real number and the 'angle' is in degrees; the notation $\sin x$ indicates that the 'angle' is in radians.

1 Sketch the function defined by

$$f:x \to -1 \text{ if } x<-1$$
$$\to x \text{ if } -1 \leqslant x \leqslant 1$$
$$\to 1 \text{ if } 1<x$$

(a) Is there an inverse function?
(b) Is f even or odd or neither?

2 If the domain is $\mathbb{R}_0^+$, the set of all non-negative real numbers, and $f:x \to e^x$, find the range of f, and the inverse function f^{-1}.

3 Are the following functions even, odd or neither? Find the inverse function when it exists.

(a) $f:x \to 1+x^2$,
(b) $f:x \to x(1+x^2)$,
(c) $f:x \to x \sin x$,
(d) $f:x \to x \cos x$,
(e) $f:x \to \frac{1}{1+x^2}$,
(f) $f:x \to \frac{x}{1+x^2}$,
(g) $f:x \to \frac{x}{1-x^2}$,
(h) $f:x \to x\sqrt{(1+x^2)}$,
(i) $f:x \to e^{x^2}$,
(j) $f:x \to e^{-x^2}$.

4 A function f is defined by $f:x \to x^2+ax+b$. Find a and b, given that $f(1)=2$ and $f(2)=8$.

5 A function f is defined by $f:x \to x^2+4x+5$. Find the range when the domain is $\mathbb{R}$.

6 Given $f(x)=3x$, $g(x)=x+1$ and $h(x)=e^x$, express each of the following functions as composite functions in f, g and h:
(a) $3(e^x+1)$, (b) $3e^x+1$, (c) e^{3x+1}.

7 The function f is defined over the domain $\mathbb{R}$ by $f:x \rightarrow e^x+1$.
(a) Find f^{-1}.
(b) Find the domain of f^{-1}.
(c) Sketch f and f^{-1}.

8

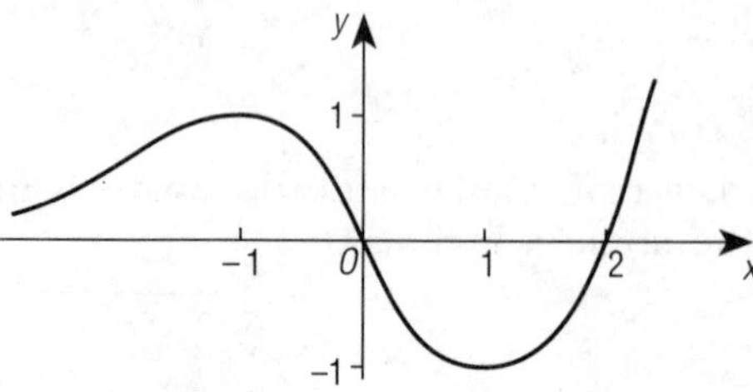

Figure 1.15

Figure 1.15 shows a rough sketch of the curve with equation $y=f(x)$. Sketch on separate axes
(a) $y=f(x+1)$, (b) $y=f(x)+1$, (c) $y=-f(x)$, (d) $y=[f(x)]^2$, (e)* $y=|f(x)|$.

9 Functions f, g and h are defined over $\mathbb{R}^+$ by
$f(x)=x^2$, $g(x)=x+1$, and $h(x)=1/x$
Sketch on separate clearly-labelled diagrams the graphs of
(a) $y=f(x)$, (b) $y=g(x)$, (c) $y=g[g(x)]$, (d) $y=f[h(x)]$, (e) $y=h[f(x)]$.

10 Functions f and g are defined over $\mathbb{R}^+$ by $f:x \rightarrow x+1$ and $g:x \rightarrow \ln x$. Sketch on the same diagrams
(a) f and f^{-1}, (b) fg and $g^{-1}f^{-1}$, (c) gf and $f^{-1}g^{-1}$.

*$y \equiv |f(x)| = f(x)$ when $f(x) \geqslant 0$
$= -f(x)$ when $f(x) < 0$

The quadratic function 2

Solving a quadratic equation 15

Completing the square 15

Finding a formula 15

The roots of a quadratic equation 16

Maximum and minimum values of a quadratic function 16

Solution of two simultaneous equations: one linear, one quadratic 17

Symmetric functions of the roots of a quadratic equation 18

Notes

The quadratic equation $ax^2+bx+c=0$ has

two real distinct roots if $b^2 > 4ac$

equal roots if $b^2 = 4ac$

and no real roots if $b^2 < 4ac$

The sum of the roots is $-b/a$: the product of the roots is c/a.

The graph is concave upwards if a is positive, downwards if a is negative.

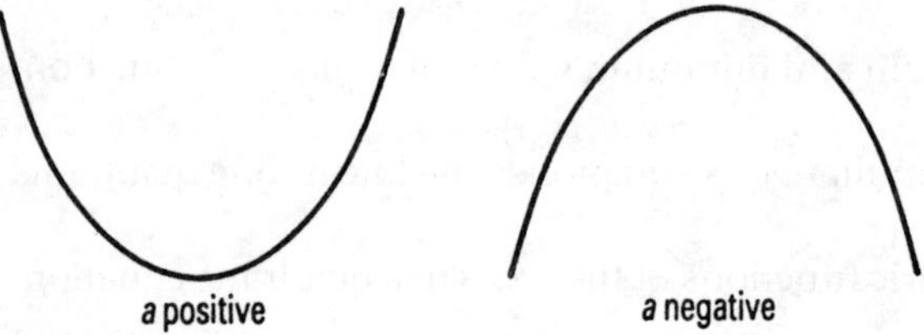

Figure 2.1

Solving a quadratic equation

Many calculators have the facility to solve quadratic equations merely by comparing the equation given with $ax^2+bx+c=0$ and identifying the values a, b and c. When such a calculator is available, it should, of course, always be used. The method of completing the square, on which the traditional 'formula' depends, should be understood, however, for there are many useful applications of this.

Completing the square

Since $(x+3)^2=x^2+6x+9$, the expression $x^2+6x+10$ can be written

$$x^2+6x+10=x^2+6x+9+1$$
$$=(x+3)^2+1$$

This form, a perfect square and a constant, has many uses in calculus and other branches of mathematics. In particular, here we can see that since a perfect square is never negative $x^2+6x+10\geqslant 1$, the minimum value 1 occurring only when $x+3=0$, i.e. $x=-3$.

In general, since $(x+a)^2=x^2+2ax+a^2$, to write x^2+bx+c as a perfect square and a constant, we find half the coefficient of x. Here,

$$x^2+bx+c=(x+\tfrac{1}{2}b)^2+c-\tfrac{1}{4}b^2$$

If the coefficient of x^2 is other than 1, take out a factor a.

Example. Write as a perfect square and a constant:
(a) $x^2-8x-17$, (b) $2x^2-8x-17$.

(a) $x^2-8x-17 =(x-4)^2-17-16$, as half the coefficient of x is -4,

$$=(x-4)^2-33$$

(b)
$$2x^2-8x-17=2[x^2-4x-17/2]$$
$$=2[(x-2)^2-17/2-4]$$
$$=2[(x-2)^2-25/2]$$
$$=2(x-2)^2-25$$

Finding a formula

Since
$$ax^2+bx+c=a\left(x^2+\frac{bx}{a}\right)+c$$
$$=a\left(x+\frac{b}{2a}\right)^2+c-\frac{b^2}{4a}$$

$$ax^2+bx+c=0 \text{ only if } \frac{b^2}{4a}\geqslant c, \text{ i.e. } b^2-4ac\geqslant 0$$

The expression b^2-4ac is called the discriminant of the quadratic. If $b^2-4ac>0$, the quadratic equation has two real distinct roots; if $b^2-4ac = 0$, the quadratic equation has two equal roots; and if $b^2-4ac < 0$, the quadratic equation has no real roots.

If $$ax^2+bx+c = 0$$

$$\left(x+\frac{b}{2a}\right)^2 = \frac{b^2-4ac}{4a^2}$$

i.e. $$x = \frac{-b\pm\sqrt{b^2-4ac}}{2a}$$

a formula which enables us to solve any quadratic equation.

The roots of a quadratic equation

A quadratic equation whose roots are 2 and 3 is

$$(x-2)(x-3) = 0$$

which can be written $x^2-5x+6 = 0$

Notice that the sum of the roots is -5 and the product is 6. In general, the equation whose roots are α and β can be written

$$(x-\alpha)(x-\beta) = 0$$

which can be expanded $x^2-(\alpha+\beta)x+\alpha\beta = 0$.

If the coefficient of x^2 is a number other than 1, we write

$$ax^2+bx+c = a[x^2+(b/a)x+c/a]$$

so that $$a[x^2+(b/a)x+c/a] = a[(x-\alpha)(x-\beta)] = a[x^2-(\alpha+\beta)x+\alpha\beta]$$

Again, the sum of the roots is $-b/a$ and the product is c/a.

Example. Find the values of x for which $2x^2-5x-2=0$

Comparing this equation with $ax^2+bx+c=0$, we have $a=2$, $b=-5$ and $c=-2$. Substituting in the formula,

$$x = \frac{-(-5)\pm\sqrt{(-5)^2-4(2)(-2)}}{2(2)}$$

$$= \frac{5\pm\sqrt{41}}{4}$$

$$= 2.85 \text{ or } -0.35, \text{ to 2 d.p.}$$

Check: Note that the sum of the roots is 2.5, and $-b/a=5/2=2.5$; the product of the roots is $-0.35\times2.85=-0.9975$, and $c/a=-2/2=-1$.

Maximum and minimum values of a quadratic function

Writing ax^2+bx+c as $a(x+b/2a)^2+c-b^2/4a$, we see that if a is positive, $ax^2+bx+c\geqslant c-b^2/4a$

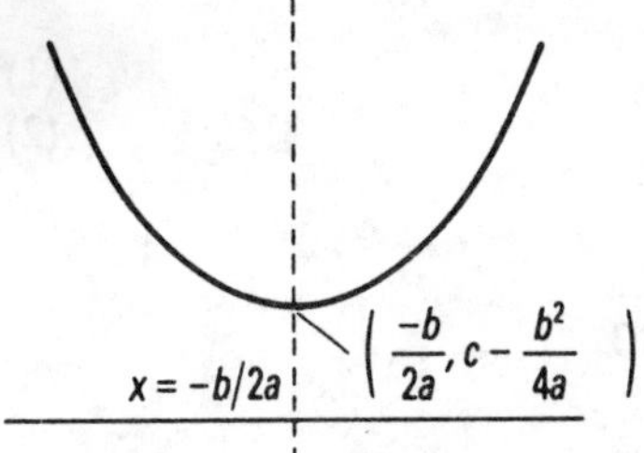

Figure 2.2

equality occurring only when $x=-b/2a$; if a is negative, then $ax^2+bx+c \leqslant c-b^2/4a$, equality again occurring only when $x=-b/2a$.

Example. Find the least value of $2x^2+12x+7$.

$$\begin{aligned} 2x^2+12x+7 &= 2(x^2+6x)+7 \\ &= 2(x+3)^2-18+7 \\ &= 2(x+3)^2-11 \end{aligned}$$

Since $(x+3)^2$ is a perfect square, it is never negative. Therefore, $2x^2+12x+7 \geqslant -11$, the least value, -11, occurring only when $x=-3$.

Exercise 2.1

1 Solve the following quadratic equations, giving the solutions to an appropriate degree of accuracy:
(a) $2x^2-4x-1=0$, (b) $x^2-4x-4=0$, (c) $x^2+5x+2=0$, (d) $3x^2-4x-5=0$, (e) $2x^2+7x-10=0$, (f) $5x^2+3x-1=0$.

2 Write down the sum and product of the roots of each of the quadratic equations:
(a) $2x^2+6x-11=0$, (b) $x^2-7x-13=0$, (c) $x^2-2x-8=0$, (d) $x^2+5x+10=0$.

3 Write each quadratic expression $f(x)$ in the form $a(x+b)^2+c$:
(a) $x^2+10x+29$, (b) $x^2+10x+21$, (c) $x^2-10x-21$, (d) $2x^2+10x+40$, (e) $2x^2+10x+25$, (f) $7-2x-x^2$, (g) $25-10x-x^2$, (h) $25-10x-2x^2$.

4 Find the maximum or minimum value of each of the expressions in Q.3, and give the value of x for which that maximum or minimum occurs.

5 Sketch the graph of each of the quadratic functions $f(x)=0$ given in Q.3. Mark each axis of symmetry and write down its equation.

Solution of two simultaneous equations: one linear, one quadratic

To solve a pair of simultaneous equations, one of which is linear and the other quadratic, find one variable in terms of the other from the linear equation and substitute in the quadratic.

Example. Solve the simultaneous equations

$x+2y=3$ (1)

$x^2+3y^2=13$ (2)

From equation (1), $x=3-2y$ (3)

Substituting in (2), $(3-2y)^2+3y^2=13$

$\therefore$ $9-12y+4y^2+3y^2=13$

i.e. $7y^2-12y-4=0$

i.e. $(y-2)(7y+2)=0$

$y=2$ or $-2/7$.

Substituting $y=2$ in (3), $x=-1$

Substituting $y=-2/7$ in (3), $x=3\frac{4}{7}$

The solutions are

$x=-1$ and $y=2$

or $x=3\frac{4}{7}$ and $y=-\frac{2}{7}$.

NB. Take care to pair the solutions correctly: it is not sufficient to say just

$x=-1$ or $3\frac{4}{7}$, $y=2$ or $-\frac{2}{7}$

Exercise 2.2

1 Solve for x and y

(a) $3x+y=5$, $x^2+y^2=5$, (b) $3x+y=5$, $x^2+2xy+y^2=9$, (c) $3x+y=5$, $xy=2$, (d) $2x-y=7$, $x^2+y^2=13$, (e) $2x+y=3$, $x^2+xy+y^2=21$.

2 Solve for x and y

(a) $3x+y=5$, $x^2+y^2=6$, (b) $2x+y=5$, $x^2+2xy-y^2=4$, (c) $4x-y=1$, $xy=7$.

3 Show there are no real solutions to the equations

$3x+y=5$, $4x^2+y^2=1$

4 Solve for x and y

$2x+y=5$, $x^2+2xy+y^2=9$

Illustrate your solutions by a sketch. [Hint: factorise $x^2+2xy+y^2$.]

5 Find the range of values of k for which there are real solutions to $x+y=k$, $x^2+y^2=9$. Illustrate your solution by a sketch.

Symmetric functions of the roots of a quadratic equation

If the roots of $ax^2+bx+c=0$ are α and β, we have seen that

$$ax^2+bx+c = a(x-\alpha)(x-\beta)$$
$$= a[x^2-(\alpha+\beta)x+\alpha\beta]$$

Equating the coefficients of x, $b=-a(\alpha+\beta)$, i.e. $\alpha+\beta=-b/a$

Equating constants $c=a\alpha\beta$ i.e. $\alpha\beta = c/a$,

thus

the sum of the roots of a quadratic is $-b/a$,
the product of the roots is c/a.

Given the quadratic equation, we can write down the sum and product of its roots, $-b/a$ and c/a, respectively; given the roots α and β, we can write down a quadratic equation

$$x^2-(\alpha+\beta)x+\alpha\beta=0$$

which has roots α and β.

Example 1. (a) The sum of the roots of the equation $3x^2+8x+5=0$ is $-8/3$, the product of the roots is 5/3.

(b) The quadratic equation whose roots are $\frac{1}{2}$ and 3 can be written $x^2-3\frac{1}{2}x+\frac{3}{2}=0$; it may be more convenient to write this as $2x^2-7x+3=0$.

Example 2. If the roots of $3x^2-4x-7=0$ are α and β, find the equation whose roots are $\alpha+1$, $\beta+1$.

Comparing $3x^2-4x-7=0$ with $ax^2+bx+c=0$, we see $\alpha+\beta=4/3$, $\alpha\beta=-7/3$.
We want the equation

$$x^2-(\alpha+1+\beta+1)x+(\alpha+1)(\beta+1)=0$$

Now $\alpha+1+\beta+1=\alpha+\beta+2=10/3$,
and $(\alpha+1)(\beta+1)=\alpha\beta+\alpha+\beta+1=-7/3+4/3+1=0$,
so the equation we require is

$$x^2-10/3x=0, \text{ i.e. } 3x^2-10x=0$$

If we had solved the first equation, we would have found the roots to be -1 and 7/3; thus the equation with roots one more than these has roots 0 and 10/3, and so must be $x(x-10/3)=0$, i.e. $3x^2-10x=0$. The method used in the example can be used if the roots are not rational, and even when the roots are not real.

Example 3. If the roots of $2x^2-5x+1=0$ are α and β, find an equation whose roots are α^2+1, β^2+1.

Comparing $2x^2-5x+1=0$
with $ax^2+bx+c=0$,

we see $$\alpha+\beta=\frac{5}{2}$$

$$\alpha\beta=\frac{1}{2}$$

Now $$\alpha^2+\beta^2=(\alpha+\beta)^2-2\alpha\beta$$

$$=\left(\frac{5}{2}\right)^2-2\left(\frac{1}{2}\right)$$

$$=\frac{21}{4}$$

$$\therefore \quad (\alpha^2+1)+(\beta^2+1)=\frac{21}{4}+2=\frac{29}{4},$$

and $$(\alpha^2+1)(\beta^2+1)=\alpha^2\beta^2+\alpha^2+\beta^2+1$$

$$=\left(\frac{1}{2}\right)^2+\frac{21}{4}+1=\frac{26}{4}$$

The required equation is

$$x^2-\frac{29}{4}x+\frac{26}{4}=0$$

i.e. $$4x^2-29x+26=0$$

Exercise 2.3

1 If α and β are the roots of $x^2-3x+1=0$, form an equation whose roots are
(a) $\alpha+1, \beta+1$, (b) $\frac{1}{\alpha}, \frac{1}{\beta}$, (c) $1+\frac{1}{\alpha}, 1+\frac{1}{\beta}$

2 Form an equation whose roots are each one more than the roots of $2x^2-3x-1=0$.

3 If α and β are the roots of $3x^2-x+5=0$, form an equation whose roots are
(a) α^2, β^2, (b) α^2+1, β^2+1, (c) $\frac{1}{\alpha^2}, \frac{1}{\beta^2}$.

4 Form an equation whose roots are the reciprocals of the roots of
(a) $3x^2+4x+13=0$, (b) $5x^2+4x+1=0$.

5 The roots of the equation $3x^2+4x-2=0$ are α and β. The roots of $3x^2+bx+c=0$ are $3\alpha+\beta$ and $\alpha+3\beta$ and $\alpha+3\beta$. Find b and c.

Miscellaneous exercise 2.4

1 Find the range of values of k if each of the following equations has two real roots:
(a) $x^2+2x+k=0$, (b) $3x^2-2x+k=0$, (c) $x^2-kx+1=0$, (d) $x^2+3x+1=k$.

2 If $x \in \mathbb{R}$, find the greatest value of
(a) $4-x^2$, (b) $4-(x-1)^2$, (c) $4+2x-x^2$, (d) $3+4x-x^2$.
Write down in each case the value of x which gives the greatest value for the expression.

3 If $x \in \mathbb{R}$, find the least value of each of the following expressions, and the value of x which gives that least value:
(a) x^2+4, (b) $(x+1)^2+3$, (c) x^2+2x+4, (d) x^2+4x+3.

4 Solve for x and y
(a) $3x+y=5, x^2+y^2=5$, (b) $3x+y=5, x^2+2xy+y^2=9$, (c) $3x+y=5, xy=2$.

5 Show that there are no real solutions to the equations
$$2x+y=4, 4x^2+y^2=4$$

6 Show that there are no real solutions to the equations
$$x+y=4, x^2+y^2=1$$
and illustrate this statement by a geometrical sketch.

7 Find the range of value of k for which there are solutions of
$$x+y=k, x^2+y^2=4$$
and illustrate your result geometrically.

8 If α and β are the roots of $x^2+4x+1=0$, form the equation whose roots are $\alpha+1$, $\beta+1$.

9 Form the equation whose roots are each one less than a root of the equation $x^2-5x-2=0$.

10 If the roots of $3x^2+4x-2=0$ are α and β, form the equation whose roots are $1/\alpha$ and $1/\beta$.

11 Form the equation whose roots are each the reciprocal of a root of $5x^2-4x-2=0$.
12 If α and β are the roots of $x^2-5x-1=0$, form the equation whose roots are α^2+1 and β^2+1.
13 Sketch the graph of $y=x^2-2x+2$ to show the least value of y if $x\in\mathbb{R}$. If x is restricted so that $x>2$, what is now the least value of y?
14 Find the range of values of k if the equation $x^2-2kx+k=0$ has real roots.
15 Find the values of k if the equation $x^2-2kx+k^2=1$ has real roots.
16 Find the values of k for which the equation $kx^2+2x+3=0$ has roots differing by 4.
17 Find the range of values of x for which $x+2y=1$ and $x^2-4y^2\leqslant 5$.
18 Solve simultaneously $2x+y=4$ and $2x^2=xy-1$.
19 The roots of the quadratic equation $x^2+px+q=0$ are α and β. If $\alpha-\beta=1$ and $\alpha^2+\beta^2=41$, find p and q.
20 The roots of the quadratic equation $x^2-3x+1=0$ are α and β. Find the quadratic equation whose roots are α^3/β and β^3/α.
21 If the roots of the equation $x^2+ax+b=0$ are α and $k\alpha$, show that $(k+1)^2b=ka^2$.
22 Given that the equations $x^2+ax+b=0$ and $x^2+3ax+4b=0$ have a common root, show that $9b=2a^2$.

The factor theorem, indices and logarithms 3

The factor theorem 25

Repeated factors 26

Indices 26

Summary of the laws of indices 27

Logarithms 27

Changing the base of logarithms 28

Rationalising the denominator 29

Equations containing surds 30

Use of logarithms to determine the relation between two variables 30

Notes

The factor theorem

When a polynomial f(x) is such that f(a)=0, ($x-a$) is a factor of f(x); conversely, if ($x-a$) is a factor of f(x), then f(a)=0.

When $(x-a)^2$ is a factor of f(x), so that ($x-a$) is a repeated factor, f(a)=0 and f′(a)=0.

When a polynomial f(x) is divided by $x-a$, the **remainder** is f(a).

Indices

The laws of **indices** are

$$a^m \times a^n = a^{m+n},\ a^m \div a^n = a^{m-n} \text{ and } (a^m)^n = a^{mn}$$

From these we deduce

$$a^0 = 1,\ a^{-m} = 1/a^m \text{ and } a^{1/m} = \sqrt[m]{a}, \text{ especially } a^{1/2} = \sqrt{a}$$

Logarithms

By definition of the log function, $\boldsymbol{y=a^x \Leftrightarrow x=\log_a y}$

e.g. since $100=10^2$, $\log_{10} 100=2$

From the laws of indices, we deduce

$$\log x + \log y = \log (xy);\ \log x - \log y = \log (x/y);\ \log (x^n) = n \log x$$

Change of base

$$\log_b x = \frac{\log_a x}{\log_a b}$$

The factor theorem

When a polynomial $f(x)$ is divided by a linear expression, say $x-a$, the remainder R will be a constant, for if there are any terms in x in the remainder, we can divide again by $x-a$. Thus

$$f(x)\equiv(x-a)\,Q(x)+R$$

where $Q(x)$ is the quotient. Since this is an identity, it is true for all values of x, so substitute $x=a$,

i.e. $\quad f(a)=0\times Q(a)+R$

$\therefore \quad R=f(a)$

If $x-a$ is a **factor** of $f(x)$, the remainder R will be zero, i.e.

$$f(A)=0$$

For example, take $f(x)=x^3-2x$. To see whether $x-2$ is a factor, we write

$$x^3-2x=(x-2)\,Q(x)+R$$

Put $x=2$ in both sides,

$$8-4=R$$

So $R\neq0$, and $x-2$ is not a factor of x^3-2x. But if we test whether $x-2$ is a factor of x^3-4x, we have

$$x^3-4x=(x-2)\,Q(x)+R$$

Now when $x=2$,

$$8-8=R$$

the remainder is zero, and $x-2$ is a factor of x^3-4x.

This result is most useful for finding linear factors of a polynomial using the property that if $x-a$ is a factor, $f(a)=0$.

NB. When the coefficient of the highest power in the polynomial is 1, any root of the equation $f(x)=0$ must be a factor of the constant term, e.g. if x^3+ax^2+bx+c has a linear factor $x-k$, k must be a factor of c.

Example. Find the linear factors of $x^3-6x^2+3x+10$.

Try the factors of the constant term, ±1, ±2, ±5. Denoting $x^3-6x^2+3x+10$ by $f(x)$,

$f(1)=(1)^3-6(1)^2+3(1)+10\neq0$

$\therefore \quad (x-1)$ is not a factor

$f(-1)=(-1)^3-6(-1)^2+3(-1)+10=0$

$\therefore \quad (x+1)$ is a factor

Similarly $\quad f(2)=0$, so $(x-2)$ is a factor

and $\quad f(5)=0$, so $(x-5)$ is a factor

Since $f(x)$ is a cubic there are only three linear factors, and since the coefficient of x^3 is 1,

$$x^3-6x^2+3x+10\equiv(x+1)(x-2)(x-5)$$

Repeated factors

If $(x-a)^2$ is a factor of $f(x)$,

$$f(x) \equiv (x-a)^2 Q(x)$$

Let $f'(x)$ denote the derived function, i.e. $f'(x) \equiv df/dx$,

$$\therefore \quad f'(x) \equiv (x-a)^2 Q'(x) + 2(x-a)Q(x)$$
$$\equiv (x-a)[(x-a)Q'(x) + 2Q(x)]$$

$\therefore$ $(x-a)$ is a factor of $f'(x)$

thus not only is $f(a)=0$, but also $f'(a)=0$.

Example. Find the values of constants A and B if $(x+1)^2$ is a factor of $2x^4+7x^3+6x^2+Ax+B$

If $\quad f(x)=2x^4+7x^3+6x^2+Ax+B$

$\quad f'(x)=8x^3+21x^2+12x+A$

Since $(x+1)$ is a factor of $f(x)$, $f(-1)=0$

i.e. $\quad 2(-1)^4+7(-1)^3+6(-1)^2+A(-1)+B=0$

$\quad A-B=1$

Since $(x+1)$ is also a factor of $f'(x)$, $f'(-1)=0$

i.e. $\quad 8(-1)^3+21(-1)^2+12(-1)+A=0$

$\quad A=-1$

Substituting $A=-1$ in (1), we have $B=-2$.

Exercise 3.1

1 Use the factor theorem to find the linear factors of
(a) x^2-5x+6, (b) x^2-x-12, (c) $x^3-6x^2+11x-6$, (d) x^4-5x^2+4,
(e) $x^4-3x^3+2x^2$.

2 Use the factor theorem to find one linear factor of each of the following:
(a) x^3-4x^2+3, (b) x^3-4x^2+3x, (c) x^3-4x^2+2x+1, (d) $x^5-4x^4+3x^3+x-1$,
(e) x^3+5x^2+3x-1.

3 Find the repeated factor of
(a) x^3-3x+2, (b) x^3+4x^2+5x+2, (c) $x^3-x^2-8x+12$, (d) $x^3-10x^2-15x-36$,
(e) $x^3+6x^2-15x-100$.

Indices

We write $a\times a\times a\times a$ as a^4, and, more generally, $a\times a\times a\times a \ldots a$, the product of n a's as a^n. Thus it follows that, for example,

$$a^2\times a^3=(a\times a)\times(a\times a\times a)=a^5$$

and $$a^3\div a^2=\frac{a\times a\times a}{a\times a}=a$$

and, in general, $$a^m\times a^n=a^{m+n}$$
$$a^m\div a^n=a^{m-n}$$

adding indices when multiplying and subtracting indices when dividing.

Since $a^m \div a^m = 1$, as they are the same terms,
and $a^m \div a^m = a^0$, subtracting indices, we can write

$$a^0 = 1$$

Since $a^{1/2} \times a^{1/2} = a^1$, adding indices

$$= a, \text{ the usual notation,}$$

$a^{1/2}$ is that term which, multiplied by itself, is equal to a, i.e. the square root of a.
Since $a^2 \times a^{-2} = a^0 = 1$,

$$a^{-2} = 1/a^2$$

and in general, $a^{-n} = 1/a^n$

Summary of the laws of indices

These can be summarised:

$$a^m \times a^n = a^{m+n};\ a^m \div a^n = a^{m-n};\ (a^m)^n = a^{mn}$$

$$a^0 = 1;\ a^{-n} = 1/a^n;\ a^{1/n} = \sqrt[n]{a}$$

The reader will be familiar with positive integer indices; familiarity with the others can easily be obtained using a calculator.

Example. (a) $9^{1/2}=3$, (b) $64^{1/3}=4$, (c) $5^0=1$, (d) $5^{-1}=1/5=0.2$, (e) $10\,000^{1/4}=10$, (f) $100^{-1/2}=1/10=0.1$.

All these should be verified using the index key on a calculator.

Exercise 3.2

1 When $x=64$, evaluate
(a) $x^{1/2}$, (b) $x^{1/3}$, (c) $x^{-1/2}$, (d) $(x^{2/3})^{-1}$, (e) $(x^{-1})^{1/6}$.
2 When $x=125$, evaluate
(a) $x^{1/3}$, (b) x^{-1}, (c) $x^{-2/3}$, (d) $(x^{-1})^{1/3}$, (e) $(x^{1/3})^{-1}$.
3 Write in index form:
(a) $\sqrt{x}$, (b) $\sqrt[3]{x}$, (c) $\sqrt[3]{x^2}$, (d) $\dfrac{1}{x^2}$, (e) $\dfrac{1}{\sqrt{x}}$.
4 By writing $y=x^{1/2}$, solve $x-5x^{1/2}+6=0$.
5 By writing $y=x^{1/3}$, solve $x^{1/3}-5+4x^{-1/3}=0$.

Logarithms

The logarithmic function can be defined by saying if $y=a^x$, then $x=\log_a y$.
For example, since $1000=10^3$, $\log_{10} 1000=3$;
since $0.1=10^{-1}$, $\log_{10} 0.1=-1$
From the laws of indices we can deduce

$$\log_a x + \log_a y = \log_a(xy);\ \log_a x - \log_a y = \log_a\left(\frac{x}{y}\right)$$

and $\log_a(x^n) = n\log_a x$

The Napierian or natural logarithm $\log_e x$ is usually written $\ln x$; $\log_{10}x$ is usually written $\lg x$.

Example 1. Find the value of (a) $\log_2 \sqrt[3]{2}$, (b) $\log_4 \sqrt{2}$.

(a) Express $\sqrt[3]{2}$ as a power of 2.

Since $\sqrt[3]{2}=2^{1/3}$ and $\log_a(a^n)=n$

$$\log_2(2^{1/3})=\frac{1}{3}$$

(b) Express $\sqrt{2}$ as a power of 4.

Since $\sqrt{2}=2^{1/2}=4^{1/4}$

$$\log_4\sqrt{2}=\log_4(4)^{1/4}=\tfrac{1}{4}$$

Example 2. Express $\log_{10}x$ as a multiple of $\log_e x$

If $\log_{10}x=N$, $10^N=x$,

i.e. $\log_e(10^N)=\log_e x$

i.e. $N\log_e 10=\log_e x$

$$\log_{10}x=\frac{1}{\log_e 10}\log_e x$$

This can of course be written

$$\lg x=\frac{\ln x}{\ln 10}$$

Changing the base of logarithms

From the definition of a logarithm, we see that we can have logarithms to any base. On calculators we have logarithms base e and logarithms base 10 and we may find other bases useful at times.

If $\log_a x=N$, $x=a^N$

Then $\log_b x=\log_b a^N$

$=N\log_b a$

i.e. $N=\dfrac{\log_b x}{\log_b a}$

i.e. $\log_a x=\dfrac{\log_b x}{\log_b a}$

Example 1. $\log_3 8=\log_{10} 8/\log_{10} 3$

$=1.893$, to 4 s.f., by calculator.

Check: Since $3^2=9$, $\log_3 9=2$, so 1.893 is reasonable.

Example 2. $\ln 8=\ln 2\times\log_2 8$

$=3\ln 2$

This can be verified by calculator.

Exercise 3.3

1 Using a calculator, find, correct to 4 s.f.

(a) $\log_2 5$, (b) $\log_2 40$, (c) $\log_2 4000$, (d) $\log_3 2$, (e) $\log_3 6$, (f) $\log_3 18$, (g) $\log_3 36$.

2 Show that $\log_a b = 1/\log_b a$ for all values of a and b.

Rationalising the denominator

Since $(x-y)(x+y)=x^2-y^2$,

$$\frac{1}{\sqrt{2}+1}=\frac{(\sqrt{2}-1)}{(\sqrt{2}+1)(\sqrt{2}-1)}$$

$$=\frac{\sqrt{2}-1}{2-1}$$

$$=\sqrt{2}-1$$

This sometimes helps in evaluating expressions containing surds, as below, but more important, helps when manipulating complex numbers.

Example 1. Find the sum of

$$\frac{1}{\sqrt{2}+1}+\frac{1}{\sqrt{3}+\sqrt{2}}+\frac{1}{\sqrt{4}+\sqrt{3}}\cdots\frac{1}{\sqrt{100}+\sqrt{99}}$$

Using the result above, we can see that

$$\frac{1}{\sqrt{3}+\sqrt{2}}=\frac{(\sqrt{3}-\sqrt{2})}{(\sqrt{3}+\sqrt{2})(\sqrt{3}-\sqrt{2})}=\sqrt{3}-\sqrt{2}$$

$\therefore$ The sum of the series is

$$(\sqrt{2}-1)+(\sqrt{3}-\sqrt{2})+(\sqrt{4}-\sqrt{3})\ldots(\sqrt{100}-\sqrt{99})$$
$$=\sqrt{100}-1=9$$

Example 2. Write in the form $a+ib$

(a) $\frac{1}{2+i}$, (b) $\frac{1+2i}{2-i}$, (c) $\frac{2}{(3+i)^2}$

(a) Multiply numerator and denominator by $2-i$, the complex conjugate of $2+i$. Then

$$\frac{1}{2+i}=\frac{2-i}{(2+i)(2-i)}=\frac{2-i}{5}=\frac{1}{5}(2-i)$$

(b) The complex conjugate of the denominator is $2+i$, so

$$\frac{1+2i}{2-i}=\frac{(1+2i)(2+i)}{(2-i)(2+i)}=\frac{5i}{5}=i$$

We can check that $1+2i=i(2-i)$, so $\frac{1+2i}{2-i}=i$.

(c) We can either say $(3+i)^2=9+6i-1=8+6i$, and multiply numerator and denominator by $8-6i$, or we can multiply both by $(3+i)^2$ as below:

$$\frac{2(3-i)^2}{(3-i)^2(3+i)^2}=\frac{2(9-6i-1)}{(10)^2}=\frac{2(8-6i)}{100}=\frac{1}{25}(4-3i)$$

Equations containing surds

An equation that contains surds can often be expressed as a polynomial by squaring both sides of the equation, though we have to remember that the square of $+\sqrt{(x+a)}$ is also the square of $-\sqrt{(x+a)}$, so that the roots we obtain may not be the roots of the original equation. *Check that the roots obtained do satisfy the equation BEFORE it was squared.*

Example. Solve $x+\sqrt{x+1}=5$.

We must have the term containing the square root alone on one side of the equation, so rewrite it as

$$\sqrt{x+1}=5-x$$

Squaring both sides,
$$x+1=(5-x)^2$$
$$=25-10x+x^2$$

i.e.
$$x^2-11x+24=0$$
$$(x-3)(x-8)=0$$
$$x=3 \text{ or } 8$$

Checking, when $x=3$, $x+\sqrt{x+1}=3+\sqrt{4}=5$, so that $x=3$ is a a root of the original equation, but when $x=8$, $x+\sqrt{x+1}=8+\sqrt{9}\neq 5$, so that $x=8$ is *not* a root of the original equation. It can easily be seen that $x=8$ is a root of $x-\sqrt{x+1}=5$. Thus the only root of $x+\sqrt{x+1}=5$ is $x=3$.

Exercise 3.4

1 Find the exact value of

(a) $\dfrac{1}{\sqrt{3}+1}$, (b) $\dfrac{\sqrt{2}}{\sqrt{2}-1}$, (c) $\dfrac{\sqrt{5}}{3-\sqrt{5}}$

2 Write in the form $a+ib$

(a) $\dfrac{1}{2+i}$, (b) $\dfrac{2+i}{2-i}$, (c) $\dfrac{1-3i}{3+i}$, (d) $\dfrac{2+i}{4+3i}$, (e) $\dfrac{2+i}{(3-4i)^2}$

3 Solve the following equations:

(a) $x-\sqrt{x-1}=3$, (b) $x-2\sqrt{x-3}=3$, (c) $\sqrt{x-2}+\sqrt{x+3}=5$.

Use of logarithms to determine the relation between two variables

If two variables x and y are thought to be related by a law of the form $y=mx+c$, then points corresponding to pairs of values of x and y should lie on a straight line. If the relation between the variables is of the form $y=ax^n$, we can deduce that $\log y=\log a+n \log x$, so if $\log y$ is plotted against $\log x$, we should have a straight line graph whose intercept is $\log a$ and whose gradient is n.

Example. A certain company was started in 1950, and its annual profits at five-yearly intervals are given below:

1950	£250
1955	£1200
1960	£7000
1965	£40 000
1970	£105 000
1975	£1 000 000

If the annual profits are £y and the number of years after 1950 is n, is there a relation of the form $y=ax^n$?

If $y=ax^n$, $\log y=\log a+n \log x$. Here we know y and n, so plot $\log y$ against n. Figure 3.1 shows that all the points except one lie close to a straight line, so that apart from 1970, there does seem to be a relation of the form $y=ax^n$ between the annual profits and the number of years since the start of the company.

Since n is the number of years after 1950, the table of values is:

n	0	5	10	15	20	25
y	250	1200	7000	40 000	105 000	10^6
$\log y$	2.4	3.1	3.8	4.6	5.0	6

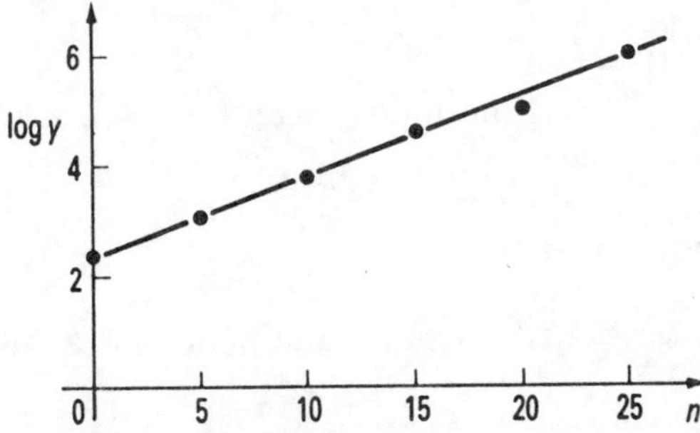

Figure 3.1

Exercise 3.5

1 Find the value of

(a) $\log_{10} 100$, (b) $\log_{10} 10\,000$, (c) lg 0.01, (d) lg 0.0001, (e) lg 1.

2 Find the value of

(a) $\log_2 8$, (b) $\log_2 32$, (c) $\log_2 \frac{1}{2}$, (d) $\log_2 \frac{1}{4}$, (e) $\log_2 1$.

3 Find the value of

(a) $\log_3 27$, (b) $\log_c c^3$, (c) $\log_a a^5$, (d) $\ln e^2$, (e) $\ln 1$.

4 Use logarithms to write each of the following in a linear form in $x, y, \log x$ or $\log y$:
(a) $y=ax^n$, (b) $xy=a$, (c) $x^ny=a$, (d) $ay=b^x$, (e) $a^y=bx$, (f) $a^y=kb^x$.
5 There is thought to be a relation of the form $P=kV^n$ between the volume V, in cm^3, and the pressure P, in suitable units of a given mass of gas. The following readings were taken:

V	100	120	140	160	180	200
P	39.3	30.6	24.5	19.7	16.6	14.1

Plot $\log P$ against $\log V$ to estimate values for k and n.
6 There is thought to be a relation of the form $y=ab^x$ between two variables x and y. The following readings have been taken:

x	1	2	3	4	5
y	6	20	63	200	600

Plot $\log y$ against x to obtain values for a and $\log b$. Hence find b.
7 There is thought to be a relation of the form $xy^n=a$ between two variables x and y. The following readings of x and y are available. Plot $\log y$ against $\log x$, and determine the values of a and n:

x	1	5	10	20	50
y	3	2	1.65	1.35	1.05

Miscellaneous exercise 3.6

1 Find the linear factors of $x^3-10x^2+23x-14=0$.
2 If $f(x)=x^3-13x^2+40x-36$, find $f'(x)$. Obtain the linear factors of $f'(x)$, and verify that one of them is a repeated factor of $f(x)$.
3 Find the value of k if $(x-2)$ is a factor of $x^3-3x^2+kx-10$.
4 Find the values of A and B if $(x-2)^2$ is a factor of
$$x^4-11x^2+Ax+B$$
5 Show that $(x+2)$ is a factor of $6x^4+11x^3-13x^2-16x+12$, and hence solve the equation
$$6x^4+11x^3-13x^2-16x+12=0$$
6 When $x=64$, evaluate
(a) $x^{1/2}$, (b) $x^{1/3}$, (c) x^{-2}, (d) $(x^{2/3})^{-1}$, (e) $(x^{-1})^{1/6}$.
7 Express in index form
(a) $\sqrt[4]{x}$, (b) $\frac{1}{x^3}$, (c) $\sqrt[3]{x^2}$, (d) $\sqrt[2]{x^3}$, (e) $\sqrt[3]{x^6}$.

8 Integrate with respect to x

(a) $\sqrt[4]{x}$, (b) $\sqrt[3]{x}$, (c) $\frac{1}{\sqrt{x}}$, (d) $\frac{1}{\sqrt[3]{x}}$, (e) $\sqrt[3]{x^2}$.

9 Find

$$\int \frac{1}{\sqrt{(x+1)}-\sqrt{x}}\,dx$$

10 Find the value of
(a) $\log_2 8$, (b) $\log_8 2$.

11 Find the value of a and b if
(a) $\log_a 3=27$, (b) $\log_b 2=8$.

12 Express $\log_5 x$ as a multiple of $\log_{10} x$. Hence find $\log_5 2$.

13 Find
(a) $\log_3 9$, (b) $\log_3 8$.

14 Find the value of the constants A and B if $x-1$ and $x-3$ are factors of $2x^4-11x^3+Ax^2+Bx-6$.

15 Find the values of the constants A and B if x^2-5x+6 is a factor of $x^4-6x^3+10x^2+Ax+B$.

16 Find the value of the constants A and B if $(x-2)^2$ is a factor of $2x^4+Ax^3+11x^2+Bx-4$.

17 If $x=16$ and $y=\frac{1}{25}$, find the value of
(a) $x^{1/2}$, (b) $x^{-1/2}$, (c) $xy^{1/2}$, (d) y^{-2}, (e) $x^{1/2}(x+1)$,
(f) $x^{-2}(x+9)^{1/2}$.

18 Find

(a) $\int x^{1/2}(x+1)dx$, (b) $\int \frac{x+1}{x^{1/2}}\,dx$,

(c) $\int \frac{x+1}{x^2}\,dx$, (d) $\int \frac{x+1}{x}\,dx$.

19 Find
(a) $\log_2\sqrt{8}$, (b) $\log_8\sqrt{2}$, (c) $\log_4(2\sqrt{2})$, (d) $\log_2\sqrt{4}$.

20 Which of the following statements are true for all values of a, x and y?
(a) $y=a^x \Leftrightarrow \ln y=x\ln a$,
(b) $y=a^x \Leftrightarrow \log_a y=x$,
(c) $y=(a^x)^2 \Leftrightarrow \ln y=2x\ln a$.

21 If $y=10^x$, which of the following would give a straight line graph?
(a) Plotting y against $\log x$.
(b) Plotting $\log y$ against $\log x$.
(c) Plotting $\log y$ against x.

22 Solve the equation

$$2x-\sqrt{(3x+1)}=6$$

23 Solve the equation

$$2\sqrt{2x}+\sqrt{5x-1}=7$$

Induction 4

Induction 37

Notes

To prove a result for **all** values of n, first suppose that it is true for **some one** specific value of n, say $n=k$,

e.g. to prove $\sum_{r=1}^{n} r=\frac{1}{2}n(n+1)$

if this is true for some **one** value of n, say $n=k$

$\sum_{r=1}^{k} r \equiv 1+2+3...+k=\frac{1}{2}k(k+1)$

Then the sum of the first $(k+1)$ integers, i.e. $\sum_{1}^{k+1} r$, is found by adding the $(k+1)$th integer on to what we think is the sum of the first k,

i.e. $\sum_{1}^{k+1} r=\frac{1}{2}k(k+1)+(k+1)$

$=\frac{1}{2}(k+1)(k+2)$

which we expect.

But the sum of the first one integer(s) is 1, which equals $\frac{1}{2}\times1\times1(1+1)$, so it is true when $n=1$.

Since it is true when $n=1$, it is true when $n=2$.

Since it is true when $n=2$...

So it is true for **all positive integral** values of n.

Induction

$$\begin{aligned} 1 &= 1=1^2 \\ 1+3 &= 4=2^2 \\ 1+3+5 &= 9=3^2 \\ 1+3+5+7 &=16=4^2 \end{aligned}$$

It looks possible that the sum of the first n odd integers is always equal to n^2.

The method of induction first requires that we have an idea of the result we wish to prove, and this will be given in an examination, of course. In this example, we guessed a possible conclusion from a few special cases.

The first n odd integers are 1, 3, 5,... $(2n-1)$, and the next odd integer, the $(n+1)$th, is $(2n+1)$. If our guess is correct, the sum of the first 10 odd integers is 100; the 11th odd integer is 21, so that the sum of the first 11 odd integers is 100+21, i.e. 121, which is 11^2, so that if our guess was correct for the first 10 odd integers, it is also correct for the first 11 odd integers.

Suppose that the guess is correct for the first k odd integers, i.e. $1+3+5\ldots(2k-1)=k^2$. Then the sum of the first $(k+1)$ odd integers is

$$\begin{aligned} &1+3+5+7\ldots+(2k-1)+(2k+1) \\ &\quad =k^2 \qquad\qquad + 2k+1 \\ &\quad =(k+1)^2 \end{aligned}$$

so that if the guess was correct for the first k odd integers, it is also correct for the first $(k+1)$ odd integers. But the 'sum' of the first one odd integer(s) is 1, i.e. 1^2, so the guess is true for the first one odd integer; therefore it is true for the first two odd integers. Since it is true for the first two odd integers, it is true for the first three odd integers; and so on for all positive integral values of n.

There are two essential stages of the proof by induction:

1 Suppose that the result is true for some one specific value of n, and carry out the operation (often adding the next term) to see whether it is true for the next value of n.

2 Find a starting value, e.g. the sum of the first two terms, the expansion of $(x+a)^2$, the angle-sum of a three-sided polygon (a triangle).

Example 1. Prove by induction that

$$\sum_{r=1}^{n} r^3 \equiv 1^3+2^3+3^3\ldots+n^3=[\tfrac{1}{2}n(n+1)]^2$$

Suppose this is true for some one specific value of n, and call this value k. Then the sum of the first k terms is

$$1^3+2^3+3^3\ldots+k^3=[\tfrac{1}{2}k(k+1)]^2$$

In this case, the sum of the first $(k+1)$ terms will be

$$\begin{aligned} &1^3+2^3+3^3\ldots+k^3+(k+1)^3 \\ &=[\tfrac{1}{2}k(k+1)]^2+(k+1)^3 \\ &=\tfrac{1}{4}(k+1)^2[k^2+4(k+1)] \end{aligned}$$

$$=\tfrac{1}{4}(k+1)^2(k^2+4k+4)$$
$$=\tfrac{1}{4}(k+1)^2(k+2)^2$$

which we expected, since this is the result obtained by writing $(k+1)$ in place of n in the formula. Thus if the formula is true for some one value of n, it will be true for the 'next' value of n. But $1^3=1=\tfrac{1}{4}(1)^2(2)^2$ so the formula is true when $n=1$, therefore it is true when $n=2$. Since it is true when $n=2$, it is true when $n=3$; since it is true when $n=3$, it is true when $n=4$, and so on for all positive integral values of n.

Example 2. Prove by induction that all numbers of the form $n(n+1)(n+2)$ are multiples of 6.

It often helps if we familiarize ourselves with the problem by trying simple numerical values of n first; here, when $n=1$, the number is $1\times2\times3=6$; when $n=2$, the number is $2\times3\times4=24$, a multiple of 6.

Suppose it is true for some one value of n, say $n=k$, so that $k(k+1)(k+2)$ is a multiple of 6, i.e. $k(k+1)(k+2)=6m$ where m is an integer. Then we want to show that $(k+1)(k+2)(k+3)$ is also a multiple of 6. Now

$$(k+1)(k+2)(k+3)=k(k+1)(k+2)+3(k+1)(k+2)$$
$$=6m+3(k+1)(k+2)$$

But if k is odd, $(k+1)$ is even; if k is even, so is $(k+2)$, so $(k+1)(k+2)$ contains one factor that is even, and therefore must be even, and $3(k+1)(k+2)$ is three times an even number, and so has a factor 6. Thus both terms on the right-hand side have a factor 6, so $(k+1)(k+2)(k+3)$ is a multiple of 6. But we found that this result was true when $n=2$, so it is true when $n=3$; since it is true when $n=3$, it is true when $n=4$, and so it is true for all positive integral values of n.

Example 3. Prove the binomial theorem, that if n is a positive integer

$$(x+y)=x^n+\binom{n}{1}x^{n-1}y+\binom{n}{2}x^{n-2}y^2+\ldots$$
$$\ldots+\binom{n}{r}x^{n-r}y^r+\ldots+x^n$$

where $$\binom{n}{r}\equiv{}^nC_r=\frac{n!}{r!(n-r)!}$$

If this is true for some one value of n, say $n=k$, then

$$(x+y)^k=x^k+\binom{k}{1}x^{k-1}y+\binom{k}{2}x^{k-2}y^2+\ldots+\binom{k}{r}x^{k-r}y^r+\ldots+y^k$$

Multiplying both sides of the equation by $(x+y)$ to obtain $(x+y)^{k+1}$

$$(x+y)^{k+1} = (x+y)\left(x^k+\binom{k}{1}x^{k-1}y+\binom{k}{2}x^{k-2}y^2+\dots\right.$$

$$\left.\dots+\binom{k}{r}x^{k-r}y^r+\dots+y^k\right)$$

$$=x^{k+1}+\binom{k}{1}x^k y+\binom{k}{2}x^{k-1}y^2+\dots+\binom{k}{r}x^{k-r+1}y^r+\dots+xy^k$$

$$+x^k y+\binom{k}{1}x^{k-1}y^2\dots$$

$$\dots+\binom{k}{r-1}x^{k-(r-1)}y^r+\dots+y^{k+1}$$

But $\binom{k}{1}+1=k+1=\binom{k+1}{1}$, and more generally

$$\binom{k}{r}+\binom{k}{r-1}=\binom{k+1}{r} \text{ (see page 87)}$$

$$\therefore \quad (x+y)^{k+1}=x^{k+1}+\binom{k+1}{1}x^k y+\binom{k+1}{2}x^{k+1}y^2+\dots$$

$$\dots+\binom{k+1}{r}x^{k+1-r}y^r+\dots+y^{k+1}$$

which is the form we expect.

$\therefore$ If it is true for some one value of n, it is true for the 'next'. But

$$(x+y)^2=x^2+2xy+y^2$$

$$=x^2+\binom{2}{1}xy+y^2$$

$\therefore$ It is true for $n=2$. Since it is true for the value $n=2$ it is true for all positive integral values of n greater than 2.

NB. Sometimes the case $n=1$ is so trivial that it may not be easy to see that any result being proved for general values of n is true even in that case, as when finding the sum of the first one terms in a series, and as here $(x+y)^1=x+y$.

Exercise 4.1

Prove by induction, n being always a positive integer:

1 $\sum_1^n r \equiv 1+2+3+4\dots n=\frac{1}{2}n(n+1)$

2 $\sum_1^n r \equiv 1^2+2^2+3^2+4^2+\dots n^2=\frac{1}{6}n(n+1)(2n+1)$

3 $\sum_1^n r(r+1) \equiv 1\times2+2\times3+3\times4\dots n(n+1)=\frac{1}{3}n(n+1)(n+2)$

4 $\sum_1^n r(r+2) \equiv 1\times3+2\times4+3\times5\dots n(n+2)=\frac{1}{6}n(n+1)(2n+7)$

5 $\sum_1^n r(r+1)(r+2) \equiv 1\times2\times3+2\times3\times4+3\times4\times5\dots n(n+1)(n+2)=\frac{1}{4}n(n+1)(n+2)(n+3)$

6 $\sum_1^n ap^r \equiv a+ap+ap^2+ap^3 \ldots ap^r = a\dfrac{p^{n+1}-1}{p-1}$

7 $\sum_1^n [a+(r-1)d] \equiv a+(a+d)+(a+2d)+(a+3d)\ldots = a+(n-1)d = \frac{1}{2}n[2a+(n-1)d]$

8 When £P is invested at r% per annum compound interest, the value of the investment, including interest after n years, is £$P\left(1+\frac{r}{100}\right)^n$.

9 All numbers of the form $3^{2n}+7$ are multiples of 8.

10 All numbers of the form 17^n-1 are multiples of 16.

11 x^n-1 is always divisible by $x-1$. Hint: write

$$\begin{aligned} x^{k+1}-1 &= x^{k+1}-x^k+x^k-1 \\ &= x^k(x-1)+x^k-1 \end{aligned}$$

12 x^n-y^n is always divisible by $x-y$.

13 $3^{4n+3}+53$ is a multiple of 80.

14 The sum of the interior angles of an n-sided polygon is $(2n-4)$ right angles.

15 If $\mathbf{A} = \begin{pmatrix} 1 & 1 & 1 \\ 0 & 1 & 1 \\ 0 & 0 & 1 \end{pmatrix}, \quad \mathbf{A}^n = \begin{pmatrix} 1 & n & \frac{1}{2}n(n+1) \\ 0 & 1 & n \\ 0 & 0 & 1 \end{pmatrix}$

Series 5

Arithmetic series 44

Sum of an arithmetic series 44

Geometric series 45

Sum of a geometric series 45

Sum to infinity 45

Convergent series 47

Binomial series 48

Expansion when x is large 49

Use of the binomial theorem to find approximations 49

Logarithmic series 50

Exponential and trigonometric series 51

Notes

Arithmetic series

$$a+(a+d)+(a+2d)+...+[a+(n-1)d].$$

with n terms, is an arithmetic series; the sum is $\frac{1}{2}n[2a+(n-1)d]$.
If the last term l is known, the sum is $\frac{1}{2}n(a+l)$.

Geometric series

$$a+ar+ar^2+ar^3+...+ar^{n-1}$$

with n terms, is a geometric series; the sum is $a\dfrac{r^n-1}{r-1}$

If the common ratio r is such that $-1<r<1$, the series **converges** and is said to have a **'sum to infinity'** S_∞ where

$$S_\infty=\frac{a}{1-r}$$

Binomial series

$$(x+a)^n=x^n+nx^{n-1}a+\frac{n(n-1)}{1\times2}x^{n-2}a^2+...$$

$$...+\frac{n!}{r!(n-r)!}x^{n-r}a^r...+a^n$$

for all values of x and a, when n is a positive integer;

$$(1+x)^n=1+nx+\frac{n(n-1)}{1\times2}x^2+\frac{n(n-1)(n-2)}{1\times2\times3}x^3...$$

for all values of n if $-1<x<1$, and when $x=-1$ and/or $+1$ for some values of n.

Logarithmic series

$$\ln(1+x)=x-\tfrac{1}{2}x^2+\tfrac{1}{3}x^3-...+(-1)^{r-1}\frac{x^r}{r}...$$

when $-1<x\leqslant1$.

Exponential series

$$e^x = 1 + x + \frac{x^2}{2!} + \frac{x^3}{3!} + \ldots + \frac{x^r}{r!} + \ldots$$

for all values of x.

Trigonometric series

$$\sin x = x - \frac{x^3}{3!} + \frac{x^5}{5!} - \frac{x^7}{7!} + \ldots$$

$$\cos x = 1 - \frac{1}{2}x^2 + \frac{x^2}{4!} - \ldots$$

for all values of x.

Arithmetic series

The sequence (or progression) 1, 5, 9, 13 ..., in which the difference between any two consecutive terms is constant, here 4, is an example of an arithmetic sequence. Other examples are

1.1, 1.2, 1.3, ...

10, 7, 4, 1, −2, −5 ...

In general, an arithmetic series* (or progression) will be written

$$a+a+d+a+2d+a+3d\ldots+a+(n-1)d$$

when consecutive terms differ by a common difference d, and the nth term is $a+(n-1)d$.

Sum of an arithmetic series

To find the sum S of the series $a+(a+d)+(a+2d)\ldots$to n terms, write

$$S=a+(a+d)+(a+2d)\ldots a+(n-1)d$$

Then $S=a+(n-1)d+a+(n-2)d\ldots a$

reversing the order of the terms.

Adding

$$2S=[2a+(n-1)d]+[2a+(n-1)d]+\ldots[2a+(n-1)d]$$
$$=n[2a+(n-1d]$$

so that

$$S=\frac{n}{2}[2a+(n-1)d]$$

Sometimes it is convenient to denote the nth term by l, so that

$$S=\frac{n}{2}[a+l]$$

Example 1. The series 1, 5, 9, 13 is an arithmetic series, common difference 4. The twentieth term is $1+19\times4$, i.e. 77, and the sum of the first 20 terms is

$$\tfrac{1}{2}\times20\times\{2\times1+19\times4\},\text{ i.e. }780$$

Example 2. How many terms in the arithmetic series 2, 3.5, ... must be taken if the sum is to be 123?

We know that $a=2$, and can see that $d=1.5$, so using

$$S=\tfrac{1}{2}n\{2a+(n-1)\times d\}$$

we have $123=\tfrac{1}{2}n\{4+(n-1)\times1.5\}$

$$=\tfrac{1}{2}n\{1.5n+2.5\}$$

i.e. $3n^2+5n-492=0$

$$(3n+41)(n-12)=0$$

$n=12$ or $-41/3$. But since n is the number of terms, n must be positive, so that $n=12$, we have to take 12 terms if the sum is to be 123.

*Series (or progression) is the sum of the sequence.

Geometric series

The sequence 1, 2, 4, 8,... in which each term is double the previous term, is an example of a geometric sequence. Other examples are

$$8, 4, 2, 1, \tfrac{1}{2}, \tfrac{1}{4}, \ldots$$

$$18, -6, 2, -\tfrac{2}{3}, \ldots$$

In general, a geometric series can be written

$$a+ar+ar^2+ar^3+\ldots+ar^{n-1}$$

when consecutive terms are in a constant ratio r, and the nth term is ar^{n-1}.

Sum of a geometric series

To find the sum S of the series $a+ar+ar^2\ldots$ to n terms, write

$$S=a+ar+ar^2+\ldots+ar^{n-1}$$

Then $rS= \quad ar+ar^2+\ldots+ar^{n-1}+ar^n$

Subtracting,

$$S-rS=a-ar^n$$

i.e. $S(1-r)=a(1-r^n)$

i.e. $S=a\dfrac{(1-r^n)}{(1-r)}$

When $r>1$, $1-r^n$ and $1-r$ will both be negative, and we may find the form

$$S=a\frac{r^n-1}{r-1}$$

slightly easier to use.

The formulae for the sum of an arithmetic series and the sum of a geometric series can easily be proved by induction.

Sum to infinity

When $r<1$, the series $a+ar+ar^2+ar^3\ldots$ can be shown to converge, i.e. approach as closely as we wish, to a fixed value; this is called the sum to infinity, sometimes written S_∞. It can be shown that

$$S_\infty=a\frac{1}{1-r}.$$

Example 1. The series 2, 1, $\frac{1}{2}$, $\frac{1}{4}$ is a geometric series, common ratio $\frac{1}{2}$. The tenth term is $2\times(\frac{1}{2})^9$, i.e. $(\frac{1}{2})^8$, and the sum of the first 10 terms is

$$2\frac{1-(\frac{1}{2})^{10}}{1-\frac{1}{2}}$$

i.e. $4-(\frac{1}{2})^8$. We can see that as the number of terms summed increases, the sum gets closer and closer to 4; this is called the sum to infinity, and the sum to infinity of the geometric series a, ar, ar^2, … in which $r<1$, is

$$\frac{a}{1-r}.$$

Example 2. Show the sum of the first 20 terms of the geometric series 3, 6, 12, … is greater than 3×10^6, given $2^{10}>1000$.

Using the formula $\quad S=a\dfrac{r^n-1}{r-1}$

$$S=3\frac{2^{20}-1}{2-1}$$

$$=3(2^{20}-1)$$

Since $\quad 2^{10}=1024>1000$, $2^{20}>10^6$, so $S>3\times10^6$.

Example 3. Find the sum of the first (a) 4 terms, (b) 5 terms, (c) 6 terms, and (d) show that the sum to infinity of the series $1+\frac{1}{3}+\frac{1}{9}$ … is $1\frac{1}{2}$.

(a) The sum of the first 4 terms is $\dfrac{1-\frac{1}{3}^4}{1-\frac{1}{3}}$, i.e. $\dfrac{40}{27}$, about 1.48…

(b) The sum of the first 5 terms is $\dfrac{1-\frac{1}{3}^5}{1-\frac{1}{3}}$, i.e. $\dfrac{121}{81}$, about 1.49^{38}…

(c) The sum of the first 6 terms is $\dfrac{1-\frac{1}{3}^6}{1-\frac{1}{3}}$, i.e. $\dfrac{364}{243}$, about 1.4979…

(d) The sum to infinity $S_\infty=1\dfrac{1}{1-\frac{1}{3}}$, i.e. $1\frac{1}{2}$.

The decimal equivalents 1.48…, 1.4938…, 1.4979…, show the manner in which the sums approach closer and closer to the 'sum to infinity', $1\frac{1}{2}$. This can also be seen from the equivalent fractions

$$\frac{3}{2}=\frac{40.5}{27}=\frac{121.5}{81}=\frac{364.5}{243}$$

The arithmetic mean of a set of n numbers x_1, x_2, x_3 … is $\dfrac{1}{n}\{x_1+x_2+x_3+\ldots+x_n\}$; the geometric mean of the same set of numbers is $\sqrt[n]{x_1\,x_2\,x_3\,\ldots\,x_n}$. For example, the arithmetic mean of 3, 6, 96, is $\frac{1}{3}(3+6+96)$, i.e. 35; the geometric mean is $\sqrt[3]{3\times6\times96}$, i.e. 12.

Example 4. Prove that the arithmetic mean of two positive unequal numbers a, b is always greater than their geometric mean.

The arithmetic mean A is $\frac{1}{2}(a+b)$; the geometric mean G is $\sqrt{ab}$. Consider A^2-G^2. Then

$$A^2-G^2=\tfrac{1}{4}(a+b)^2-ab$$
$$=\tfrac{1}{4}(a^2+2ab+b^2)-ab$$
$$=\tfrac{1}{4}(a-b)^2>0 \text{ since } a\neq b$$

Since both A and G are positive,

$$A^2-G^2>0\Rightarrow A^2>G^2\Rightarrow A>G$$

Convergent series

We saw, on page 45, that the sum of a certain series became 'closer and closer to 4'. The general geometric series a, ar, ar^2 has sum S, where

$$S=a\frac{1-r^n}{1-r}=a\frac{1}{1-r}-a\frac{r^n}{1-r}$$

If $-1<r<1$, $a\frac{r^n}{1-r}$ becomes as small as we wish, and we say that the series has a 'sum to infinity' $a\frac{1}{1-r}$. The series is then called a **convergent** series.

Example. Find the range of values for which the series

$$1+\frac{x}{3}+\frac{x^2}{9}+\frac{x^3}{27}\dots$$

has a sum to infinity and an expression in x for that sum.

The series is a geometric series, common ratio $x/3$, so that there will only be a sum to infinity if $-1<x/3<1$, i.e. $-3<x<3$.

If x takes a value in that range, the sum to infinity is

$$\frac{1}{1-x/3}, \text{ i.e. } \frac{3}{3-x}$$

Exercise 5.1

1 Which of the following series is an arithmetic series, which a geometric series, and which neither?

(a) 1, 2.5, 5, …, (b) 1, 2, 3, 5, …, (c) 3, 18, 108, …, (d) 0.6, 1.2, 1.8, …,
(e) −0.8, 0.8, 1.8, …

2 If the rth term of a series is denoted by u_r, in which of the following cases is the series arithmetic and which geometric?

$u_r=$(a) $2r$, (b) $2-r$, (c) 2^r, (d) 2^{-r}, (e) $1-\frac{1}{2}r$.

3 The third term of an arithmetic series is 3 and the sixth term is 12. Find the first term and the sum of the first 10 terms.

4 The fifth term of an arithmetic series is 8 and the ninth term is 14. Find the fourth term and the sum of the first 20 terms.

5 Find the first negative term in the arithmetic series 8, 6.5, 5, …

6 The fourth term of a geometric series is 3 and the sixth term is $\frac{3}{16}$. Find the two possible values of the common ratio and of the first term.

7 How many terms of the arithmetic series 1, 5, 9, … must be taken if the sum is 190? What is the least number of terms of this series that must be taken if the sum is to exceed 900?

8 Find the first term in the arithmetic series 2, 7, 12 which is greater than 1000.

9 Find the first term in the geometric series 2, 10, 50 which is greater than 1000.

10 What is the least number of terms in the geometric series 2, 6, 18, … if the sum exceeds 1000?

Binomial series

The binomial theorem states that, if n is a positive integer, for all values of x and y,

$$(x+y)^n=x^n+\binom{n}{1}x^{n-1}y+\binom{n}{2}x^{n-2}y^2+\ldots+\binom{n}{r}x^{n-r}y^r+\ldots+y^n$$

(proved by Induction on page 38). It is also true (though the proof is too difficult at this stage) that

$$(1+x)^n=1+nx+\frac{n(n-1)}{1\times 2}x^2+\frac{n(n-1)(n-2)}{1\times 2\times 3}x^3\ldots$$

for all values of n if $-1<x<1$; it can be shown that this is also true if $x=1$ when $n>-1$ and when $x=-1$ when $n>0$.

Example 1. Find the range of values for x for which $(1-2x)^{1/2}$ can be expanded as a power series in x, and the first four terms in that series.

Since $n=\frac{1}{2}$, $n>0$ so that the expansion is valid when $-1\leqslant -2x\leqslant 1$, i.e. $-\frac{1}{2}\leqslant x\leqslant \frac{1}{2}$.
When x has a value in this range:

$$(1-2x)^{1/2}=1+\tfrac{1}{2}(-2x)+\frac{\frac{1}{2}(-\frac{1}{2})}{1\times 2}(-2x)^2+\frac{\frac{1}{2}(-\frac{1}{2})(-\frac{3}{2})}{1\times 2\times 3}(-2x)^3\ldots$$
$$=1-x-\tfrac{1}{2}x^2-\tfrac{1}{2}x^3$$

Example 2. Assuming x to be sufficiently small compared with a for the expansion to be valid, find the first four terms in the expansion in ascending powers of x of

$$\frac{a^3}{(a^2+x^2)^{3/2}}$$

Since the binomial expansion, when n is not an integer, is written in the form $(1+\quad)^n$, write $(a^2+x^2)^{3/2}$ as

$$a^3\left(1+\frac{x^2}{a^2}\right)^{3/2}$$

Then
$$\frac{a^3}{a^3\left(1+\frac{x^2}{a^2}\right)^{3/2}}=\left(1+\frac{x^2}{a^2}\right)^{-3/2}$$

$$=1+\left(-\frac{3}{2}\right)\left(\frac{x^2}{a^2}\right)+\frac{(-\frac{3}{2})(-\frac{5}{2})}{1\times 2}\left(\frac{x^2}{a^2}\right)^2+\frac{(-\frac{3}{2})(-\frac{5}{2})(-\frac{7}{2})}{1\times 2\times 3}\left(\frac{x^2}{a^2}\right)^3\ldots$$

$$=1-\frac{3x^2}{2a^2}+\frac{15x^4}{8a^4}-\frac{35x^6}{16a^6},\text{ to four terms}$$

Expansion when *x* is large

When x is 'large', $1/x$ is 'small', so that it is often possible to expand $(1+1/x)^n$ as a power series in $1/x$.

Example. If x is sufficiently large for the expansion to be valid, find the first four terms in the expansion of $\dfrac{x}{(2+x)^2}$ in ascending powers of $1/x$.

$$\frac{x}{(2+x^2)}=\frac{x}{x^2\left(\frac{2}{x^2}+1\right)}=\frac{1}{x}\left(1+\frac{2}{x^2}\right)^{-1}$$

$$=\frac{1}{x}\left[1+(-1)\left(\frac{2}{x^2}\right)+\frac{(-1)(-2)}{1\times 2}\left(\frac{2}{x^2}\right)^2+\frac{(-1)(-2)(-3)}{1\times 2\times 3}\left(\frac{2}{x^2}\right)^3\cdots\right.$$

$$\simeq\frac{1}{x}-\frac{2}{x^3}+\frac{4}{x^5}-\frac{8}{x^7}$$

Use of the binomial theorem to find approximations

Before the ready availability of electronic calculators, the binomial expansion could be used to give approximations to various arithmetic expressions. Now the calculator can be used to check easily an expansion, even if arithmetic approximations are not required.

Example. Find the first four terms in the binomial expansion of $(1-3x)^{-1/3}$ in ascending powers of x.

Using the binomial theorem,

$$(1-3x)^{-1/3}=1+(-\tfrac{1}{3})(-3x)+\frac{(-\frac{1}{3})(-\frac{4}{3})}{1\times 2}(-3x)^2+\frac{(-\frac{1}{3})(-\frac{4}{3})(-\frac{7}{3})(-3x)^3}{1\times 2\times 3}\cdots$$

$$=1+x+2x^2+\tfrac{14}{3}x^3\ldots$$

Putting $x=0.01$,

$$(1-0.03)^{-1/3}=(0.97)^{-1/3}$$
$$=1.010\,204\,7\ldots$$

Substituting in the expansion,

$$=1+0.01+2(0.01)^2+\tfrac{14}{3}(0.01)^3$$
$$=1.010\,204\,69\ldots$$

so our expansion looks likely to be correct.

Exercise 5.2

1 Expand each of the following, giving the expansions in their simplest form:
(a) $(2+x)^3$, (b) $(1+2x)^3$, (c) $(2-3x)^3$, (d) $(1-3x)^4$, (e) $(2-3x)^4$,
(f) $(2+3x)^4$.

2 Find the first four terms when each of the following expressions is expanded in ascending powers of x, and the range of values for which each expansion is valid:
(a) $(1-2x)^{-1}$, (b) $(1-2x)^{-2}$, (c) $(1-2x)^{-1/2}$, (d) $(1-2x)^{1/2}$,
(e) $(1-2x^2)^{-1}$, (f) $(2-x)^{-1}$.

3 Find the first three terms when each of the following is expanded in ascending powers of x and state the range of values of x for which the expansion is valid:
(a) $(1+x^2)^{-1}$, (b) $(1+x^2)^{-2}$, (c) $(1+x^2)^{-3}$, (d) $(1-2x^2)^{-1}$, (e) $x(1-3x^2)^{-1}$,
(f) $x^2(1-x^2)^{-1}$.

4 Find the first four terms when each of the following expressions is expanded in ascending powers of $1/x$:
(a) $(x-1)^{-1}$, (b) $(x^2+2)^{-1}$, (c) $(x+1)^{-2}$, (d) $(x^2-2)^{-2}$.

5 Find the expansions in ascending powers of x of $(1-4x)^{1/2}$ and $1-2x(1-ax)^b$, up to and including the term containing x^3. Find the values of a and b if these expansions are identical for the terms that have been found.

Logarithmic series

It can be proved by Maclaurin's theorem (page 285) that if $-1<x\leqslant 1$:

$$\ln(1+x)=x-\frac{x^2}{2}+\frac{x^3}{3}\ldots(-1)^{r-1}\frac{x^r}{r}\ldots$$

(Check by substituting $x=-0.01$ in $\ln(1+x)$ and in the expansion.)

Example. Find the expansion of $\ln\left(\frac{(1+x^2)^{1/2}}{1-2x}\right)$ in ascending powers of x, up to and including the term in x^4, assuming that the value of x is such that the expansion is valid.

$$\begin{aligned}\ln\frac{(1+x^2)^{1/2}}{1-2x}&=\tfrac{1}{2}\ln(1+x^2)-\ln(1-2x)\\&=\tfrac{1}{2}\left[x^2-\frac{x^4}{2}\ldots\right]\\&\qquad-\left[-2x-\tfrac{1}{2}(-2x)^2+\tfrac{1}{3}(-2x)^3-\tfrac{1}{4}(-2x)^4\ldots\right]\\&=\frac{x^2}{2}-\frac{x^4}{4}\ldots-\left[-2x-2x^2-\tfrac{8}{3}x^3-4x^4\ldots\right]\\&=2x+\tfrac{5}{2}x^2+\tfrac{8}{3}x^3+\tfrac{15}{4}x^4\ldots\end{aligned}$$

For the expansion to be valid, $-1<y\leqslant 1$, i.e. $-1<x^2\leqslant 1$ and also $+1<-2x\leqslant 1$. Both these conditions are satisfied only if $-\frac{1}{2}\leqslant x<\frac{1}{2}$.

Exponential and trigonometric series

We can also use Maclaurin's theorem to prove that

$$e^x=1+x+\frac{x^2}{2!}+\frac{x^3}{3!}\cdots\frac{x^r}{r!}\cdots$$

$$\cos x=1-\frac{x^2}{2!}+\frac{x^4}{4!}\cdots$$

and $$\sin x=x-\frac{x^3}{3!}+\frac{x^5}{5!}$$

These expansions are valid for all (real) values of x.

Example. Find the coefficient of x^n in the expansion of e^{1+2x} in ascending powers of x.

$$e^{1+2x}=e(e^{2x})$$

$$=e\left(1+2x+\frac{(2x)^2}{2!}+\frac{(2x)^3}{3!}\cdots\right)$$

$$=e+2ex+\frac{2^2ex^2}{2!}+\frac{2^3ex^3}{3!}\cdots\frac{2^nex^n}{n!}$$

thus the coefficient of x^n is $\dfrac{2^ne}{n!}$

More questions and examples on the logarithmic, exponential and trigonometric series are given in Chapter 24.

Exercise 5.3

1 Write down the first four non-zero terms in each of the following, assuming the values of x to be such that the expansion is valid:
(a) $\ln(1-x)$, (b) $\ln(1-2x)$, (c) $\ln(1+3x)$, (d) $\ln(1+3x^2)$,
(e) $\ln(1-4x^2)$, (f) e^{2x}, (g) e^{x+1}, (h) e^{x^2+1}, (i) $\sin(2x)$,
(j) $\cos(x^2)$.
In each case, check by taking an appropriate value for x, such as $x=0.01$.

2 Factorise $1-3x+2x^2$ and hence find the first four terms in the expansion of $\ln(1-3x+2x^2)$ as a power series in x. Check by finding the value of $\ln(0.72)$.

3 Find the first four terms in the expansion of $\ln\left(\dfrac{1+3x}{1-2x}\right)$ and give a numerical check for your expansion.

4 Write down the first four non-zero terms in the expansions of sin x and cos x, obtain the product sin x cos x up to and including the term in x^8 and compare with the expansion of sin $2x$.

5 Find the first four non-zero terms in the expansions of
(a) $\frac{1}{2}(e^x+e^{-x})$, (b) $\frac{1}{2}(e^x-e^{-x})$.

Miscellaneous exercise 5.4

1 Show that the sum of the first n odd numbers, i.e. $1+3+5 \dots 2n-1$ is n^2.

2 Use the formula in Q.1 to show that the sum of the odd numbers from 1 to 125 inclusive is equal to the sum of the odd numbers from 169 to 209 inclusive.

3 A man saves £600 one year, and each subsequent year saves £200 more than the previous year. How much does he save in 20 years?

4 Given that a,b and c are three consecutive terms in a geometric series, show that log a, log b and log c are three consecutive terms in an arithmetic series.

5 Find the sum of the first 10 terms in the series $\log 2 + \log 4 + \log 8 + \dots$

6 How many terms of the series $\lg 2 + \lg 4 + \lg 8 \dots$ must be taken if the sum is to exceed 10?

7 Find the sum of all the numbers between 200 and 300 that are divisible by 7.

8 The nth term of an arithmetic series is x and the sum of the first n terms of that series is S. Find an expression in x, n and S for the first term of that series.

9 Find the sum to infinity of the geometric series $\frac{1}{4}+\frac{1}{16}+\frac{1}{64} \dots$ How many terms of this series must be taken if the sum is greater than 0.333 33?

10 Find the value of x if $(x-3)$, $(x+2)$ and $(3x-4)$ are consecutive terms in a geometric series.

11 The rth term of an arithmetic series is $3r-1$. Find the first term and the sum of the first 20 terms.

12 If 1, x, 7, 10 are the first four terms of an arithmetic series, how many terms must be taken for the sum of the series to exceed 1000?

13 The rth term of a geometric series is $8(\frac{1}{2})^r$. Find the 10th term of the series, and the sum to infinity of the series.

14 Find the term that does not contain x in the expansion of

$$\left(x^2-\frac{1}{x}\right)^4\left(x+\frac{1}{x}\right)^3$$

15 Given $a<b$, find a and b if the first three terms in the expansion of

$$\frac{1+ax}{\sqrt{1+bx}}$$

in ascending powers of x are $1+2x-\frac{3}{2}x^2$.

16 Express $2(1-2x)^{1/2}-(4+5x)^{-1/2}$ as a power series in x, up to and including the term in x^2.

17 Given that x is sufficiently small, find the constants a, b and c if

$$\left(\frac{1+3x}{8+3x}\right)^{1/3} \approx a+bx+cx^2$$

18 Show that the first three terms in the expansion of $(1-8x)^{1/4}$ in ascending powers of x are the same as the first three terms in the expansion of $\dfrac{1-5x}{1-3x}$.

19 Find a and b if the first three terms in the expansion of

$$\frac{(1+ax)^4}{(1+bx)^3} \text{ are } 1-x+6x^2$$

given a and b are both positive.

20 Find correct to the nearest whole number, the sum of the first 20 terms of the geometric series $1+e^{1/2}+e+e^{3/2}\ldots$; find also the range of values of x for which the geometric series $1+e^x+e^{2x}\ldots$ has a sum to infinity S, and find the value of S, correct to four significant figures when $x=-0.5$.

21 Find the values of a and b if the first three terms in the expansion of $e^{ax}/(1-bx^2)$ are $1+\frac{1}{2}x+\frac{3}{8}x^2$.

22 Write down the first three terms in the expansion of $u=\left(1+\dfrac{x}{n}\right)^n$ in ascending powers of x. Show that if all terms in x^3 and higher powers of x are neglected, then

$$u+\frac{1}{u}=2e^x.$$

23 Write down and simplify the expansions of $\ln(2-x)$ and $\ln[(2-x)(1-x)]$, up to and including the terms in x^3. Put $x=0.2$, to find an approximation for $\ln(1.2)$, and check your approximation using a calculator.

24 Find the values of a and b if $e^x \ln(1+x)=ax+bx^2$, when x is sufficiently small for terms in x^3 to be neglected.

25 Find the values of a and b if $(x+a\sin x)(1-\cos x)=bx^5$, when terms in x^6 and higher powers are neglected.

Partial fractions 6

Equations and identities 57

Partial fractions 58

Applications of partial fractions 62

Notes

Equations and identities

An equation is only satisfied by **some** values of x; an identity is true for **all** values of x.

Partial fractions

Remember that the degree of the numerator of the fraction must be less than the degree of the denominator; if it is not less, we must first divide, e.g.

$$\frac{x^2}{(x-1)(x+1)} = \frac{x^2-1+1}{(x-1)(x+1)} = 1 + \frac{1}{(x-1)(x+1)}$$

$$= 1 + \frac{\frac{1}{2}}{x-1} - \frac{\frac{1}{2}}{x+1}$$

Suitable partial fractions are:

$$\frac{c}{(x-a)(x-b)} = \frac{A}{(x-a)} + \frac{B}{(x-b)}$$

$$\frac{c}{(x-a)(x^2+b)} = \frac{A}{(x-a)} + \frac{Bx+C}{(x^2+b)}$$

$$\frac{c}{(x-a)(x-b)^2} = \frac{A}{(x-a)} + \frac{B}{(x-b)} + \frac{C}{(x-b)^2}$$

Equations and identities

$x^2-1=0$ is true for only two values of x, $x=1$ or -1;
$x^2-1=x^2$ is not true for any value of x;
$x^2-1=(x-1)(x+1)$ is true for all values of x and is called an *identity*. It is often written $\equiv$.

Quadratic equations have at most two distinct real roots, and polynomials in x of degree n will be satisfied by at most n different values of x. If an equation in x is satisfied by *more* than n different values of x, then it is an identity and is satisfied by all values of x. Thus two expressions are identically equal if the coefficients of each term are equal, or if they have the same values for all values of x.

Example 1. Show that $x(x-1)-2(x-1)(x-2)+x(x-2)=3x-4$ is true for all values of x.

Method 1: Expanding the brackets on the L.H.S.,

$$\begin{aligned}&x(x-1)-2(x-1)(x-2)+x(x-2)\\&\quad=x^2-x-2x^2+6x-4+x^2-2x\\&\quad=3x-4, \text{ the same expression as the R.H.S.}\end{aligned}$$

Method 2: This is an equation of degree two, so it will be an identity if it is satisfied by *more than two values* of x.

Put $x=0$; L.H.S.$=-4$, R.H.S.$=-4$
Put $x=1$; L.H.S.$=-1$, R.H.S.$=-1$
Put $x=2$; L.H.S.$=2$ R.H.S.$=2$

Thus the equation is satisfied by at least three values of x and so is an identity.

NB. The values $x=0$, 1 and 2 were chosen so that as many as possible of the brackets on the L.H.S. were zero.

Example 2. Show that $x(x-1)-2(x-1)(x-2)+x(x-2)=3x-5$ is not satisfied by any values for x.

Expanding the L.H.S. as before,

$$\text{L.H.S.}=3x-4$$

so the equation becomes

$$3x-4=3x-5$$

which is not true, whatever the value of x.

Exercise 6.1

1 Show that the following are true for all values of x:
(a) $x(x+1)-2(x+1)(x+2)+x(x+2)=-3x-4$,
(b) $x(x-1)-3(x-1)(x-2)+2x(x-2)=4x-6$.

2 Show that the following are not true for any value of x:
(a) $x(x-1)+2x(x-3)=3x^2-7x+1$,
(b) $x(x+2)+(x-3)(x+3)=2x^2+2x$.

3 Show that each of the following is true for some values of x, and find those values:
(a) $(x-1)(x+1)=8$,
(b) $(x-1)(x+2)=4$,
(c) $(x-1)(x+2)=x^2+4$,
(d) $(x-1)(x+2)=x^2-2$.

4 Which of the following are identities?
(a) $x^3=(x+1)(x^2-x+1)$,
(b) $x^3+1=(x+1)(x^2-x+1)$,
(c) $x^3+x=(x+1)(x^2-x+1)$.

Partial fractions

We can see that $$\frac{1}{x}+\frac{1}{x+1}\equiv\frac{2x+1}{x(x+1)}$$

and that $$\frac{1}{x}-\frac{1}{x+1}\equiv\frac{1}{x(x+1)}$$

Can we find constants A and B so that, say,

$$\frac{2x-1}{x(x+1)}\equiv\frac{A}{x}+\frac{B}{x+1}?$$

If this is so, multiply both sides by $x(x+1)$

$$2x-1\equiv A(x+1)+Bx$$

Put $x=0$, then $A=-1$; put $x=-1$, then $B=3$, so that

$$2x-1\equiv-(x+1)+3x$$

i.e. $$\frac{2x-1}{x(x+1)}=\frac{-1}{x}+\frac{3}{x+1}$$

There are three types of fractions that we have to express as partial fractions at this stage:

(1) where the factors of the denominator are linear and all different, e.g.

$$\frac{1}{(x-2)(x+3)}$$

(2) where one of the factors in the denominator is quadratic, e.g.

$$\frac{1}{(x-2)(x^2+3)}$$

(3) where one of the factors in the denominator is repeated, e.g.

$$\frac{1}{(x-2)(x+3)^2}$$

In each case, before we can express a 'fraction' in partial fractions we have to ensure that it is a fraction, i.e. that the degree of the numerator is less than the degree of the denominator. (If this is not already so, then we have to divide – see Example 5 on page 62.) We can then assume that the degree of the numerator of every fraction is at least one less than the degree of its denominator, e.g.

$$\frac{A}{x-2} \text{ and } \frac{Bx+C}{x^2+3} \text{ type (2);}$$

occasionally B or C may be zero. In type (3), however, we need only have constant terms in each denominator, so that the partial fractions will be of the form

$$\frac{A}{(x-2)}+\frac{B}{(x+3)}+\frac{C}{(x+3)^2}$$

Example 1. Find the values of A and B if

$$\frac{5}{(x-2)(x+3)} \equiv \frac{A}{(x-2)}+\frac{B}{(x+3)}$$

Method 1: Multiply both sides by $(x-2)(x+3)$, and find the values for A and B if

$$5 = A(x+3)+B(x-2) \qquad (1)$$

is true for all values of x

i.e. $\quad 5 \equiv Ax + 3A + Bx - 2B$

Equating coefficients of x, $\quad 0 = A + B$

Equating constants, $\quad 5 = 3A - 2B$

Solving, $\quad A = 1$ and $B = -1$

$$\therefore \quad \frac{5}{(x-2)(x+3)} = \frac{1}{x-2} - \frac{1}{x+3}$$

Method 2: In (1), put $x=-3$,

then $\quad 5=B(-5)$, i.e. $B=-1$

Put $x=2$, then $\quad 5=A(5)$, i.e. $A=1 \qquad (2)$

Method 3 ('Cover up' or 'finger' method): Dividing equation (1) by $(x+3)$ we have

$$\frac{5}{(x+3)} = A + \frac{B(x-2)}{(x+3)}$$

When $x=2$,

$$\frac{5}{(2+3)} = A, \text{ as in (2), giving } A=1.$$

We see that the value of A is that obtained by 'covering up' the factor $(x-2)$ in $\frac{5}{(x-2)(x+3)}$ and substituting $x=2$ in what remains to get

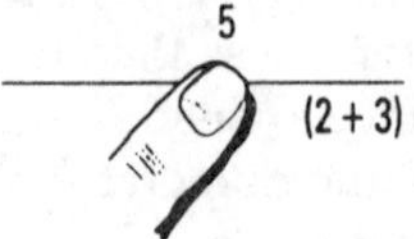

Figure 6.1

and the value of B is that obtained by covering up the factor $(x+3)$ in $\frac{5}{(x-2)(x+3)}$ and substituting $x=-3$ in what remains, i.e.

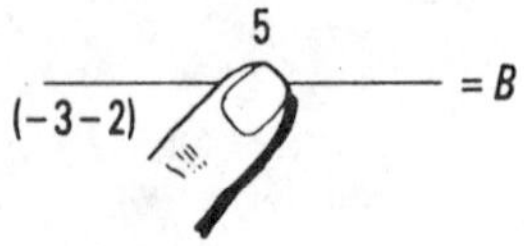

$$\frac{5}{(-3-2)\qquad} = B$$

Figure 6.2

i.e. $B=-1$.

Since we often 'cover up' with a finger this is sometimes called the 'finger' method.

Example 2. Find the values of A, B and C if

$$\frac{12}{(x+1)(x-2)(x-3)} = \frac{A}{(x+1)} + \frac{B}{(x-2)} + \frac{C}{(x-3)}$$

Cover up the factor $(x+1)$ and put $x=-1$ in what remains

$$\frac{12}{\qquad(-3)(-4)} = A, \text{ i.e. } A=1$$

Cover up the factor $(x-2)$ and put $x=2$ in what remains

$$\frac{12}{(3)\qquad(-1)} = B, \text{ i.e. } B=-4$$

Cover up the factor $(x-3)$ and put $x=3$ in what remains

$$\frac{12}{(4)(1)\qquad} = C, \text{ i.e. } C=3$$

$$\frac{12}{(x+1)(x-2)(x-3)} = \frac{1}{(x+1)} - \frac{4}{(x-2)} + \frac{3}{(x-3)}$$

Check: Multiply both sides by $(x+1)((x-2)(x-3)$

$$12 = 1(x-2)(x-3)-4(x+1)(x-3)+3(x+1)(x-2)$$

The coefficient of x^2 on the L.H.S. is 0; on the R.H.S. is $1-4+3=0$

Example 3. Find the values of A, B and C if

$$\frac{3}{(x+1)(x^2+2)} \equiv \frac{A}{(x+1)} + \frac{Bx+C}{(x^2+2)}$$

Notice that we have to take the numerator of the second term as $Bx+C$ since the degree of the denominator is two.

The value of A can be found by the 'cover up' method, but we shall here use a combination of methods 1 and 2.

Multiply both sides by $(x+1)(x^2+2)$

$$3 = A(x^2+2)+(x+1)(Bx+C)$$

Put $x=-1$, then $\quad 3 = A[(-1)^2+2]$, i.e. $A=1$

Equating the coefficients of x^2,

$$0 = A+B, \quad \therefore B=-1$$

Equating the constants, $3 = 2A+C$, $\therefore$ C=1

Check: Equate the coefficients of x. On the L.H.S., 0; on the R.H.S. $B+C=-1+1=0$.

$$\therefore \quad \frac{3}{(x+1)(x^2+2)} \equiv \frac{1}{(x+1)} + \frac{-x+1}{(x^2+2)}$$

Example 4. Find the values of A and B if

$$\frac{3x+7}{(x+1)^2} \equiv \frac{A}{(x+1)} + \frac{B}{(x+1^2)}$$

Method 1: Multiply both sides by $(x+1)^2$

$$3x+7 \equiv A(x+1)+B$$

Put $x=-1$, $\quad 4 = B$

Equating the coefficients of x, $\quad 3 = A$

$$\therefore \quad \frac{3x+7}{(x+1)^2} \equiv \frac{3}{(x+1)} + \frac{4}{(x+1)^2}$$

Method 2: Substitute $x+1=y$

Then $\quad \dfrac{3x+7}{(x+1)^2} \equiv \dfrac{3y+4}{y^2} \equiv \dfrac{3}{y} + \dfrac{4}{y^2} \equiv \dfrac{3}{(x+1)} + \dfrac{4}{(x+1)^2}$

With a little practice this can be worked through without actually making the substitution, i.e.

$$\frac{3x+7}{(3x+1)^2} \equiv \frac{3(x+1)+4}{(x+1)^2} \equiv \frac{3}{x+1} + \frac{4}{(x+1)^2}$$

Example 5. Express in partial fractions

$$\frac{x^4}{(x-1)(x^2+2)}$$

In this case the degree of the numerator is 4, of the denominator is 3, so we must first divide. We can use long division, or the identity $x^4 \equiv (x+1)(x^3-x^2+2x-2)-x^2+2$, since $(x-1)(x^2+2) \equiv x^3-x^2+2x-2$.

Then $$\frac{x^4}{(x-1)(x^2+2)} \equiv \frac{(x+1)(x^3-x^2+2x-2)-x^2+2}{(x-1)(x^2+2)}$$

$$\equiv x+1-\frac{x^2-2}{(x-1)(x^2+2)}$$

Now if $$\frac{x^2-2}{(x-1)(x^2+2)} \equiv \frac{A}{x-1} + \frac{Bx+C}{x^2+2}$$

$$x^2-2 \equiv A(x^2+2) + (Bx+C)(x-1)$$

Put $x=1$, then $A=-\frac{1}{3}$
Equating the coefficients of x^2 $1=A+B \therefore B=\frac{4}{3}$
Equating the constants $-2=2A-C \therefore C=\frac{4}{3}$

To check, equate the coefficients of x, $0=-B+C$, which is so.

$$\frac{x^4}{(x-1)(x^2+2)} = x+1 + \frac{\frac{1}{3}}{x-1} - \frac{\frac{4}{3}(x+1)}{x^2+2}$$

Applications of partial fractions

Partial fractions are often useful when finding binomial expansions or when integrating.

Example 1. Express in partial fractions and find the first two non-zero terms in the expansion as a power series in x of

$$\frac{x}{(x-2)(x-3)}$$

Use the 'cover up' method and put $x=2$;

$$A = \frac{2}{(2-3)} = -2$$

Put $x=3$, $$B = \frac{3}{(3-2)} = 3$$

$$\therefore \quad \frac{x}{(x-2)(x-3)} = \frac{-2}{x-2} + \frac{3}{x-3}$$

Remember that the denominators must be written in the form (1−   ) before the binomial expansion is used.

$$\text{R.H.S.} = \frac{1}{1-\frac{x}{2}} - \frac{1}{1-\frac{x}{3}}$$

$$= \left(1-\frac{x}{2}\right)^{-1} - \left(1-\frac{x}{3}\right)^{-1}$$

$$= 1+(-1)\left(-\frac{x}{2}\right) + \frac{(-1)(-2)}{1\times 2}\left(-\frac{x}{2}\right)^2 \ldots$$

$$-1-(-1)\left(-\frac{x}{3}\right) - \frac{(-1)(-2)}{1\times 2}\left(-\frac{x}{3}\right)^2 \ldots$$

$$= \frac{x}{6} + \frac{5x^2}{36}, \text{ neglecting higher powers of } x.$$

Example 2. Find

$$\int \frac{1}{(x-1)(x-2)}\,dx$$

Since $\dfrac{1}{(x-1)(x-2)} = \dfrac{-1}{x-1} + \dfrac{1}{x-2}$

using the 'cover up' or any other method,

$$\int \frac{1}{(x-1)(x-2)}\,dx = \int \left(\frac{-1}{x-1} + \frac{1}{x-2}\right)dx$$

$$= -\ln|x-1| + \ln|x-2| + C$$

$$= \ln\left|\frac{x-2}{x-1}\right| + C$$

Exercise 6.2

1 Find the constants A, B and C as appropriate in the following:

(a) $\dfrac{1}{(x+1)(x+2)} \equiv \dfrac{A}{x+1} + \dfrac{B}{x+2}$,

(b) $\dfrac{x}{(x+1)(x+2)} \equiv \dfrac{A}{x+1} + \dfrac{B}{x+2}$,

(c) $\dfrac{x^2}{(x+1)(x+2)} \equiv 1 + \dfrac{A}{x+1} + \dfrac{B}{x+2}$,

(d) $\dfrac{1}{(x+1)(x^2+2)} \equiv \dfrac{A}{x+1} + \dfrac{Bx+C}{x^2+2}$,

(e) $\dfrac{x}{(x+1)^2} \equiv \dfrac{A}{x+1} + \dfrac{B}{(x+1)^2}$,

(f) $\dfrac{x}{(x+1)(x+2)(x+3)} \equiv \dfrac{A}{x+1} + \dfrac{B}{x+2} + \dfrac{C}{x+3}$,

(g) $\dfrac{1}{x(x+1)^2} \equiv \dfrac{A}{x} + \dfrac{B}{x+1} + \dfrac{C}{(x+1)^2}$,

(h) $\dfrac{x^3}{(x-1)(x+1)} \equiv x + \dfrac{A}{x-1} + \dfrac{B}{x+1}$.

2 Express in partial fractions:

(a) $\dfrac{2x+3}{(x-2)(x-3)}$, (b) $\dfrac{2x+3}{(x-2)(x^2+3)}$, (c) $\dfrac{2x+3}{(x-2)(x-3)^2}$,

(d) $\dfrac{2x+3}{(x-2)(x^2-9)}$, (e) $\dfrac{2x^2+3}{(x-2)(x-3)}$, (f) $\dfrac{2x^3}{(x-2)(x-3)}$.

Exercise 6.3

Express in partial fractions, then find the binomial expansion of each of the following, up to and including the term in x^2:

1 $\dfrac{1}{(1+x)(1+2x)}$.

2 $\dfrac{1}{(1-x)(-3x)}$.

3 $\dfrac{1}{(1-2x)(1-3x)}$.

4 $\dfrac{1}{(1+2x)(1-3x)}$.

5 $\dfrac{1}{(1+x)(1+x^2)}$.

6 $\dfrac{1}{(1-x)(1-2x^2)}$.

7 $\dfrac{x}{(1-2x)(1+3x)}$.

8 $\dfrac{x}{(1+4x)(1-x)}$.

9 $\dfrac{x}{(2+x)(1+x)}$.

10 $\dfrac{x}{(2+x)(5+x)}$.

11 $\dfrac{1}{(1-2x)(1-7x)}$.

12 $\dfrac{1}{(1-ax)(1-bx)}$.

Express in partial fractions and then integrate $\dfrac{1}{f(x)}$, where $f(x) \equiv$

13 $x(x+1)$.

14 $x(x^2+1)$.

15 $(x-1)(x-2)$.

16 $(x-1)(x-5)$.

17 $(x-3)(2x-3)$.

18 $(x-1)(x^2+1)$.

19 $(2x-1)(2x-3)$.

20 $(2x-1)(x+2)$.

Miscellaneous exercise 6.4

1 Express in partial fractions

(a) $\dfrac{1}{(x-1)(x+2)}$, (b) $\dfrac{x}{(x-1)(x+2)}$, (c) $\dfrac{x+3}{(x-2)(x+1)}$, (d) $\dfrac{x+1}{x(x+3)}$,

(e) $\dfrac{3}{(x-1)(x+3)}$, (f) $\dfrac{x}{(x-2)(x+3)}$, (g) $\dfrac{2}{(x-1)(x^2+1)}$, (h) $\dfrac{x}{(x-2)(x^2+1)}$,

(i) $\dfrac{x^2}{(x-1)^2(x-2)}$, (j) $\dfrac{1}{x(x-1)^2}$, (k) $\dfrac{12(x+x^2)}{(x-1)(x+3)(x+5)}$, (l) $\dfrac{x^2}{(x+1)^2(x+3)}$.

2 Find the binomial expansion of each of the following, up to and including the term in x^2:

(a) $\dfrac{1}{(2x-1)(x-1)}$, (b) $\dfrac{x}{(2x-1)(x-1)}$, (c) $\dfrac{1}{(2x-1)(x^2+1)}$, (d) $\dfrac{1}{(2x-1)(x+1)^2}$.

3 Find the following integrals:

(a) $\displaystyle\int \frac{1}{(2x-1)(2x+1)}\,dx$, (b) $\displaystyle\int \frac{1}{x(x^2+1)}\,dx$, (c) $\displaystyle\int \frac{1}{x(x^2-1)}\,dx$,

(d) $\displaystyle\int \frac{x}{(x-1)^2}\,dx$.

Inequalities and curve sketching 7

Inequalities 70

Curve sketching 73

Polynomials of the form $y=a(x-b)(x-c)(x-d)$ 73

Some common curves 74

Translations 75

Transformations 75

Summary 76

The graph of $y=(x-b)/(x-a)$ 78

The curve $y=ax/(x^2+a^2)$ 79

Curves described by the products of functions 80

Notes

Inequalities

If $ax=b$ and $a \neq 0, x = b/a$

but if $ax < b, x < b/a$ **only if *a* is positive.**

If $(x-a)(x-b)=0, x=a$ or b

but if $(x-a)(x-b)<0, a<x<b$

and if $(x-a)(x-b)>0, x<a$ or $x>b$

Curve sketching

Become familiar with as many sketches as possible, and notice the relation between the sketch-graphs of similar functions, e.g.

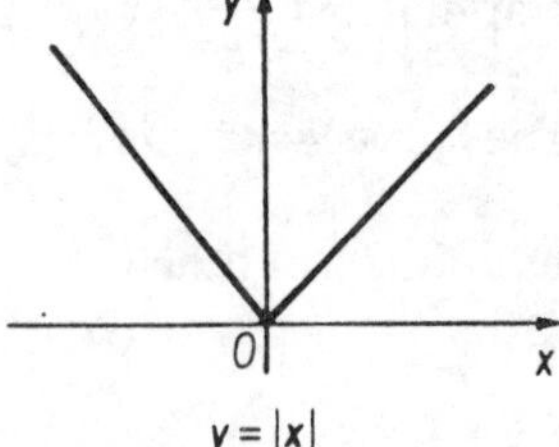

and

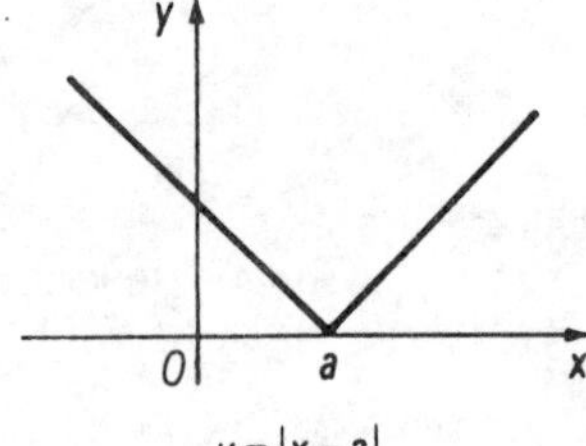

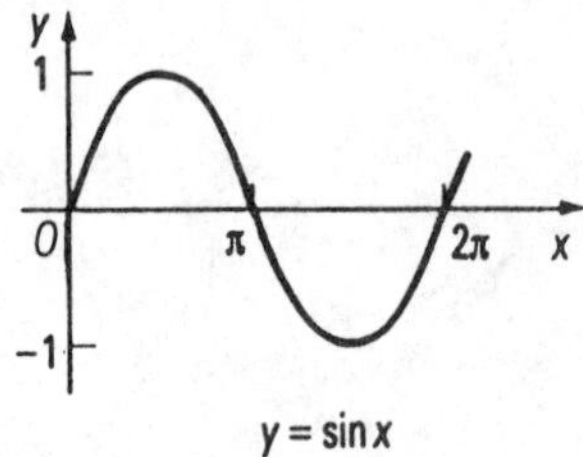

and

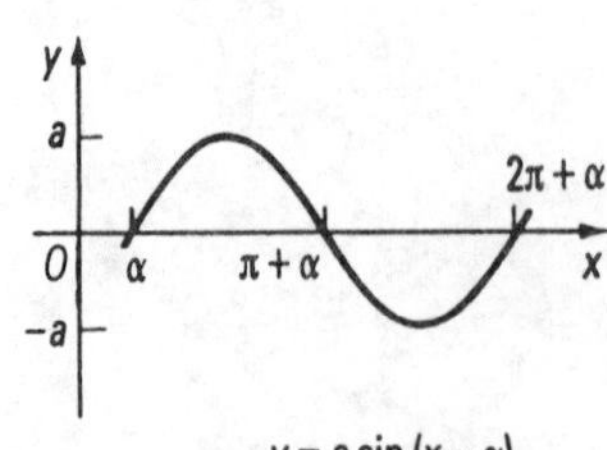

Figure 7.1

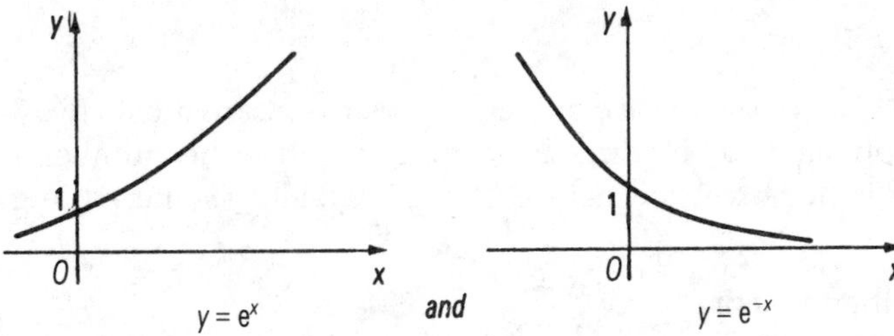

Figure 7.1 continued

Investigate ...

(1) the domain over which the function is defined, and the range of values attained ...
(2) any symmetry ...
(3) where the curve crosses the coordinate axes ...
(4) whether there are any asymptotes parallel to either coordinate axis ...
(5) the shape of the curve when x is small, to find the tangent(s) at the origin.

Inequalities

If $ax=b$ and $a \neq 0$, $x=b/a$, but if $ax<b$, $x<b/a$ only if a is positive. Care must always be taken, when multiplying and dividing by a number, that the number is positive; if the number is negative, the nature of the inequality is altered, e.g. $-3x<6 \Leftrightarrow x>-2$.

If $(x-a)(x-b)=0$, then $x=a$ or b

but if $(x-a)(x-b)<0$, then $a<x<b$

and $(x-a)(x-b)>0$, then $x<a$ or $x>b$, if $a<b$

It is often helpful to sketch the graph to find the range of values that satisfy an inequality.

$(x-a)(x-b)>0$ if
$x<a$ or $x>b$, if a is less than b

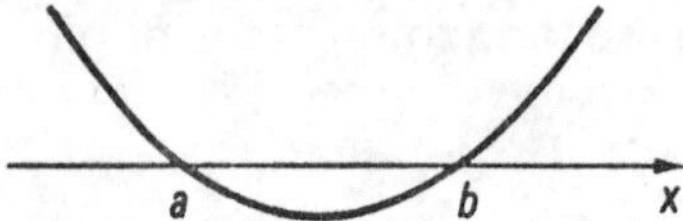

Figure 7.2

Example. Find the range of values of x for which

$$\frac{1}{x-2} > \frac{2}{x}$$

Method 1: If $x>2$, both $x-2$ and x are positive,

$$\frac{1}{x-2} > \frac{2}{x} \Rightarrow x > 2(x-2) \Rightarrow x<4$$

$\therefore$ $$2<x<4$$

If $0<x<2$, $x-2$ is negative and

$$\frac{1}{x-2} > \frac{2}{x} \Rightarrow x<2(x-2) \Leftrightarrow x>4$$

which is not consistent with $0<x<2$.

If $x<0$, x and $x-2$ are both negative, so

$$\frac{1}{x-2} > \frac{2}{x} \Rightarrow x>2x-4 \Leftrightarrow x<4$$

which is so, since x is already <0, $\therefore x<0$ or $2<x<4$ satisfy the original inequality.

Method 2: Sketching the curves $y=\dfrac{1}{x-2}$ and $y=2/x$, serves as a check.

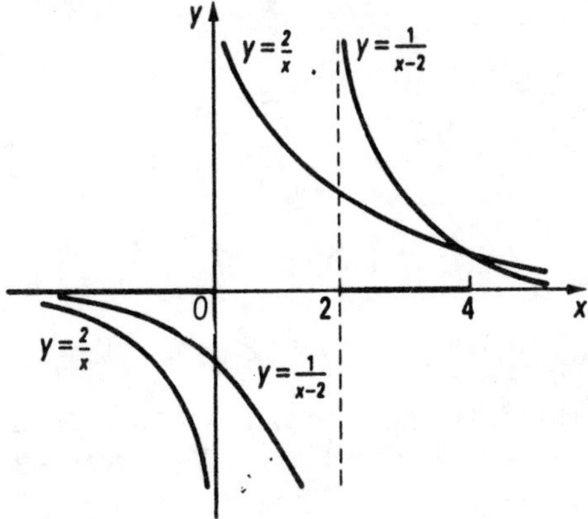

Figure 7.3

From the graphs we can see that $\frac{1}{x-2}$ is always greater than $2/x$ when x is negative, and also that it is greater when $2<x<4$. The value $x=4$ has to be found by solving the equation $\frac{1}{x-2}=\frac{2}{x}$, i.e. $x=2(x-2)$, $x=4$.

Exercise 7.1

1 Find the range of values of x for which
(a) $3x-1>x+7$, (b) $4x\geqslant 3(x-1)$, (c) $5-3x<2x-7$, (d) $x(x-1)>0$,
(e) $x(x+3)<0$, (f) $x^2-3x+2\geqslant 0$, (g) $5-4x-x^2\geqslant 0$, (h) $x^2-6x>16$,
(i) $x^2+4\leqslant 4x$, (j) $x+5/x<6$.

2 Given that x is positive, find the range of values of x for which
(a) $2(x-1)<x+4$, (b) $2(x-1)>-4$, (c) $(x+1)(x-2)\geqslant 0$,
(d) $(x+2)(x-1)\leqslant 0$, (e) $(x+3)(x+2)>0$.

3 Find the range of values of x if
(a) $x-3\leqslant -\frac{2}{x}$, (b) $x-5>\frac{6}{x}$, (c) $\frac{3}{x-1}\geqslant\frac{1}{x}$,
(d) $\frac{3}{x-1}>\frac{2}{x+1}$, (e) $\frac{1}{x+2}<\frac{3}{x-1}$.

$y=|x|$

The expression $|x|$ is defined by

$$|x| = x \text{ if } x\geqslant 0$$
$$= -x \text{ if} <0$$

$|x|$ is read 'mod x' and is a special case of $|z|$, the modulus of the complex number z. The graph of $y=|x|$ is given in Figure 7.4.

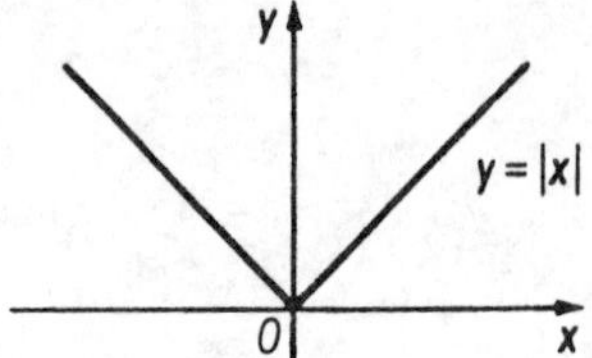

Figure 7.4

Example 1. Find the range of values for which $|x|>|x-2|$

We could do this in three stages, considering the ranges of values $x\leqslant 0$, $0\leqslant x\leqslant 2$ and $x\geqslant 2$, but it is easier if we draw the graphs of $y=|x|$ and $y=|x-2|$. We can see from Figure 7.5 that $|x|>|x-2|$ if and only if $x>1$.

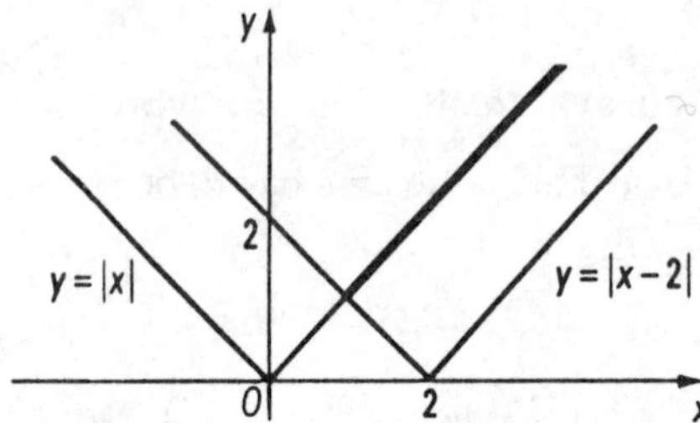

Figure 7.5

Example 2. Find the range of values for which $|x|<|2x-3|$

The graph of $y=|2x-3|$ is slightly more difficult to draw than that of $y=|x-2|$, and we see that we need to find the coordinates of the points of intersection, P and Q, by calculation. To find the x coordinate of Q, solve $y=x$ and $y=2x-3$, and obtain $x=3$. To find the x coordinate of P, solve $y=x$ and $y=3-2x$. (Since $x<3/2$, $2x-3$ is negative, so $|2x-3|=3-2x$.) These meet where $x=1$. From Figure 7.6 we see that

$$|x|<|2x-3| \text{ if } x<1 \text{ or if } x>3$$

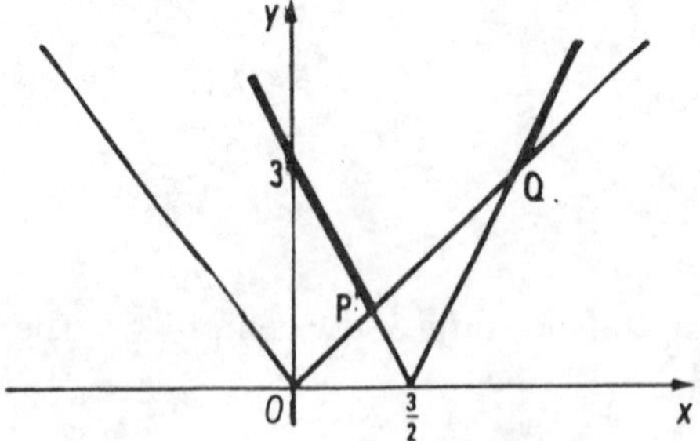

Figure 7.6

Exercise 7.2

1 Find the range of values of x for which

(a) $|x|>1$, (b) $|x|\leqslant 1$, (c) $|2x|\geqslant 1$, (d) $|2x|<3$, (e) $|x|<2x$,
(f) $|2x|\geqslant x$, (g) $|x|<x-1$, (h) $|x|\geqslant 2x+1$, (i) $|x-1|>x+1$, (j) $|x-3|>|x+2|$,
(k) $|x-2|<|2x+1|$, (l) $|x+2|\geqslant|3x-1|$.

Curve sketching

It is vital to be familiar with some common curves; in the examples above, the graph of $y=\dfrac{1}{x-2}$ was deduced from that of $y=\dfrac{1}{x}$ and the graph of the straight line $y=2x-3$ was deduced from the straight line through the origin $y=x$.

Polynomials of the form $y=a(x-b)(x-c)(x-d)$

This graph crosses the x-axis only where $x=b$, c or d; if a is positive, for large x (i.e. $x>d$), y is positive and the graph has the form shown in Figure 7.7(a). If a is negative, the form of the graph is that in Figure 7.7(b), the reflection of Figure 7.7(a) in the x-axis.

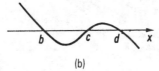

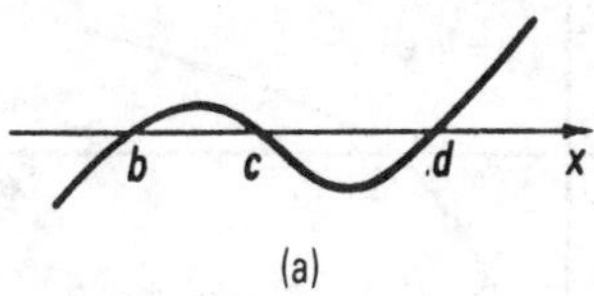

(a)

b c d x

(b)

Figure 7.7

Some common curves

Figure 7.8 shows some common curves with which we must be familiar.

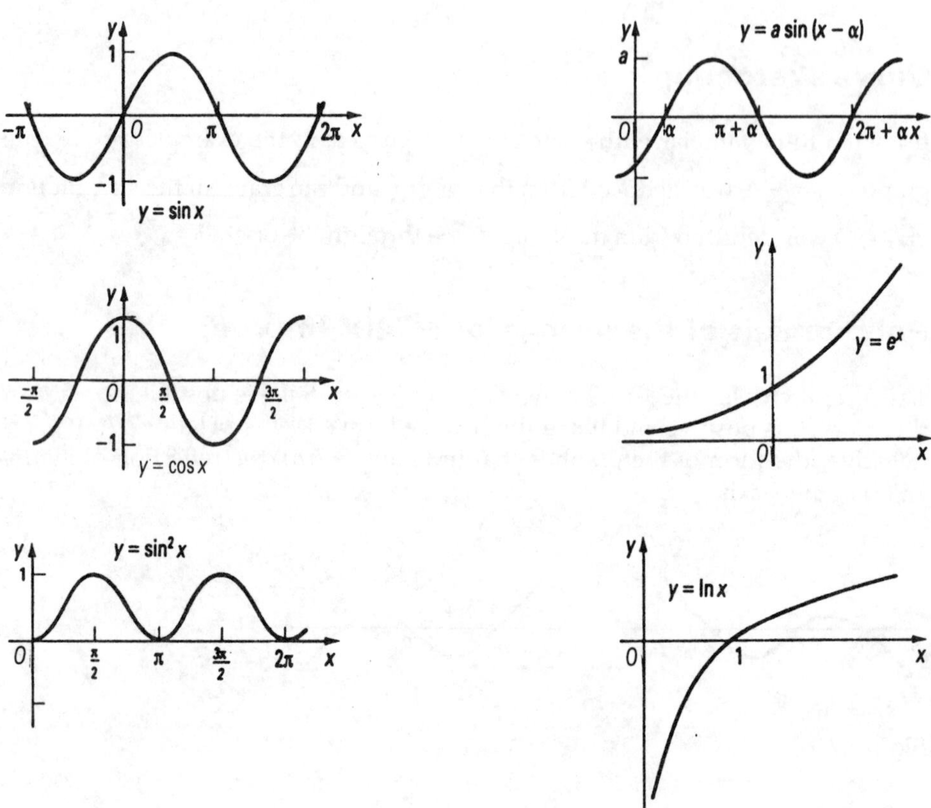

Figure 7.8

Many other curves can be deduced from these. Indeed, since

$$\cos x = \sin\left(x+\frac{\pi}{2}\right)$$
$$= \sin\left[x-\left(-\frac{\pi}{2}\right)\right]$$

$y=\cos x$ can be obtained from $y=\sin x$ by a translation of $-\frac{\pi}{2}$ to the 'right', i.e. $\frac{\pi}{2}$ to the 'left'. $y=e^{-x}$ can be obtained from $y=e^x$ by reflection in the y-axis, $y=\ln(x-1)$ from $y=\ln x$ by a translation of $+1$ to the 'right', i.e. x increasing.

Translations

Comparing $y=x$ and $y=x+1$ (Figure 7.9), the second graph is the result of translating the first by 1 unit, parallel to the y-axis. In general,

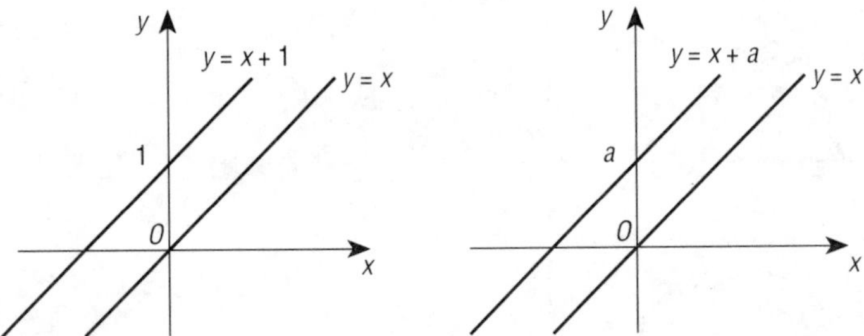

Figure 7.9

$y=x+a$ is the result of translating $y=x$ by a parallel to the y-axis, and the graph of $y=f(x)+a$ is the image of $y=f(x)$ after a translation a parallel to the y-axis.

Comparing the graphs of $y=x^2$ and $y=(x-1)^2$ (Figure 7.10), we see that the second has been obtained from the first by a translation of 1 unit parallel to the x-axis; the axis of symmetry of the first is $x=0$, of the second is $x-1=0$, i.e. $x=1$. Similarly, the graph of $y=(x-a)^2$ is obtained from $y=x^2$ by a translation $+a$ parallel to the y-axis. In general, $y=f(x-a)$ is obtained from $y=f(x)$ by a translation $+a$ parallel to the x-axis, as can be seen by replacing $x-a$ by X.

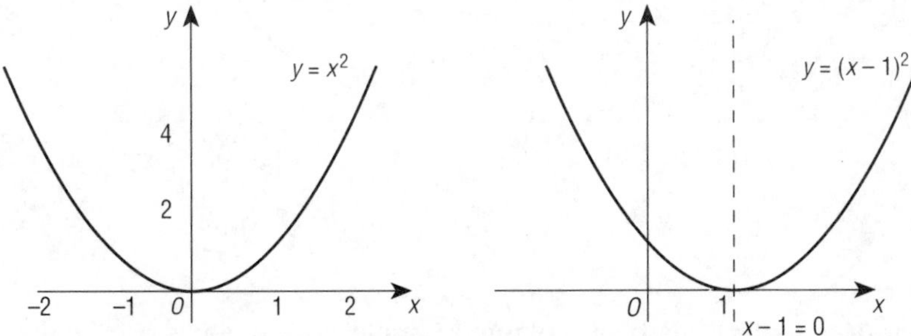

Figure 7.10

Transformations

Compare the graphs of $y=x$ and $y=2x$ (Figure 7.11). For any value of x, the ordinate on the second graph will be twice the corresponding ordinate on the first. The values of y will have been enlarged by a factor 2. Similarly $y=2 \sin x$ is obtained from $y=\sin x$ by an enlargement factor 2 parallel to the y-axis. In general, $y=kf(x)$ is the result of enlarging $y=f(x)$ by a factor k, parallel to the y-axis. This is clear from the expression $kf(x)$, or by comparing $y=f(x)$ and $y/k=f(x)$, and writing $Y=y/k$.

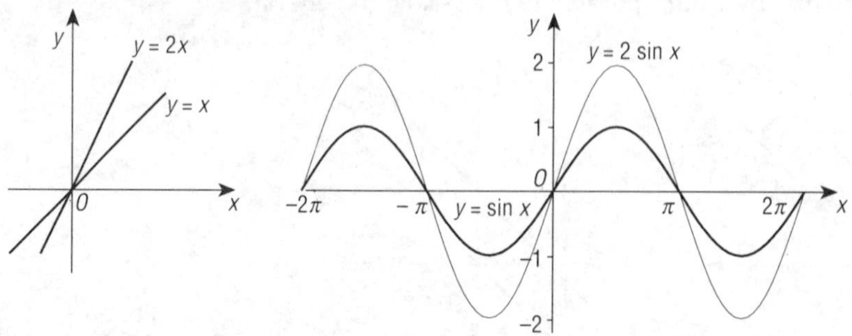

Figure 7.11

By contrast, $y=f(kx)$ is obtained from $y=f(x)$ by reducing the scale along the x-axis by the factor k; $y=\sin 2x$ oscillates twice as x increases from 0 to 2π, whereas $y=\sin x$ only oscillates once (Figure 7.12).

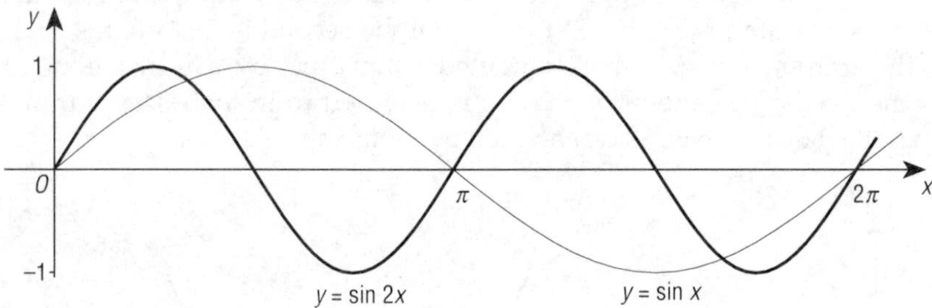

Figure 7.12

Summary

If $y=kf(x)$, the curve $y=f(x)$ has been enlarged parallel to the y-axis, i.e. $y=kY$, where $Y=f(x)$; if $y=f(kx)$, the curve has been reduced by a factor k parallel to the x-axis, where $X=kx$, i.e. $x=X/k$.

If $y=f(x)+a$, i.e. $y-a=f(x)$, the curve $y=f(x)$ has been translated a distance a parallel to the y-axis, increasing y.

If $y=f(x-a)$, the curve $y=f(x)$ has been translated a distance a parallel to the x-axis, increasing the value of x.

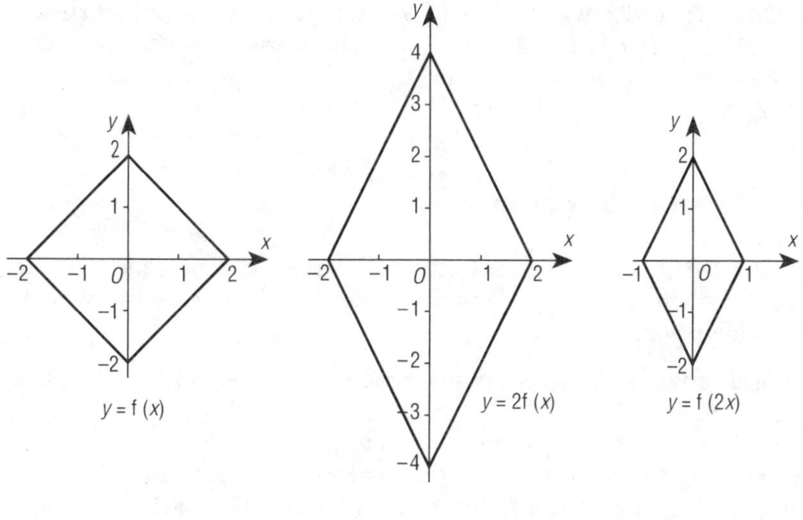

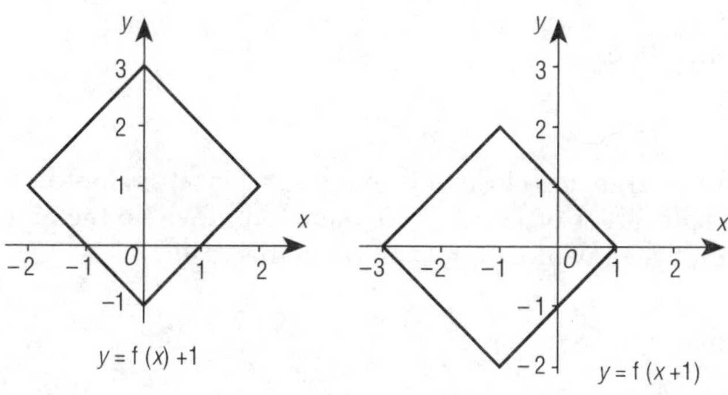

Figure 7.13

Exercise 7.3

1 Sketch the following curves, and write down the coordinates of the points in which they cross the x-axis:
(a) $y=x(x-2)$, (b) $y=x(x+2)$, (c) $y=x(x-1)(x-2)$, (d) $y=x(x+1)(x-3)$, (e) $y=x^2(x-1)$.

2 Sketch the following curves, for values of x from 0 to 360:
(a) $y=\cos x°$; (b) $y=\cos(x+30)°$, (c) $y=1+\cos x°$, (d) $y=2\cos x°$, (e) $y=[\cos x°]^2$.

3 Sketch the following curves:
(a) $y=|x|$, (b) $y=|x|+1$, (c) $y=|x+1|$, (d) $y=2|x|$, (e) $y=|-2x|$.

4 Sketch the following curves:
(a) $y=\ln 2x$, (b) $y=2\ln x$, (c) $y=2+\ln x$.

5 Sketch (on the same axes) the following pairs of curves, indicating the relation between each pair of curves:

(a) $y=x$, $y=x-2$, (b) $y=2x$, $y=-2x$, (c) $y=\frac{1}{3}x$, $y=x$, (d) $y=x^2$, $y=x^2+2$,
(e) $y=x^2$, $y=(x-2)^2$, (f) $y=x^2$, $y=2x^2$, (g) $y=\sin x$, $y=\sin(x-\pi/4)$,
(h) $y=\sin x$, $y=-\sin x$, (i) $y=\sin x$, $y=\sin \frac{1}{2}x$, (j) $y=e^x$, $y=e^{2x}$,
(k) $y=e^x$, $y=\ln x$, (l) $y=\ln x$, $y=\ln |x|$.

The graph of $y=(x-b)/(x-a)$

The method adopted in sketching this curve illustrates the procedure to be followed in cases where the curve cannot be sketched immediately by comparison with a known curve.

(1) Domain and range. Are there any restrictions on the values of x or y? In this case, $x \neq a$.

(2) Symmetry. It is not easy to spot any symmetry.

(3) Crossing the coordinate axes. When $y=0$, $x=b$; when $x=0$, $y=ba$.

(4) Asymptotes. When $x=a$, y is infinite. Writing the equation of the curve as

$$y = \frac{x-a+a-b}{x-a}$$

i.e.
$$y = 1 + \frac{a-b}{x-a}$$

we see that when x is large, y is close to 1, that is, $y=1$ is an asymptote.

(5) Shape for small values of x and y. We have found where the graph crosses the axes, and cannot get any more information in this case.

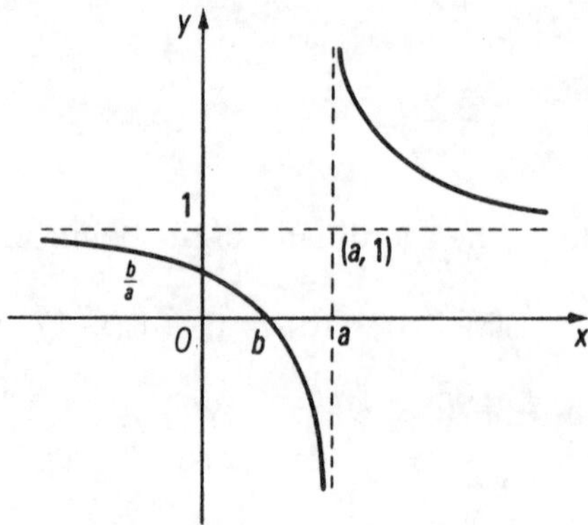

Figure 7.14

To draw the curve, let us suppose that a and b are both positive, and a greater than b. Then we can easily sketch in the asymptote $x=a$, and the points at which the curve crosses the axes. Since $a>b$, when x is large and positive, y is little more than 1; when x is large and negative, y is a little less than 1. This enables us to complete the sketch, as in Figure 7.14.

Having sketched the curve, we see that it has rotational symmetry about $(a, 1)$, but we could hardly have anticipated that from the equation, unless possibly we had written it in the form

$$y-1=\frac{a-b}{x-a}$$

The curve $y=ax/(x^2+a^2)$

Follow the same procedure:

(1) Domain and range? Clearly the domain can be the set of all real numbers, and there are no obvious restrictions on the range.

(2) Symmetry? The function $f:x\to ax/(x^2+a^2)$ is an odd function, so that the curve is symmetrical about the origin. Alternatively, we can say that using the x, y notation, when $x\to -x$, $y\to -y$ so the curve has rotational symmetry order two about the origin.

(3) Crossing the coordinate axes? When $x=0$, $y=0$, and this is the only point at which it crosses the axes.

(4) Asymptotes? There is no value of x for which y is infinite, so there are no asymptotes parallel to the y-axis. When x is large, y is small, so $y=0$ is an asymptote.

(5) Shape for small values of x? When x is small compared with a, $y\approx ax/a^2=x/a$, so that $y=x/a$ is the tangent at the origin. We can now sketch the curve, as in Figure 7.15.

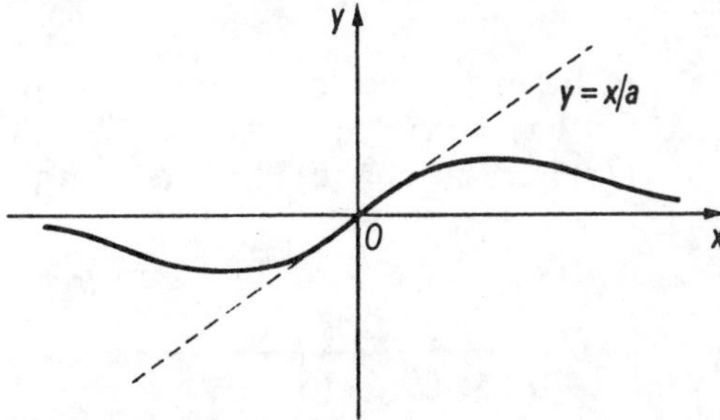

Figure 7.15

Having sketched the curve, we see that there are restrictions on the range, but we could not easily have spotted them, and they did not affect our ability to sketch the curve.

Curves described by the products of functions

If the equation of a curve is the product of functions, e.g. $y=xe^{-x}$, it is often helpful to sketch the graph of each function, here $y=x$ and $y=e^{-x}$, and deduce the required sketch from these, as in Figure 7.16.

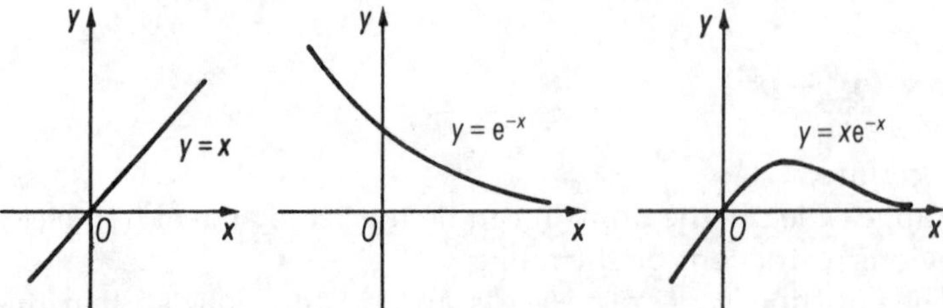

Figure 7.16

Exercise 7.4

1 Give

(i) the domain and range of each of the following;
(ii) any symmetry the curve has;
(iii) the coordinates of the points where it meets the coordinate axes;
(iv) the equations of any asymptotes parallel to the coordinate axes;
(v) the shape of the curve near the origin, in suitable cases:

(a) $y=\dfrac{x-2}{x-3}$, (b) $y=\dfrac{x^2}{x-1}$, (c) $y=\dfrac{x-1}{x^2}$, (d) $y=x^2(x-3)$,

(e) $y=\dfrac{3x-5}{(x-2)(x-3)}$, (f) $y=\dfrac{3x-5}{(x-1)(x-3)}$.

2 Each of the following functions f(x) can be expressed in terms of simpler functions f(x) and g(x). Sketch the graphs of $y=f(x)$, $y=g(x)$ and $y=F(x)$.
(a) $F(x)=x\sin x$, (b) $F(x)=e^x\sin x$, (c) $F(x)=x^2\sin x$, (d) $F(x)=e^{-x}\sin x$.

Miscellaneous exercise 7.5

1 Find the range of values of x for which

(a) $3(x+1)<x-1$, (b) $x-1\geqslant 3x-9$, (c) $x^2-5x+6>0$, (d) $\dfrac{5}{x-1}\geqslant\dfrac{1}{x+1}$,

(e) $x-5>\dfrac{6}{x}$.

2 Given that x is positive, find the range of values of x if

(a) $2(x+1)<x+5$, (b) $x^2-4x+3\geqslant 0$, (c) $x-2>\dfrac{3}{x}$, (d) $\dfrac{2}{x+4}<\dfrac{1}{x+1}$.

3 Given that x is greater than 2, find the range of values of x if

(a) $2(x+1)<x+5$, (b) $x^2-4x+3\geqslant 0$.

4 Find the range of values of x for which

(a) $|x|>2$, (b) $|x|>2x$, (c) $|x|>6-2x$, (d) $|3-2x|>|x+5|$, (e) $|x-2|\leq|2x+1|$.

5 Sketch the following curves, marking the points at which each meets the coordinate axes:

(a) $y=(x-2)(x+4)$, (b) $y=x(x-1)(x+3)$, (c) $y=x^2(x-1)$, (d) $y=x^2(x^2-1)$, (e) $y=(1-x)(2-x)(3-x)$, (f) $y=x^2|x-1|$.

6 Sketch the following curves, for values of x, $-360°\leq x\leq 360°$ showing the greatest and least values of y:

(a) $y=\sin\frac{1}{2}x$, (b) $y=\sin 2x$, (c) $y=\cos^2 x$, (d) $y=1+\cos x$, (e) $y=2\sin(x+120°)$.

7 Sketch the following curves, showing the points at which each meets the coordinate axes, and indicate the nature of the curve when x is large:

(a) $y=e^{-x}$, (b) $y=e^{x^2}$, (c) $y=\ln(x^2)$, (d) $y=\ln(1/x)$.

8 By first using two rough sketches, sketch the following, showing the points at which each meets the coordinate axes and indicating the nature of the curve when x is large and positive:

(a) $y=x\sin x$, (b) $y=x\ln x$, (c) $y=e^{-x}\sin x$.

9 Sketch the following curves, indicating in each the five features listed on page 78 where appropriate:

(a) $y=\dfrac{1}{x-2}$, (b) $y=\dfrac{x+1}{x-2}$, (c) $y=\dfrac{x}{x^2+4}$, (d) $y=\dfrac{x}{x^2-4}$, (e) $y^2=x^2(4-x^2)$.

Arrangements and selections 8

Arranging n objects in a straight line 85

Arranging r objects chosen from n 85

Arranging n objects, r of which are identical 85

Selecting r objects from n different objects 86

Selecting any number of objects from n 86

Relations between the binomial coefficients 87

Notes

Arrangements

n objects all different can be arranged in $n!$ different ways.

n objects, p of one kind, q of another, and the rest all different, can be arranged in $\frac{n!}{p!q!}$ different ways, e.g. there are $\frac{8!}{2!2!2!}$ different ways of arranging the letters in CALCULUS.

Selections

r objects can be selected from n different objects in $\frac{n!}{r!(n-r)!}$ ways, if the order of selection does not matter.

If any number of objects is to be selected from n, all different, that can be done in 2^n-1 different ways.

If any number of objects is to be selected from n objects, p of one kind, q of another and the rest all different, that can be done in $(p+1)(q+1)2^{n-p-q}-1$ different ways.

Relations between binomial coefficients

$\binom{n}{r}=\binom{n}{n-r}$ formerly ${}^nC_r={}^{n-r}C_n$

$\binom{n}{r-1}+\binom{n}{r}=\binom{n+1}{r}$ formerly ${}^nC_{r-1}+{}^nC_r={}^{n+1}C_r$

Arranging *n* objects in a straight line

The first object can be chosen in n ways, the second in $(n-1)$ ways, the third in $(n-2)$ ways, and so on, till finally the nth object is the only one left. Thus n objects can be arranged in a line in $n(n-1)(n-2)\ldots 3\times2\times1$ ways, i.e. $n!$ ways.

Arranging *r* objects chosen from *n*

If we wish to select just r objects out of n and arrange them in order, we can choose the first in n ways, the second in $(n-1)$ ways ... and finally the rth in $(n-r+1)$ ways, so that the number of different arrangements is $n(n-1)(n-2)(n-3)\ldots(n-r+1)$, i.e. $\frac{n!}{(n-r)!}$. These arrangements are sometimes called permutations, and the expression $\frac{n!}{(n-r)!}$ can be written ${}^nP_r$ or ${}_nP_r$.

Example 1. In how many ways can a first, second and third prize be awarded to a class of 15 pupils?

The first prize can be awarded in 15 ways, the second in 14 ways and the third in 13 ways. Thus there are $15\times14\times13$ different ways of awarding the prizes, i.e. 2730.

NB. $15\times14\times13=\frac{15!}{12!}={}^{15}P_{12}$

Example 2. In how many ways can 10 persons be seated at a circular table?

In this example, since the table is circular there is no 'head'. Place one person and fix all the others relative to him (or her). The person on his left can be chosen in 9 ways, the person on his left in 8 ways ... so that there are $9\times8\times7\ldots\times1$ ways, i.e. 9!, 362 880.

In general, n persons can be arranged round a circular table in $(n-1)!$ ways; n beads can be threaded on a circular wire in $\frac{1}{2}(n-1)!$ since the two sides of the wire are considered to be indistinguishable.

Arranging *n* objects, *r* of which are identical

Suppose we have six objects, two of which are identical. Denote the objects by A, B, C, D, X_1 and X_2, suffixes being added to the two otherwise-identical objects denoted by X. Then there are 6! ways of arranging these different objects. But for every arrangement say A X_1 B C X_2 D there is another arrangement A X_2 B C X_1 D that will be indistinguishable when the suffices are removed, so that then the number of different arrangements will be $\frac{1}{2}\times6!$ More generally, the number of ways of arranging n objects, p of which are identical, is $\frac{n!}{p!}$.

Example. Find the number of ways of arranging 10 different pencils, 4 of which are identical red pencils, and the other six are all different.

Using the result above, the number of different arrangements is

$$\frac{10!}{4!} \text{ i.e. } 10\times9\times8\times7\times6\times5$$

$$\text{i.e. } 151\,200$$

Selecting *r* objects from *n* different objects

If we choose three objects, say A, B, C from a set of n, selecting them in the order A, B, C, gives us the same final selection as if we select them in the order A, C, B, or the order B, C, A. There are $3\times2\times1$ different orders in which we can select these three objects; ABC, ACB, BAC, BCA, CAB, CBA, so that the number of different final selections that we can have of three objects from n is

$$\frac{n!}{(n-3)!}\div 6 \text{ i.e. } \frac{n!}{(n-3)!3!}$$

In general, the number of different selections of r objects from n is

$$\frac{n!}{(n-r)!r!}$$

These selections are sometimes called combinations. The expression $\frac{n!}{(n-r)!\,r!}$ is now generally written $\binom{n}{r}$, though the notations ${}^nC_r$ and ${}_nC_r$ may still sometimes be seen.

Selecting any number of objects from *n*

The first object can either be selected or not selected; likewise the second, and third ... and so on. Thus there are 2×2 ... different selections, i.e. 2^n. But in one of these, all the objects will have been rejected, i.e. none will have been selected, so the number of different selections is only 2^n-1.

Alternatively, the number of ways of selecting 1 object is written $\binom{n}{1}$ etc. We require $\binom{n}{1}+\binom{n}{2}+\binom{n}{3}+ \dots \binom{n}{n}$. Using the binomial theorem to expand $(1+x)^n$

$$(1+x)^n=1+\binom{n}{1}x+\binom{n}{2}x^2 \dots \binom{n}{n}x^n$$

Put $x=1$,

$$2^n=1+\binom{n}{1}+\binom{n}{2}+\binom{n}{3}+ \dots +\binom{n}{n}$$

i.e.

$$\binom{n}{1}+\binom{n}{2}+\binom{n}{3} \dots \binom{n}{n}=2^n-1$$

Example. Find the number of different outcomes of 13 football matches, if each match can end in a home win, a draw or an away win.

This is a variation of the problem of choosing any numbers of objects, as instead of there being two possible outcomes for each object, there are three possible results of each match, so that there are

$$3\times3\times\ldots=3^{13}\text{ possible outcomes}$$

Relations between the binomial coefficients

(1) Since if we select any r objects from n, we automatically reject $(n-r)$ objects,

$$\binom{n}{r}=\binom{n}{n-r}$$

This is illustrated by the symmetry of the binomial coefficients in Pascal's triangle.

(2) $$\binom{n}{r-1}+\binom{n}{r}=\binom{n+1}{r}$$

To choose r objects from $(n+1)$ different objects, denote the objects by $a_1, a_2, \ldots a_n$, b. Then either we choose b or we do not choose b. If we choose b, we have to choose $(r-1)$ objects from the n as, which is done in $\binom{n}{r-1}$ ways; if we do not choose b, we must choose all r objects from the n as, in $\binom{n}{r}$ different ways.

Thus $$\binom{n+1}{r}=\binom{n}{r-1}+\binom{n}{r}$$

This result is used in the binomial theorem (page 39). It can also be proved by writing each binomial coefficient in terms of factorials.

Exercise 8.1

1 Find the number of different arrangements of the letters
(a) ON, (b) TEA, (c) SEAT, (d) TABLE, (e) CARPET, (f) BRISTOL.

2 How many different arrangements can be made of two letters chosen from
(a) TEA, (b) SEAT, (c) TABLE, (d) CARPET, (e) BRISTOL?

3 How many different arrangements can be made of the letters
(a) MEET, (b) PAPER, (c) COFFEE, (d) RHUBARB, (e) IMMOBILE, (f) ARRANGING?

4 In how many ways can 6 people be seated at a round table?

5 A host has to seat 3 men and 3 women at a round table. In how many ways can this be done, if men and women are to sit alternately?

6 A hostess has to sit 3 married couples at a round table with men and women sitting alternately. In how many ways can this be done, if no husband is to sit next to his wife?

7 In how many ways can 8 different books be placed on a shelf, if two particular books are to be placed next to each other?
8 In how many ways can 9 different coins be given to Abe, Bess and Chris so that Abe has 2, Bess has 3 and Chris has 4?
9 What is the greatest possible number of points of intersection of
(a) 4, (b) 5, (c) 6, (d) n straight lines?
10 How many triangles can be drawn by joining sets of three points chosen from 12, given that no three of these points lie in a straight line?

Miscellaneous exercise 8.2

1 Find the number of different arrangements of the letters ASTER.
2 Find the number of different arrangements of the letters WALLFLOWER.
3 Find the number of ways in which 8 different beads can be arranged on a circular wire.
4 Find the number of arrangements on a circular wire of 8 beads, 3 of which are identical red beads and the other 5 are all different.
5 In how many ways can a team of four be chosen from eight players?
6 In how many ways can two teams of four be chosen from eight players?
7 In how many ways can two teams of four be chosen from nine players?
8 In how many ways can a selection of fruit be made up from an apple, a banana, an orange and a pear?
9 In how many ways can a selection of fruit be made up from 2 apples, 3 bananas, 4 oranges and 5 pears?
10 Find the number of selections of three cards chosen from a pack of 52 different playing cards. Find also the number of selections of three cards from a suit of 13 different cards.
11 In how many ways can four boys and four girls be arranged in a circle? In how many of these will boys and girls occur alternately?
12 In how many ways can n boys and n girls be arranged in a circle? In how many of these will the boys and girls occur alternately?

Structure 9

Binary operations 91

Closure 91

Commutative operations 91

Associative operations 92

Identity element 92

Inverse element 92

Group: definition 93

Order of an element, order of a group 93

Cyclic groups, generators 94

Isomorphic groups 94

Group of symmetries, group of permutations 95

Notes

A set S is **closed** under an operation $*$ if $a*b \in S$ for all $a, b \in S$.

An operation is **associative** if $a*(b*c)=(a*b)*c$ for all $a, b, c \in S$.

An operation is **commutative** if $a*b=b*a$ for all $a, b \in S$.

The **identity** element e is such that $a*e=e*a=a$ for all elements $a \in S$.

The **inverse** of an element a, written a^{-1}, is such that $a*a^{-1}=a^{-1}*a=e$.

A set S is a **group** under an operation $*$ if
(a) S is closed under $*$,
(b) the operation $*$ is associative over S,
(c) there is an identity element e,
(d) for every element $a \in S$, there is an inverse $a^{-1} \in S$.

Commutative groups are called **Abelian** groups.

Binary operations

A binary operation is an operation defined on two elements of a set, e.g. 'add 2 to 3', 'subtract 2 from 6'. A binary operation is often denoted by $*$, and may be defined in words, as above, or algebraically.

Example. A binary operation $*$ is defined over **R**, the set of all real numbers, by $x*y=2x-y$. Find $x*y$ if $x=3$ and $y=4$.

$$\text{Since } x*y=2x-y$$
$$3*4=6-4$$
$$=2$$

Closure

When a binary operation $*$ is defined over a set S, the set S is closed under $*$ if $a*b$ belongs to S, for all $a, b \in S$. Thus the set $\mathbb{R}$ is closed under the binary operation'add', for the sum of any two real numbers is a real number. The set $\mathbb{Z}$ of integers is closed under 'add', for the sum of any two integers is an integer. However, $\mathbb{Z}$ is not closed if, say, $x*y=x/y$, for if $x=5$ and $y=3$, both elements of $\mathbb{Z}$, $x*y=5/3$, which is not an element of $\mathbb{Z}$.

Example. (a) The set of all even numbers is closed under addition, subtraction and multiplication, but not under division, e.g. $6/2=3$.

(b) The set of all positive integers is closed under addition and multiplication, but not if $x*y=x-y$, e.g. $3-7$ is negative, nor if $x*y=x/y$, for $3/7$ is not an integer.

(c) The set of all powers of 2 is closed under multiplication and if $x*y=x/y$, but not under addition, nor if $x*y=x-y$.

Notice that one counter-example is sufficient to prove that a set is not closed under a particular operation. The proofs that in certain circumstances the sets are closed, are left as an exercise.

Commutative operations

If the order in which we combine the elements does not affect the result, i.e. $x*y=y*x$ for all x, y, the operation is called **commutative**. Thus addition is commutative, for $x+y=y+x$, but subtraction is not commutative, for $x-y\neq y-x$ for x, y. Notice that above, we could describe an operation as 'addition', but not, strictly, as subtraction, for the word does not say whether $x*y=x-y$ or $y-x$.

Associative operations

If we wish to combine three elements under a binary operation, we have to combine them in pairs. Thus to find $1+2+3$ we find either $(1+2)+3$ or $1+(2+3)$. If the order is immaterial, as in this example, the operation is associative, but notice that, e.g., 'subtraction' is not associative, for $1-(2-3)\neq(1-2)-3$. If an operation is associative,

$$a*(b*c)=(a*b)*c$$

for all a, b and c.

Example. A binary operation $*$ is defined over $\mathbb{R}$ by $x*y=\frac{1}{2}(x+y)$. Investigate whether $\mathbb{R}$ is closed under $*$, and whether $*$ is associative or commutative.

If x and y are any real numbers, $\frac{1}{2}(x+y)$ is also a real number, so $\mathbb{R}$ is closed under $*$. Notice though that if the same operation is defined over $\mathbb{Z}$, it is not closed, for $\frac{1}{2}(2+1)$ is not an integer.

Since $\frac{1}{2}(x+y)=\frac{1}{2}(y+x)$, the operation is commutative, but

$$x*(y*z)=x*\tfrac{1}{2}(y+z)=\tfrac{1}{2}x+\tfrac{1}{4}y+\tfrac{1}{4}z,$$

whereas $(x*y)*z=\frac{1}{4}(x+y)+\frac{1}{2}z$, so the operation is not associative.

Identity element

When zero is added to any number, the value of the number is not altered. When any number is multiplied by one, the number is not altered. 0 is called the identity element under addition; 1 is the identity element under multiplication. The identity element (usually denoted by e) has the property that $a*e=e*a=a$ for all a.

Inverse element

$4\times\frac{1}{4}=1$ and $\frac{1}{4}\times4=1$, 1 being the multiplicative identity under multiplication. $\frac{1}{4}$ is called the multiplicative inverse of 4 (and 4 is the multiplicative inverse of $\frac{1}{4}$). The inverse of an element a(usually denoted by a^{-1}) is the element such that $a*a^{-1}=a^{-1}*a=e$. Thus the additive inverse of 4 is -4, since $4+(-4)=(-4)+4=0$, 0 being the identity element under addition.

Example. Multiplication mod 5 is defined over the set of integers S $\{1,2,3,4\}$. Show that S is closed under this operation. Find the identity element, and the inverse of each element.

The table below shows the result of $x*y$, for all $x, y \in S$

	1	2	3	4
1	1	2	3	4
2	2	4	1	3
3	3	1	4	2
4	4	3	2	1

From this we see that $x*y$ belongs to S, for all $x, y \in S$, so that the set is closed under $*$. We see that 1 is the element that leaves all others unaltered, i.e. $x*1=1*x=x$, for all x, so that 1 is the identity element under $*$.

We see that $2*3=3*2=1$, so that the inverse of 2 is 3, and the inverse of 3 is 2. However, $1*1=1$ and $4*4=1$, so that the inverse of 4 is 4, and the inverse of 1 is 1, i.e. 1 and 4 each is its own inverse.

Group: definition

A set of elements S is a group under an operation $*$ if four conditions are satisfied:

(a) S is closed under $*$,
(b) the operation $*$ is associative over S, i.e. $a*(b*c)=(a*b)*c$ for all $a, b, c \in S$,
(c) there is an identity element $e \in S$, i.e. an element e such that $a*e=e*a=a$ for all $a \in S$,
(d) every element $a \in S$ has an inverse a^{-1} in S.

If in addition the operation $*$ is commutative, then the group is called a commutative (or Abelian) group.

Notice that in the example above, all these conditions are satisfied, so that the numbers 1, 2, 3, 4 form a group under multiplication mod 5.

Order of an element, order of a group

An element a of S is said to have order n if n is the smallest positive integer such that $a^n=e$, where $a^2=a*a$, $a^3=a^2*a=a*a^2$ and a^n is defined by $a^n=a*a^{n-1}$, etc. Thus in a group $\{1, 2, 3, 4\}$ under multiplication mod 5,

1 has order 1,
2 has order 4, since $2^4=1$,
3 has order 4, since $3^4=1$
and 4 has order 2, since $4^2=1$

The number of elements in a group is called the order of the group.

Cyclic groups, generators

In a cyclic group, all the elements are 'powers' of one element, e.g. the rotations R through 60° in a plane, where the operation $*$ is 'first one rotation, then the other', $R^2=R*R$, a rotation of 120°, $R^3=R*R^2$, a rotation of 180°, and so on. The element R, corresponding to a rotation of 60°, is called a **generator** of the group, for all other elements can be expressed as powers of R, and the group consists of the six elements R, R^2, R^3, R^4, R^5 and R^6, the last being the identity element. Notice that R^5 would also serve to generate this group, but none of the other elements is a generator. Only cyclic groups have generators.

Example. Show that the numbers $1, -1, i, -i$ form a group under multiplication.

Make up a table as below:

	1	-1	i	$-i$
1	1	-1	i	$-i$
-1	-1	1	$-i$	i
i	i	$-i$	-1	1
$-i$	$-i$	i	1	-1

Taking the group axioms in turn we see

(a) the set is closed under multiplication,
(b) the operation is associative, though this is tedious to check and is often given in examinations,
(c) there is an identity element, 1,
(d) every element has an inverse, namely $1^{-1}=1$, $(-1)^{-1}=-1$, $(i)^{-1}=-i$ and $(-i)^{-1}=i$.

All four criteria are satisfied, so the numbers form a group under multiplication. Notice that i and $-i$ are generators of this group, but not 1 or -1.

Isomorphic groups

Two groups are said to be isomorphic if they have essentially the same structure, which can best be seen, for finite groups, by looking at the group table. If, by renaming the elements and possibly altering the order of the rows and columns in one table, the two tables become identical, then the groups are isomorphic.

Consider the numbers $\{0, 1, 2, 3\}$ under addition mod 4. Then the table is that given in Table 9.1.

Table 9.1

	0	1	2	3
0	0	1	2	3
1	1	2	3	0
2	2	3	0	1
3	3	0	1	2

The group table for the numbers 1, 2, 3, 4 under multiplication mod 5 is given in Table 9.2(a). We can see that by altering the order in which the elements are written the table becomes of the same structure as that in Table 9.2(b). By contrast, Table 9.3 cannot be rearranged to take

Table 9.2(a)

	1	2	3	4
1	1	2	3	4
2	2	4	1	3
3	3	1	4	2
4	4	3	2	1

Table 9.2(b)

	1	2	4	3
1	1	2	4	3
2	2	4	3	1
4	4	3	1	2
3	3	1	2	4

the same form as the first group table, and so is not isomorphic to the first group. Notice also there are no generators of this group.

Table 9.3

	e	a	b	c
e	e	a	b	c
a	a	e	c	b
b	b	c	e	a
c	c	b	a	e

The group to which the integers 0, 1, 2, 3 under addition mod 4 belong is called the cyclic group of order 4; the group illustrated in Table 9.3 is called the Klein four-group (after Felix Klein, 1849–1925). It can be shown that all groups of order 4 are isomorphic to one or other of these groups. The difference in the structure of these two groups can be seen by noticing that in the Klein four-group, each element is its own inverse, so that all elements are of order 2, whereas in the cyclic group there are two elements of order 4; we have already commented that there are no generators of the Klein four-group.

Group of symmetries, group of permutations

The symmetry of an equilateral triangle is such that the triangle is unaltered when rotated in its own plane through 120° (Figure 9.1). This rotation can be described by the permutation ABC→BCA, in which each letter 'moves on' one

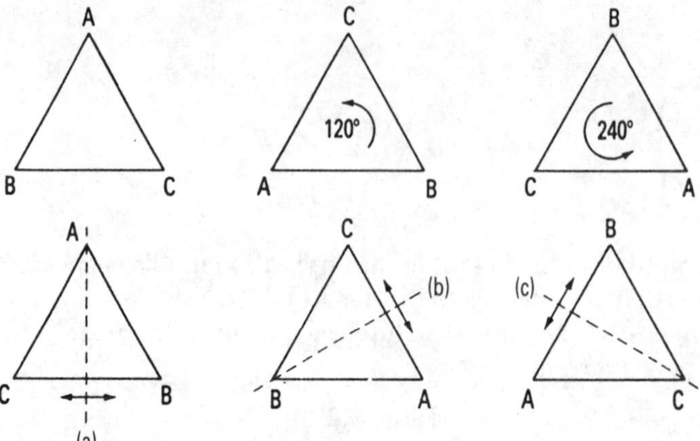

Figure 9.1

place. Similarly, the triangle can be rotated through 240°, described by ABC→ACB, each letter 'moving on' two places. The triangle can also be reflected in axis (a), this reflection being described by ABC→ACB, in which the first letter is unaltered, and the other two interchanged. Similar reflections are described by ABC→CBA (reflection in axis (b)) and ABC→BAC (reflection in (c)), each corresponding to one of the symmetries of the triangle. Let us adopt the following notation. The permutation (which corresponds, as each does, to one of the symmetries of the triangle) ABC→BCA we denote by T_1,

the permutation ABC→CAB we denote by T_2
ABC→ACB T_3
ABC→CBA T_4
ABC→BAC T_5
and the 'identity permutation' ABC→ABC T_0

Then Table 9.4 shows that these permutations (and of course the corresponding symmetries) form a group under the operation 'first one, then the other'.

Table 9.4

	T_0	T_1	T_2	T_3	T_4	T_5
	ABC	BCA	CAB	ACB	CBA	BAC
T_0	T_0	T_1	T_2	T_3	T_4	T_5
T_1	T_1	T_2	T_0	T_4	T_5	T_3
T_2	T_2	T_0	T_1	T_5	T_3	T_4
T_3	T_3	T_5†	T_4	T_0	T_2††	T_1
T_4	T_4	T_3	T_5	T_1	T_0	T_2
T_5	T_5	T_4	T_3	T_2	T_1	T_0

where, for example, the element marked †, $T_3 * T_1$ means 'first T_1 then T_3' and describes ABC→BCA→BAC, equivalent to the single permutation T_5 (corresponding to a reflection in (c)) and the element marked †† T_3*T_4 means 'first T_4 then T_3' and describes ABC→CBA→CAB, equivalent to T_2. Notice that the table is not symmetrical about the leading diagonal, showing that the group is not a commutative (i.e. Abelian) group.

We see in Table 9.4 that the set $\{T_0, T_1, T_2\}$ is closed, and is an example of a *subgroup*. Other subgroups are $\{T_0, T_3\}$, $\{T_0, T_4\}$ and $\{T_0, T_5\}$. The order of the original group p is 6; the orders of the subgroups are 3, 2 and 2 and 2, respectively. It is not a coincidence that these are factors of 6, but the proof of this (Lagrange's theorem) is outside present syllabuses.

Miscellaneous exercise 9.1

1 The operation $*$ is defined over $\mathbb{R}$ by $x*y=1/x+1/y$. Is $\mathbb{R}$ closed under this operation? Is the operation associative or commutative?

The same operation $*$ is now defined over $\mathbb{Z}$. Is $\mathbb{Z}$ closed under $*$?

2 The operation $*$ is defined over $\mathbb{R}^+$ by $x*y=\sqrt{xy}$, the positive square root being taken. Is $\mathbb{R}^+$ closed under $*$? If the operation is defined over $\mathbb{Z}$, is $\mathbb{Z}$ closed under $*$?

Investigate whether $*$ is associative or commutative.

3 If $\mathbf{A}=\begin{pmatrix} 0 & 1 \\ -1 & 0 \end{pmatrix}$ show that the set $\{\mathbf{A}, \mathbf{A}^2, \mathbf{A}^3, \mathbf{A}^4\}$ forms a group under matrix multiplication, and that this group is isomorphic to that formed by $\{1, -1, i, -i\}$ under multiplication.

4 Show that the numbers {1, 3, 5, 7} form a group under multiplication mod 8. Give the inverse of each element, the order of each element, and say to which of the groups of order four it is isomorphic.

5 Say why each of the following does not form a group:

(a) the numbers {1, 2, 3} under multiplication mod 4,

(b) the real numbers under the operation $*$ where $a*b=a+b-ab-1$,

(c) the real numbers under the operation ~, where ~ means the positive difference, e.g. $7\sim2=5$ and $2\sim7=5$.

6 If a and b are any elements in any group, show that the inverse of $(a*b)$, written $(a*b)^{-1}$, is $b^{-1}*a^{-1}$.

7 Functions f_1, ... are defined by

$$f_1:x\to x, \quad f_2:x\to\frac{1}{x}, \quad f_3:x\to -x \quad \text{and} \quad f_4:x\to -\frac{1}{x}$$

Show that these form a group under the usual rule for composition of functions, and find to which group of order four it is isomorphic.

8 The symmetries of a rectangle ABCD (Figure 9.2)

are	rotation through 180°, described by	ABCD→CDAB
	reflection in Ox	ABCD→DCBA
	reflection in Oy	ABCD→BADC
and	the identity element	ABCD→ABCD

Draw up a table to show that these form a group of order four. To which of the two groups, the cyclic group or the Klein four-group, is this isomorphic?

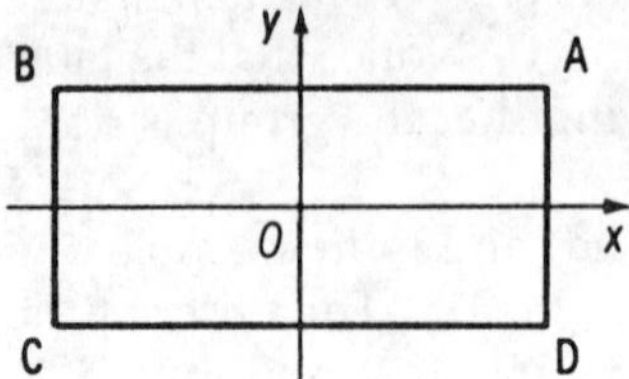

Figure 9.2

9 Describe the symmetries of the rhombus in the same manner as we have described the symmetries of the rectangle. Show that these form a group of order four, and find to which group this is isomorphic.

Plane cartesian coordinates; the straight line and circle 10

The distance between two points 101

The midpoint of the line joining two points 101

The point dividing a line-segment in the ratio $\lambda:\mu$ 102

The centroid of a triangle 102

Equation of a straight line 103

The straight line with given gradient m 104

The straight line in intercept form 104

Parallel and perpendicular lines 104

The angle between two straight lines 105

The equation of a circle 105

Equation of the tangent at (x', y') 106

Notes

If P_1 has coordinates (x_1, y_1) etc., the **distance between the two points P_1 and P_2** is

$$\sqrt{[(x_1-x_2)^2+(y_1-y_2)^2]}$$

the **midpoint** of $P_1 P_2$ is

$$\tfrac{1}{2}(x_1+x_2), \tfrac{1}{2}(y_1+y_2)$$

the coordinates of the **point dividing $P_1 P_2$ in the ratio $\lambda:\mu$** are

$$\frac{\mu x_1+\lambda x_2}{\lambda+\mu}, \frac{\mu y_1+\lambda y_2}{\lambda+\mu}$$

the **centroid** of the triangle $P_1 P_2 P_3$ is

$$\tfrac{1}{3}(x_1+x_2+x_3), \tfrac{1}{3}(y_1+y_2+y_3)$$

the equation of the **straight line through P_1, P_2** is

$$\frac{y-y_1}{y_2-y_1}=\frac{x-x_1}{x_2-x_1}$$

the equation of the **straight line through P_1, with gradient m** is

$$y-y_1=m(x-x_1)$$

Two line gradients m_1, m_2 are **parallel** if $m_1=m_2$, are **perpendicular** if $m_1m_2=-1$.

The **equation of the circle** centre (h, k) radius r is

$$(x-h)^2+(y-k)^2=r^2$$

The circle equation $x^2+y^2+2gx+2fy+c=0$ has

centre $(-g, -f)$, **radius** $\sqrt{[g^2+f^2-c]}$

The equation of the **tangent** at (x', y') to the circle $x^2+y^2=r^2$ is

$$xx'+yy'=r^2$$

The equation of the **tangent** at $(x'y')$ to $x^2+y^2+2gx+2fy+c=0$ is

$$xx'+yy'+g(x+x')+f(y+y')+c=0$$

The distance between two points

By Pythagoras' theorem, from Figure 10.1, we see that the distance between the points $P_1(x_1, y_1)$ and $P_2(x_2, y_2)$ is given by

$$P_1P_2 = \sqrt{[(x_1 - x_2)^2 + (y_1 - y_2)^2]}$$

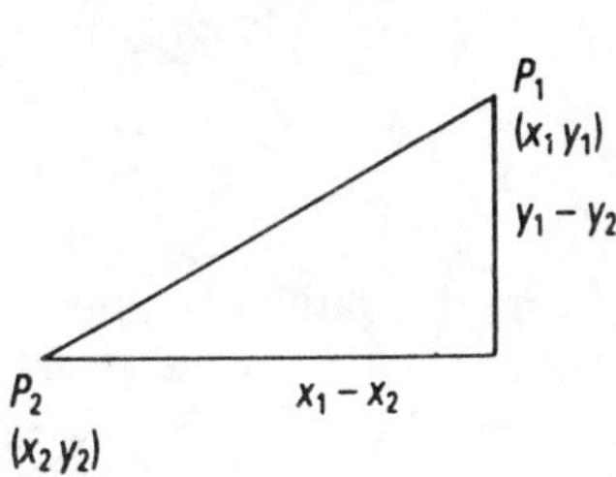

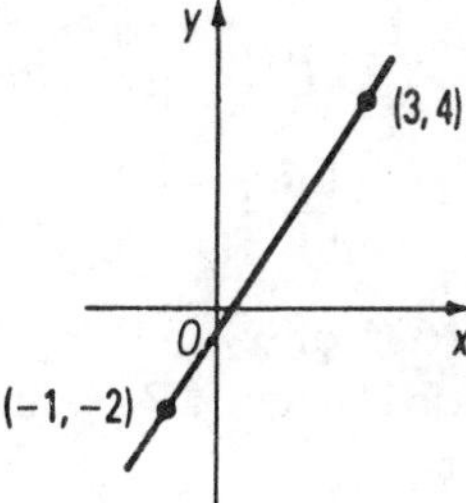

Figure 10.1

Example. The distance between the points (−1, −2) and (3, 4) is given by

$$(P_1P_2)^2 = [3 - (-1)]^2 + [4 - (-2)]^2$$

i.e.

$$P_1P_2 = \sqrt{52}$$

NB. It is usually wise to draw a diagram; be very careful of the signs of the numbers.

The midpoint of the line joining two points

If the coordinates of the midpoint M (Figure 10.2) are (X, Y),

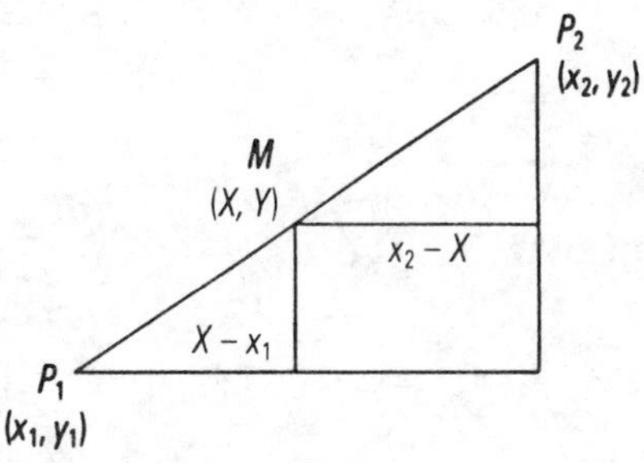

Figure 10.2

considering the X coordinate,

$$X - x_1 = x_2 - X$$

i.e. $$X = \tfrac{1}{2}(x_1 + x_2)$$

Similarly, $$Y = \tfrac{1}{2}(y_1 + y_2)$$

The point dividing a line-segment in the ratio $\lambda:\mu$

Considering Figure 10.2 again, if instead of being the midpoint, M divides P_1P_2 in the ratio $\lambda:\mu$,

$$\frac{X-x_1}{x_2-X}=\frac{\lambda}{\mu}$$

whence $$X=\frac{\lambda x_2+\mu x_1}{\lambda+\mu}$$

Similarly, $$Y=\frac{\lambda y_2+\mu y_1}{\lambda+\mu}$$

NB. Note the order of x_2 and x_1. If M divides P_1P_2 in the ratio $\lambda:\mu$, then λ multiplies the coordinates of P_2, μ the coordinates of P_1.

The centroid of a triangle

If A' is the midpoint of BC (Figure 10.3), the coordinates of A' are

$$\tfrac{1}{2}(x_1+x_2),\ \tfrac{1}{2}(y_1+y_2)$$

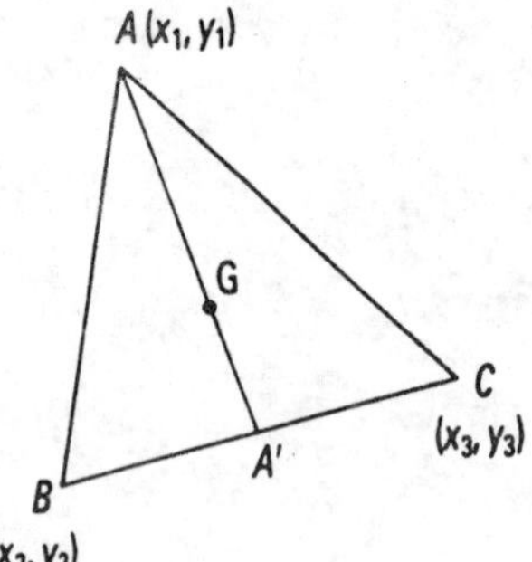

Figure 10.3

If G divides AA' in the ratio 2:1, the x-coordinate of G is

$$\frac{2[\frac{1}{2}(x_1+x_2)]+x_3}{2+1},\text{ i.e. }\tfrac{1}{3}(x_1+x_2+x_3)$$

Similarly, the y-coordinate of G is $\frac{1}{3}(y_1+y_2+y_3)$.

By symmetry, the point G defined in this way divides BB' in the ratio 2:1, and divides CC' in the ratio 2:1.

Exercise 10.1

1 Calculate the distances between the following pairs of points:
(a) (1,2) and (5,5), (b) (1,−2) and (−2,−6), (c) (−1,−3) and (3,−6),

(d) (4,0) and (−8,−5), (e) (2,−3) and (4,−4), (f) (0.8,1.6) and (3.2,2.6).

2 Give the coordinates of the midpoint of the line-segments joining the following pairs of points:
(a) (1,3) and (7,3), (b) (1,3) and (−3,−7), (c) (−2,−5) and (−6,−7),
(d) (−4,−7) and (2,1).

3 Give the coordinates of the two points of trisection of the line-segments joining
(a) (1,3) and (7,12), (b) (−1,3) and (5,−6), (c) (−2,−3) and (4,9).

4 Give the coordinates of the points dividing the line-segments between the pairs of points in the given ratios:
(a) (1,3) and (5,−1) in the ratio 1:3,
(b) (1,3) and (5,−1) in the ratio 3:1,
(c) (−1,4) and (9,9) in the ratio 2:3,
(d) (−1,4) and (9,9) in the ratio 3:2,
(e) (2,3) and (4,1) in the ratio 2:−1.

5 Give the coordinates of the centroid of the triangles whose vertices are
(a) (0,0), (4,5) and (8,7), (b) (1,3), (4,7) and (−5,−1).

Equation of a straight line

The gradient of any straight line through the points (x_1, y_1), (x_2, y_2) is

$$\frac{y_2-y_1}{x_2-x_1}$$

If P is any point on the straight line P_1P_2 (Figure 10.4), then the gradients of PP_1 and P_2P_1 are equal, i.e.

$$\frac{y-y_1}{x-x_1}=\frac{y_2-y_1}{x_2-x_1}$$

which is conveniently written

$$y-y_1=\frac{y_2-y_1}{x_2-x_1}(x-x_1)$$

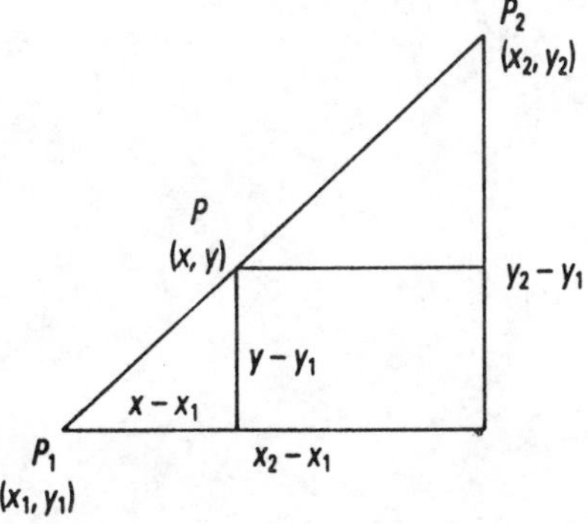

Figure 10.4

The straight line with given gradient *m*

If we require the equation of the straight line through the point (x_1, y_1) with gradient m, any point (x, y) on the line has the property that the line joining it to (x_1, y_1) has gradient m,

i.e. $$\frac{y-y_1}{x-x_1}=m$$

i.e. $$y-y_1=m(x-x_1)$$

The straight line in intercept form

If the straight line makes intercepts a and b on the x and y axes respectively, it passes through the points $(a, 0)$, $(0, b)$. The equation reduces to the form

$$\frac{x}{a}+\frac{y}{b}=1$$

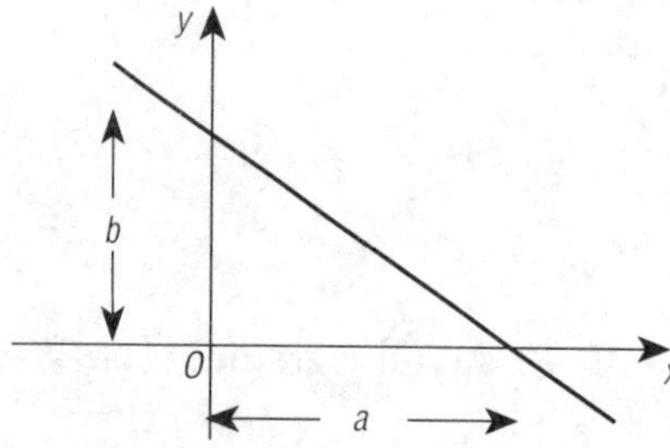

Figure 10.5

Parallel and perpendicular lines

If two straight lines are parallel, their gradients m_1 and m_2 are equal, i.e. $m_1=m_2$.

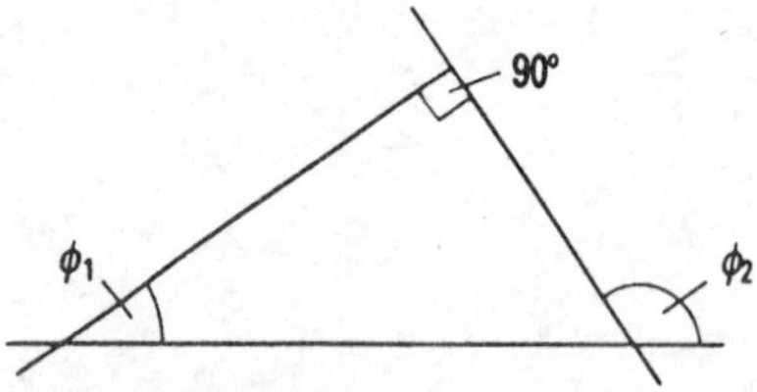

Figure 10.6

If two straight lines are perpendicular, i.e. if $\phi_2=90°+\phi_1$ (Figure 11.6), $\tan(\phi_2-\phi_1)$ is infinite. But

$$\tan(\phi_2-\phi_1)=\frac{\tan\phi_2-\tan\phi_1}{1+\tan\phi_2\tan\phi_1}$$

i.e. the lines are perpendicular if and only if $\tan\phi_2\tan\phi_1+1=0$,

i.e $\quad m_1m_2=-1$

The angle between two straight lines

Generalizing the result above, if the angle between the two straight lines is α, not necessarily equal to 90°, then

$$\tan\alpha=\tan(\phi_2-\phi_1)$$

$$=\frac{m_2-m_1}{1+m_1m_2}$$ (see page 165)

Exercise 10.2

1 Find the equation of the straight line through each of the following pairs of points:
(a) (1,3) and (3,5), (b) (1,3) and (5,11), (c) (2,5) and (−1,−4),
(d) (3,2) and (6,−1), (e) (3,4) and (5,0).

2 Find the equation of the straight line through each point with the given gradient:
(a) (2,3), gradient 2, (b) (3,−1), gradient $\frac{1}{2}$, (c) (3,−2), gradient −1,
(d) (4,−5), gradient 0, (e) (4,−3), gradient $-\frac{1}{2}$.

3 Find the gradient of the straight line making intercepts on the coordinate axes of
(a) 5 and 2, (b) $\frac{1}{2}$ and $\frac{1}{3}$, (c) −2 and 1.

4 Find the equation of the straight lines through the given point parallel and perpendicular to each given straight line:
(a) Through (1,2); $y=x$. (b) Through (2,−1); $y=3x$. (c) Through (2,3); $y=-x$.
(d) Through (−1,−2); $y=\frac{1}{2}x$.

5 Find the tangent of the acute angle between
(a) $y=x+1$ and $y=2x+1$, (b) $y=\frac{1}{2}x+1$ and $y=\frac{1}{3}x$, (c) $y=-x+2$ and $y=-2x$,
(d) $x+2y=5$ and $x+3y=10$.

The equation of a circle

From the definition of a circle, if the point $P(x,y)$ lies on a circle centre (h,k) radius r (Figure 10.7).

$$(x-h)^2+(y-k)^2=r^2 \qquad (1)$$

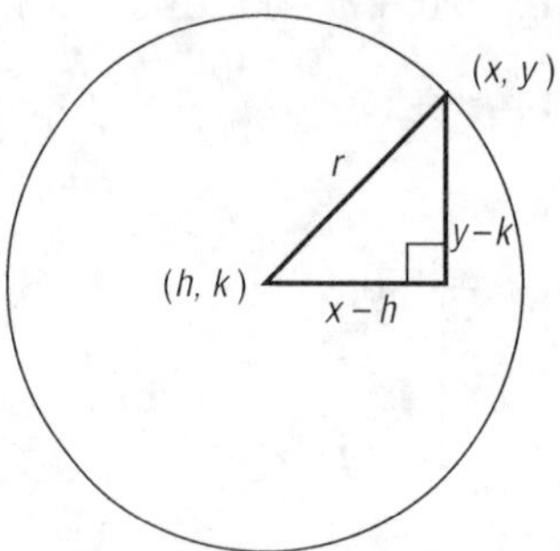

Figure 10.7

In particular, the equation of the circle centre (0,0) radius r is

$$x^2+y^2=r^2$$

Equation (1) can be rearranged as

$$x^2+y^2-2hx-2ky+h^2+k^2-r^2=0$$

so that if the equation is given in the form

$$x^2+y^2+2gx+2fy+c=0 \qquad (2)$$

we can deduce the centre is $(-g,-f)$ and the radius r is given by

$$h^2+k^2-r^2=c, \text{ i.e. } r=\sqrt{(g^2+f^2-c)}$$

Example 1. The equation of the circle centre (3, −1) radius 4 is

$$(x-3)^2+(y+1)^2=4^2$$

i.e. $$x^2+y^2-6x+2y-6=0$$

Example 2. Find the centre and radius of the circle

$$4x^2+4y^2-8x+2y=1$$

First divide by the coefficient of x^2:

$$x^2+y^2-2x+\tfrac{1}{2}y=\tfrac{1}{4}$$

Comparing with (2),

the centre is $(1, -\frac{1}{4})$, the radius is $\sqrt{\{1^2+(-\frac{1}{4})^2+\frac{1}{4}\}}$, i.e. $\frac{1}{4}\sqrt{21}$

Equation of the tangent at (x', y')

The gradient at any point (x', y') can be found by differentiating, i.e.

$$2x+2y\frac{dy}{dx}+2g+2f\frac{dy}{dx}=0$$

whence

$$\frac{dy}{dx}=-\frac{(x'+g)}{(y'+f)}\text{at } (x', y')$$

and the equation of the tangent is

$$y-y'=-\left(\frac{x'+g}{y'+f}\right)(x-x')$$

i.e. $xx'+yy'+g(x+x')+f(y+y')+c=0$ (3)

Example. Find the equation of the tangent to the circle $x^2+y^2+4x+6y-7=0$ at the point $(2, -1)$.

Substituting in (3), we have

$$2x-y+2(x+2)+3(y-1)-7=0$$

i.e. $2x+y-3=0$

Exercise 10.3

1 Write down the equation of the circles with the given centre and radii:
(a) centre (1,2), radius 3,
(b) centre (−2,4), radius 5,
(c) centre (−2,−1), radius 4.

2 Find the coordinates of the centre and the radius of each of the following circles:
(a) $x^2+y^2-6x-8y=0$, (b) $x^2+y^2-2x+4x+4=0$, (c) $4x^2+4y^2-7x-8y-2=0$.

3 Find the equation of the circle through each set of three points:
(a) (6,0), (0,4) and (0,9), (b) (3,3), (1,4) and (0,2).

4 Find the equation of the tangent to $x^2+y^2=25$ at (−3,4).

5 Find the equation of the tangent to $x^2+y^2+4x-6y-12=0$ at (1,7).

Miscellaneous exercise 10.4

1 Write down the distance between the following pairs of points:
(a) (7,4) and (4,0), (b) (7,4) and (−5, −1).

2 Write down the coordinates of the midpoints of the line-segments joining
(a) (3,1) and (5,−3), (b) (−5,1) and (4,1).

3 Find the coordinates of the point dividing (4,1) and (7,7) in the ratio 2:1.

4 Find the coordinates of the point joining (4,1) and (7,7) in the ratio 2:−1. Mark these points in a diagram.

5 Find the coordinates of the centroid of the triangle whose vertices are
(a) (2,1), (4,3) and (3,−1), (b) (4,5), (−1,−4) and (−3,−1).

6 Find the equation of each of the following straight lines:
(a) Through (1,3) and (−2,4).
(b) Through (1,−1) with gradient 2.
(c) Through (2,0) and (0,3).
(d) Through (2,−1) at +45° to the x-axis.
(e) Through (1,−2) parallel to $3y=2x-4$.

(f) Through $(1, -1)$ perpendicular to $3y=2x-4$.

7 Find the tangent of the acute angle between each of the following pairs of lines:
(a) $y=3x-4$ and $y=2x+1$, (b) $3y=x+4$ and $2y+x=1$.

8 Write down the equation of the circle centre $(-3, 2)$ radius 4.

9 Find the coordinates of the centre and the radius of the circle $x^2+y^2-6x+2y-15=0$

10 Find the equation of the circle radius 3 concentric with $x^2+y^2-5x-7y=1$

11 Find the equation of the tangent to $x^2+y^2=25$ at the point $(-3, 4)$.

12 Find the equation of the tangent to $x^2+y^2-6x+2y+6=0$ at the point $(3, 1)$.

13 Find the point on the circle $x^2+y^2-16x+12y+75=0$ which is
(a) nearest to, (b) furthest from, the origin.

14 Find the equation of the circle through the points $(0, 1)$, $(1, 2)$ $(3, 1)$.

15 Find the equations of the circles touching both coordinate axes and passing through the point $(2, 1)$.

16 Find the two values of m for which the line $my=11-3x$ is a tangent to the circle

$$x^2+y^2-8x-12y+25=0$$

17 Find the equations of the two tangents from the origin to the circle

$$(x-3)^2+(y-2)^2=1$$

Parabola and rectangular hyperbola 11

Definition of a parabola 111

Translation of axes 111

Tangent with given gradient m 112

Tangent at the point (x', y') 112

Normal to a parabola 113

Rectangular hyperbola: definition 113

Symmetry of the rectangular hyperbola 114

Asymptotes of a rectangular hyperbola 115

The equation of a rectangular hyperbola, given the asymptotes 116

The tangent at (x', y') 116

The equation of the normal 116

Notes

The locus of a point that moves in a plane so that its distance from a fixed point S, the focus, is equal to its distance from a fixed straight line, the directrix, is a **parabola** (Figure 11.1).

If the axes are chosen so that the equation is $y^2=4ax$, the coordinates of the **focus** are
$(a, 0)$; the equation of the **directrix** is $x=-a$.

The **tangent** to this curve with **given gradient** m is

$$y=mx+a/m$$

the tangent at a **given point** (x', y') is

$$yy'=2a(x+x')$$

It is often helpful to use the **parametric form** (at^2+2at) (see Chapter 13).

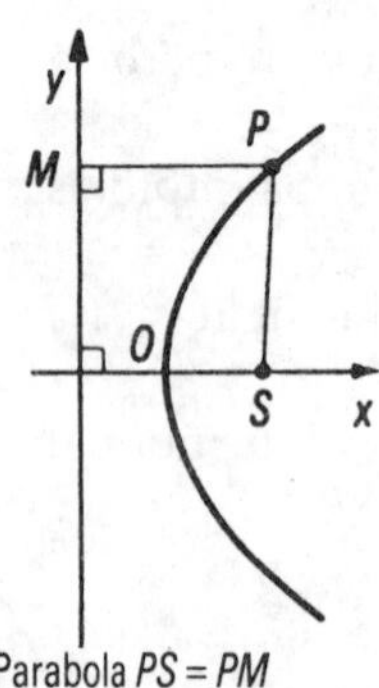

Parabola $PS = PM$

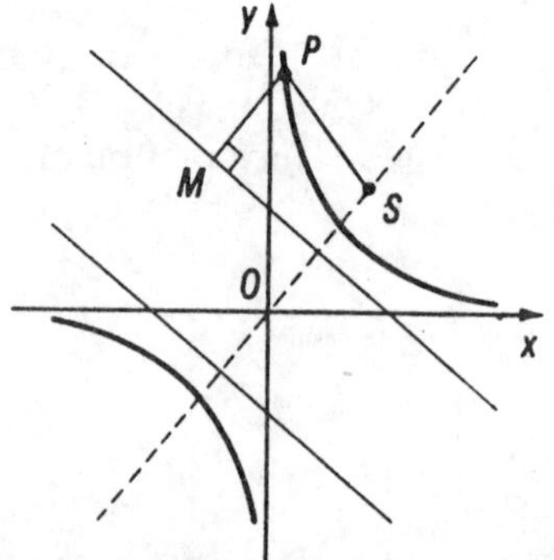

Rectangular hyperbola $PS = ePM$, where $e = \sqrt{2}$

Figure 11.1

If the axes are chosen so that the equation of a rectangular hyperbola is $xy=c^2$, the coordinates of the **foci** are $(c\sqrt{2}, c\sqrt{2})$ and $(-c\sqrt{2}, -c\sqrt{2})$; the **directrices** are $x+y=c\sqrt{2}$ and $x+y=-c\sqrt{2}$.

The ratio PS:PM is called the **eccentricity** e of a conic; the eccentricity of a rectangular hyperbola is $\sqrt{2}$.

The **asymptotes** of the rectangular hyperbola $xy=c^2$ are $x=0$ and $y=0$.

The **tangent** at the point (x', y') to $xy=c^2$ is

$$xy'+yx'=2c^2$$

It is often helpful to use the parametric form $(ct, c/t)$ (see Chapter 13).

Definition of a parabola

A parabola can be defined as the locus of a point that moves so that its distance from a fixed point, called the focus S, is equal to its distance from a fixed line, the directrix.

In Figure 11.2, if S is the focus and X the foot of the perpendicular from S on to the fixed line, the parabola will be symmetrical about SX. The parabola clearly passes through A, the midpoint of SX, for $SA=AX$, so A has the property common to all points on the parabola. Taking A as origin, and AS produced as the x-axis, if the coordinates of any point on the parabola are (x, y), since $PS=PM$, where M is the foot of the perpendicular from P on to the directrix,

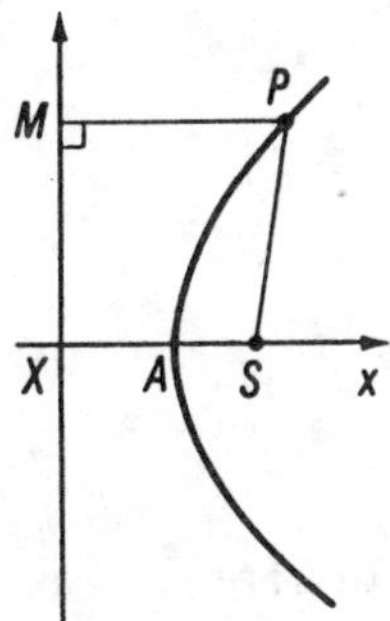

Figure 11.2

$$PS^2=PM^2$$

i.e. $$(x-a)^2+y^2=(x+a)^2$$

i.e. $$y^2=4ax$$

Translation of axes

If the axis of symmetry of the parabola is $y=b$, instead of the x-axis $y=0$, and the vertex is at (c,b) instead of $(0,0)$ (see Figure 11.3), the equation of the parabola is

$$(y-b)^2=4A(x-c)$$

where A is the distance of the vertex from the directrix.

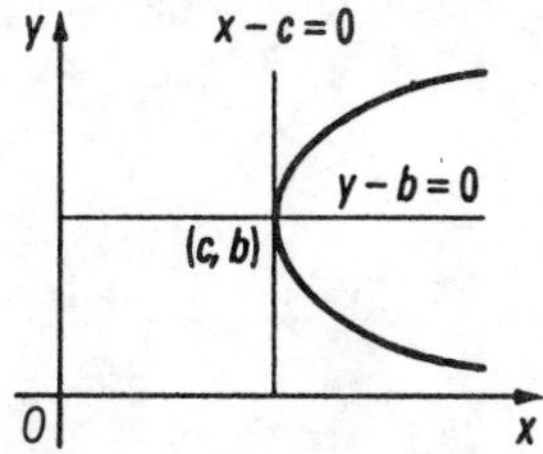

Figure 11.3

Tangent with given gradient *m*

Any straight line with gradient m can be written in the form $y=mx+c$, for some c. We want to find the value of c for which this line is a tangent

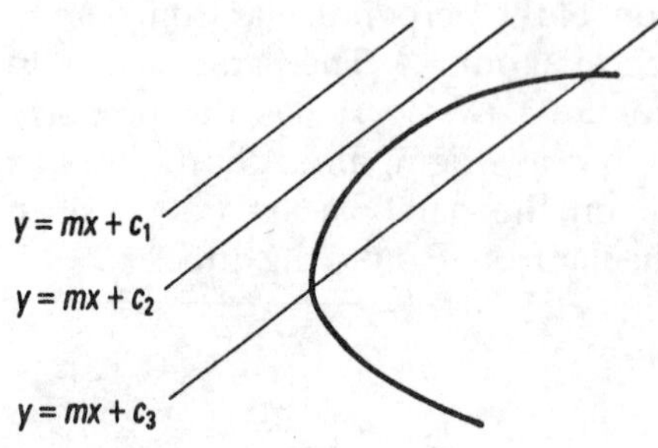

Figure 11.4

to $y^2=4ax$ (Figure 11.4). The line meets the parabola where $(mx+c)^2=4ax$,

i.e. where $\quad m^2x^2+2x(mc-2a)+c^2=0$

If the straight line is a tangent, the quadratic equation will have two equal roots, i.e.

$$4(mc-2a)^2=4m^2c^2$$

i.e. $\quad c=a/m$

so the equation of the tangent is

$$y=mx+a/m$$

Tangent at the point (x', y')

Differentiating the equation of the parabola to find the gradient,

$$2y\frac{dy}{dx} = 4a$$

i.e. $\quad \dfrac{dy}{dx}=\dfrac{2a}{y}$

so the equation of the tangent at (x', y') is

$$y-y' = \frac{2a}{y'}(x-x')$$

i.e. $\quad yy' = 2a(x+x')$, using $(y')^2=4ax'$

Normal to a parabola

The normal at any point is the line through that point perpendicular to the tangent there, so that the normal at (x', y') is

$$y-y' = -\frac{y'}{2a}(x-x')$$

For all except the simplest numerical cases, it is almost invariably easier to use the parametric form (see page 132).

Example. Find the equation of the tangent and normal to the parabola $y^2=12x$ at the point (3,6).

Comparing $y^2=12x$ with $y^2=4ax$, we see $a=3$, so using equation (1), the tangent is

$$6y=6(x+3)$$

i.e. $y=x+3$

Since the gradient of this tangent is 1, the gradient of the normal at the point is -1, so the equation of the normal is

$$y-6=-1(x-3)$$

i.e. $x+y=9$

Exercise 11.1

1 Find the equation of the parabola with the given focus and directrix x:
(a) Focus (4,0), directrix $x=-4$, (b) $(-2,0)$, $x=2$, (c) (0,1), $y=-1$, (d) $(0,-3)$, $y=3$, (e) (2,0), $x=-4$, (f) (4,0), $x=-2$, (g) $(-3,0)$, $x=5$, (h) (0,4), $y=-8$, (i) (0,4), $y=8$, (j) (2,2), $x=-2$.

2 Find the equation of the axis of symmetry of each of the following parabolae, and the coordinates of each vertex:
(a) $y^2=4(x-1)$, (b) $y^2=12(4-x)$, (c) $(y-1)^2=12(x-4)$, (d) $4y=(x-2)^2$, (e) $4(y-1)=(x-2)^2$.

3 Find the tangent with gradient 2 to each of these parabolae:
(a) $y^2=4x$, (b) $y^2=12x$, (c) $4y^2=x$.

4 Find the tangent to the parabola $y^2=8x$ with gradient
(a) 1, (b) 2, (c) $\frac{1}{2}$.

5 Show that there are two tangents to the parabola $y^2=4x$ through $(-1,2)$ and that these two tangents are perpendicular.

Rectangular hyperbola: definition

If instead of satisfying $PS=PM$, the point P is such that $PS=ePM$, P describes a general conic; if $e=1$, we have seen the locus is a parabola.

If $0<e<1$, the locus is an ellipse,
if $e=1$, a parabola,
if $e>1$, a hyperbola, where if
$e=\sqrt{2}$, we have a special case, a rectangular hyperbola.

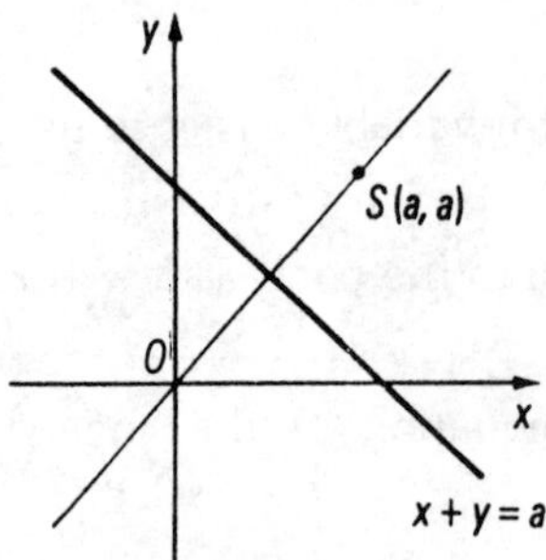

Figure 11.5

Take the coordinates of S as (a, a); the equation of the directrix as $x+y=a$ (Figure 11.5). Then the perpendicular distance of any point (x',y') from the straight line $x+y=a$ is

$$\frac{x'+y'-a}{\sqrt{2}}$$

so that if $PS=\sqrt{2}PM$, i.e. $PS^2=2PM^2$

i.e. $$(x-a)^2+(y-a)^2=2\left(\frac{x+y-a}{\sqrt{2}}\right)^2$$

whence $$xy=\tfrac{1}{2}a^2$$

The form $xy=c^2$ or $y=c^2/x$ is more commonly used; in this case the focus is $(c\sqrt{2}, c\sqrt{2})$ and the directrix is $x+y=c\sqrt{2}$.

Symmetry of the rectangular hyperbola

Since the equation $xy=c^2$ is satisfied by $(-x', -y')$ for all (x', y') such that $x'y'=c^2$, the curve is symmetrical about the origin. Corresponding to the one focus S we already have, $(c\sqrt{2}, c\sqrt{2})$ there will also be a second focus S' $(-c\sqrt{2}, -c\sqrt{2})$, and a second directrix $x+y=-c\sqrt{2}$ (Figure 11.6).

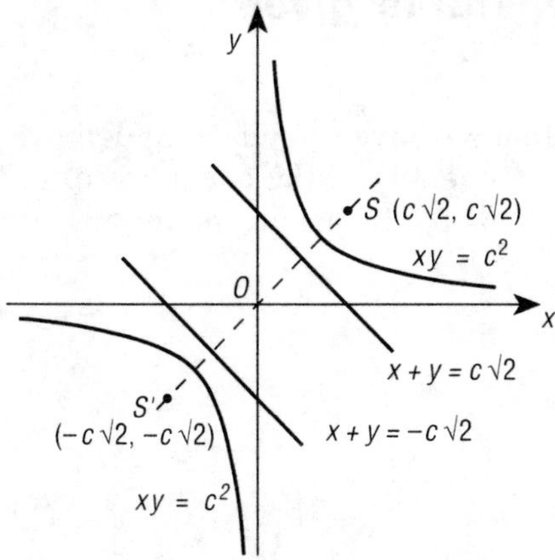

Figure 11.6

Asymptotes of a rectangular hyperbola

Writing the equation in the form $y=c^2/x$, we see that as x becomes large, c^2/x becomes small, as small as we wish, so that the curve becomes as close as we wish to $y=0$. The straight line $y=0$ is called an asymptote; similarly $x=0$ is also an asymptote.

Translating the axes, to obtain the hyperbola $(x-a)(y-b)=c^2$, we see that can be written

$$y-b=c^2/(x-a)$$

so that as x becomes large, $y-b$ becomes as small as we wish, and one asymptote is $y=b$; similarly, the other asymptote is $x=a$ (Figure 11.7).

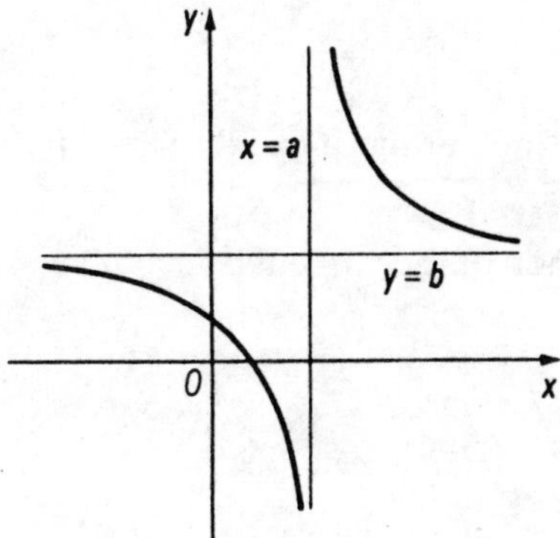

Figure 11.7

The equation of a rectangular hyperbola, given the asymptotes

Given the asymptotes $x=a$, $y=b$, we can see that we have a family of hyperbolae $(x-a)(y-b)=k$, for differing values of k. More generally, if the equations of the two asymptotes are $a_1x+b_1y+c_1=0$, $a_2x+b_2y+c_2=0$, the family of rectangular hyperbolae with these as asymptotes is

$$(a_1x+b_1y+c_1)(a_2x+b_2y+c_2)=k$$

The tangent at (*x′*, *y′*)

Differentiating $xy=c^2$,

$$x\frac{dy}{dx}+y=0$$

$\frac{dy}{dx}=-\frac{y'}{x'}$ at (x', y')

so the equation of the tangent is

$$y-y'=-\frac{y'}{x'}(x-x')$$

i.e. $xy'+yx'=2c^2$, using $x'y'=c^2$

The equation of the normal

Since the normal is perpendicular to the tangent, the gradient is x'/y' and the equation is

$$xx'-yy'=(x')^2-(y')^2$$

Example. Find the equation of the tangent and the normal at (3,12) to the curve $xy=36$.

Comparing $xy=36$ with $xy=c^2$, $c=6$, so the equation of the tangent is

$$3y+12x=72$$

i.e. $y+4x=24$

and the normal, having gradient $\frac{1}{4}$, is

$$y-12=\frac{1}{4}(x-3)$$

i.e. $4y=x+45$.

This can be obtained from $xx'-yy'=(x')^2-(y')^2$,

i.e.
$$3x-12y=3^2-12^2$$
$$3x-12y=-135$$
$$x-4y=-45$$

Exercise 11.2

1 Find the coordinates of the foci and equations of the directrices of the rectangular hyperbolae
(a) $xy=8$, (b) $xy=-8$, (c) $4xy=1$.

2 Find the equations of the asymptotes of the hyperbolae rectangular
(a) $(x-1)(y-2)=1$, (b) $(x-2)(y+4)=100$, (c) $(x-2)(y-3)=-1$.
Sketch each curve.

3 Find the equation of the rectangular hyperbola with $x=2$ and $y=1$ as asymptotes, passing through
(a) (3,2), (b) (0,0).
Sketch each curve.

4 Find the equation of the tangent and of the normal to
(a) $xy=4$ at (4,1), (b) $xy=32$ at (4,8), (c) $xy=-1$ at $(2,\frac{1}{2})$.

5 Points A (2,2), B (4,1) and C (−4,−1) lie on the rectangular hyperbola $xy=4$. The line through A perpendicular to BC meets the hyperbola again at D.
(a) Find the coordinates of D.
(b) Show that BD is perpendicular to AC and CD is perpendicular to AB.

Miscellaneous exercise 11.3

1 Find the equation of the parabola focus (4,0), directrix $x=-4$.

2 Find the equation of the parabola focus (4,3) directrix $x=-2$.

3 Find the value of c if $y=2x+c$ is a tangent to the parabola $y^2=6x$.

4 Find the equation of the tangent to the parabola $y^2=8x$ at the point (2,4). Find also the equation of the normal at this point.

5 Find an equation satisfied by l, m, n and a if $lx+my+n=0$ is a tangent to $y^2=4ax$.

6 The tangent at the point (x',y') meets the asymptotes $y=0$, $x=0$ at P_1,P_2 respectively. Prove that the area of the triangle OP_1P_2 is independent of x' and y'.

7 With the data of Q.6 prove that (x',y') is always the midpoint of P_1,P_2.

8 The tangent at $P_1(x_1y_1)$ meets an asymptote at Q_1; the tangent at P_2 (x_2, y_2) meets that asymptote at Q_2; show that P_1P_2 always passes through the midpoint of Q_1,Q_2.

9 The tangent at $P(x',y')$ meets the asymptotes at T_1,T_2: the normal at P meets the asymptotes at N_1,N_2,N_1 being on OT_1. Prove that $OT_1{:}OT_2=ON_2{:}N_1O$.

10 Find the relation satisfied by l, m, n, and c if $lx+my+n=0$ touches $xy=c^2$.

Ellipse and hyperbola 12

Ellipse and hyperbola: definitions 122

The equation of an ellipse 122

The equation of a hyperbola 122

Symmetry of an ellipse 123

Sum of the focal distances of an ellipse 123

Equation of the tangent at (x',y') 123

Equation of the normal at (x',y') 124

Tangent to an ellipse with given gradient m 124

Hyperbolae: foci, directrices and asymptotes 125

Equations of tangent and of normal 126

Notes

The **eccentricity** of an ellipse is less than 1, i.e. $e>1$.

If the equation of an ellipse is

$$\frac{x^2}{a^2}+\frac{y^2}{b^2}=1,$$

the **foci** are $(ae,0)$ and $(-ae,0)$; the **directrices** are $x=a/e$, $x=-a/e$.

The **tangent at the point** (x',y') is

$$\frac{xx'}{a^2}+\frac{yy'}{b^2}=1,$$

the **tangents with given gradient** m are

$$y=mx\pm\sqrt{(a^2m^2+b^2)}.$$

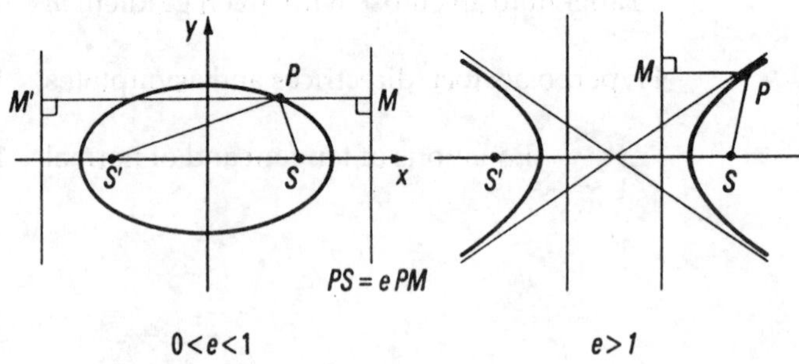

Figure 12.1

The **eccentricity** of a hyperbola is greater than 1, i.e. $e>1$.

If the equation of a hyperbola is

$$\frac{x^2}{a^2}-\frac{y^2}{b^2}=1,$$

the **foci** are also at $(ae,0)$ and $(-ae,0)$; the **directrices** are $x=a/e$, $x=-a/e$.

The **tangent** at (x',y') is

$$\frac{xx'}{a^2}-\frac{yy'}{b^2}=1,$$

the **tangents with given gradient** m are

$$y=mx\pm\sqrt{(a^2m^2-b^2)}.$$

The **asymptotes** of $\frac{x^2}{a^2}-\frac{y^2}{b^2}=1$ are

$$\frac{x^2}{a^2}-\frac{y^2}{b^2}=0, \text{ i.e. } \frac{x}{a}-\frac{y}{b}=0 \text{ and } \frac{x}{a}+\frac{y}{b}=0$$

Ellipse and hyperbola: definitions

In Chapter 11, we saw that the locus of a point P whose distance from a fixed point S, the focus, is proportional to its distance from a fixed line, the directrix, is called an ellipse if the constant of proportion e is such that $0<e<1$; a hyperbola if $e>1$, with the special case $e=\sqrt{2}$ giving a form called a rectangular hyperbola, the asymptotes of which are at right angles. The ellipse and hyperbola clearly have much in common, and we shall see many similarities between the corresponding equations.

The equation of an ellipse

The simplest form for the equation of an ellipse occurs when we take one focus at $(ae,0)$, and the corresponding directrix as $x=a/e$ (Figure 12.2). Then $PS^2=(x-ae)^2+y^2$, $PM=(a/e-x)$, so that since $PS^2=e^2PM^2$,

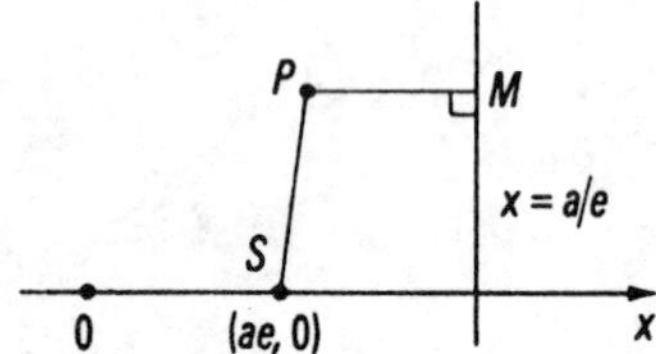

Figure 12.2

$$(x-ae)^2+y^2=e^2(a/e-x)^2$$

i.e. $$x^2(1-e^2)+y^2=a^2(1-e^2) \quad (1)$$

Writing $b^2=a^2(1-e^2)$, and dividing by b^2, we have

$$\frac{x^2}{a^2}+\frac{y^2}{b^2}=1$$

The equation of a hyperbola

To find the equation of a hyperbola, we proceed exactly as above, until we have obtained equation (1). Now, since $e>1$ we cannot write $b^2=a^2(1-e^2)$, we have to write $b^2=a^2(e^2-1)$, and the equation of the hyperbola is

$$\frac{x^2}{a^2}-\frac{y^2}{b^2}=1$$

Symmetry of an ellipse

Since the equation of an ellipse only contains even powers of x, if (x',y') lies on this ellipse, so does $(-x',y')$, and the curve is symmetrical about the y-axis; similarly the curve is symmetrical about the x-axis, as it only contains even powers of y. Thus there will be a second focus S' at $(-ae,0)$ and a second directrix $x=-a/e$.

Sum of the focal distances of an ellipse

We may be familiar with the rough method used to draw an ellipse, with a length of string pinned at each end to a board, allowing a pencil to move along the string. This method uses the property that $PS+PS'$ is constant (Figure 12.3).

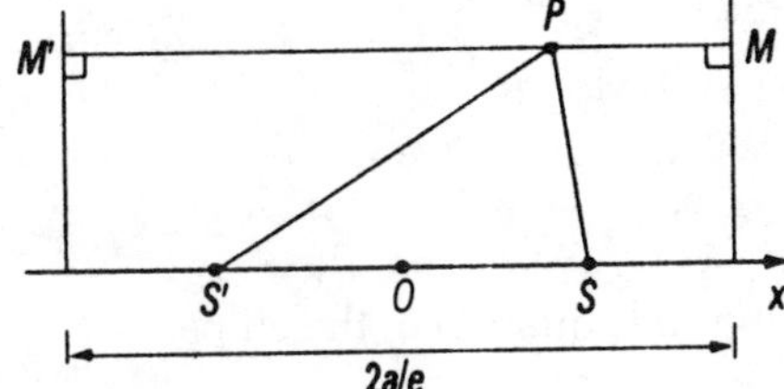

Figure 12.3

Since $$PS=ePM, \text{ and } PS'=ePM$$
$$PS+PS'=e(PM+PM')$$
$$=e(2a/e)$$

Since the distance between the two directrices is constant, for all positions of P,

$$PS+PS'=2a$$

Equation of the tangent at (x', y')

Differentiating the equation of the ellipse

$$\frac{2x}{a^2}+\left(\frac{2y}{b^2}\right)\frac{\mathrm{d}y}{\mathrm{d}x}=0$$

so the gradient at (x',y') is $-b^2x'/a^2y'$, and the equation of the tangent is

$$y-y'=-\left(\frac{b^2x'}{a^2y'}\right)\left(x-x'\right)$$

which reduces to $$\frac{xx'}{a^2}+\frac{yy'}{b'}=1$$

after using $$\frac{(x')^2}{a^2}+\frac{(y')^2}{b^2}=1$$

Equation of the normal at (x', y')

Since the gradient of the normal is $(a^2y')/(b^2x')$, the equation is

$$y-y' = \frac{a^2y'}{b^2x'}(x-x')$$

which reduces to $a^2xy'-b^2yx' = (a^2-b^2)x'y'$

This form should not be committed to memory, but rather the method should be used in any numerical examples.

Example. Find the equation of the tangent and normal at (1,1) to the ellipse $2x^2+y^2=3$.

Differentiating, $$4x+2y\frac{dy}{dx}=0$$

so the gradient at (1,1) is -2, and the equation of the tangent is

$$y-1=-2(x-1)$$

i.e. $$2x+y=3$$

This could have been obtained by rearranging the equation of the ellipse

$$\frac{x^2}{(\frac{3}{2})}+\frac{y^2}{3} = 1$$

and using $$\frac{xx'}{a^2}+\frac{yy'}{b^2} = 1$$

to give $$\frac{1x}{(\frac{3}{2})}+\frac{1y}{3} = 1$$

i.e. $$2x+y = 3$$

To find the normal, since this is perpendicular to the tangent the gradient is $\frac{1}{2}$, so the equation is

$$y-1=\tfrac{1}{2}(x-1)$$

i.e. $$2y=x+1$$

Tangent to an ellipse with given gradient m

The equation of the tangent will be of the form $y=mx+c$, for some c. This meets the ellipse where

$$\frac{x^2}{a^2}+\frac{(mx+c)^2}{b^2}=1$$

i.e. $$(b^2+a^2m^2)x^2+2a^2mcx+a^2(c^2-b^2)=0$$

If this line is to be a tangent, the quadratic equation must have equal roots, and

$$4a^4m^2c^2=4(b^2+a^2m^2)a^2(c^2-b^2)$$

whence $\quad c^2=a^2m^2+b^2$

so the equation of a tangent with gradient m is

$$y=mx+\sqrt{(a^2m^2+b^2)}$$

There are, of course, two tangents with given gradient m,

$$y=mx\pm\sqrt{(a^2m^2+b^2)} \tag{2}$$

since $\quad c=\pm\sqrt{(a^2m^2+b^2)}$

Example. Find the equation of the tangent with gradient 2 to the ellipse $x^2/4+y^2/9=1$

Any straight line with gradient 2 has equation of the form $y=2x+c$. This will be a tangent to the ellipse if

$$\frac{x^2}{4}+\frac{(2x+c)^2}{9}=1$$

has equal roots, i.e. if

$$25x^2+16cx+4(c^2-9)=0$$

has equal roots. Thus

$$(16c)^2=4\times25\times4(c^2-9)$$
$$16c^2=25c^2-225$$
$$c^2=25,\ c=\pm5$$

the two tangents with gradient 2 are $y=2x\pm5$.

Alternatively, comparing with the standard form of the equation of the ellipse, we have $a^2=4$, $b^2=9$, and $m=2$, so using equation (2), the equation of the tangents is

$$y=2x\pm\sqrt{(4\times2^2+9)}$$

i.e. $\quad y=2x\pm5$

Hyperbolae; foci, directrices and asymptotes

We have seen that the equation of a hyperbola can be written in the form

$$\frac{x^2}{a^2}-\frac{y^2}{b^2}=1 \tag{3}$$

where $b^2=a^2(e^2-1)$, the foci are $(\pm ae,0)$, and the directrices are $x=\pm a/e$. If we are given the equation in the form (3), then we can deduce the foci, using $b^2=a^2(e^2-1)$. The equation of the hyperbola can be written

$$\left(\frac{x}{a}-\frac{y}{b}\right)\left(\frac{x}{a}+\frac{y}{b}\right)=1$$

so that
$$\frac{x}{a}-\frac{y}{b}=\frac{1}{\frac{x}{a}+\frac{y}{b}}$$

or
$$\frac{x}{a}+\frac{y}{b}=\frac{1}{\frac{x}{a}-\frac{y}{b}}$$

Thus if x and y are each large and of the same sign, $1/(x/a+y/b)$ is as small as we wish, so that $x/a-y/b=0$ is an asymptote. Similarly $x/a+y/b=0$ is the other asymptote (Figure 12.4).

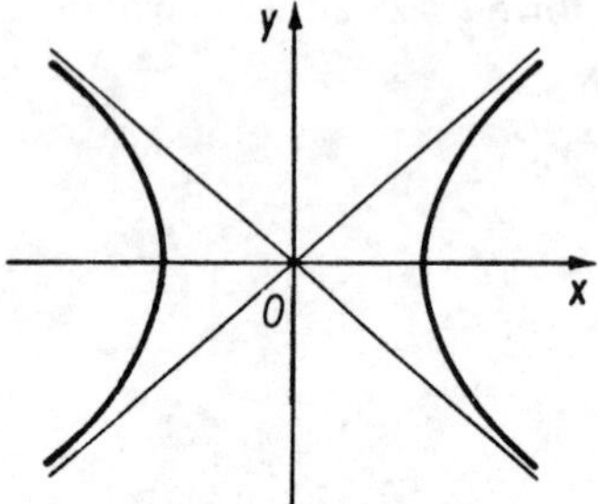

Figure 12.4

As with the ellipse, the hyperbola is symmetrical about the x-axis and the y-axis.

Equations of tangent and of normal

We can show in exactly the same manner as for the ellipse that the equation of the tangent at the point (x',y') is

$$\frac{xx'}{a^2}-\frac{yy'}{b^2}=1 \tag{4}$$

and the equation of the tangents with a given gradient m are

$$y=mx\pm\sqrt{(a^2m^2-b^2)} \tag{5}$$

The equation of the normal at (x',y') is

$$a^2y'x+b^2x'y=(a^2+b^2)x'y'$$

Example. Find the foci, directrices and asymptotes of the hyperbola $9x^2-25y^2=225$, and the equation of the tangent at $(\frac{25}{3}, 4)$.

Rearranging the equation of the hyperbola,

$$\frac{x^2}{25}-\frac{y^2}{9}=1$$

and comparing with (3), we see $a^2=25$, $b^2=9$, so that

$$25=9(e^2-1)$$

and $\quad e=\frac{1}{3}\sqrt{34}$.

Thus the foci are $(\pm\frac{5}{3}\sqrt{34}, 0)$ and the directrices are $x=\pm 15/\sqrt{34}$, and the asymptotes

$$\frac{x^2}{25}-\frac{y^2}{9}=0$$

i.e. $\quad \frac{x}{5}-\frac{y}{3}=0$ and $\frac{x}{5}+\frac{y}{3}=0$

To find the tangent at (25/3,4), we can differentiate (3) to find the gradient , or substituting in (4), we have

$$\frac{x}{25}\left(\frac{25}{3}\right)-\frac{y}{9}(4)=1$$

i.e. $\quad 3x-4y=9$

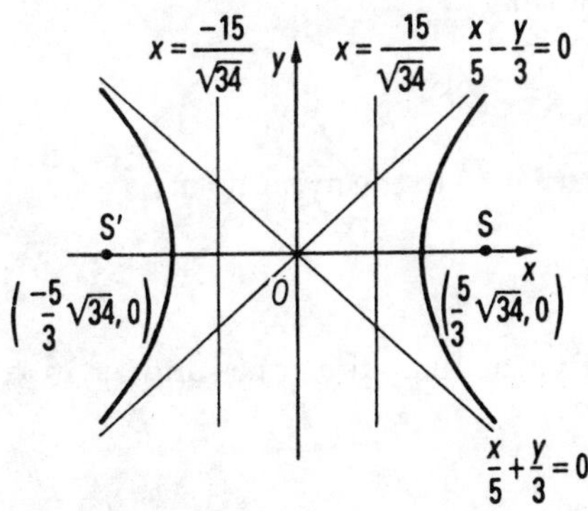

Figure 12.5

Exercise 12.1

1 Find the coordinates of the foci and the eccentricity of

$$4x^2+9y^2=36$$

and of $\quad 9x^2+4y^2=36$

Draw sketches illustrating the two ellipses.

2 Find the equation of the tangent and of the normal at (2,1) to the ellipse $2x^2+3y^2=11$.

Deduce the equation of the tangent and normal at $(2, -1)$.

3 Find the equations of the tangents with gradient 4 to the ellipse

$$\frac{x^2}{9}+\frac{y^2}{25}=1$$

4 Find the equations of the axes of symmetry, the coordinates of the foci, and the equations of the directrices of the ellipse

$$\frac{(x+2)^2}{16}+\frac{(y-1)^2}{7}=1$$

5 Find the points of contact of the tangents of gradient 1 with the ellipse

$$\frac{x^2}{64}+\frac{y^2}{225}=1$$

and obtain the equations of the two normals to this ellipse which have gradient -1.

6 Find the foci, directrices and asymptotes of

$$\frac{x^2}{4}-\frac{y^2}{9}=1$$

and $$\frac{x^2}{9}-\frac{y^2}{4}=1$$

and illustrate the two hyperbolae by sketches.

7 Find the equation of the tangent and the normal to

$$2x^2-y^2=1$$

at the point (1,1).

8 Find the equations of the tangents with gradient 3 to the hyperbola

$$\frac{x^2}{25}-\frac{y^2}{64}=1$$

9 Find the equations of the axes of symmetry, the foci, directrices and asymptotes of

$$\frac{(x-1)^2}{16}-\frac{(y+2)^2}{25}=1$$

illustrating these results by a sketch.

10 Find the points of contact of the tangents with gradient 1 to the hyperbola $x^2/25-y^2/16=1$, and deduce the normals to the curve with gradient -1.

Parametric forms 13

Circle 131

Equation of the tangent 131

Parabola 132

Equation of the tangent 132

Equation of the normal 133

Equation of a chord 134

The rectangular hyperbola $x=ct$, $y=c/t$ 134

Equation of the tangent 135

Equation of the normal 135

The ellipse 137

Equation of tangent and of normal 137

The semi-cubical parabola 138

Notes

Any point on the **circle** $x^2+y^2=r^2$ can be taken in the form $(r\cos\theta, r\sin\theta)$, any point on the **parabola** $y^2=4ax$ as $(at^2,2at)$, any point on the **rectangular hyperbola** $xy=c^2$ as $(ct,c/t)$, any point on the **ellipse** $x^2/a^2+y^2/b^2=1$ as $(a\cos\theta,b\sin\theta)$, any point on the **semi-cubical parabola** $y^2=x^3$ as (t^2,t^3).

When these parameters are used, the **tangent** at $(r\cos\theta, r\sin\theta)$ is

$$x\cos\theta+y\sin\theta=r$$

the **tangent** at $(at^2,2at)$ is

$$ty=x+at^2$$

the **normal** at $(at^2,2at)$ is

$$y+tx=2at+at^3$$

the **tangent** at $(ct,c/t)$ is

$$x+t^2y=2ct$$

Circle

We can see in Figure 13.1 that the point P $(r \cos \theta, r \sin \theta)$ lies on the circle centre (0,0) radius r. When $\theta=0$, the point is at A, $(r,0)$. As θ increases, the point P moves anti-clockwise around the circle, reaching B when $\theta=\pi/2$, and so on as θ increases. Any value of θ gives one point on the curve; any point on the curve corresponds to one value of θ between 0 and 2π. θ is called a *parameter*, and many properties of curves can often be investigated easily if we use a parametric form.

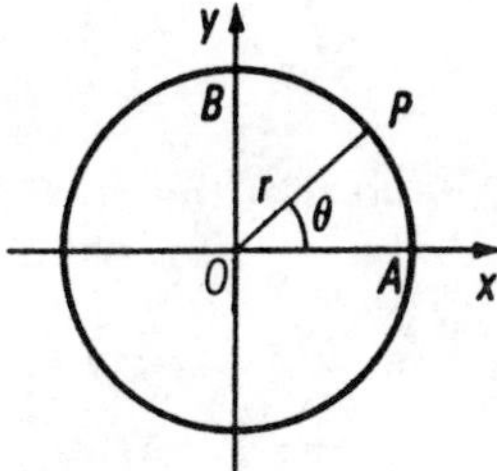

Figure 13.1

Equation of the tangent

Any point on the circle $x^2+y^2=r^2$ can be written in this form. To find the equation of the tangent at the point $(r \cos \theta, r \sin \theta)$, we can substitute in the form $xx'+yy'=r^2$ to obtain,

$$xr \cos \theta+yr \sin \theta=r^2$$

i.e. $$x \cos \theta+y \sin \theta=r^2$$

or we can differentiate the parametric form. To find $\mathrm{d}y/\mathrm{d}x$, we use

$$\frac{\mathrm{d}y}{\mathrm{d}x}=\frac{\mathrm{d}y/\mathrm{d}\theta}{\mathrm{d}x/\mathrm{d}\theta}$$

Now since $x=r \cos \theta$, $\mathrm{d}x/\mathrm{d}\theta=-r \sin \theta$,
and since $y=r \sin \theta$, $\mathrm{d}y/\mathrm{d}\theta=r \cos\theta$, so that

$$\frac{\mathrm{d}y}{\mathrm{d}x}=-\frac{r \cos \theta}{r \sin \theta}=-\cot \theta$$

and the equation of the tangent at $(r \cos \theta, r \sin \theta)$ is

$$y-r \sin \theta=-\cot \theta\,(x-r \cos \theta)$$

i.e. $x \cos \theta+y \sin \theta=1$, using $\cos^2 \theta+\sin^2 \theta=1$

Parabola

Consider the parabola $y^2=4ax$. The points $(\frac{1}{4}a,a)$, $(a,2a)$, $(4a,4a)$ all lie on the parabola, and any point of the form $(at^2,2at)$ lies on the parabola. For the three points given as examples, we see that $t=\frac{1}{2}$, 1, and 2 respectively.

Equation of the tangent

As with the circle, we can recall the equation of the tangent $yy'=2a(x+x')$, and substituting $x'=at^2$, $y'=2at$, we have

$$2aty=2a(x+at^2)$$

i.e. $$ty=x+at^2$$

Alternatively, we can use $\frac{dy}{dx}=\frac{dy/dt}{dx/dt}$, where $\frac{dy}{dt}=2a$, $\frac{dx}{dt}=2at$, so that the equation of the tangent at $(at^2,2at)$ is

$$y-2at=\frac{1}{t}(x-at^2)$$

i.e. $$ty=x+at^2$$

Example. Show that any two perpendicular tangents to the parabola $y^2=4ax$ intersect on the directrix.

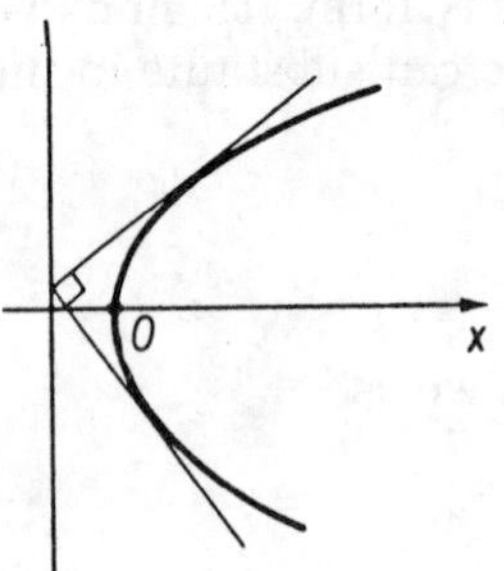

Figure 13.2

If the points of contact are $(at^2,2at)$, $(am^2,2am)$, the equation of the tangents are $ty=x+at$ and $my=x+am$. If these are perpendicular, $(1/t)(1/m)=-1$, i.e. $mt=-1$. Now the tangents meet where

$$ty=x+at^2 \qquad (1)$$

and $$my=x+am^2 \qquad (2)$$

If the point of intersection lies on the directrix, then the x coordinate must be $-a$. Multiplying (1) by m and (2) by t and subtracting,

$$0=x(m-t)+amt(t-m)$$

i.e. $0=x+a$, using $mt=-1$

i.e. $x=-a$ for all t, m such that $mt=-1$.

Equation of the normal

Since the gradient of the tangent is $1/t$, the gradient of the normal is $-t$, and the equation of the normal is

$$y-2at=-t(x-at^2)$$

i.e. $$y+tx=2at+at^3 \qquad (1)$$

Example. The normal to $y^2=4ax$ at $(at^2,2at)$ meets the coordinate axes in G and H. Find the locus of the midpoint of GH as t varies.

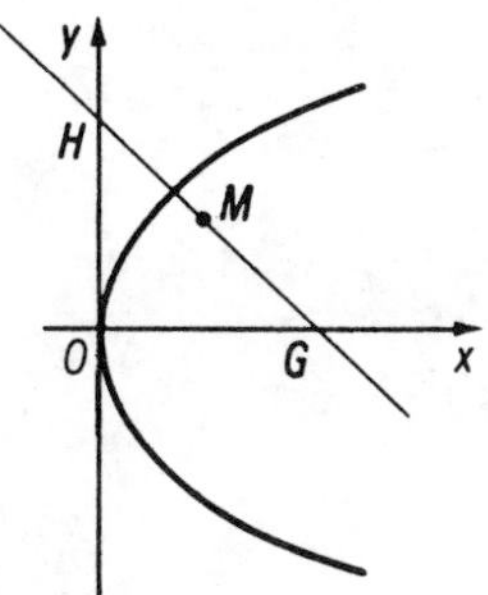

Figure 13.3

If G is the point at which the normal meets $y=0$, from equation (1) we see that at G, $x=a(2+t^2)$. At H, where $x=0$, $y=2at+at^3$, i.e. $y=at(2+t^2)$. The coordinates of the midpoint M of GH are therefore

$$x=\tfrac{1}{2}a(2+t^2),\ y=\tfrac{1}{2}at(2+t^2)$$

These would serve as the parametric form for the locus, but the cartesian form can be obtained easily by noticing that $at^2=2x-2a$,

so that $$y^2=\tfrac{1}{4}a^2t^2(2+t^2)^2$$

i.e. $$y^2=\tfrac{1}{4}a(2x-2a)\frac{4x^2}{a^2}$$

i.e. $$ay^2=2x^2(x-a)$$

Equation of a chord

The equation of the straight line through the points $(ap^2,2ap)$, $(aq^2,2aq)$ is

$$\frac{y-2ap}{2aq-2ap}=\frac{x-ap^2}{aq^2-ap^2}$$

i.e. $$y-2ap=\frac{2a(q-p)}{a(q-p)(q+p)}(x-ap^2)$$

$$a(q+p)(y-2ap)=2(x-ap^2)$$
$$(p+q)y=2x+2apq$$

Notice first, that this equation is symmetrical in p and q, secondly, that as q tends to p, this equation becomes that of the tangent at $(ap^2,2ap)$.

Example. The chord joining points P and Q on a parabola always passes through the focus. Show that the tangents at P and Q are always perpendicular.

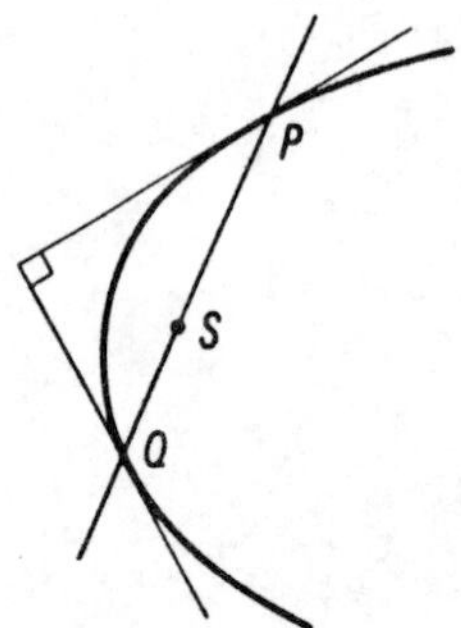

Figure 13.4

Since the chord passes through $(a,0)$,

$$(p+q)\times 0=2a+2apq,\text{ i.e. } pq=-1$$

But we have seen that the gradient of the tangent at P is $1/p$, at Q is $1/q$, so that $pq=-1 \Rightarrow (1/p)(1/q)=-1$, the tangents at P and Q are always perpendicular.

The rectangular hyperbola $x=ct$, $y=c/t$

All points on the curve $xy=c^2$ can be described by the parametric form $x=ct$, $y=c/t$. When t is positive, P lies in the first quadrant; when t is negative, P lies in the third quadrant. We see that when t is small and positive, P lies close to the y-axis (since ct is small); the positive vertex A corresponds to $t=1$, and when t is large and positive, the point P is close to the x-axis (Figure 13.5).

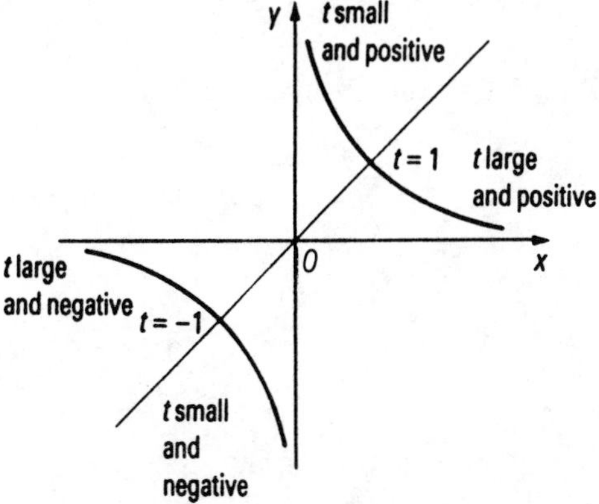

Figure 13.5

Equation of the tangent

Since $x=ct$, $dx/dt=c$; since $y=c/t$, $dy/dt=-c/t^2$,

$$\frac{dy}{dx}=\frac{-c/t^2}{c}=-\frac{1}{t^2}$$

and the equation of the tangent is

$$y-\frac{c}{t}=\left(-\frac{1}{t^2}\right)\left(x-ct\right)$$

i.e. $\quad t^2y+x=2ct$

This could also have been obtained by putting $x=ct$, $y=c/t$ in the equation $xy'+yx'=2c^2$.

Equation of the normal

The gradient of the normal is t^2, so the equation of the normal is

$$y-c/t=t^2(x-ct)$$

i.e. $\quad ty-t^3x=c(1-t^4)$

Example. P is any point on a rectangular hyperbola, $x=ct$, $y=c/t$. The normal at P meets the hyperbola again at Q. If M is the midpoint of PQ, show that PO is perpendicular to OM for all positions of P.

The normal at P is $ty-t^3x=c(1-t^4)$. Take Q as $(cq,c/q)$. This lies on the normal at P if

$$ct/q-ct^3q=c(1-t^4)$$

i.e. $\quad t^3q^2+(1-t^4)q-t=0$

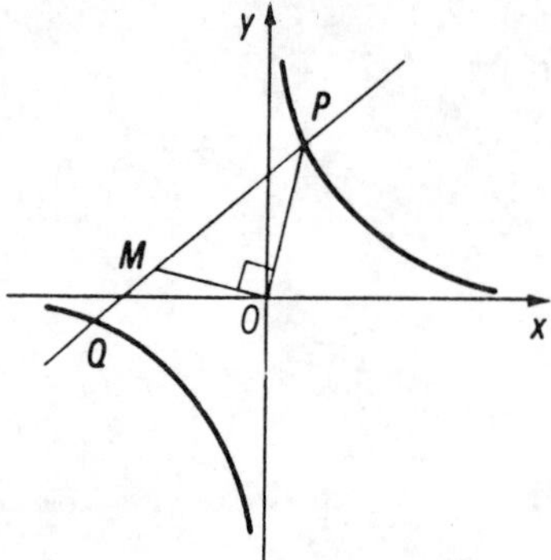

Figure 13.6

We know that one root of this equation is $q=t$, since one of the two points in which this line meets the hyperbola is P, so that one factor must be $(q-t)$, thus

$$(q-t)(t^3q+1)=0$$
$$q=t \text{ or } -\frac{1}{t^3}$$

so the coordinates of Q are $(-c/t^3, -ct^3)$.

Now the coordinates of M are

$$\frac{1}{2}c\left(t-\frac{1}{t^3}\right), \frac{1}{2}c\left(\frac{1}{t}-t^3\right)$$

so the gradient of OM is

$$\frac{\frac{1}{2}c\left(\frac{1}{t}-t^3\right)}{\frac{1}{2}c\left(t-\frac{1}{t^3}\right)}$$
$$=\frac{t^2(1-t^4)}{t^4-1}=-t^2$$

The gradient of OP is $\frac{c/t}{ct}=\frac{1}{t^2}$, and since

$$\left(-t^2\right)\left(\frac{1}{t^2}\right)=-1$$

OM is perpendicular to OP for all positions of P.

Notice that when solving the quadratic for q, we recalled that we knew one value of q, so that we knew one factor, and therefore could find the other easily.

Exercise 13.1

1 Write down suitable parametric forms for the following:
(a) $x^2+y^2=25$, (b) $x+y=\frac{1}{4}$, (c) $y^2=4x$, (d) $y^2=-36x$, (e) $x^2=y$,

(f) $xy=9$, (g) $4xy=25$, (h) $xy=-c^2$, (i) $9xy=-4$, (j) $(x-1)(y-2)=c^2$.

2 Find the cartesian equations of the following curves:
(a) $x=2\cos\theta$, $y=2\sin\theta$, (b) $x=3\sin\theta$, $y=3\cos\theta$, (c) $x=4t$, $y=1/t$,
(d) $x=t+1$, $y=1+1/t$, (e) $x=4t$, $y=4t^2$.

3 Find the equation of the tangent and of the normal to each of the following curves at the given points:
(a) $x^2+y^2=25$ at $(3,-4)$, (b) $y^2=12x$ at $(3,6)$, (c) $x^2=4y$ at $(8,16)$,
(d) $xy=1$ at $(2,\frac{1}{2})$, (e) $xy=16$ at $(-8,-2)$.

4 Find the equations of the two tangents to $y^2=4x$ from the point $(-1,0)$.

5 Find the equations of the two tangents from $(-1,\frac{3}{2})$ to $y^2=4x$.

The ellipse

We see that $x=\cos\theta$, $y=b\sin\theta$ satisfies

$$\frac{x^2}{a^2}+\frac{y^2}{b^2}=1$$

for all values of θ, since

$$\frac{(a\cos\theta)^2}{a^2}+\frac{(b\sin\theta)^2}{b^2}=1$$

for all θ. Unlike most other parameters, though, θ has a geometric interpretation, and Figure 13.7 shows a circle, centre O, radius a (called the auxiliary circle) and the relation of θ to the point P' on that circle with the same x coordinate as P.

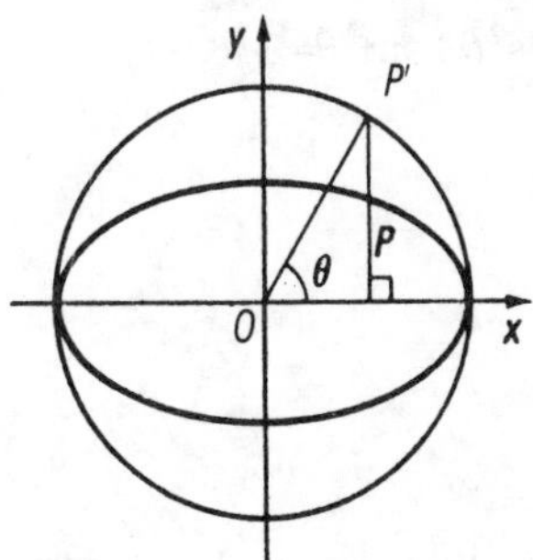

Figure 13.7

Equation of tangent and of normal

Using the form on page 123 and substituting $x'=a\cos\theta$, $y'=b\sin\theta$, the equation of the tangent is

$$\frac{x\cos\theta}{a}+\frac{y\sin\theta}{b}=1$$

The equation of the normal is found to be

$$ax \sin \theta - by \cos \theta = (a^2 - b^2) \sin \theta \cos \theta$$

Example. The tangent at a variable point P meets the axes at Q and R. S is the fourth vertex of the rectangle $OQSR$. Show that as P varies, the locus of Q is $a^2y^2 + b^2x^2 = x^2y^2$.

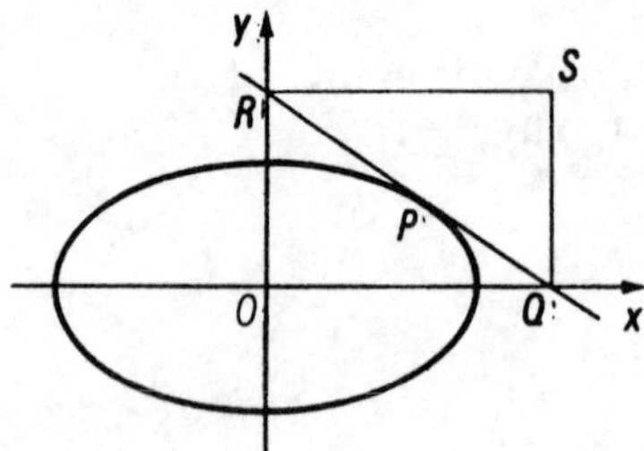

Figure 13.8

The equation of the tangent at P is

$$\frac{x \cos \theta}{a} + \frac{y \sin \theta}{b} = 1$$

this meets $y=0$ at $(a/\cos \theta, 0)$ and $x=0$ at $(0, b/\sin \theta)$ so the coordinates (X, Y) of S are

$$X = \frac{a}{\cos \theta}, \; Y = \frac{b}{\sin \theta}$$

To find the locus of S, eliminate $\cos \theta$ and $\sin \theta$, using $\cos^2\theta + \sin^2\theta = 1$,

i.e. $$\left(\frac{a}{X}\right)^2 + \left(\frac{b}{Y}\right)^2 = 1$$

the locus of S is $a^2y^2 + b^2x^2 = x^2y^2$.

The semi-cubical parabola

All points on the curve $y^2 = x^3$ can be described parametically by $x = t^2$, $y = t^3$. This curve is symmetrical about the x-axis, and only exists for positive values of x.

Example. Find the equation of the tangent at the point (t^2, t^3) on the curve $x^3 = y^2$, and the coordinates of the other point at which the tangent meets the curve again (Figure 13.9).

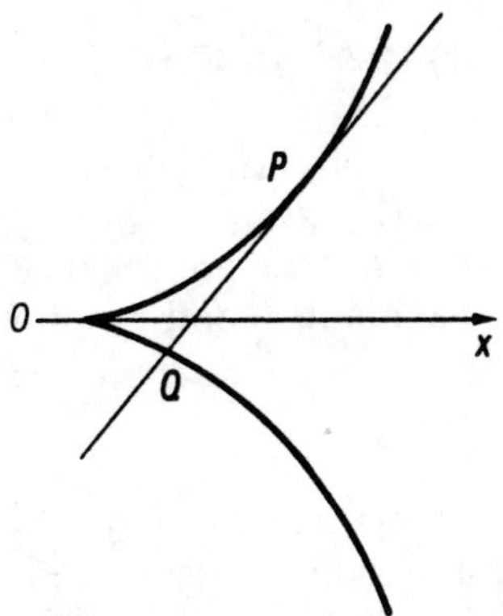

Figure 13.9

We have to use

$$\frac{dy}{dx}=\frac{\frac{dy}{dt}}{\frac{dx}{dt}}$$

$dy/dt=3t^2$, $dx/dt=2t$, so $dy/dx=\frac{3}{2}t$, and the equation of the tangent is

$$y-t^3=\frac{3}{2}t(x-t^2)$$

i.e. $\quad 2y-3tx+t^3=0$

If this meets the curve again at Q, take Q as (q^2, q^3), and since Q lies on the tangent at P,

$$2q^3-3tq^2+t^3=0$$

Since the tangent touches the curve at P, there are two roots $q-t$, so that $(q-t)^2$ is a factor of $2q^3-3tq^2+t^3$, and we can find the other linear factor easily by considering the coefficient of q^3, and the constant term, thus

$$2q^3-3tq^2+t^3=0$$

$$\Rightarrow \quad (q-t)^2(2q+t)=0$$

$$\Rightarrow \quad q=t \text{ (twice) or } -\tfrac{1}{2}t$$

the coordinates of Q are $(-\frac{1}{2}t)^2,(-\frac{1}{2}t)^3$, i.e. $(\frac{1}{4}t^2, -\frac{1}{8}t^3)$.

Exercise 13.2

1 Write down suitable parametric forms for the following:
(a) $x^2/16+y^2/25=1$, (b) $4x^2+25y^2=100$, (c) $25y^2=8x^3$, (d) $y^2=x^5$,
(e) $2x^2+3y^2=1$.

2 Find the cartesian equations of the following:
(a) $x=2\cos\theta$, $y=3\sin\theta$, (b) $x=\frac{1}{2}\cos\theta$, $y=\sin\theta$, (c) $x=2t^2$, $y=3t^3$,
(d) $x=2t$, $y=t^3$, (e) $x=t+1$, $y=t$.
3 Find the equations of the tangent and normal to $4x^2+9y^2=36$ at $(\frac{3}{2}, \sqrt{3})$.
4 Find the equation of the tangent and normal to $y^2=x^3$ at $(1,1)$.
5 Find the equation of the tangent to $x=a\cos^3 t$, $y=a\sin^3 t$ at the point whose parameter is α. If this tangent meets the coordinate axes at points X and Y, show that the length XY is constant for all values of α.

Miscellaneous exercise 13.3

1 Points P and Q on the parabola $y^2=4ax$ have parameters p and q. Find the equation of the chord PQ, and show that if PQ passes through the focus, $pq=-1$.
2 The tangent at a point P on $y^2=4ax$ meets the y-axis at Y; the normal to the curve at P meets the x-axis at X. Show that the locus of the midpoint of XY is $2y^2=a(x-a)$.
3 The normal at a point P on $y^2=4ax$ meets the x-axis Ox at N. Show that $2a<PN^2/ON<4a$, whatever the position of P.
4 The tangent at a variable point P $(ct,c/t)$ on $xy=c^2$ meets the asymptotes at T_1,T_2. Find the coordinates of T_1 and T_2 in terms of t and show that the area of the triangle OT_1T_2 is constant for all positions of P.
5 With the data of Q.2 show that P is always the midpoint of T_1T_2.
6 The normal at a variable point P on $xy=c^2$ meets $y=x$ at Q. Show that $PQ=PO$, where O is the origin.
7 The tangent at a variable point P meets the x-axis at T_1, the y-axis at T_2; the normal at P meets the x-axis at N_1, the y-axis at N_2. Show that $OT_1\times ON_1 = OT_2\times ON_2$.
8 An ellipse is given by the parametric form $x=2\cos\theta$, $y=3\sin\theta$. Find the equation of the tangent to the ellipse at the point parameter θ. If this tangent passes through the point $(2,1)$, show that θ satisfies an equation of the form $l\cos\theta+m\sin\theta=n$. Solve this equation to find the two points P and Q at which the tangent passes through $(2,1)$.
9 The tangent at a variable point $P(a\cos\theta, b\sin\theta)$ meets the tangent at $A(a,0)$ at T, and the tangent at $A'(-a,0)$ at T'. Show that $AT\times A'T'$ is constant for all positions of P.
10 Given that the tangent at P to the curve $x=t^2$, $y=t^3$ passes through the point $(1,0)$, find the two possible parameters for P, given that P is not the origin.
11 Find the equation of the tangent at P, the point $t=\sqrt{2}$, to the curve $x=3t^2$, $y=2t^3$. Find also the parameter of the point Q at which this tangent meets the curve again, and show that the tangent at P is the normal at Q.
12 Points P and Q on the circle $x^2+y^2=r^2$ have parameters θ and ϕ respectively. Prove that the equation of the chord PQ can be written

$$x\cos\tfrac{1}{2}(\theta+\phi)+y\sin\tfrac{1}{2}(\theta+\phi)=r\cos\tfrac{1}{2}(\theta-\phi)$$

Polar coordinates 14

Polar coordinates: pole and axis 143

The curve $r=a(1+\cos\theta)$ 144

The curve $r^2=a^2\cos 2\theta$ 144

The straight line $r=p\operatorname{cosec}(\theta-\alpha)$ 144

The circle $r=2a\cos\theta$ 145

The spirals $r=a\theta$, $r=ae^{k\theta}$ 146

The area of a sector 147

Notes

To change cartesian coordinates to polars,

$$x = r\cos\theta,\ y = r\sin\theta$$

To change polar coordinates to cartesians,

$$r^2 = x^2 + y^2,\ \tan\theta = \frac{y}{x}$$

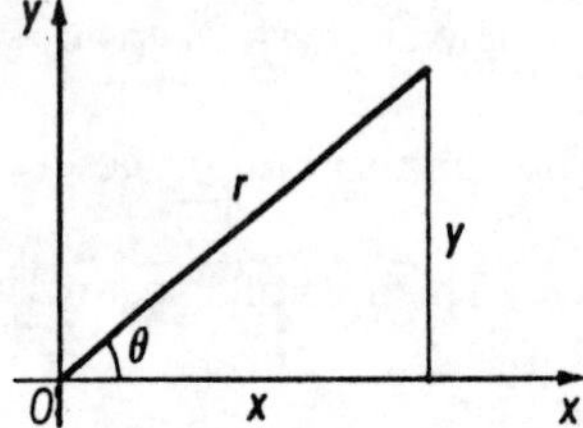

Figure 14.1

The area of a sector bounded by the curve $r = f(\theta)$, and the radii $\theta = \alpha$ and $\theta = \beta$ is $\frac{1}{2}\int_{\alpha}^{\beta} r^2 d\theta$

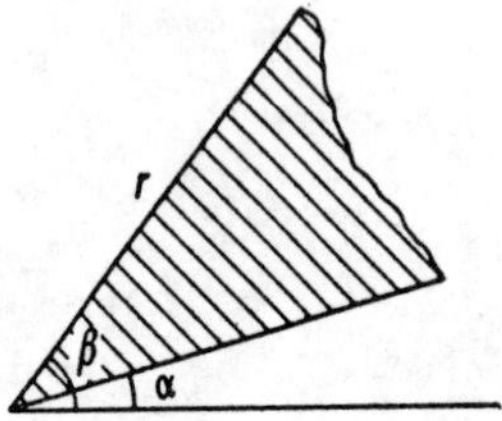

Figure 14.2

Polar coordinates: pole and axis

Cartesian coordinates determine the position of a point relative to two fixed straight lines, the coordinate axes; polar coordinates determine the position of a point P by its distance from a fixed point O (the pole), and the angle made by the line joining P to the pole with a fixed line (Figure 14.3). Although it is easy to convert from cartesian coordinates to polars, using

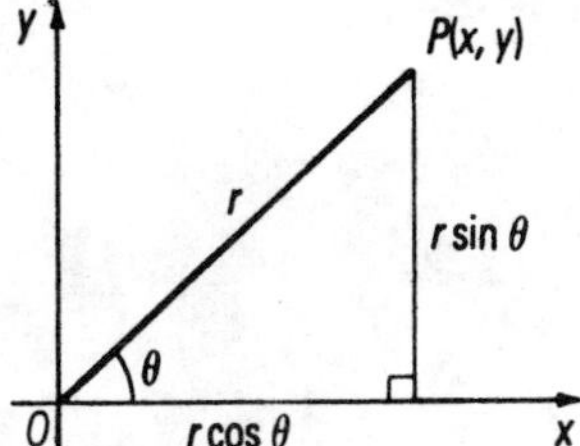

Figure 14.3

$$x=r\cos\theta,\ y=r\sin\theta$$

and from polars to cartesians, using

$$r=\sqrt{(x^2+y^2)},\ \tan\theta=\frac{y}{x}$$

it is usually better to think in terms of polar coordinates, to realize that the equation $r=a$ describes all points a distance a from the pole, so is the equation of a circle, radius a, centre O; that $\theta=\alpha$ describes all points P such that OP makes a fixed angle α with the baseline, and so describes a straight line inclined to the baseline at an angle α (Figure 14.4).

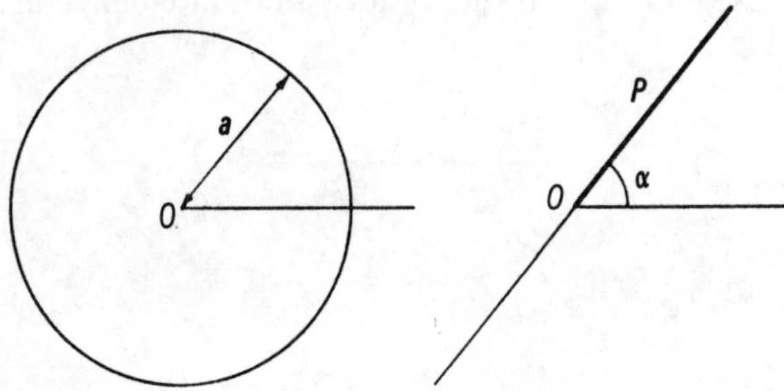

Figure 14.4

The curve $r=a(1+\cos\theta)$

Given the equation of a curve in the form $r=a(1+\cos\theta)$, we can see that any one value of α determines one value of r, so that for any one given angle made by OP with the baseline, we can find the distance of P from O for that angle. Thus when $\theta=0$, $\cos\theta=1$ and $r=2a$; as θ increases, $\cos\theta$ decreases and so r decreases, taking the value a when $\theta=\pi/2$, and the value 0 when $\theta=\pi$; r then increases again, being equal to a when $\theta=3\pi/2$, finally $r=2a$ when $\theta=2\pi$. We have the curve sketched in Figure 14.5. This is called a cardioid.

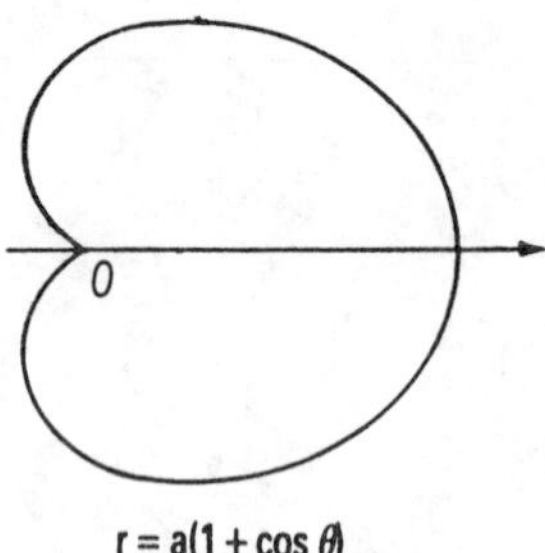

Figure 14.5

The curve $r^2=a^2\cos 2\theta$

Following this procedure for $r^2=a^2\cos 2\theta$, when $\theta=0$ we have $r=a$ (strictly $\pm a$, but we usually adopt the convention that r is positive). As θ increases, r decreases, until $r=0$ when $\theta=\pi/4$. When $\pi/4<\theta<3\pi/4$, $\cos 2\theta$ is negative, so there are no real values of r in the interval $\pi/4<\theta<3\pi/4$. As θ increases from $3\pi/4$, r increases, until when $\theta=\pi$, $r=a$. Continuing the curve for values of θ between π and 2π, we obtain the curve in Figure 14.6.

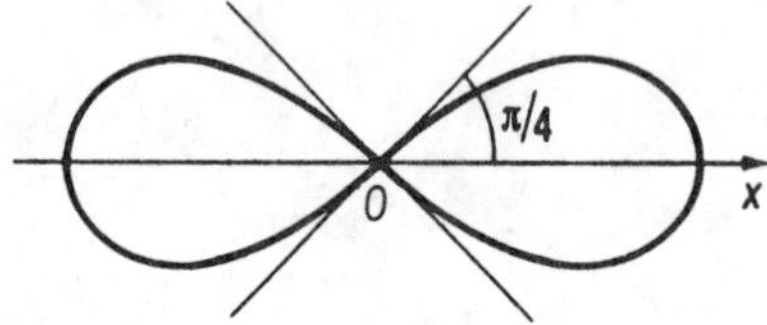

Figure 14.6

The straight line $r=p\operatorname{cosec}(\theta-\alpha)$

Some polar equations use properties of the curve they describe that require some trigonometry. Consider the straight line a perpendicular distance p from the origin, inclined at an angle α to the baseline. Then all points P on this line are such that their distance r from the origin is given by $p=r\sin(\alpha-\theta)$, so the equation of this straight line is $r=p/\sin(\alpha-\theta)$, or $r=p\operatorname{cosec}(\alpha-\theta)$.

Expanding the equation $p=r\sin(\alpha-\theta)$, we have

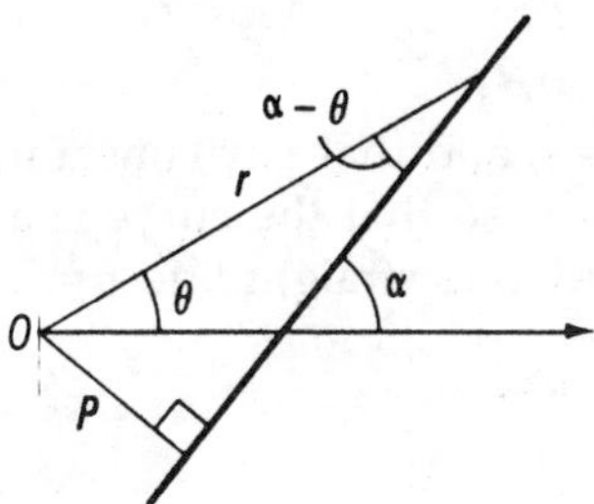

Figure 14.7

$$p=r\sin\alpha\cos\theta-r\cos\alpha\sin\theta$$

Writing $x=r\cos\theta$, $y=r\sin\theta$, we obtain

$$p=x\sin\alpha-y\cos\alpha$$

which we recognize as a straight line in cartesian form.

The circle $r=2a\cos\theta$

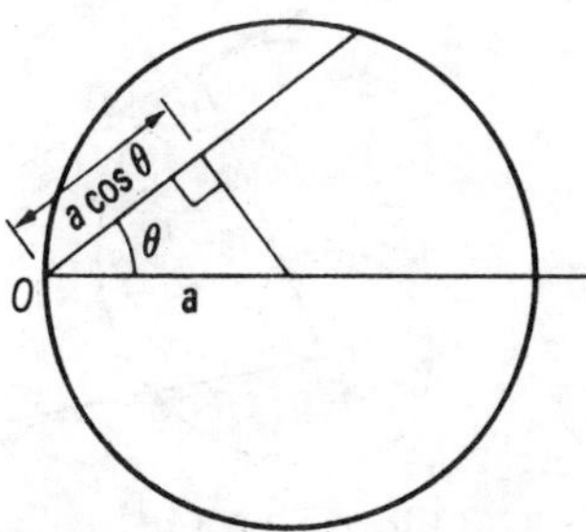

Figure 14.8

If P is any point on the circle centre $(a,0)$, radius a, from Figure 14.8 we see that $\frac{1}{2}r=a\cos\theta$, so the equation is $r=2a\cos\theta$. If we wish to express this in cartesian form,

$$r=2a\cos\theta\Rightarrow r^2=2ar\cos\theta$$
$$\Rightarrow x^2+y^2=2ax$$

i.e. $\quad x^2+y^2-2ax=0$

a circle centre $(a,0)$, radius a. Notice that since we know $x=r\cos\theta$ and $y=r\sin\theta$, it is often helpful to multiply by r (or r^2) so that we can substitute for $r\cos\theta$ and $r\sin\theta$ rather than $\cos\theta$ and $\sin\theta$.

The spirals $r=a\theta$, $r=ae^{k\theta}$

The equation $r=a\theta$ tells us that as θ increases, so does r, and that any constant increase of θ, say 2π, produces a constant increase in r, so that the curve is a spiral, of constant width $2\pi a$ between points along any one straight line $\theta=\alpha$. This is called the spiral of Archimedes (Figure 14.9).

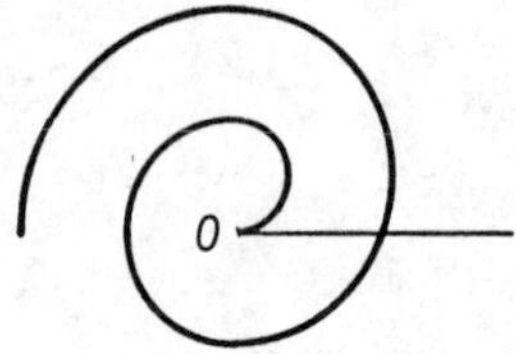

Figure 14.9

By contrast, the equation $r=ae^{k\theta}$ tells us that any increase in θ, say of 2π multiplies r by a factor that often is very large, since

$$\begin{aligned} r &= ae^{k(2\pi+\alpha)} = ae^{2k\pi}e^{k\alpha} \\ &= (e^{2k\pi})\,(ae^{k\alpha}) \end{aligned}$$

and unless k is very small, $e^{2k\pi}$ will be large. Thus we now have a spiral of rapidly increasing width, as in Figure 14.10.

Figure 14.10

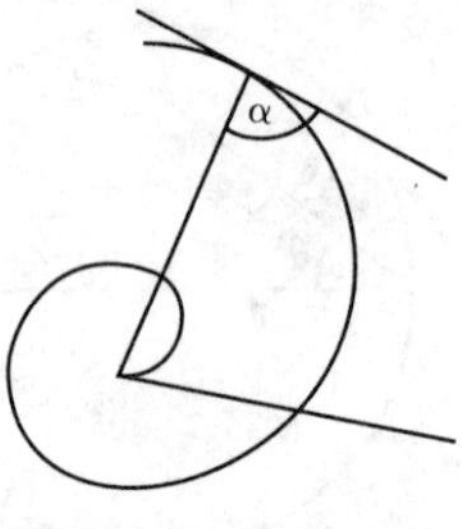

Figure 14.11

This curve is called the equiangular spiral, because the angle α between a tangent and the radius vector (Figure 14.11) is constant for all positions of the point P, and $\alpha=\arctan k$, when the equation is $r=ae^{k\theta}$.

Exercise 14.1

1 Sketch the following curves, by using the property given in the equation of the curve:

(a) $r=2$, (b) $\theta=\pi/2$, $r>0$, (c) $r=3$, $-\pi/4<\theta<3\pi/4$, (d) $\theta=\pi/3$, $1<r<2$.

2 Sketch the following curves, by finding the values for r corresponding to values of θ between 0 and 2π:
(a) $r=1+\sin\theta$, (b) $r=2+\sin\theta$, (c) $r=1+2\sin\theta$, (d) $r=\sin 2\theta$, (e) $r^2=2/\sin 2\theta$.
3 Sketch the following curves:
(a) $r=2(1+\cos\theta)$, (b) $r=2+3\cos\theta$, (c) $r=3+2\cos\theta$.
4 Sketch the spirals $r=2\theta$ and $r=\frac{1}{2}e^{\theta}$ for $0<\theta<2\pi$.
5 By writing $x=r\cos\theta$, $y=r\sin\theta$, express the following curves in polar form:
(a) $x^2-y^2=a^2$, (b) $xy=c^2$, (c) $x^2+y^2+4x=0$.
6 Express the following polar equations in cartesian form:
(a) $r^2\sin 2\theta=1$, (b) $r^2\cos 2\theta=1$, (c) $r^2=a^2\sin 2\theta$.

The area of a sector

To find the area of a sector bounded by the curve and two radii $\theta=\alpha$ and $\theta=\beta$, a small increase $\delta\theta$ in θ produces a corresponding increase δA in the area A, where $\delta A\simeq\frac{1}{2}r^2\delta\theta$. It can be shown that $dA/d\theta=\frac{1}{2}r^2$, so $A=\int_{\alpha}^{\beta}\frac{1}{2}r^2 d\theta$

Example. Find the area enclosed by the curve $r=a(1+\cos\theta)$.

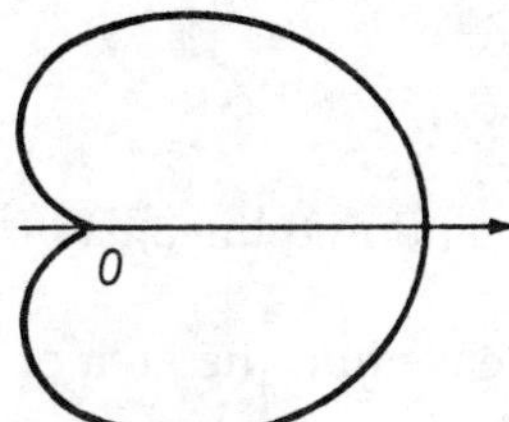

Figure 14.12

This curve, a cardioid, we sketched on page 144. The area A enclosed by the curve is

$$\int_0^{2\pi}\frac{1}{2}a^2(1+\cos\theta)^2 d\theta$$
$$=\int_0^{2\pi}\frac{1}{2}a^2[1+2\cos\theta+\tfrac{1}{2}(1+\cos 2\theta)]d\theta$$

using $\cos^2\theta=\frac{1}{2}(1+\cos 2\theta)$,

$$A=\tfrac{1}{2}a^2\int_0^{2\pi}\left[\tfrac{3}{2}\theta+2\cos\theta+\tfrac{1}{2}\cos 2\theta\right]d\theta$$
$$=\tfrac{1}{2}a^2\left[\tfrac{3}{2}\theta+2\sin\theta=\tfrac{1}{4}\sin 2\theta\right]_0^{2\pi}$$
$$=\tfrac{1}{2}a^2\times\tfrac{3}{2}\times 2\pi$$
$$=\tfrac{3}{2}\pi a^2$$

It is always important to check solutions where this can be done easily. Here we see that the region enclosed is considerably less than that enclosed by a circle radius $2a$, but greater than that enclosed by a circle radius a.

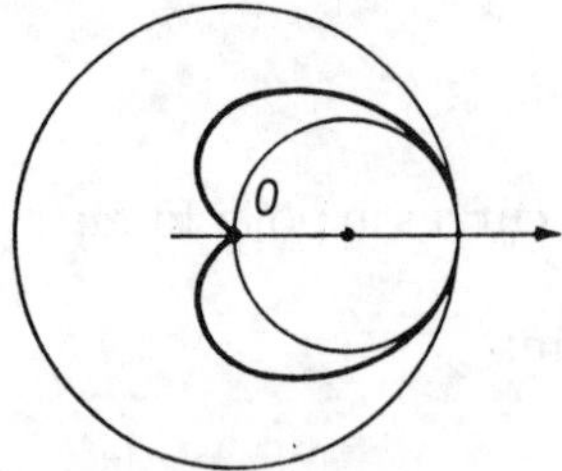

Figure 14.13

Exercise 14.2

1 Find the area of the regions bounded by the following:
(a) the circle $r=a$, (b) the circle $r=a\cos\theta$, (c) $r^2=a^2\sin 2\theta$, $-\pi/4<\theta<\pi/4$,
(d) $r^2=a^2\sin 2\theta$, $0<\theta<\pi/2$, (e) $r=a\theta$, $\theta=2\pi$.

Miscellaneous exercise 14.3

1 Sketch the following curves, for values of $0\leqslant\theta\leqslant\frac{1}{2}\pi$:
(a) $r\cos\theta=c$, (b) $r\cos\theta=a+b\cos\theta$.

2 Find the cartesian equation of the curve $r\cos\theta=a+b\cos\theta$.

3 Sketch the curve $r^2=a^2\cos 2\theta$ and find the area of a loop.

4 Show that the curve $r=1+2\cos\theta$ consists of two loops, and find the area of the inside loop.

5 Find the polar equation of the ellipse $x^2/a^2+y^2/b^2=1$. Hence find the area of the ellipse.

Trigonometry I 15

Definition of the trigonometric functions 152

General solution of the equation sin θ=sin α 154

General solution of the equation cos θ=cos α 154

General solution of the equation tan θ=tan α 154

Radian measure 156

The sine formula 157

The cosine formula 158

Notes

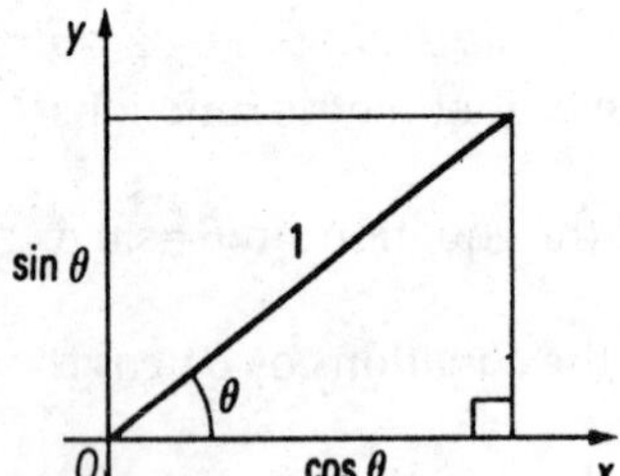

Figure 15.1

Cosine θ is defined as the projection on to the x-axis of a unit vector at an angle θ to Ox; **sine** θ as the projection on to the y-axis. From these definitions we see

$$\cos(-\theta)=\cos\theta=\cos(360°-\theta)=\cos(360°+\theta)$$

and $$\sin\theta=\sin(180°-\theta)=\sin(360°+\theta)=\sin(540°-\theta)$$

Tan θ is defined as $\sin\theta/\cos\theta$

Some useful **exact** values:

$$\sin 0°=\cos 90°=0$$
$$\sin 30°=\cos 60°=\tfrac{1}{2}$$
$$\sin 60°=\cos 30°=\tfrac{1}{2}\sqrt{3}$$
$$\sin 90°=\cos 0°=1$$

Sine formula

$$\frac{a}{\sin A}=\frac{b}{\sin B}=\frac{c}{\sin C}=2R,$$ R being the radius of the circumcircle of triangle ABC

Cosine formula

$$a^2=b^2+c^2-2bc\cos A$$

i.e. $$\cos A=\frac{b^2+c^2-a^2}{2bc}$$

General solution of equations

If $\sin\theta=\sin\alpha$, $\theta=360n°+\alpha$ or $(360n+180n)°-\alpha$
If $\cos\theta=\cos\alpha$, $\theta=360n°\pm\alpha$
If $\tan\theta=\tan\alpha$, $\theta=180n°+\alpha$

Radian measure

An arc of a circle equal in length to the radius of the circle subtends an angle of **1 radian** at the centre of the circle. Thence

$$\pi\text{ rad}=180°;\ 1\text{ rad}=\left(\frac{180}{\pi}\right)^{\circ}\simeq 57.3°$$

The length of an arc subtending an angle of θ rad at the centre is $r\theta$; the area of the sector, angle θ, is $\frac{1}{2}r^2\theta$.

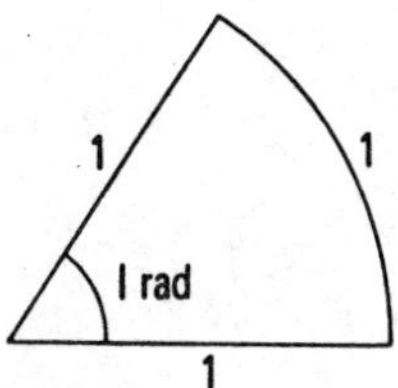

Figure 15.2

Definition of the trigonometric functions

The trigonometric functions cosine and sine are best defined in terms of projections on to the coordinate axes. Thus if *OP* is a straight line unit length, inclined at an angle θ to *Ox*, cosine θ is defined as the projection of *OP* on to *Ox*, sine θ as the projection on to *Oy* (Figure 15.3). We can see from this definition that for any angle θ,

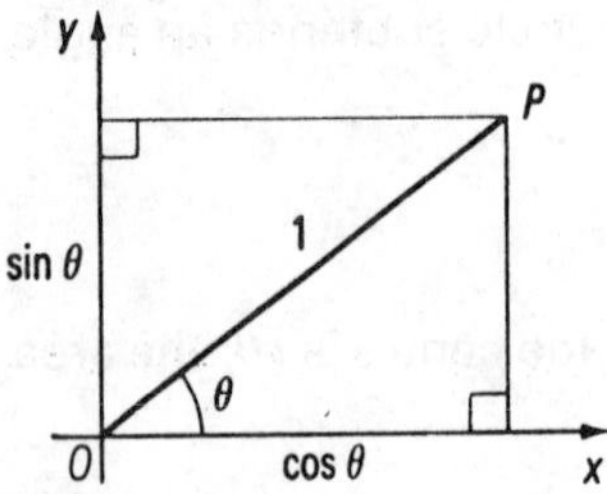

Figure 15.3(a)

$$\cos(-\theta)=\cos\theta=(360°-\theta)=\cos(360°+\theta)\ldots$$

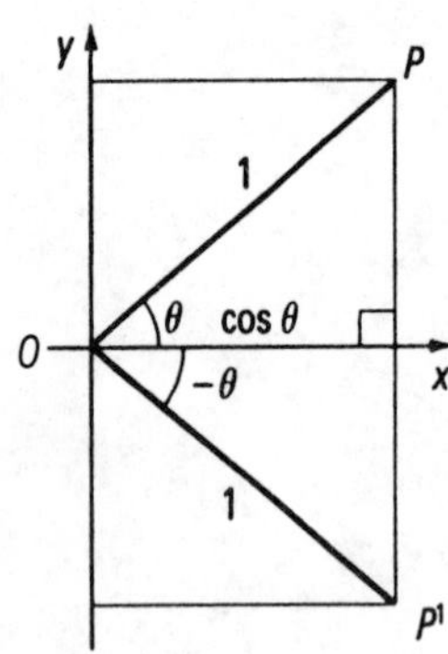

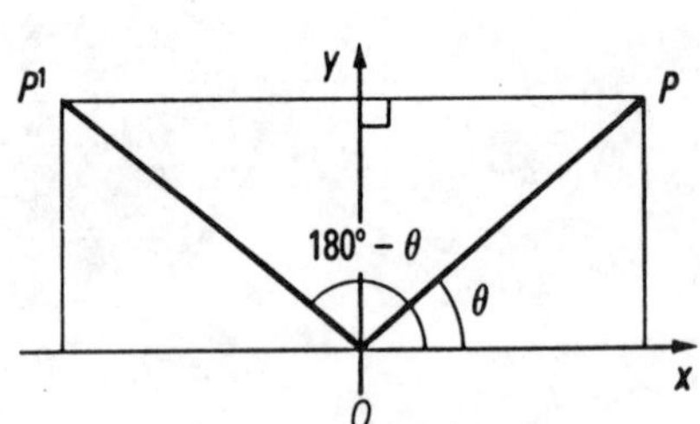

Figure 15.3(b)

and

$$\sin\theta=\sin(180°-\theta)=\sin(360°+\theta)=\sin(540°-\theta)\ldots$$

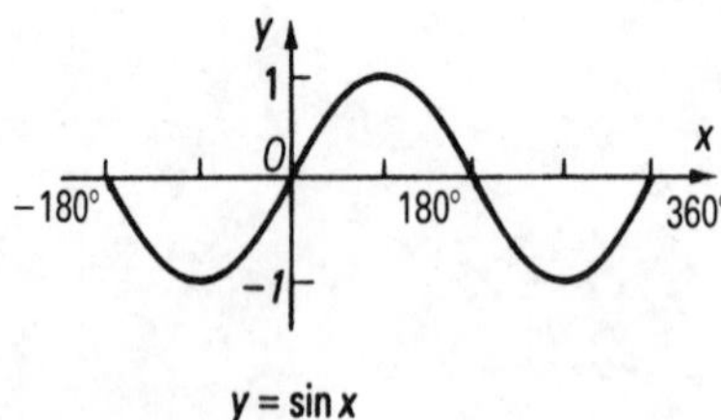

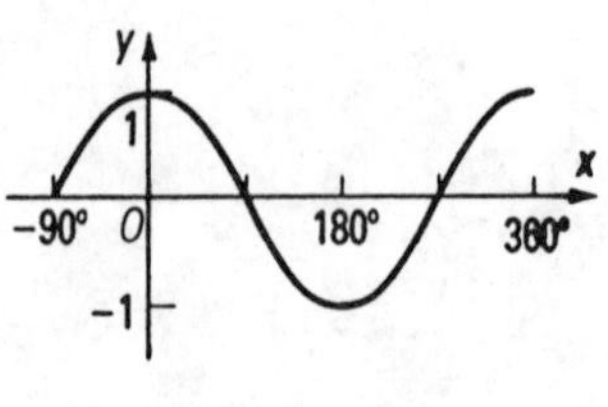

Figure 15.4

The graphs of sine and cosine are given in Figure 15.4.

Having defined cosine and sine, we now define

$$\tan \theta = \frac{\sin \theta}{\cos \theta}, \ \cot \theta = \frac{\cos \theta}{\sin \theta}$$

$$\sec \theta = \frac{1}{\cos \theta}, \ \operatorname{cosec} \theta = \frac{1}{\sin \theta}$$

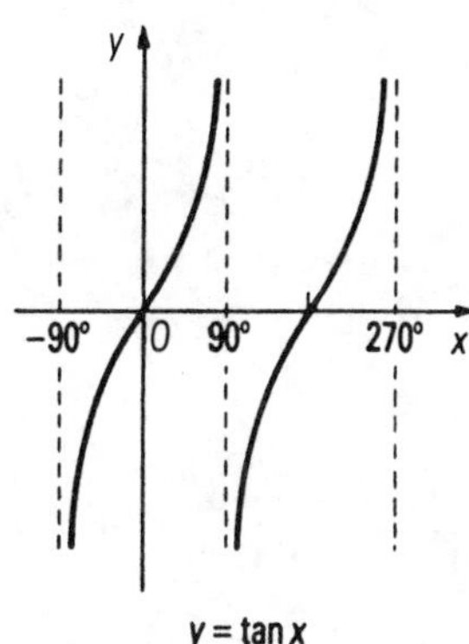

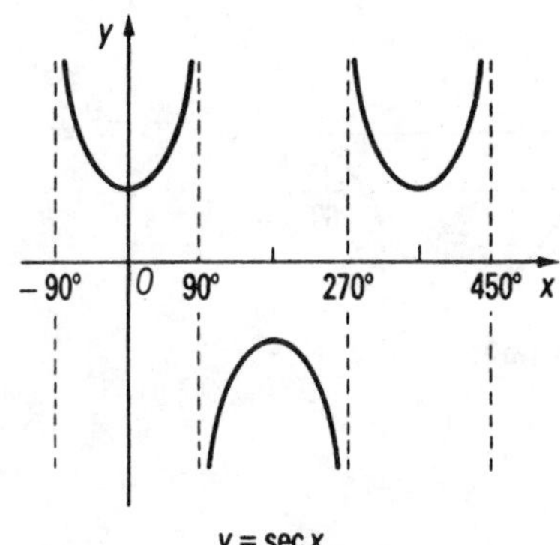

Figure 15.5

The graphs of tan and sec are given in Figure 15.5; the graphs of cot and cosec are similar and can be deduced from these.

Exercise 15.1

1 Using graph paper, draw the graph of $y=\cos \theta$, for values of θ between $-360°$ and $+360°$.

Using this graph, draw sketch-graphs of the following:

(a) $y=2 \cos \theta$, (b) $y=2+\cos \theta$, (c) $y=\cos (\theta+30°)$.

2 As in Q.1, draw the graph of $y=\sin \theta$, for values of between $-360°$ and $+360°$.

Using this graph, draw sketch-graphs of the following:

(a) $y=2 \sin \theta$, (b) $y=2+\sin \theta$, (c) $y=\sin (\theta+30°)$.

3 As in Q.1, draw the graph of $y=\tan \theta$ for value of θ from $-360°$ to $+360°$.

Using this graph, draw sketch-graphs of the following:

(a) $y=2 \tan \theta$, (b) $y=2+\tan \theta$, (c) $y=\tan (\theta+30°)$.

4 From the graphs in Qs.1, 2 and 3, sketch the graphs of the following:

(a) $y=\sec \theta$, (b) $y=\operatorname{cosec} \theta$, (c) $y=\cot \theta$, (d) $y=\sec 2\theta$,
(e) $y=2 \operatorname{cosec} \theta$, (f) $y=\cot (\theta+90°)$.

General solution of the equation sin θ=sin α

Looking at the graph of sin θ in Figure 15.6, we see that for any value k such that $-1\leqslant k\leqslant 1$, we have at least one value α such that sin $\alpha=k$. But we also see (Figure 15.6) that sin $(180°-\alpha)=k=\sin\alpha$, so that if α is any one solution (invariably taken in the first or fourth quadrant), of the equation sin $\alpha=k$, then further solutions are $180°-\alpha$, $360°+\alpha$, $540°-\alpha$ ... and the general solution is

$360n°+\alpha$ or $(2n+1)180°-\alpha$

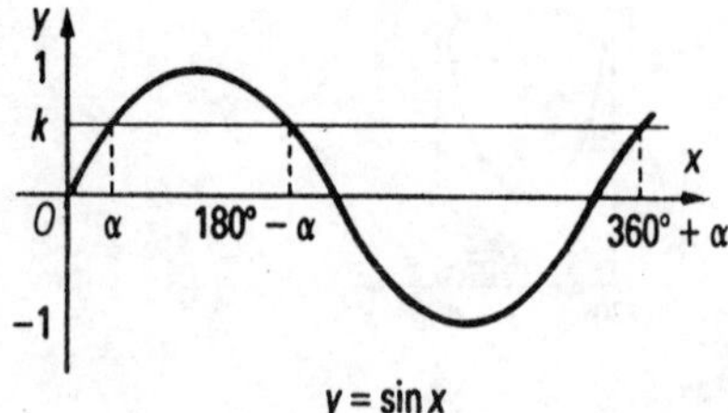

Figure 15.6

General solution of the equation cos θ=cos α

Looking at the graph of cos θ in Figure 15.7, we see that for any value k such that $-1\leqslant k\leqslant 1$, we have at least one value α such that cos $\alpha=k$. But we also see (Figure 15.7) that cos $(-\alpha)=k=\cos\alpha$, so that if α is any one solution (invariably taken in the first or second quadrant) to the equation cos $\alpha=k$, then further solutions are $360°-\alpha$, $360°+\alpha$, $720°-\alpha$, $720°+\alpha$ ... and the general solution is $360n°\pm\alpha$.

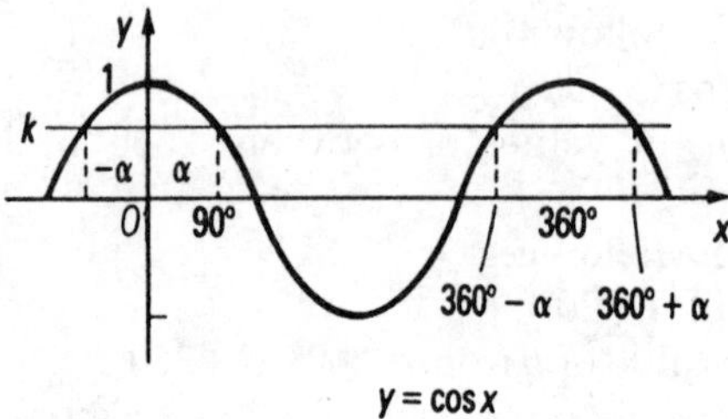

Figure 15.7

General solution of the equation tan θ=tan α

From the graph of tan θ in Figure 15.8, we see that for any value k we can find first one solution α such that tan $\alpha=k$, then further values $180°+\alpha$, $360°+\alpha$, so that the general solution of the equation $\tan\theta=\tan\alpha$, where $\tan\alpha=k$ is $\theta=180n°+\alpha$, for any integer value of n.

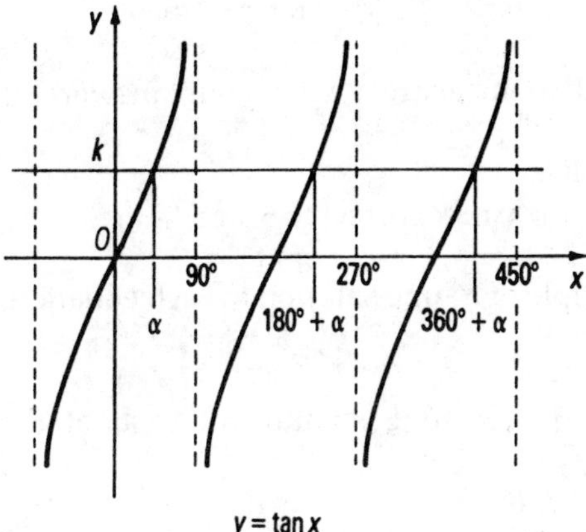

Figure 15.8

Example. Find general solutions, in degrees, of (a) $\sin\theta=-0.5$, (b) $\cos\theta=0.5$, (c) $\tan\theta=-1$.

(a) From calculator or tables we obtain one solution of $\sin\theta=-0.5$ as $\theta=-30°$. From the graph, we see that other solutions are 210°, 330°, 570°, ... and −150°, −390°, ... The general solution is

$$\theta=(360n-30)° \text{ or } [(2n+1)180+30]°$$

(b) We first obtain one solution of $\cos\theta=0.5$ as $\theta=60°$. From the graph, we see that other solutions are 300°, 420°, 660°, ... −60°, −420° ... The general solution is

$$\theta=(360n\pm 60)°$$

(c) One solution of $\tan\theta=-1$ is $\theta=-45°$. From the graph we see that other solutions are 135°, 315°, 495°, 675°, ... −225°, −405°, ... and the general solution is

$$\theta=(180n-45)°$$

Exercise 15.2

1 Find, from calculator or tables, one solution of each of the following, then deduce from graphs all the solutions between 0 and 360°:
(a) $\sin x=0.4$, (b) $\cos x=0.6$, (c) $\tan x=0.5$, (d) $\sin x=-0.6$, (e) $\cos x=-0.4$, (f) $\tan x=-2.5$, (g) $\sin x=0.9$, (h) $\cos x=-0.1$, (i) $\tan x=0.4$, (j) $\sin x=\frac{3}{4}$.

2 Find, from calculator or tables, one solution of each of the following, then deduce from sketch-graphs all the solutions between −90° and +90°:
(a) $\sin 2x=0.5$, (b) $\cos 2x=\frac{1}{4}$, (c) $\tan 3x=1$, (d) $\sin(x+30°)=0.9$, (e) $\cos(x-45°)=0.9$, (f) $\tan(x-70°)=2$, (g) $\sin(2x-90°)=0.5$,

(h) $2\cos(x+30°)=1$, (i) $1.5+\cos(2x-10°)=1.8$, (j) $[\tan(x+30°)]^2=3$.

3 First, from calculator or tables, find one solution in degrees to each of the following, then deduce from graphs the general solutions:
(a) $\sin\theta=0.8$, (b) $\cos\theta=-0.9$, (c) $\tan\theta=2$, (d) $\tan\theta=-1.5$,
(e) $\cos\theta=0.7$, (f) $\sin\theta=-0.4$.

4 Express the following angles in radian measure giving your answers as multiples of π:
(a) 45°, (b) 210°, (c) −90°, (d) 240°.

5 Express the following angles in radian measure, correct to 3 s.f.:
(a) 40°, (b) 200°, (c) −10°, (d) −100°.

6 First find, in radian measure as a multiple of π, one solution to each equation, then give the general solution:
(a) $\sin\theta=1$, (b) $\cos\theta=0.5$, (c) $\tan\theta=1$.

7 Find, in radian measure correct to 3 d.p., one solution of each of the following equations:
(a) $\sin\theta=0.3$, (b) $\cos\theta=-0.6$, (c) $\tan\theta=-2$.

8 Find, as a multiple of π, one solution of each of the following, then give all the solutions between -2π and $+2\pi$, also in terms of π:
(a) $\sin x=0.5$, (b) $\cos x=1/\sqrt{2}$, (c) $\tan x=1$, (d) $[\sin x]^2=\frac{1}{2}$,
(e) $[\cos x]^2=\frac{3}{4}$.

9 Find in terms of π, all the solutions between 0 and $\pi/2$ of
(a) $\sin 2x=1$, (b) $\sin(x+\pi/2)=\frac{1}{2}$, (c) $\cos 2x=0.5$, (d) $\tan 3x=1$,
(e) $\tan 4x=-1$.

10 Find, in radians correct to 2 d.p., all the solutions between 0 and 3 of each of the following equations:
(a) $\sin 2\theta=0.9$, (b) $\cos 2\theta=-0.8$, (c) $\tan 2\theta=5$.

Radian measure

Although we are probably most familiar with the degree as the unit in which to measure angles, we shall certainly have come across radians, if only as a button on the face of a calculator! To define a radian, we say that if an arc of a circle, of unit radius, has length one unit, then the angle subtended by that arc at the centre of the circle is one radian, written 1 rad (Figure 15.9). Since the circumference of this circle is 2π, the angle subtended by the complete circumference is 2π rad, so that

$$360°=2\pi \text{ rad}$$

Using this relation, we see, for example,

$$60°=\pi/3 \text{ rad},\ 150°=5\pi/6 \text{ rad},\ 270°=3\pi/2 \text{ rad}$$

and, using calculators,

$$50°\simeq 0.873 \text{ rad},\ 150°\simeq 2.62 \text{ rad and } 250°\simeq 4.36 \text{ rad}$$

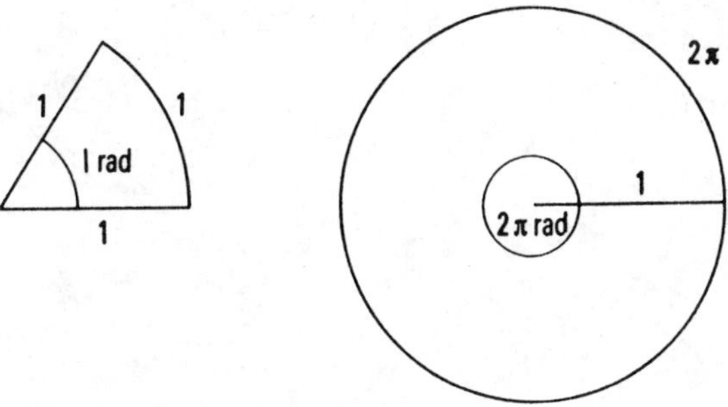

Figure 15.9

Similarly,

$$\pi/2 \text{ rad}=90°, 2\pi/3 \text{ rad}=120°,$$

and by calculators,

$$1 \text{ rad}\simeq 57.3, 1.4 \text{ rad}=1.4\times 180/\pi \simeq 80°$$

The sine formula

The sine formula states that, in any triangle *ABC*,

$$\frac{a}{\sin A}=\frac{b}{\sin B}=\frac{c}{\sin C}=2R$$

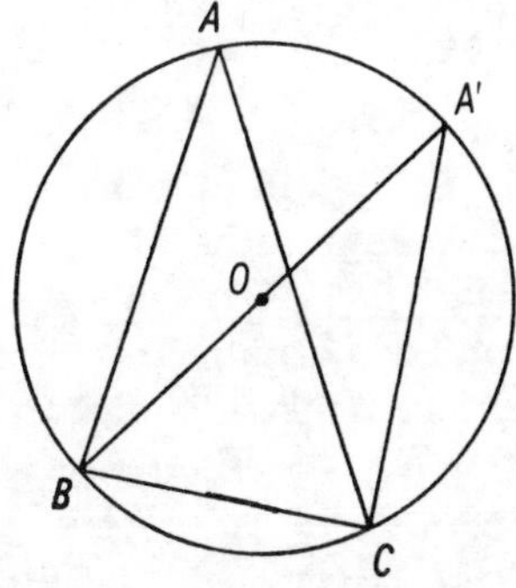

Figure 15.10

It is most easily proved by drawing the circumcircle of the triangle *ABC* (Figure 15.10), and drawing the diameter BA' through B. Then since angle $BCA'=90°$ (angle in a semi-circle) and angle $BA'C=$angle BAC (angles in same segment), $BC=BA' \sin A$, i.e. $$2R=\frac{a}{\sin A}$$

Similarly, $2R=b/\sin B$ and $2R=c/\sin C$, so

$$\frac{a}{\sin A}=\frac{b}{\sin B}=\frac{c}{\sin C}=2R$$

The cosine formula

The cosine formula states that in any triangle ABC,

$$a^2=b^2+c^2-2bc\cos A$$

If we wish to find an angle knowing the three sides of the triangle, then we can rearrange the formula

$$\cos A=\frac{b^2+c^2-a^2}{2bc}$$

Similar formulae exist with b, c, $\cos B$ or $\cos C$ as the subject of the formula.

To prove the cosine formula, draw a line through B perpendicular to AC, meeting AC, produced if necessary, at D (see Figure 15.11b). Then $AD=c\cos A$, and $DC=b-c\cos A$ (Figure 15.11a).

Since $$BD^2=BC^2-DC^2$$
and $$BD^2=BA^2-AD^2$$
$$BC^2-DC^2=BA^2-AD^2$$
i.e. $$a^2-(b-c\cos A)^2=c^2-(c\cos A)^2$$
whence $$a^2-b^2+2bc\cos A-c^2\cos^2 A=c^2-c^2\cos^2 A$$

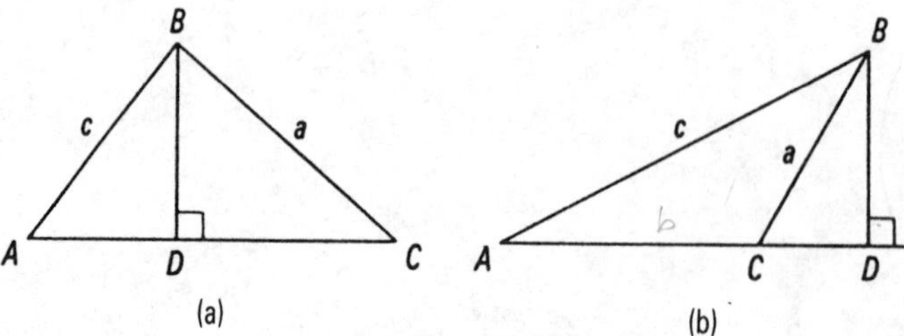

Figure 15.11

i.e. $$a^2=b^2+c^2-2bc\cos A$$

The proof needs to be adapted slightly if angle A or C is obtuse. We are certainly familiar with both these formulae, but it may be useful to be reminded of special cases where we may have some ambiguity. Since, for example, $\sin 30°=\sin 150°=0.5$, we may have two possible values for any angle; often only one of these is correct.

Example. In the triangle ABC, the length of BC is 4 cm, the length of AC is 7 cm and $C=40°$. Find the remaining sides and angles.

Using the cosine formula first,

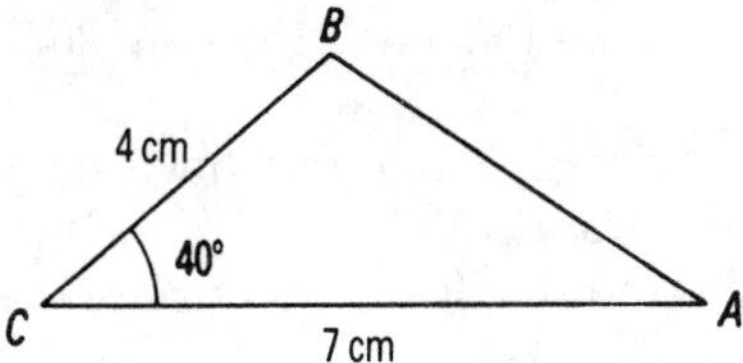

Figure 15.12

$$c^2=4^2+7^2-2\times4\times7\cos 40° \quad (1)$$
$$\simeq 22.10$$
$$c\simeq 4.70$$

Now calculate the angle opposite the smaller of the two given sides, as this cannot be obtuse.

$$\sin A=\frac{4\sin 40°}{4.70} \quad (2)$$

$$A=33.2°$$

Since the angle-sum of the triangle is 180°, $B=106.8°$. The length of AB is 4.70 cm, angle $A=33.2°$ and angle $B=106.8°$.

NB. Take particular care when evaluating expressions like (1) and (2) with a calculator; always make a rough estimate of the expected answer.

NB. Do not use the sine formula to solve isosceles triangles; draw the axis of symmetry and use the right-angled triangles so formed. Do not use the sine formula to solve right-angled triangles; it is a waste of time.

NB. Do not use the cosine formula to solve isosceles triangles; draw the axis of symmetry and use the right-angled triangles so formed. Do not use the cosine formula to solve right-angled triangles; it is a waste of time.

Exercise 15.3

In this exercise, a,b,c denote the sides BC,CA,AB of the triangle ABC.

1 Find the unknown sides and angles in triangle ABC if

(a) $a=8.52$ cm, $B=28°$, $C=64°$,
(b) $b=7.24$ cm, $B=86°$, $C=48°$,
(c) $c=8.4$ cm, $B=112°$, $C=42°$,
(d) $a=4.2$ cm, $b=4.8$ cm, $C=130°$,
(e) $a=11.2$ cm, $b=13.4$ cm, $C=32°$,
(f) $b=20.8$ cm, $c=12.6$ cm, $A=48.25°$,

(g) $A=26°$, $a=4.3$ cm, $b=5.2$ cm,
(h) $a=4.13$ cm, $b=18.1$ cm, $c=17.6$ cm,
(i) $a=5.42$ cm, $b=11.2$ cm, $c=10.9$ cm,
(j) $A=51°$, $a=2.7$ cm, $b=3.1$ cm.

2 A straight road runs from east to west through points *A* and *B*, which are 1.5 km apart. The bearings of a point *C* from *A* and *B* are 215° and 202°, respectively. Calculate the distance of *C* from *B*.

3 Calculate the angles between the diagonals of a parallelogram whose sides are 10.2 cm and 5 cm, given an angle in the parallelogram is 70°.

4 The hands of a clock are 4 cm and 10 cm long. Find the distance between the tips of the hands at
(a) 03 00h, (b) 04 00h.

5 Points *A* and *B* are 300 m apart. A hot-air balloon is vertically above a point in *AB*, and the angles of elevation of the hot-air balloon from *A* and *B* are 62° and 48°. Calculate the height of the hot-air balloon above *AB*.

6 In the triangle *ABC*, $a=3$ cm, $b=5$ cm and angle $C=45°$. Find the remaining sides and angles.

7 In the triangle *ABC*, $a=6$ cm, $b=7$ cm and $c=8$ cm. Find the angles of the triangle.

8 A glider pilot at a point *P*, 1000 m above sea-level, observes two beacons at points *Q* and *R*. He estimates that his horizontal distance from *Q* is 3000 m, its angle of elevation from *P* is 10° and its bearing from *P* is 020. He estimates his horizontal distance from *R* is 1000 m, its angle of depression is 15° and its bearing from *P* is 080. Find the heights of *Q* and *R* above sea-level, and the angle of elevation of *Q* from *R*.

Trigonometry II | 16

Sums and products formulae 163

Double angle formulae 164

Identities 166

Half angle formulae 168

Notes

Sums and products formulae

$$\sin(A+B) = \sin A\cos B + \cos A\sin B$$
$$\sin(A-B) = \sin A\cos B - \cos A\sin B$$
$$\cos(A+B) = \cos A\cos B - \sin A\sin B$$
$$\cos(A-B) = \cos A\cos B + \sin A\sin B$$

$$\tan(A+B) = \frac{\tan A + \tan B}{1 - \tan A\tan B}$$

$$\sin 2A = 2\sin A\cos A$$
$$\cos 2A = \cos^2 A - \sin^2 A = 2\cos^2 A - 1 = 1 - 2\sin^2 A$$

$$\tan 2A = \frac{2\tan A}{1-\tan^2 A}$$

$$\sin x + \sin y = 2\sin\tfrac{1}{2}(x+y)\cos\tfrac{1}{2}(x-y)$$
$$\sin x - \sin y = 2\cos\tfrac{1}{2}(x+y)\sin\tfrac{1}{2}(x-y)$$
$$\cos x + \cos y = 2\cos\tfrac{1}{2}(x+y)\cos\tfrac{1}{2}(x-y)$$
$$\cos x - \cos y = -2\sin\tfrac{1}{2}(x+y)\sin\tfrac{1}{2}(x-y)$$

Half angle formulae

If $t = \tan\tfrac{1}{2}A$,

$$\sin A = \frac{2t}{1+t^2}$$

$$\cos A = \frac{1-t^2}{1+t^2}$$

$$\tan A = \frac{2t}{1-t^2}$$

Auxiliary angle

$$a\sin\theta + b\cos\theta = R\sin(\theta+\alpha)$$

where $R = \sqrt{a^2+b^2}$, and $\cos\alpha : \sin\alpha : 1 = a : b : R$.

$$-\sqrt{(a^2+b^2)} \leqslant a\sin\theta + b\cos\theta \leqslant \sqrt{(a^2+b^2)}$$

for all values of θ.

Sums and products formulae

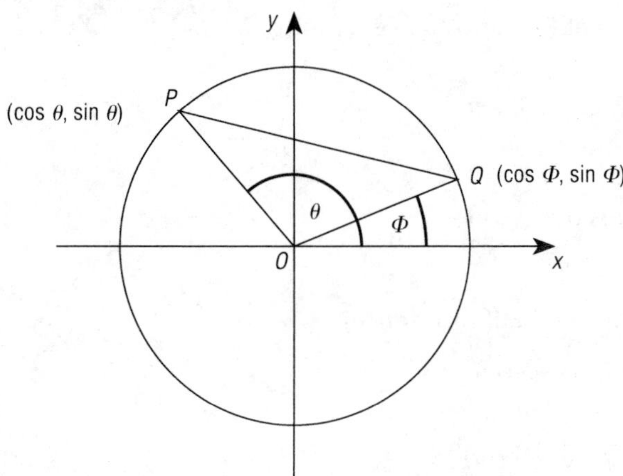

Figure 16.1

Any two points P and Q on a circle centre O radius 1 can be written in parametric form $(\cos\theta, \sin\theta)$, $(\cos\phi, \sin\phi)$, where θ and ϕ are the angles made by OP, OQ, respectively, with the x-axis (Figure 16.1). Then angle $POQ=(\theta-\phi)$. Now

$$PQ^2=(\cos\theta-\cos\phi)^2+(\sin\theta-\sin\phi)^2$$
$$=\cos^2\theta-2\cos\theta\cos\phi+\cos^2\phi+\sin^2\theta-2\sin\theta\sin\phi+\sin^2\phi$$
$$=2-2\cos\theta\cos\phi-2\sin\theta\sin\phi,\ \text{since } \cos^2\theta+\sin^2\theta=1,\ \text{etc.} \qquad \text{(A)}$$

But using the cosine formula on triangle POQ,

$$PQ^2=OP^2+OQ^2-2OP.OQ\cos(\theta-\phi)$$
$$=1+1-2\cos(\theta-\phi) \qquad \text{(B)}$$

Comparing (A) and (B), we see

$$\cos(\theta-\phi)=\cos\theta\cos\phi+\sin\theta\sin\phi \qquad \text{(C)}$$

This is true for all values of θ and ϕ.

Replacing ϕ by $-\phi$ in (C),

$$\cos(\theta+\phi)=\cos\theta\cos(-\phi)+\sin\theta\sin(-\phi)$$
$$=\cos\theta\cos\phi-\sin\theta\sin\phi$$

Replacing θ by $\frac{\pi}{2}-\theta$ in (C), we have

$$\cos\left(\frac{\pi}{2}-\theta-\phi\right)=\cos\left(\frac{\pi}{2}-\theta\right)\cos\phi+\sin\left(\frac{\pi}{2}-\theta\right)\sin\phi$$

i.e. $\sin(\theta+\phi)=\sin\theta\cos\phi+\cos\theta\sin\phi$, since $\cos\left(\frac{\pi}{2}-\theta\right)=\sin\theta$, etc.

and, again replacing ϕ by $-\phi$,

$$\sin(\theta-\phi)=\sin\theta\cos\phi-\cos\theta\sin\phi$$

These equations can be summarised

$$\sin(A+B)=\sin A\cos B+\cos A\sin B \qquad (1)$$
$$\sin(A-B)=\sin A\cos B-\cos A\sin B \qquad (2)$$

$$\cos(A+B)=\cos A\cos B-\sin A\sin B \quad (3)$$
$$\cos(A-B)=\cos A\cos B+\sin A\sin B \quad (4)$$

From these four formulae we can obtain another set of four:

Adding (1) and (2), we have

$$\sin(A+B)+\sin(A-B)=2\sin A\cos B \quad (5)$$

and writing $A+B=x$, $A-B=y$

$$\sin x+\sin y=2\sin\tfrac{1}{2}(x+y)\cos\tfrac{1}{2}(x-y)$$

which is most easily remembered as

sin+sin=2 sin (half sum) cos (half difference)

where difference means 'first minus second'.

Similarly we obtain

$$\sin x-\sin y=2\cos\tfrac{1}{2}(x+y)\sin\tfrac{1}{2}(x-y) \quad (6)$$

'sin−sin=2 cos (half sum)sin(half difference)'

$$\cos x+\cos y=2\cos\tfrac{1}{2}(x+y)\cos\tfrac{1}{2}(x-y) \quad (7)$$

'cos+cos=2 cos(half sum)cos(half difference)'

and

$$\cos x-\cos y=-2\sin\tfrac{1}{2}(x+y)\sin\tfrac{1}{2}(x-y) \quad (8)$$

'cos−cos=−2 sin (half sum)sin(half difference)'

NB. Remember the minus sign in (8).

These formulae are sometimes useful in simplifying trigonometric expressions; their most important use is in finding the derivatives of the trigonometric functions, when we need to simplify expressions like $\sin(x+\delta x)-\sin x$

Double angle formulae

From (1) and (3) we can deduce the double angle formulae,

$$\sin 2A=2\sin A\cos A \quad (9)$$

and
$$\cos 2A=\cos^2 A-\sin^2 A \quad (10)$$
$$=2\cos^2 A-1$$
$$=1-2\sin^2 A$$

There are many other methods of obtaining these formulae. The method given on page 163 has the advantage over some others that it is valid for all values of θ and ϕ, not just when θ and ϕ are acute. These double angle formulae can easily be obtained from first principles, by methods like this.

Again take a unit circle, as in Figure 16.2. Angle $BOC=2$ angle BAO, being the angle at the centre. From the diagram, looking at the length BP,

$$OB\sin 2A=AB\sin A$$

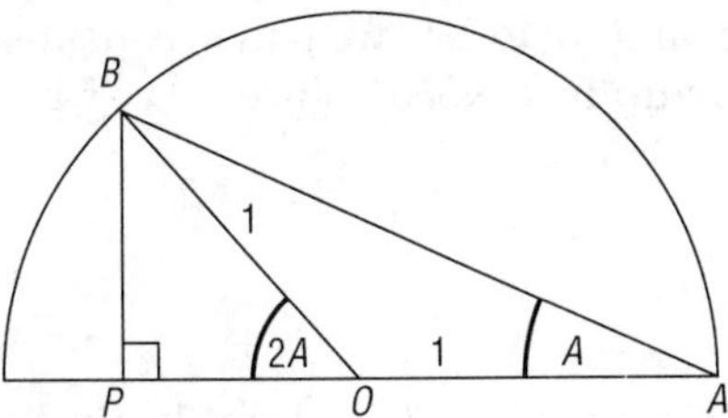

Figure 16.2

But $AB=2\cos A$
so $\sin 2A=2\sin A\cos A$
Similarly, $BP=1+\cos 2A$, OP being equal to $OB\cos 2A$,
and $BP=AB\cos A$
$=2\cos^2 A$
$\therefore\ 1+\cos 2A=2\cos^2 A$
i.e. $\cos 2A=2\cos^2 A-1$

From (1) and (3) we also have

$$\tan(A+B)=\frac{\tan A+\tan B}{1-\tan A\tan B} \tag{11}$$

whence

$$\tan 2A=\frac{2\tan A}{1-\tan^2 A} \tag{12}$$

These formulae are often useful when solving equations or establishing identities.

Example. Solve the equation, for values of x between 0° and 360°,
$\sin x+\sin 2x=\cos\frac{1}{2}x$

From (6), we see $\sin x+\sin 2x=2\sin\frac{3}{2}x\cos\frac{1}{2}x$ so that the equation becomes

$$2\sin\tfrac{3}{2}x\cos\tfrac{1}{2}x=\cos\tfrac{1}{2}x$$

i.e. either $\cos\frac{1}{2}x=0$ or $2\sin\frac{3}{2}x=1$.

If $\cos\frac{1}{2}x=0$, $\frac{1}{2}x=90°$ or $270°$, so $x=180°$ is the only solution in the interval $0\leqslant x\leqslant 360$.
If $2\sin\frac{3}{2}x=1$, $\sin\frac{3}{2}x=\frac{1}{2}$,

$$\tfrac{3}{2}x=30° \text{ or } 150° \text{ or } 390° \text{ or } 510°$$
$$x=20° \text{ or } 100° \text{ or } 260° \text{ or } 340°$$

so the complete list of solutions is

$$x=20° \text{ or } 100° \text{ or } 180° \text{ or } 260° \text{ or } 340°$$

Check: when $x=20°$

$$\sin 20°+\sin 40°\simeq 0.98$$
$$\cos 10°\simeq 0.98$$

Notice that to ensure we had all solutions in the range 0° to 360° we had to consider values of $\frac{3}{2}x$ greater than 360°, indeed all values up to $\frac{3}{2}x\times 360°$, since if $\frac{3}{2}x<540°$, $x<360°$.

Identities

When establishing identities it is most important that we should not begin by assuming what we wish to prove, for

'If 7=5,
5=7,
12=12, which is true'

yet it is plain that the original premise is false!

Almost invariably, consider the left-hand side of the identity and express it in the same form as the right-hand side.

Example. If $\cos\theta\neq -\frac{1}{2}$ or 0, show that

$$\frac{\sin\theta+\sin 2\theta}{1+\cos\theta+\cos 2\theta}=\tan\theta$$

First notice that the right-hand side is $\frac{\sin\theta}{\cos\theta}$, so that we hope to show that $\sin\theta$ is a factor of the numerator of the left-hand side, and $\cos\theta$ is a factor of the denominator. This suggests that we shall first try using

$$\sin 2\theta=2\sin\theta\cos\theta \qquad (9)$$

$$1+\cos 2\theta=2\cos^2\theta \qquad \text{from (10)}$$

so that the left-hand side (L.H.S.) is

$$\frac{\sin\theta+2\sin\theta\cos\theta}{\cos\theta+2\cos^2\theta}$$

$$=\frac{\sin\theta(1+2\cos\theta)}{\cos\theta(1+2\cos\theta)}$$

$$=\tan\theta, \text{ since } 1+2\cos\theta\neq 0$$

We may have been tempted to try

$$\sin\theta+\sin 2\theta=2\sin\tfrac{3}{2}\theta\cos\tfrac{1}{2}\theta$$

or even

$$1+\cos\theta+\cos 2\theta=1+2\cos\tfrac{3}{2}\theta\cos\tfrac{1}{2}\theta$$

but the ratio $\frac{1}{2}\theta$ is not like any term in the R.H.S., so that this method does not look worth pursuing. **All identities set at A-level nowadays are straightforward and can be established quickly, so do not get involved in heavy algebra!**

These formulae are often useful when integrating expressions (page 249).

Exercise 16.1

1 From $\sin^2 A+\cos^2 A=1$, show that
(a) $\sec^2 A=1+\tan^2 A$,
(b) $\operatorname{cosec}^2 A=1+\cot^2 A$,
(c) $\sin^4 A-\cos^4 A=\sin^2 A-\cos^2 A$,
(d) $\sin^6 A+\cos^6 A=1-3\cos^2 A\sin^2 A$.

2 Prove the following identities:

(a) $\dfrac{1}{1-\sin A}+\dfrac{1}{1+\sin A}=2\sec^2 A$,

(b) $\dfrac{\cos^2 A}{1-\sin A}-\dfrac{\cos^2 A}{1+\sin A}=2\sin A$.

(c) $\dfrac{1}{\operatorname{cosec} A-\cot A}+\dfrac{1}{\operatorname{cosec} A+\cot A}=2\operatorname{cosec} A$,

(d) $\dfrac{1}{\operatorname{cosec} A-\cot A}-\dfrac{1}{\operatorname{cosec} A+\cot A}=2\cot A$.

3 Show that $\dfrac{\cos A}{1-\sin A}=\tan A+\sec A$.

4 Show that $(\cos A+\sin A)^3-(\cos A-\sin A)^3=2\sin A(1+2\cos^2 A)$.

5 Show that $\dfrac{1}{1+\sec A}-\dfrac{1}{1-\sec A}=2\operatorname{cosec} A\cot A$.

6 Using $\sin(A+B)=\sin A\cos B+\cos A\sin B$, etc.,
obtain
(a) $\sin 3A=4\sin^3 A-3\sin A$, $3\sin A-4\sin^3 A$,
(b) $\cos 3A=4\cos^3 A-3\cos A$,
(c) $\tan 3A=\dfrac{3\tan A-\tan^3 A}{1-3\tan^2 A}$.

7 Using (12) on page 165, obtain

$$\tan 4A=\frac{4\tan A-4\tan^3 A}{1-6\tan^2 A+\tan^4 A}$$

8 Express the following as products of two trig ratios:
(a) $\sin 5x+\sin x$, (b) $\cos 5x+\cos 3x$, (c) $\sin 5x-\sin 2x$,
(d) $\cos 5x-\cos 7x$.

9 Express the following as the sum of two trig ratios:
(a) $2\sin 5x\cos 3x$, (b) $2\cos 4x\cos x$, (c) $\sin 4x\cos 5x$,
(d) $\sin x\sin 2x$.

10 Writing $\cos 4x=\cos(2x+2x)$. Express $\cos 4x$ as a polynomial in $\cos x$.

11 Solve the following equations, for values of x such that $0°\leqslant x\leqslant 360°$:
(a) $2\sin x+\sin 2x=0$, (b) $\sin x+\sin 3x+\sin 5x=0$, (c) $2\cos 2x+2\sin^2 x-1=0$,
(d) $\tan 2x+5\tan x=0$.

12 Establish the following identities:
(a) $\cos x+\cos(x+120°)+\cos(x+240°)=0$,
(b) $\sin 2x-\sin 4x+\sin 6x=\sin 4x(2\cos 2x-1)$,
(c) $\sin^2 x-\sin^2 y=\sin(x+y)\sin(x-y)$.

Half angle formulae

From equation (9), we have

$$\sin A = 2\sin\tfrac{1}{2}A\cos\tfrac{1}{2}A$$

$$= \frac{2\sin\frac{1}{2}A\cos\frac{1}{2}A}{\cos^2\frac{1}{2}A+\sin^2\frac{1}{2}A}$$

$$= \frac{2\tan\frac{1}{2}A}{1+\tan^2\frac{1}{2}A}$$

which we can write as $\sin A = \dfrac{2}{1+t^2}$, where $t=\tan\frac{1}{2}A$ (13)

Similarly we can show

$$\cos A = \frac{1-t^2}{1+t^2} \qquad (14)$$

and

$$\tan A = \frac{2t}{1-t^2} \qquad (15)$$

Equations (14) and (15) are especially useful for solving some equations, and for finding certain integrals.

Example. Solve correct to 1 d.p. the equation $3\sin x+4\cos x=2$ for $0°<x<360°$.

Method 1: Using (13) and (14) we have

$$3\frac{2t}{1+t^2}+4\frac{1-t^2}{1+t^2}=2$$

i.e. $6t+4-4t^2=2+2t^2$

i.e. $3t^2-3t-1=0$

$\tan\frac{1}{2}x \equiv t = 1.26$ or -0.26, using the formula for the solution of quadratic equations,

$$\tfrac{1}{2}x = 51.65° \text{ or } 165.22°$$
$$x = 103.3° \text{ or } 330.4°$$

Notice that to find solutions between 0° and 360° we only had to consider values of $\frac{1}{2}x$ between 0° and 180°, but in order to obtain solutions correct to 1 d.p., we had to find $\frac{1}{2}x$ to a greater degree of accuracy.

Method 2: Comparing $3\sin x+4\cos x$ with $\sin x\cos\alpha+\cos x\sin\alpha$, we see that if we write

$$3\sin x+4\cos x = 5(\sin x\cos\alpha+\cos x\sin\alpha) \qquad (16)$$
$$= 5\sin(x+\alpha)$$

our given equation reduces to

$$5 \sin (x+\alpha)=2$$

i.e. $$\sin (x+\alpha)=0.4$$

α being such that $\cos \alpha=0.6$, $\sin \alpha=0.8$, i.e. $\alpha \simeq 53.13°$.

Thus $\sin (x+53.13°)=0.4$

$$x+53.13°=23.58° \text{ or } 156.42° \text{ or } 383.58° \text{ or } \ldots$$

the values of x between 0° and 360° being 103.3° or 330.4°. Notice that to obtain values of x in the required range we had to consider values of $x+\alpha$ in the range 53.13° to 413.13°, and also that, as before, we worked to 2 d.p. to obtain a final answer correct to 1 d.p. Much of the arithmetic done in detail above should be carried out on a calculator.

The angle α we introduced above is called the auxiliary angle. The form (16) is useful not only for solving equations of this type, but it also enables us to see that

$$-5 \leqslant 3 \sin x+4 \cos x \leqslant 5$$

since $$-5 \leqslant 5 \sin (x+\alpha) \leqslant 5$$

the maximum value of 5 being attained when $x=90°-\alpha$, the minimum value when $x=270°-\alpha$.

Exercise 16.2

1 Solve the following equations, correct to the nearest degree, for values of x such that $-180° \leqslant x \leqslant 180°$:
(a) $3 \sin x+4 \cos x=1$, (b) $\sin x+\cos x=0.5$, (c) $3 \cos x-2 \sin x=1$,
(d) $3 \sin x-5 \cos x=5$, (e) $3 \sin 2x+4 \cos 2x=1$.

2 Find the greatest and least values of each of the following:
(a) $3 \sin x+4 \cos x$ [write $3 \sin x+4 \cos x=5 \sin(x+\alpha)$], (b) $3 \sin 2x+4 \cos 2x$,
(c) $\sin x+\cos x$, (d) $\sin x-2 \cos x$, (e) $2 \cos x-3 \sin x$.

3 Find the greatest and least values of each of the following, and the values of x between 0° and 360° for which those greatest and least values are attained:
(a) $4 \sin x+3 \cos x$, (b) $4 \sin x-3 \cos x$, (c) $\sin x-\cos x$, (d) $\sin 2x-\cos 2x$,
(e) $\sin 2x-2 \cos 2x$.

4 Find the least positive value of $\dfrac{1}{2 \sin x+\cos x}$ and the values of x at which that least value is attained.

5 Given that $\sin x=0.8$, $\cos x=-0.6$, find the exact value of the following:
(a) $\sin 2x$, (b) $\cos 4x$, (c) $\sin(x+45°)$, (d) $\sin(x+120°)+\sin(x-120°)$.

Complex numbers 17

Introduction 173

Complex conjugate 173

Operations on complex numbers 173

Equality of complex numbers 174

Representation in an Argand diagram 175

Product and quotient of two complex numbers 176

Powers of complex numbers 176

Loci 177

Algebraic method 180

Notes

Complex conjugate

If $z=a+ib$, the complex conjugate of z, written z^* (or $\bar{z}$) is $\bar{z}=a-ib$.

Modulus and argument

The modulus of $|z|$, written $|z|$, is $\sqrt{(a^2+b^2)}$.

The argument of z, written arg z, is arctan (b/a), **only if *x* is positive**. Draw a diagram for all other cases.

Products and quotients

$$R(\cos\theta+i\sin\theta)r(\cos\phi+i\sin\phi)=Rr[\cos(\theta+\phi)+i\sin(\theta+\phi)]$$

$$\frac{R(\cos\theta+i\sin\theta)}{r(\cos\phi+i\sin\phi)}=\frac{R}{r}[\cos(\theta-\phi)+i\sin(\theta-\phi)]$$

$$[R(\cos\theta+i\sin\theta)]^2=R^2(\cos 2\theta+i\sin 2\theta)$$

Loci

$|z|=1$ represents a circle, centre (0,0), radius 1.
$|z-a-ib|=r$ represents a circle, centre (a, b), radius r.
arg $z=\alpha$ is a straight line through (0,0), inclined at an angle α to the real axis.
$|z-z_1|=|z-z_2|$ is the perpendicular bisector of the straight line joining the points representing the complex numbers z_1, z_2.

Introduction

Complex numbers can be regarded merely as an extension of the real number system, necessary if we are to consider the solution of certain equations. Just as a child may say 'there are no solutions to the equation $3x=4$' until introduced to 'fractions', so we may say 'there are no solutions to the equation $x^2=-4$' until we are introduced to the number i such that $i\times i=-1$. What is remarkable is that this extension of the number-field enables us to solve all polynomials, even those with complex coefficients, and also equations like $3^x=-2$ and $\sin x=-3$.

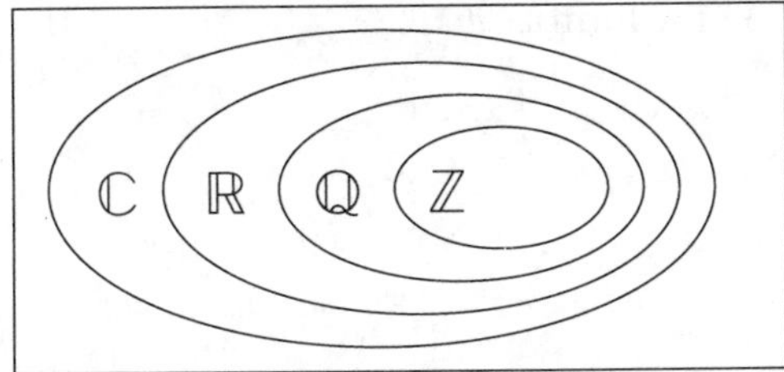

$\mathbb{Z}$ = {all integers}
$\mathbb{Q}$ = {all rationals}
$\mathbb{R}$ = {all reals}
$\mathbb{C}$ = {all complex numbers}

Figure 17.1

The Venn diagram (Figure 17.1) shows $\mathbb{Z}$, the set of all integers, e.g. 3, as a subset of the rationals, e.g. $\frac{3}{2}$, $\frac{3}{4}$; the rationals $\mathbb{Q}$ as a subset of the reals $\mathbb{R}$, e.g. π is a real number but not a rational, and the real numbers, e.g. 3, as a subset of $\mathbb{C}$, the set of complex numbers, e.g. $3+i$, $3+2i$, $3+3i$.

Complex conjugate

If $z^2=-4$, $z=2i$ or $-2i$; if $z^2+z+1=0$, $z=\frac{1}{2}[-1+i\sqrt{3}]$ or $\frac{1}{2}[-1-i\sqrt{3}]$. Associated with each complex number $z=a+ib$, we define its complex conjugate z^* (sometimes written $\bar{z}$), where $z^*=a-ib$. This has the property that

$$z+z^*=(a+ib)+(a-ib)=2a, \text{ which is real}$$

and $$zz^*=(a+ib)(a-ib)=a^2+b^2, \text{ which is also real}$$

In particular, this shows that if quadratic equations with real coefficients have complex roots, then those roots are complex conjugates, the sum and products of those roots being real. If the quadratic equations have complex coefficients, then in general the roots will not be complex conjugates.

Operations on complex numbers

Addition and subtraction are defined by

$$(a+ib)+(c+id)=(a+c)+i(b+d)$$

and $$(a+ib)-(c+id)=(a-c)+i(b-d)$$

i.e. add (or subtract) the real and imaginary parts separately:

multiplication is defined by

$$(a+ib)(c+id)=ac-bd+i(bc+ad)$$

NB. Take special care that $ib\times id=-bd$; although we may be confident that we will never make a mistake, it is terribly easy to write $ib\times id=+bd$.

To divide two complex numbers, we almost invariably multiply numerator and denominator by the complex conjugate of the denominator, as in this example.

Example. If $z_1=2+i$ and $z_2=4+3i$, find, in the form $a+ib$,

(a) $\frac{z_1}{z_2}$, (b) $2+1/z_1$

To express $\frac{z_1}{z_2}$ in this form,

$$\frac{z_1}{z_2}=\frac{2+i}{4+3i}=\frac{(2+i)(4-3i)}{(4+3i)(4-3i)}$$

$$=\frac{8-6i+4i+i\times(-3i)}{16+9}$$

$$=\tfrac{11}{25}-\tfrac{3}{25}i$$

Similarly, $$2+\frac{1}{z_1}=2+\frac{2-i}{(2+i)(2-i)}$$

$$=2+\tfrac{2}{5}-\tfrac{1}{5}i$$

$$=\tfrac{12}{5}-\tfrac{1}{5}i$$

adding the two real numbers.

Equality of complex numbers

Two complex numbers are equal only if the real parts of each are equal and the imaginary parts of each are equal, thus if

$$x+iy=2+3i,\ x=2 \text{ and } y=3$$

Exercise 17.1

1 Find in the form $a+ib$ the solutions of the following equations:
(a) $z^2=-25$, (b) $4z^2+9=0$, (c) $(z-1)^2=-4$, (d) $(2z-3)^2=-25$,
(e) $(z-2i)^2=49$, (f) $(z-2i)^2=-49$.

2 If $z=2-i$, find in the form $a+ib$

(a) $z+2i$, (b) z^2, (c) $\bar{z}$, (d) $1/z$, (e) $\frac{1}{z+1}$.

3 If $z_1=3+2i$, $z_2=1-3i$, find in the form $a+ib$,

(a) z_1+z_2, (b) z_1z_2, (c) $z_1\bar{z}_2$, (d) $\dfrac{1}{z_1}+\dfrac{1}{z_2}$, (e) $\dfrac{1+z_1}{z_2-2i}$.

4 If $z_1=3+2i$ and $z_2=1+3i$, find real numbers a, b, c, d such that

(a) $az_1+bz_2=9-i$, (b) $\dfrac{c}{z_1}+\dfrac{d}{z_2}=9-13i$.

5 If $\dfrac{z}{z-2}=2+i$, find z in the form $a+ib$.

6 If $z=3-2i$, find $\bar{z}$, $z\bar{z}$ and $z+\bar{z}$. Hence obtain the quadratic equation whose roots are z and $\bar{z}$.

Representation in an Argand diagram

In the same way that real numbers can be represented along

−3 −2 −1 −0.5 0 1 √2 2 3 π

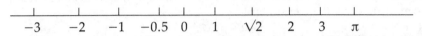

a number-line, we can represent complex numbers using two dimensions so that a point (x,y) represents the complex number $x+iy$. The distance of the point P, representing the complex number z, from the origin is called the modulus of z, written $|z|$; the angle made by OP with the positive x-axis is called the argument (the term amplitude was used until fairly recently).

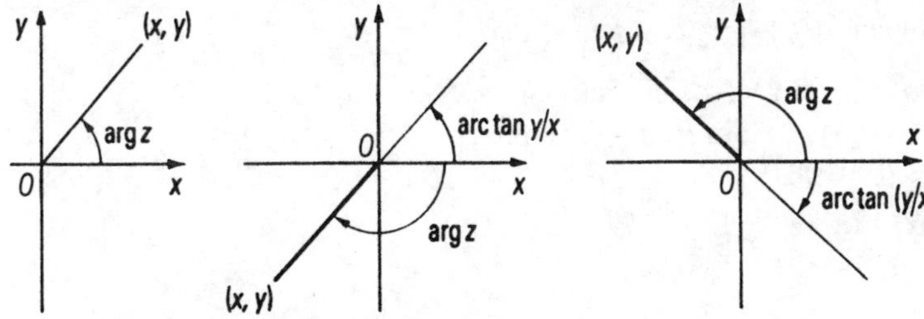

Figure 17.2

Thus if $z=x+iy$, $|z|=\sqrt{(x^2+y^2)}$

$\arg(z)=\arctan(y/x)$ if x is positive

$=\arctan(y/x)-\pi$ if both x and y are negative,

$=\arctan(y/x)+\pi$ if x is negative but y is positive.

Always draw a diagram when finding the argument of a complex number.

Example. Find the modulus and argument of (a) $1+i$, (b) $-1-i$, (c) $-1+i$.

In each case, the modulus is $\sqrt{2}$.
From Figure 17.3(a) we see $\arg(1+i)=\arctan(1/1)=\pi/4$.
From Figure 17.3(b) we see $\arg(-1-i)=\pi/4-\pi=-3\pi/4$.
From Figure 17.3(c) we see $\arg(-1+i)=-\pi/4+\pi=3\pi/4$.

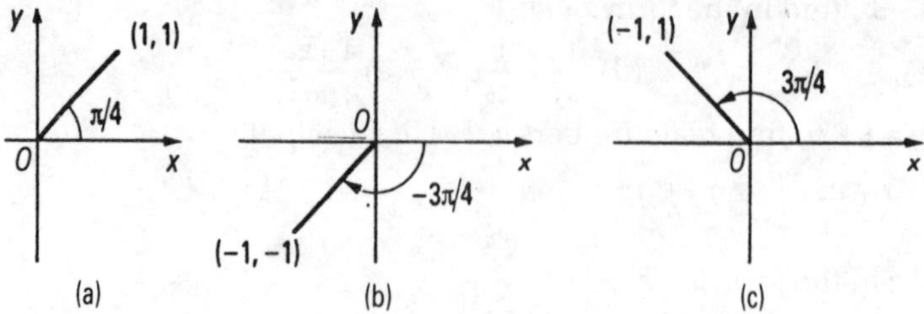

Figure 17.3

Product and quotient of two complex numbers

The modulus-argument form of a complex number enables us to divide by a complex number more easily than using the $a+ib$ form. For if $z=r(\cos\theta+i\sin\theta)$, r being the modulus and θ the argument,

$$\frac{1}{z}=\frac{1}{r(\cos\theta+i\sin\theta)}=\frac{\cos\theta-i\cos\theta}{r(\cos\theta+i\sin\theta)(\cos\theta-i\sin\theta)}$$

$$=\frac{(\cos\theta-i\sin\theta)}{r}, \text{ since } \cos^2\theta+\sin^2\theta=1$$

$$=\frac{\cos(-\theta)+i\sin(-\theta)}{r}$$

Also, if $z_1=r_1(\cos\theta+i\sin\theta)$, $z_2=r_2(\cos\phi+i\sin\phi)$,

$$\begin{aligned} z_1z_2&=r_1r_2(\cos\theta+i\sin\theta)(\cos\phi+i\sin\phi)\\ &=r_1r_2(\cos\theta\cos\phi-\sin\theta\sin\phi+i\sin\theta\cos\phi\\ &\quad+i\cos\theta\sin\phi)\\ &=r_1r_2[\cos(\theta+\phi)+i\sin(\theta+\phi)]\end{aligned}$$

and

$$\frac{z_1}{z_2}=z_1\times\frac{1}{z_2}=\frac{r_1(\cos\theta+i\sin\theta)[\cos(-\phi)+\sin(-\phi)]}{r_2}$$

$$=\frac{r_1}{r_2}[\cos(\theta-\phi)+i\sin(\theta-\phi)]$$

Thus to multiply two complex numbers in modulus-argument form, we multiply the moduli and add the arguments; to divide, we divide the moduli and subtract the arguments.

Powers of complex numbers

This result when multiplying two complex numbers gives us an easy way of finding the powers of a complex number, for

$$z^2 \equiv [r(\cos\theta + i\sin\theta)]^2 = r^2(\cos\theta + i\sin\theta)(\cos\theta + i\sin\theta)$$
$$= r^2(\cos 2\theta + i\sin 2\theta)$$

and
$$z^3 \equiv z^2 z = r^2(\cos 2\theta + i\sin 2\theta)r(\cos\theta + i\sin\theta)$$
$$= r^3(\cos 3\theta + i\sin 3\theta)$$

We can prove by induction, that for all positive integer values of n,

$$z^n \equiv [r(\cos\theta + i\sin\theta)]^n = r^n(\cos n\theta + i\sin n\theta)$$

This theorem, known as de Moivre's theorem, is true for all values of n, whether integer or not, but the general form is outside the syllabus of single-subject A-level examinations.

Exercise 17.2

1 Represent on an Argand diagram, and give the modulus and argument of
(a) 3, (b) $2i$, (c) -1, (d), $-2i$, (e) $3+4i$.

2 Represent on an Argand diagram, and give the modulus and argument of

(a) $\frac{1}{2}+i\frac{\sqrt{3}}{2}$, (b) $\sqrt{3}-i$, (c) $-2\sqrt{3}+2i$, (d) $-\frac{1}{2}-i\frac{\sqrt{3}}{2}$, (e) $-\sqrt{3}-i$.

3 If $z_1-2(\cos\pi/3+i\sin\pi/3)$
$z_2=5(\cos\pi/6+i\sin\pi/6)$
and $z_3=3(\cos\pi/4-i\sin\pi/4)$
find, in modulus-argument form

(a) z_1z_2, (b) $\frac{z_1}{z_2}$, (c) $z_1z_2z_3$, (d) z_1^2, (e) z_2^3, (f) $\frac{z_1z_2}{z_3^2}$.

4 If $z=3/2+i\frac{\sqrt{3}}{2}$, write z in modulus argument form. Illustrate this form in an Argand diagram, and use it to find
(a) z^2, (b) z^3, (c) l/z, (d) the smallest positive value of n for which z^n is real.

5 If $z=1+\cos\theta+i\sin\theta$, write z in modulus-argument form. Illustrate this form in an Argand diagram, and use it to find
(a) z^2, (b) l/z, (c) z^4.

Loci

All points whose distance from the fixed point O is constant, say 2 units, lie on a circle centre O, radius 2. Thus $|z|=2$ describes a circle centre O, radius 2.

All points P such that OP is inclined to the positive x-axis at a constant angle, say $\pi/6$, lie on a straight line through O inclined at $\pi/6$ to the positive x-axis. (Strictly, they lie on only half the straight line, since the argument of numbers represented by points on the other half is $-5\pi/6$.)

If the point P represents the complex number z, Figure 17.5 shows the relation of P to the point Q representing the number $z-2$, and to the point R representing the number $z-1+2i$.

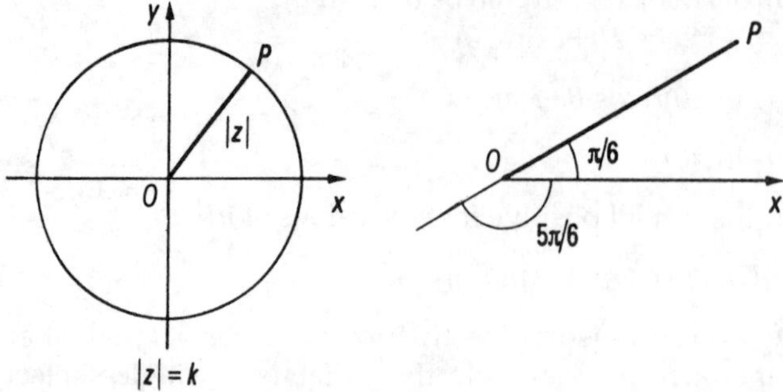

Figure 17.4

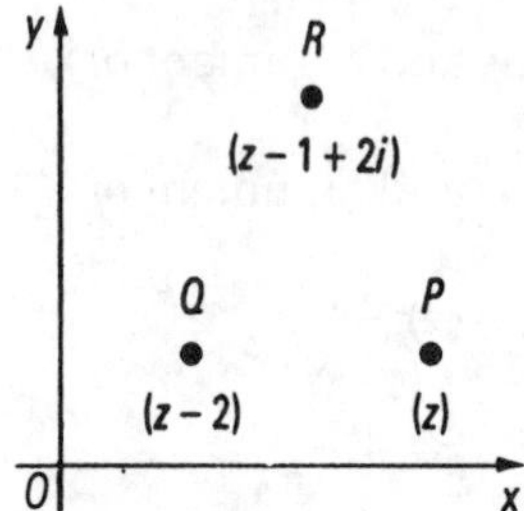

Figure 17.5

Thus if P is such that $|z-2|=1$, the point representing the complex number $Z\equiv z-2$ describes as circle centre O, radius 1, so that the point P representing z, i.e. $Z+2$, describes a circle centre (2,0), radius 1. Similarly if $|z-1+2i|=3$, P describes a circle centre $(1, -2)$, radius 3. We may be helped in interpreting these loci if we remember the relation of, say, $z-2$ to z (Figure 17.6), so that if the point representing $z-2$ describes a circle centre the origin, the point representing z will describe this circle after the point has been translated by $+2$; if $z-1+2i$ describes a circle centre O, the point z describes this circle after a translation described by $1-2i$.

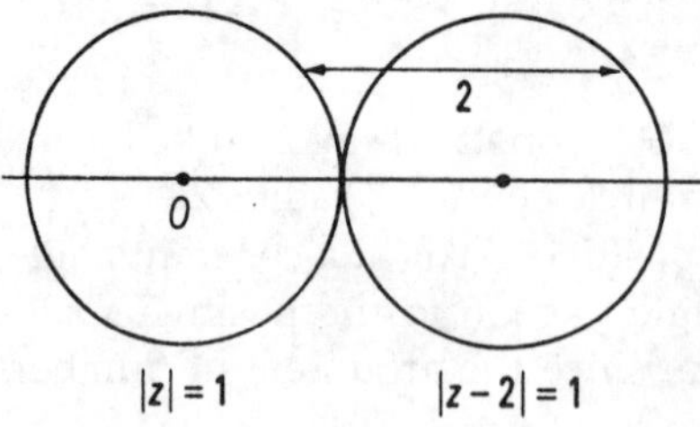

Figure 17.6

Example 1. Find the locus described by $|z-i|=2$.

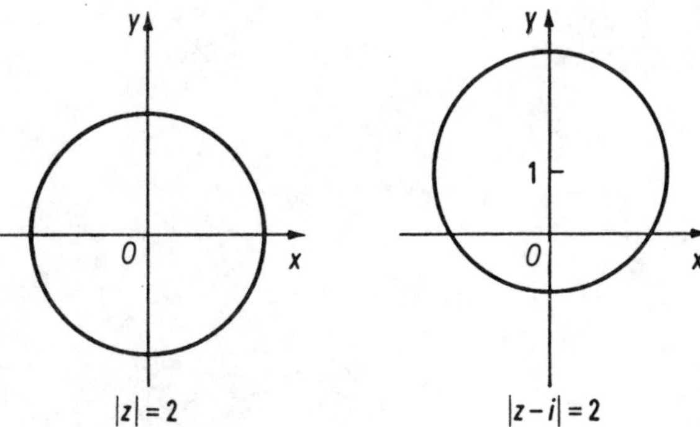

Figure 17.7

The point P' representing the number $Z \equiv z-i$ describes a circle centre O, radius 2. The point P representing the number z, i.e. $(z-1)+i \equiv Z+i$, is P' **after a translation** $+i$, so P describes a circle, centre (0,1), radius 2.

Example 2. Find the locus described by $\arg(z-1)=\pi/4$

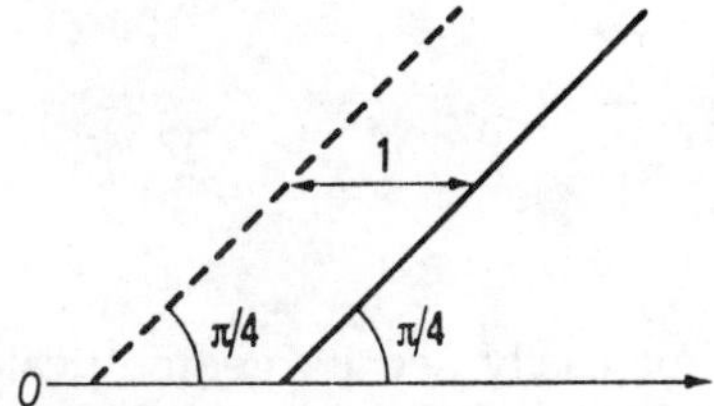

Figure 17.8

We know that $\arg Z=\pi/4$ is half of a straight line through O, so if

$$Z=z-1$$
$$z=Z+1$$

and the locus of z will be the locus of Z **after a translation +1**.

Example 3. Find the locus described by $|z-1-i|=|z+1|$.

$|z-1-i|$ is the distance of the point P from the point representing the number $1+i$, i.e. from (1,1); $|z+1|$ is the distance from the point representing the number -1, i.e. $(-1,0)$. The locus of points equidistant from points A and B is the perpendicular bisector of AB, so the locus described by

$$|z-1-i|=|z+1|$$

is the perpendicular bisector of the line joining (1,1) to $(-1,0)$.

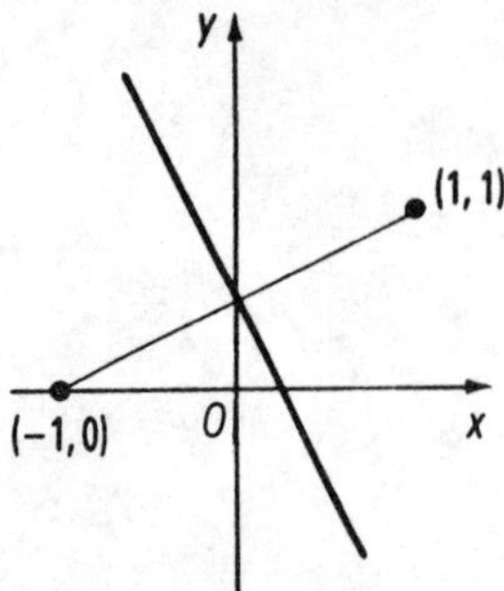

Figure 17.9

Algebraic method

Many of these loci can be found algebraically, though this is usually much longer than using the geometric property stated in the equation.

In Example 3, since $|z|=\sqrt{x^2+y^2}$

$$|z-1-i|=|z+1|$$
$$\Rightarrow |x+iy-1-i|=|x+iy+1|$$
$$(x-1)^2+(y-1)^2=(x+1)^2+y^2$$
$$x^2-2x+1+y^2-2y+1=x^2+2x+1+y^2$$

i.e. $$4x+2y=1$$

We recognise this as a straight line, but may not easily see its geometrical interpretation. The gradient of the line joining $(-1,0)$ to $(1,1)$ is $\frac{1}{2}$; its midpoint is $(0,\frac{1}{2})$, so the perpendicular bisector has equation

$$y-\tfrac{1}{2}=-2(x-0)$$

i.e. $$4x+2y=1$$

Exercise 17.3

1 Sketch the locus $|Z|=2$. Writing $Z=z-2-3i$, i.e. $z=Z+2+3i$, deduce the locus $|z-2-3i|=2$. Show this locus in the same sketch as the first locus.

2 Sketch the loci described by

(a) $|z-2|=1$, (b) $|z-2i|=1$, (c) $|z+2i|=1$, (d) $|z-2-2i|=1$.

3 Sketch the loci described by

(a) $\arg(z-1)=\pi/3$, (b) $\arg(z+1)=\pi/3$, (c) $\arg(z-1)=-2\pi/3$, (d) $\arg(z+i)=\pi/3$.

4 Sketch the loci described by

(a) $|z|=|z-2|$, (b) $|z-i|=|z+2|$.

5 Sketch the loci $\arg z=\pi/4$ and $|z+2+i|=|z-4+i|$. Use geometry to find the coordinates of the point common to both loci.

6 If $z_1=10-2i$ and $z_2=2-3i$, show that $\arg(z_1/z_2)=\pi/4$.

7 If P represents the complex number $\sqrt{3}+i$, find geometrically the two possible complex numbers represented by Q, the third vertex of the equilateral triangle OPQ.

8 Find, each in the form $a+ib$, the sum and the product of the roots of the quadratic equation.

$$(1-i)z^2-2iz+3-i=0$$

9 If z is such that $z^3=1$ but $z\neq 1$, show that $z^2+z+1=0$.

10 A square is inscribed in the circle $|z|=2$, so that the four vertices lie on the circumference of the circle; one of its vertices represents the complex number $\sqrt{2}+i\sqrt{2}$. Find the numbers represented by the other vertices.

11 A point P describes the circle $|z|=2$ in an anti-clockwise sense. Describe the loci

(a) $|z|=2$, (b) $|1/z|=2$.

12 Sketch in a diagram the region described by

$$|z-1|\leqslant 1$$

and $$\frac{-\pi}{4}\leqslant \arg z\leqslant \frac{\pi}{4}$$

13 Find the roots of the equation $z^2+2z+5=0$. Show that for any quadratic equation with real coefficients that has complex roots, the roots are complex conjugates.

14 Expand $(\cos\theta+i\sin\theta)^5$ by the binomial theorem. From this expansion, show that $\cos 5\theta=16c^2-20c^3+5c$, where $c=\cos\theta$. Obtain a similar expression for $\cos 6\theta$.

15 If $|z_1-z_2|=|z_1+z_2|$, show geometrically that the arguments of z_1 and z_2 differ by $\pi/2$.

Matrices 18

Matrices 186

Transpose 186

Determinant of a 2×2 matrix 186

Inverse of a 2×2 matrix 187

Geometrical transformation in a plane 187

Transformation of a straight line 189

Mapping a straight line onto itself 190

Determinant of a 3×3 matrix 191

Minors and cofactors 192

Adjoint of a matrix 192

Inverse of a 3×3 matrix 193

Notes

Transpose of a matrix

If $\mathbf{A}=\begin{pmatrix} a & b \\ c & d \end{pmatrix}$, the transpose, $\mathbf{A}^{\mathrm{T}}=\begin{pmatrix} a & c \\ b & d \end{pmatrix}$

Determinant of a 2×2 matrix

If $\mathbf{A}=\begin{pmatrix} a & b \\ c & d \end{pmatrix}$, $\det \mathbf{A} \equiv |\mathbf{A}| = ad-bc$

Inverse of a 2×2 matrix

$$\mathbf{A}^{-1}=\frac{1}{\det \mathbf{A}}\begin{pmatrix} d & -b \\ -c & a \end{pmatrix}$$

Determinant of a 3×3 matrix

$$\begin{vmatrix} a_1 & b_1 & c_1 \\ a_2 & b_2 & c_2 \\ a_3 & b_3 & c_3 \end{vmatrix} = a_1\begin{vmatrix} b_2 & c_2 \\ b_3 & c_3 \end{vmatrix} - b_1\begin{vmatrix} a_2 & c_2 \\ a_3 & c_3 \end{vmatrix} + c_1\begin{vmatrix} a_2 & b_2 \\ a_3 & b_3 \end{vmatrix}$$

$$=a_1b_2c_3+a_2b_3c_1+a_3b_1c_2-a_1b_3c_2-a_2b_1c_3-a_3b_2c_1$$

Inverse of a 3×3 matrix

The cofactor of an element is found by 'removing' the row and column containing that element, and finding the determinant of the 2×2 matrix, then giving it the appropriate sign

$$\begin{matrix} + & - & + \\ - & + & - \\ + & - & + \end{matrix}$$

Form the matrix of the cofactors, e.g. if $\mathbf{A}_1$ is the cofactor of a_1, $\mathbf{A}_1=b_2c_3-b_3c_2$. Transpose the matrix of the cofactors, to give

$$\begin{pmatrix} \mathbf{A}_1 & \mathbf{A}_2 & \mathbf{A}_3 \\ \mathbf{B}_1 & \mathbf{B}_2 & \mathbf{B}_3 \\ \mathbf{C}_1 & \mathbf{C}_2 & \mathbf{C}_3 \end{pmatrix} \qquad (1)$$

When this matrix is multiplied by **A**, the product is a scalar multiple of the unit matrix. Divide each term in (1) by that scalar multiple to obtain the inverse of **A**. NB. The scalar multiple is equal to det **A**.

Matrices

A matrix is defined as a rectangular array of numbers, subject to certain rules of composition, with which we should already be familiar. A matrix with r rows and s columns is called an r by s matrix, and the rule for addition (and for subtraction) requires that matrices to be added (or subtracted) together must have the same number of rows and columns. For addition (or subtraction), add (or subtract) corresponding entries, i.e.

$$\begin{pmatrix} a & b & c \\ d & e & f \end{pmatrix} + \begin{pmatrix} x & y & z \\ u & v & w \end{pmatrix} = \begin{pmatrix} a+x & b+y & c+z \\ d+u & e+v & f+w \end{pmatrix}$$

The rule for multiplication requires that if the product **AB** of two matrices **A**,**B** exists, **A** is an r by s matrix, and **B** an s by t matrix, so that the first matrix has as many columns as the second matrix has rows.

Matrix multiplication is illustrated by

$$\begin{pmatrix} a & b & c \\ d & e & f \end{pmatrix} \begin{pmatrix} x \\ y \\ z \end{pmatrix} = \begin{pmatrix} ax+by+cz \\ dx+ey+fz \end{pmatrix}$$

and

$$(x \ y) \begin{pmatrix} a & b \\ c & d \end{pmatrix} = \begin{pmatrix} ax+cy \\ bx+dy \end{pmatrix}$$

Notice that the product of an r by s matrix and an s by t matrix is an r by t matrix.

Division by a matrix is not defined. Instead, we multiply by the inverse matrix.

Transpose

The transpose of a matrix **A**, written $\mathbf{A}^T$, is formed by interchanging rows and columns, i.e. if

$$\mathbf{A} = \begin{pmatrix} a & b & c \\ d & e & f \end{pmatrix}, \ \mathbf{A}^T = \begin{pmatrix} a & d \\ b & e \\ c & f \end{pmatrix}$$

Determinant of a 2×2 matrix

Associated with every matrix is defined a determinant. For a 2×2 matrix, $\mathbf{A} \equiv \begin{pmatrix} a & b \\ c & d \end{pmatrix}$, the expression $ad-bc$ is called the determinant. A determinant only exists for square matrices, and for higher order matrices is defined in a way different from, but of course consistent with, that for a 2×2 matrix. A matrix **A** for which det $\mathbf{A}=0$ is called a singular matrix.

Inverse of a 2×2 matrix

To find the inverse $\mathbf{A}^{-1}$ of the matrix $\mathbf{A}$, where

$\mathbf{A} = \begin{pmatrix} a & b \\ c & d \end{pmatrix}$, we require a matrix, say $\begin{pmatrix} x & y \\ z & w \end{pmatrix}$ such that

$$\begin{pmatrix} a & b \\ c & d \end{pmatrix}\begin{pmatrix} x & y \\ z & w \end{pmatrix} = \begin{pmatrix} 1 & 0 \\ 0 & 1 \end{pmatrix}$$

i.e. $\begin{pmatrix} ax+bz & ay+bw \\ cx+dz & cy+dw \end{pmatrix} = \begin{pmatrix} 1 & 0 \\ 0 & 1 \end{pmatrix}$

i.e. $ax+bz = 1$ and $cx+dz = 0$,
$ay+bw = 0$ and $cy+dw = 1$

Solving for x,y,z and w we have

$$x = \frac{d}{ad-bd}, \quad y = \frac{-b}{ad-bc}, \quad z = \frac{-c}{ad-bc}, \quad w = \frac{a}{ad-bc}$$

so that if $\mathbf{A} = \begin{pmatrix} a & b \\ c & d \end{pmatrix}$, $\mathbf{A}^{-1} = \dfrac{1}{ad-bc}\begin{pmatrix} d & -b \\ -c & a \end{pmatrix}$

Forming the product $\mathbf{A}^{-1}\mathbf{A}$ we have $\mathbf{A}^{-1}\mathbf{A} = \begin{pmatrix} 1 & 0 \\ 0 & 1 \end{pmatrix}$, so that although matrix multiplication is not necessarily commutative, the inverse has the property $\mathbf{AA}^{-1} = \mathbf{A}^{-1}\mathbf{A}$

Geometrical transformations in a plane

In general, any point (x,y) in a plane can be transformed into any other point (X,Y) by multiplying by a suitable matrix $\mathbf{A}$, where

$$\mathbf{A} = \begin{pmatrix} a & b \\ c & d \end{pmatrix} \text{ and } \begin{pmatrix} a & b \\ c & d \end{pmatrix}\begin{pmatrix} x \\ y \end{pmatrix} = \begin{pmatrix} X \\ Y \end{pmatrix}$$

and the point (X,Y) is transformed back into (x,y) by multiplication by the inverse matrix $\mathbf{A}^{-1}$. Many geometrical transformations can be described precisely by the matrices effecting those transformations:

The matrix $\begin{pmatrix} a & 0 \\ 0 & 1 \end{pmatrix}$ enlarges by a factor a parallel to the x-axis.

The matrix $\begin{pmatrix} a & 0 \\ 0 & a \end{pmatrix}$ enlarges by a factor a, with centre of enlargement the origin.

The matrix $\begin{pmatrix} 1 & 0 \\ 0 & -1 \end{pmatrix}$ reflects in the x-axis.

The matrix $\begin{pmatrix} -1 & 0 \\ 0 & 1 \end{pmatrix}$ reflects in the y-axis.

The matrix $\begin{pmatrix} 0 & 1 \\ 1 & 0 \end{pmatrix}$ reflects in the line $y=x$.

The matrix $\begin{pmatrix} 0 & -1 \\ -1 & 0 \end{pmatrix}$ reflects in the line $y=-x$.

The matrix $\begin{pmatrix} \cos 2\alpha & \sin 2\alpha \\ \sin 2\alpha & -\cos 2\alpha \end{pmatrix}$ reflects in a line through the origin at an angle α to the x-axis and

the matrix $\begin{pmatrix} \cos \alpha & -\sin \alpha \\ \sin \alpha & \cos \alpha \end{pmatrix}$ rotates about the origin clockwise through an angle α.

All these transformations can be found by considering the effect of each matrix on suitable points (x,y). To illustrate the transformation we can consider the effect on unit vectors along the coordinate axes,

for $\begin{pmatrix} a & b \\ c & d \end{pmatrix}$ transforms $\begin{pmatrix} 1 \\ 0 \end{pmatrix}$ into $\begin{pmatrix} a \\ c \end{pmatrix}$ and $\begin{pmatrix} 0 \\ 1 \end{pmatrix}$ into $\begin{pmatrix} b \\ d \end{pmatrix}$

or we can find the image of a rectangle (or unit square) under the transformation.

Example 1. Find the image of the unit vectors $\begin{pmatrix} 1 \\ 0 \end{pmatrix}$ and $\begin{pmatrix} 0 \\ 1 \end{pmatrix}$ under the transformation described by the matrix $\begin{pmatrix} 0.8 & -0.6 \\ 0.6 & 0.8 \end{pmatrix}$.

Since $\begin{pmatrix} 0.8 & -0.6 \\ 0.6 & 0.8 \end{pmatrix}\begin{pmatrix} 1 \\ 0 \end{pmatrix} = \begin{pmatrix} 0.8 \\ 0.6 \end{pmatrix}$ and $\begin{pmatrix} 0.8 & -0.6 \\ 0.6 & 0.8 \end{pmatrix}\begin{pmatrix} 0 \\ 1 \end{pmatrix} = \begin{pmatrix} -0.6 \\ 0.8 \end{pmatrix}$

the vector $\begin{pmatrix} 1 \\ 0 \end{pmatrix}$ goes into $\begin{pmatrix} 0.8 \\ 0.6 \end{pmatrix}$ and the vector $\begin{pmatrix} 0 \\ 1 \end{pmatrix}$ goes into $\begin{pmatrix} -0.6 \\ 0.8 \end{pmatrix}$.

This is illustrated in Figure 18.1, and we see that the transformation

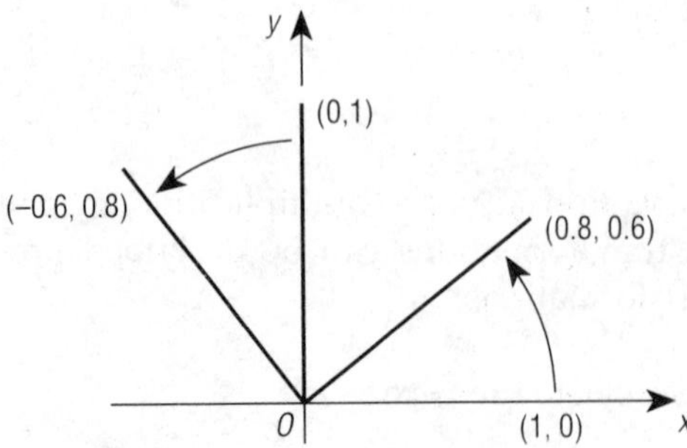

Figure 18.1

is a rotation about the origin through $\arctan\left(\frac{3}{4}\right)$, about 37°. When we place the two vectors $\begin{pmatrix} 1 \\ 0 \end{pmatrix}$ and $\begin{pmatrix} 0 \\ 1 \end{pmatrix}$ in a 2×2 matrix, we realise that the 2×2 matrix is the unit matrix, so that $\begin{pmatrix} a & b \\ c & d \end{pmatrix}$ will always map one unit vector into $\begin{pmatrix} a \\ c \end{pmatrix}$ and the other into $\begin{pmatrix} b \\ d \end{pmatrix}$.

Example 2. Find the image of the rectangle, vertices (0,0), (2,0), (2,1) and (0,1) under the transformation described by the matrix $\begin{pmatrix} 0.6 & 0.8 \\ 0.8 & -0.6 \end{pmatrix}$.

The vertices of the rectangle can be displayed in the matrix $\begin{pmatrix} 0 & 2 & 2 & 0 \\ 0 & 0 & 1 & 1 \end{pmatrix}$. Since

$$\begin{pmatrix} 0.6 & 0.8 \\ 0.8 & -0.6 \end{pmatrix}\begin{pmatrix} 0 & 2 & 2 & 0 \\ 0 & 0 & 1 & 1 \end{pmatrix} = \begin{pmatrix} 0 & 1.2 & 2 & 0.8 \\ 0 & 1.6 & 1 & -0.6 \end{pmatrix}$$

we see that the points (0,0) and (2,1) are unaltered, (2,0) maps into (1.2, 1.6) and (0.1) into (0.8, −0.6). Figure 18.2 shows that the transformation is a reflection in the line $y=\frac{1}{2}x$.

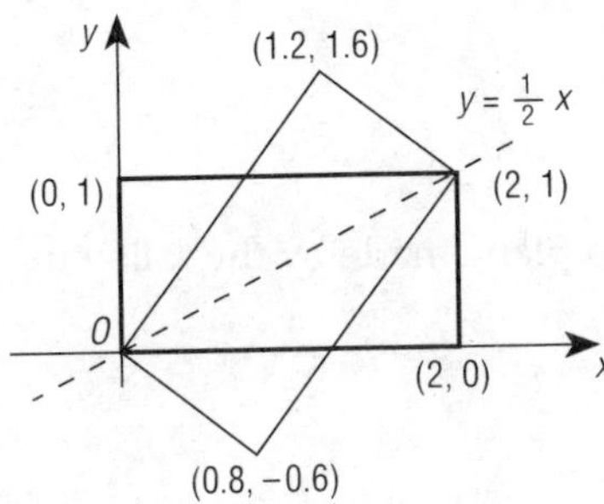

Figure 18.2

Transformation of a straight line

To find the transformation of, say, a straight line, we have to express a point on that line in parametric form. Consider, for example the transformation of the x-axis by the matrix $\begin{pmatrix} 1 & 2 \\ 3 & 4 \end{pmatrix}$. Any point on the x-axis can be written as $(X,0)$, X being a parameter. The image of this point is $\begin{pmatrix} 1 & 2 \\ 3 & 4 \end{pmatrix}\begin{pmatrix} X \\ 0 \end{pmatrix}=\begin{pmatrix} X \\ 3X \end{pmatrix}$, which always lies on the line $y=3x$. Thus the x-axis is transformed into $y=3x$

Example. Find the image of the straight line $y=2x$ under the mapping described by the matrix $\begin{pmatrix} 1 & 1 \\ -4 & 6 \end{pmatrix}$

Any point on $y=2x$ has parametric form $(\lambda,2\lambda)$, so its image is

$\begin{pmatrix} 1 & 1 \\ -4 & 6 \end{pmatrix}\begin{pmatrix} \lambda \\ 2\lambda \end{pmatrix}=\begin{pmatrix} 3\lambda \\ 8\lambda \end{pmatrix}$, which lies on the straight line $8x=3y$ for all values of λ.

Mapping a straight line onto itself

To find the equation of a straight line that is mapped onto itself by the matrix $\begin{pmatrix}1 & 1\\ -4 & 6\end{pmatrix}$, if the straight line is $y=mx$ any point on this line can be written $(\lambda, m\lambda)$ and its image will be

$$\begin{pmatrix}1 & 1\\ -4 & 6\end{pmatrix}\begin{pmatrix}\lambda\\ m\,\lambda\end{pmatrix}=\begin{pmatrix}(1+m)\lambda\\ (-4+6m)\lambda\end{pmatrix}$$

If this lies on $y=mx$,

$$-4+6m=m(1+m)$$
$$\Rightarrow m^2-5m+4=0$$
$$\Rightarrow (m-4)(m-1)=0,\ m=1 \text{ or } 4$$

so each of the lines $y=x$ and $y=4x$ is mapped onto itself by this matrix. Checking, (2,2) lies on $y=x$, and its image is $\begin{pmatrix}1 & 1\\ -4 & 6\end{pmatrix}\begin{pmatrix}2\\ 2\end{pmatrix}=\begin{pmatrix}4\\ 4\end{pmatrix}$ and (4,4) also lies on $y=x$; the point (2,8) lies on $y=4x$, and its image under this transformation is $\begin{pmatrix}1 & 1\\ -4 & 6\end{pmatrix}\begin{pmatrix}2\\ 8\end{pmatrix}=\begin{pmatrix}10\\ 40\end{pmatrix}$ and (10,40) also lies on $y=4x$.

Exercise 18.1

1 Describe geometrically the transformations in a plane made by the following matrices:

(a) $\begin{pmatrix}3 & 0\\ 0 & 3\end{pmatrix}$, (b) $\begin{pmatrix}\frac{1}{2} & 0\\ 0 & \frac{1}{2}\end{pmatrix}$, (c) $\begin{pmatrix}-1 & 0\\ 0 & 1\end{pmatrix}$,

(d) $\begin{pmatrix}0 & -2\\ 2 & 0\end{pmatrix}$, (e) $\begin{pmatrix}0 & 1\\ -1 & 0\end{pmatrix}$, (f) $\begin{pmatrix}0 & \frac{1}{2}\\ -\frac{1}{2} & 0\end{pmatrix}$.

2 Points A,B have position vectors $\mathbf{a},\mathbf{b}$, respectively, where $\mathbf{a}=\begin{pmatrix}10\\ 0\end{pmatrix}$ and $\mathbf{b}=\begin{pmatrix}0\\ 10\end{pmatrix}$; the image of A is A', etc.

(a) If $\mathbf{R}=\begin{pmatrix}0.6 & -0.8\\ 0.8 & 0.6\end{pmatrix}$, find $\mathbf{Ra}$ and $\mathbf{Rb}$.
(b) Plot points A,B,A' and B' on a sketch graph, and describe the transformation given by the matrix $\mathbf{R}$.
(c) Find $\mathbf{R}^2$ and $\mathbf{R}^2\mathbf{a}$, $\mathbf{R}^2\mathbf{b}$. Plot the corresponding points on a sketch graph, and describe the transformation given by $\mathbf{R}^2$.
(d) Find $\mathbf{R}^{-1}$, and $\mathbf{R}^{-1}\mathbf{a}$, $\mathbf{R}^{-1}\mathbf{b}$. Describe the transformation given by $\mathbf{R}^{-1}$.
(e) Find the matrix $\mathbf{S}$ such that $\mathbf{SR}$ describes a rotation through +90°, i.e. 90° in an anti-clockwise sense. What transformation does $\mathbf{RS}$ describe?

3 (a) Given $\mathbf{R}=\begin{pmatrix}2 & -1\\ 1 & 2\end{pmatrix}$, show that $\mathbf{R}^2$ represents a rotation and an enlargement.
(b) Find the enlargement factor and the angle of rotation.
(c) Deduce the geometrical transformation described by $\mathbf{R}$.

4 If $\mathbf{A} = \begin{pmatrix} 2 & -1 \\ 1 & 0 \end{pmatrix}$, show that **A** transforms every point on the straight line $y=x$ into itself, and transforms every point on the straight line $y=x+1$ into another point on the line. (Hint: take any point on $y=x+1$ in the parametric form $(\lambda, \lambda+1)$.)

5 Find the image of the x-axis under transformations described by each of the following matrices:

(a) $\begin{pmatrix} 1 & 3 \\ 2 & 4 \end{pmatrix}$, (b) $\begin{pmatrix} 0 & 1 \\ 2 & 3 \end{pmatrix}$, (c) $\begin{pmatrix} 1 & 1 \\ 2 & 2 \end{pmatrix}$.

6 Find the equations of the straight line(s) through the origin transformed into themselves by

(a) $\begin{pmatrix} 4 & 2 \\ -1 & 1 \end{pmatrix}$, (b) $\begin{pmatrix} 7 & 1 \\ -9 & 1 \end{pmatrix}$.

Determinant of a 3×3 matrix

The determinant of the 3×3 matrix

$$\begin{pmatrix} a_1 & b_1 & c_1 \\ a_2 & b_2 & c_2 \\ a_3 & b_3 & c_3 \end{pmatrix}$$

is defined as

$$a_1 \begin{vmatrix} b_2 & c_2 \\ b_3 & c_3 \end{vmatrix} - b_1 \begin{vmatrix} a_2 & c_2 \\ a_3 & c_3 \end{vmatrix} + c_1 \begin{vmatrix} a_2 & b_2 \\ a_3 & b_3 \end{vmatrix}$$

which, on expansion, is equal to

$$a_1b_2c_3 + a_2b_3c_1 + a_3b_1c_2 - a_1b_3c_2 - a_2b_1c_3 - a_3b_2c_1$$

If preferred, the determinant can be evaluated by

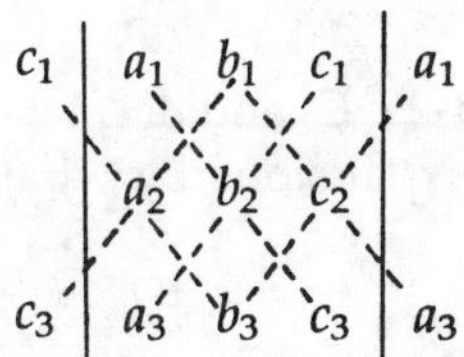

reading along the diagonals as above, signing terms + along the positive diagonals \ and – along / the negative diagonals.

Example. Find the value of the determinant of the matrix $\begin{pmatrix}1&2&3\\4&5&6\\7&8&9\end{pmatrix}$.

First, using the definition with 2×2 determinants,

$$1\begin{vmatrix}5&6\\8&9\end{vmatrix}-2\begin{vmatrix}4&6\\7&9\end{vmatrix}+3\begin{vmatrix}4&5\\7&8\end{vmatrix}$$

$$=1\times(-3)-2\times(-6)+3\times(-3)=0$$

Secondly, using the diagonals,

$$1\times5\times9+2\times6\times7+3\times4\times8-1\times6\times8-2\times4\times9-3\times5\times7$$
$$=45+84+96-48-72-105$$
$$=0$$

Minors and cofactors

The determinant found by excluding the row and column containing a_1, i.e. $\begin{vmatrix}b_2&c_2\\b_3&c_3\end{vmatrix}$ is called the minor of a_1; similarly the minor of b_1 is $\begin{vmatrix}a_2&c_2\\a_3&c_3\end{vmatrix}$, of c_1 is $\begin{vmatrix}a_2&b_2\\a_3&b_3\end{vmatrix}$.

If the minors are given the signs

$$\begin{matrix}+&-&+\\-&+&-\\+&-&+\end{matrix}$$

according to their place in the determinant, then they are called cofactors. Thus if A_1 is the cofactor of a_1, etc.,

$$A_1=+\begin{vmatrix}b_2&c_2\\b_3&c_3\end{vmatrix}\quad B_1=-\begin{vmatrix}a_2&c_2\\a_3&c_3\end{vmatrix}\quad C_1=+\begin{vmatrix}a_2&b_2\\a_3&b_3\end{vmatrix}$$

and $\det A = a_1A_1+b_1B_1+c_1C_1$.

It can be shown that $\det A = a_2A_2+b_2B_2+c_2C_2$ and $\det A = a_3A_3+b_3B_3+c_3C_3$, whereas $a_1A_2+b_1B_1+c_1C_2 = 0$. Similar expansions by what are called alien cofactors also equal zero.

Adjoint of a matrix

The transpose of the matrix formed by the cofactors of the elements of a given matrix **A** is called the adjoint of **A**, i.e. if the cofactor of a_1, an element in **A**, is denoted by A_1, etc., the adjoint of **A**, written adj **A** is

$$\begin{pmatrix}A_1&A_2&A_3\\B_1&B_2&B_3\\C_1&C_2&C_3\end{pmatrix}$$

Inverse of 3×3 matrix

There are many ways of finding the inverse of a 3×3 matrix, but this method is usually preferred at this level.

Example. Find the inverse of the matrix $\mathbf{A}=\begin{pmatrix}1&2&3\\4&5&7\\7&8&9\end{pmatrix}$.

First, form the matrix of the cofactors, $\begin{pmatrix}-11&13&-3\\6&-12&6\\-1&5&-3\end{pmatrix}$

where $\begin{vmatrix}5&7\\8&9\end{vmatrix}=-11$, $\begin{vmatrix}4&7\\7&9\end{vmatrix}=-13$, etc.

Next, transpose this matrix to obtain adj **A**, and form the product (adj **A**)**A**, i.e.

$$(\text{adj }\mathbf{A})\mathbf{A}=\begin{pmatrix}-11&6&-1\\13&-12&5\\-3&6&-3\end{pmatrix}\begin{pmatrix}1&2&3\\4&5&7\\7&8&9\end{pmatrix}=\begin{pmatrix}6&0&0\\0&6&0\\0&0&6\end{pmatrix}$$

Since the product is $6\begin{pmatrix}1&0&0\\0&1&0\\0&0&1\end{pmatrix}$, we can deduce that $\mathbf{A}^{-1}$ is found by dividing every term in adj **A** by 6,

i.e. $$\mathbf{A}^{-1}=\begin{pmatrix}-\frac{11}{6}&1&-\frac{1}{6}\\\frac{13}{6}&-2&\frac{5}{6}\\-\frac{1}{2}&1&-\frac{1}{2}\end{pmatrix}$$

The value of det **A** is 6, and some prefer to calculate det **A**, then divide each term of adj **A** by det **A**. But it is only too easy to make an arithmetic error when calculating the determinant of a 3×3 matrix, and as we are well advised to check by finding $\mathbf{AA}^{-1}$ anyway, we see that this method of finding (adj **A**)**A** (or **A** (adj **A**)), which must be of the form $\begin{pmatrix}c&0&0\\0&c&0\\0&0&c\end{pmatrix}$, gives us a check as well as saving the labour of finding, and checking, the determinant of **A**.

Exercise 18.2

1 For the matrix $\begin{pmatrix}1&3&7\\2&5&9\\4&8&0\end{pmatrix}$, find

(a) the minors, and (b) the cofactors of 1, 3, 7 and 9.

2 Find adj **A**, using **A** from Q.1.

3 Form the product (adj **A**)**A**. Deduce $\mathbf{A}^{-1}$.
4 Using each of the methods given on page 193, find det **A**.
5 Find the inverse if it exists of each of the following matrices:

(a) $\begin{pmatrix} 1 & 4 & 3 \\ -1 & 5 & 1 \\ 3 & 3 & 5 \end{pmatrix}$, (b) $\begin{pmatrix} 7 & 5 & 6 \\ 4 & 3 & 3 \\ 10 & 7 & 8 \end{pmatrix}$.

6 Show that $\begin{pmatrix} 1 & 1 & -1 \\ 2 & 2 & 1 \\ -1 & -1 & -2 \end{pmatrix}\begin{pmatrix} x \\ y \\ 0 \end{pmatrix} = \begin{pmatrix} 0 \\ 0 \\ 0 \end{pmatrix}$ for all values of x and y, interpret this geometrically.

7 If $\mathbf{A}=\begin{pmatrix} 0.8 & 0.6 \\ 0.6 & -0.8 \end{pmatrix}$, find
(a) the image of the x-axis under this mapping,
(b) the straight line that maps into the y-axis under **A**,
(c) the points and lines through the origin that are invariant under **A**.

8 Find the value of k if the matrix $\begin{pmatrix} 1 & 2 & -1 \\ 2 & -1 & -1 \\ 0 & k & 1 \end{pmatrix}$ is singular.

9 Given that $\mathbf{A}=\begin{pmatrix} 2 & 0 & 1 \\ 0 & 1 & -1 \\ 3 & 2 & 3 \end{pmatrix}$, find $\mathbf{A}^{-1}$ and use it to obtain the solutions of

$$2x+z=1$$
$$y-z=4$$
$$3x+2y+3z=-1$$

10 Assuming matrix multiplication is associative, show that the set of all matrices of the form $\begin{pmatrix} a & 0 & b \\ 0 & 1 & 0 \\ b & 0 & a \end{pmatrix}$ is a group under matrix multiplication.

Vectors 19

Vectors 198

Magnitude and direction of a vector 199

Parallel vectors and equal vectors 200

Addition and subtraction of vectors 201

Section theorem 203

Geometrical theorems 205

Equation of a straight line 207

The scalar product 210

Parallel and perpendicular vectors 210

The angle between two vectors 211

Equation of a straight line 211

Equation of a plane perpendicular to a given vector **n** 212

Equation of a plane through three points 213

Alternative method 214

Notes

Components

A vector can be expressed in terms of its components,

e.g. $x\mathbf{i}+y\mathbf{j}$ or $\begin{pmatrix}x\\y\end{pmatrix}$ or occasionally $(x\ y)$

$x\mathbf{i}+y\mathbf{j}+z\mathbf{k}$ or $\begin{pmatrix}x\\y\\z\end{pmatrix}$ or occasionally $(x\ y\ z)$

Magnitude

The magnitude of $x\mathbf{i}+y\mathbf{j}$ is $\sqrt{(x^2+y^2)}$, of $x\mathbf{i}+y\mathbf{j}+z\mathbf{k}$ is $\sqrt{(x^2+y^2+z^2)}$.

Direction of vector

The vector $x\mathbf{i}+y\mathbf{j}+z\mathbf{k}$ makes angles α, β and γ with the coordinate axes, where

$$\cos\alpha : \cos\beta : \cos\gamma : 1 = x:y:z:\sqrt{(x^2+y^2+z^2)}$$

Section theorem

The position vector of the point dividing AB in the ratio $\lambda:\mu$ is $\frac{\mu\mathbf{a}+\lambda\mathbf{b}}{\lambda+\mu}$, where $\mathbf{a},\mathbf{b}$ are the position vectors of A,B respectively.

Equation of a straight line

The position vector $\mathbf{r}$ of any point P on the straight line through the point position vector $\mathbf{a}$ parallel to the vector $\mathbf{b}$ is $\mathbf{r}=\mathrm{a}+t\mathbf{b}$.

Scalar product

By definition of the scalar product,

$$\mathbf{a}.\mathbf{b}=ab\cos\theta$$

From this, if $\mathbf{a}$, $\mathbf{b}$ are two non-zero vectors, $\mathbf{a}.\mathbf{b}=0 \Leftrightarrow \mathbf{a}$ and $\mathbf{b}$ are perpendicular.

Equation of a plane

The equation of the plane through the point A position vector $\mathbf{a}$, perpendicular to the vector $\mathbf{n}$ is $\mathbf{r.n}=\mathbf{a.n}$.

The equation of the plane through the points A, B, C is $\mathbf{r}=(1-\lambda-\mu)\mathbf{a}+\lambda\mathbf{b}+\mu\mathbf{c}$

Comparison with cartesian coordinates

Compare the straight line

$$\mathbf{r}=\begin{pmatrix}a\\b\\c\end{pmatrix}+t\begin{pmatrix}p\\q\\r\end{pmatrix}$$

with $$\frac{x-a}{p}=\frac{y-b}{q}=\frac{z-c}{r}$$

and the plane $\mathbf{r}.(a\mathbf{i}+b\mathbf{j}+c\mathbf{k})=d$
with $ax+by+cz=d$

Vectors

A vector can be defined as a physical quantity having magnitude and direction. It may most easily be considered as a displacement, e.g. 5 km due north describes a displacement precisely – if we know the starting point. Given a starting point, such as where we are sitting at present, the displacement is determined exactly. This is now called a localised vector; before we were given the starting point, it would have been called a free vector. This explains why we should say 'the position vector of a point P *relative to an origin* O is $\mathbf{p}$'. Unless we say 'relative to a starting point', strictly we do not have a unique vector. Often, though, there is no ambiguity and we will notice that the words 'relative to an origin' are not stated.

In order to describe direction by means of an angle, we need a fixed initial direction, e.g. 5 km on a bearing of 030° assumes we measure the angle from the north line; if we are working in three dimensions, then we have greater difficulties in describing the direction. It is much easier if we describe vectors in terms of their components in mutually perpendicular directions, usually Ox, Oy in two dimensions, Ox, Oy and Oz in three dimensions. We display these components in a matrix $\begin{pmatrix} x \\ y \end{pmatrix}$ or $\begin{pmatrix} x \\ y \\ z \end{pmatrix}$ occasionally (x, y) or $(x\ y\ z)$, or as multiples of $\mathbf{i}$, $\mathbf{j}$, $\mathbf{k}$, i.e. $x\mathbf{i}+y\mathbf{j}$ or $x\mathbf{i}+y\mathbf{j}+z\mathbf{k}$, where $\mathbf{i},\mathbf{j},\mathbf{k}$ are unit vectors along Ox, Oy and Oz, respectively.

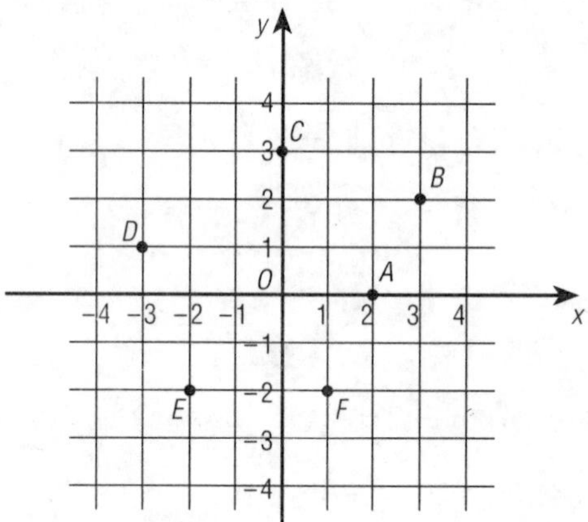

Figure 19.1

Looking at Figure 19.1, the position vector of A relative to O is $\begin{pmatrix} 2 \\ 0 \end{pmatrix}$, i.e. 2 units along Ox, 0 units along Oy. This is usually written

$$\overrightarrow{OA} \equiv \mathbf{a} = \begin{pmatrix} 2 \\ 0 \end{pmatrix} = 2\mathbf{i}$$

Similarly, $\overrightarrow{OB} \equiv \mathbf{b} = \begin{pmatrix} 3 \\ 2 \end{pmatrix} = 3\mathbf{i}+2\mathbf{j}$; $\overrightarrow{OC} \equiv \mathbf{c} = \begin{pmatrix} 0 \\ 3 \end{pmatrix} = 3\mathbf{j}$,

$\overrightarrow{OD} \equiv \mathbf{d} = \begin{pmatrix} -3 \\ 1 \end{pmatrix} = -3\mathbf{i}+\mathbf{j}$: $\overrightarrow{OE} \equiv \mathbf{e} = \begin{pmatrix} -2 \\ -2 \end{pmatrix} = -2\mathbf{i}-2\mathbf{j}$

and $\overrightarrow{OF} \equiv \mathbf{f} = \begin{pmatrix} 1 \\ -2 \end{pmatrix} = \mathbf{i}-2\mathbf{j}$

We can describe the position of a point relative to any other point; e.g. the position vector of B relative to A, written $\overrightarrow{AB}$, is $\mathbf{i}+2\mathbf{j}$, or $\begin{pmatrix} 1 \\ 2 \end{pmatrix}$. We should be familiar with both the matrix and the **i**,**j** notations.

Magnitude and direction of a vector

Looking at the position of B relative to O, B is at a distance $\sqrt{(3^2+2^2)}$, i.e. $\sqrt{13}$ units from O, in a direction making an angle arctan (2/3) with the positive x-axis. We define the magnitude of a vector in two dimension, $x\mathbf{i}+y\mathbf{j}$, as $\sqrt{(x^2+y^2)}$; in three dimensions the magnitude of $x\mathbf{i}+y\mathbf{j}+z\mathbf{k}$ is $\sqrt{(x^2+y^2+z^2)}$.

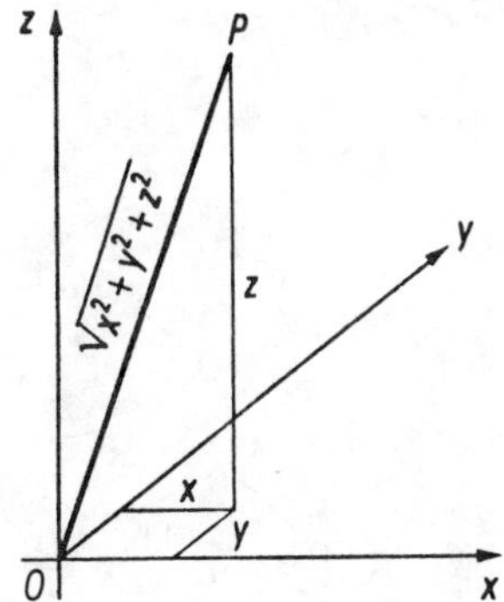

Figure 19.2

The direction of a vector in two dimensions should be found from a diagram, the angle made with the positive x-axis being arctan (y/x) when x is positive, arctan $(y/x)-\pi$ when x is negative and y positive, arctan $(y/x)-\pi$ when both are negative. *Do not try to remember these, use a diagram each time.*

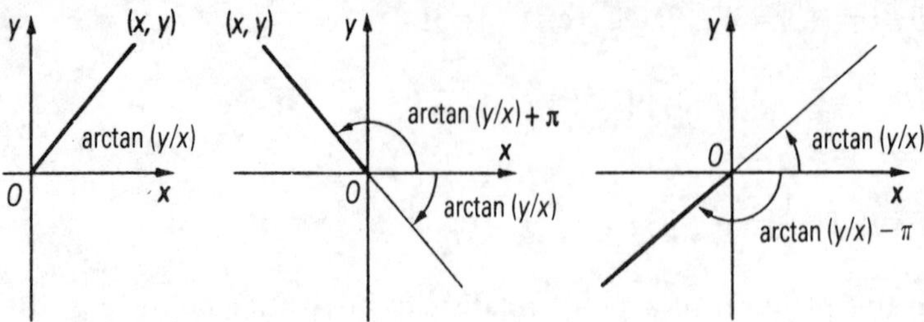

Figure 19.3

The direction of a vector in three dimensions is much harder to describe. If α, β and γ are the angles made with the coordinate axes by the vector $\begin{pmatrix} x \\ y \\ z \end{pmatrix}$, then

$$\cos \alpha = \frac{x}{\sqrt{(x^2+y^2+z^2)}}$$

$$\cos \beta = \frac{y}{\sqrt{(x^2+y^2+z^2)}}$$

$$\cos \gamma = \frac{z}{\sqrt{(x^2+y^2+z^2)}}$$

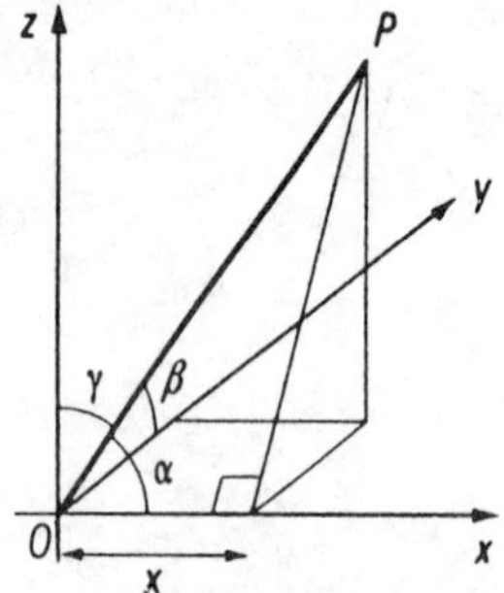

Figure 19.4

Parallel vectors and equal vectors

Two vectors are parallel if they are in the same direction, so that one is a scalar multiple of the other. Thus $6\mathbf{i}+2\mathbf{j}=2(3\mathbf{i}+\mathbf{j})$, so that $6\mathbf{i}+2\mathbf{j}$ and $3\mathbf{i}+\mathbf{j}$ are parallel. Two vectors are only equal if every element of one is equal to the corresponding element of the other; looking at Figure 19.1, $\overrightarrow{FA}=\mathbf{i}+2\mathbf{j}$, $\overrightarrow{AB}=\mathbf{i}+2\mathbf{j}$, $\therefore \overrightarrow{FA}=\overrightarrow{AB}$.

Example. Show that the points A, B, C and D with position vectors $3\mathbf{i}+2\mathbf{j}$, $4\mathbf{i}-\mathbf{j}$, $-2\mathbf{j}$ and $-\mathbf{i}+\mathbf{j}$, respectively, are the vertices of a parallelogram.

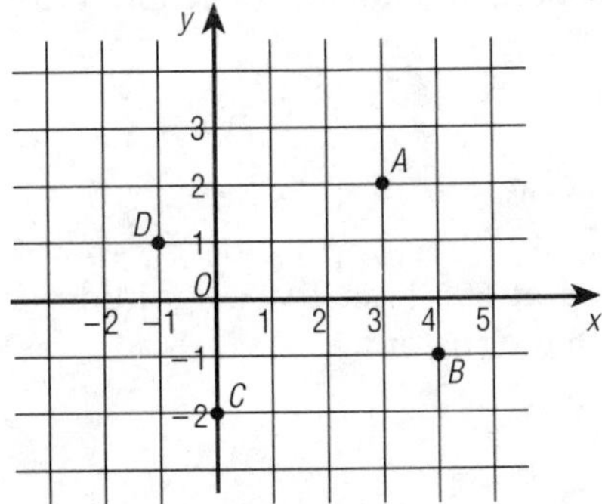

Figure 19.5

A sketch like Figure 19.5 shows that this seems likely. Writing down the vectors, $\overrightarrow{AB}=\mathbf{i}-3\mathbf{j}$, $\overrightarrow{DC}=\mathbf{i}-3\mathbf{j}$, so $AB=DC$, and AB is parallel to DC. Thus $ABCD$ must be a parallelogram. We could have shown that $\overrightarrow{DA}=4\mathbf{i}+\mathbf{j}$, $\overrightarrow{CB}=4\mathbf{i}+\mathbf{j}$, so that $AD=CB$ and AD is parallel to CB.

Addition and subtraction of vectors

When vectors are described by their magnitude and direction, they are added (or subtracted) by the parallelogram law. This can be shown to be equivalent to adding (or subtracting) their components.

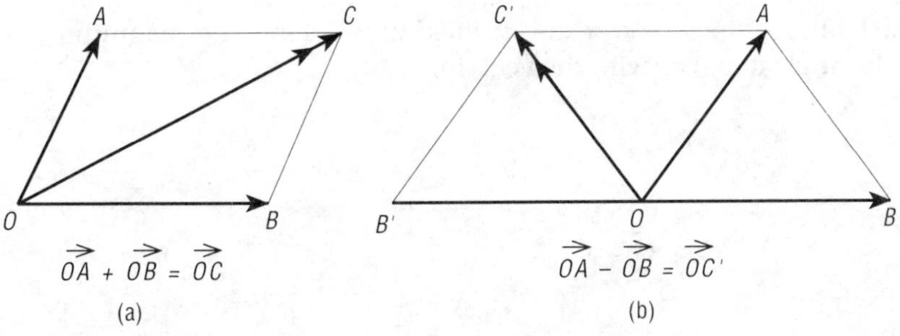

Figure 19.6

If $\overrightarrow{OA}$ and $\overrightarrow{OB}$ are any two vectors, then their sum is found by completing the parallelogram $OACB$, their sum being $\overrightarrow{OC}$. Similarly, $\overrightarrow{OA}-\overrightarrow{OB}=\overrightarrow{OA}+(-\overrightarrow{OB})$, where $-\overrightarrow{OB}$ is equal in magnitude but opposite in direction to OB (Figure 19.6a). If B' is the image of B in O, $\overrightarrow{OA}+\overrightarrow{OB'}=\overrightarrow{OC'}$, i.e. $\overrightarrow{OA}-\overrightarrow{OB}=\overrightarrow{OC'}$. Since $OC'AB$ is a parallelogram, $\overrightarrow{OC'}=\overrightarrow{BA}$, so we can write $\overrightarrow{OA}-\overrightarrow{OB}=\overrightarrow{BA}$, provided that we realise that these are equal only in magnitude and direction, and not line of action. With our usual notation, we write

$$\overrightarrow{BA}=\overrightarrow{OA}-\overrightarrow{OB}=\mathbf{a}-\mathbf{b}$$

i.e. $\overrightarrow{BA}=\overrightarrow{BO}+\overrightarrow{OA}=-\mathbf{b}+\mathbf{a}$

i.e. $\overrightarrow{BA}=\overrightarrow{OA}-\overrightarrow{OB}-\mathbf{a}-\mathbf{b}$

Example 1. $\mathbf{u}$ and $\mathbf{v}$ are unit vectors inclined at 60°. Find the magnitude of (a) $\mathbf{u}+\mathbf{v}$, (b) $\mathbf{u}-\mathbf{v}$, and the angle each makes with the vector $\mathbf{u}$.

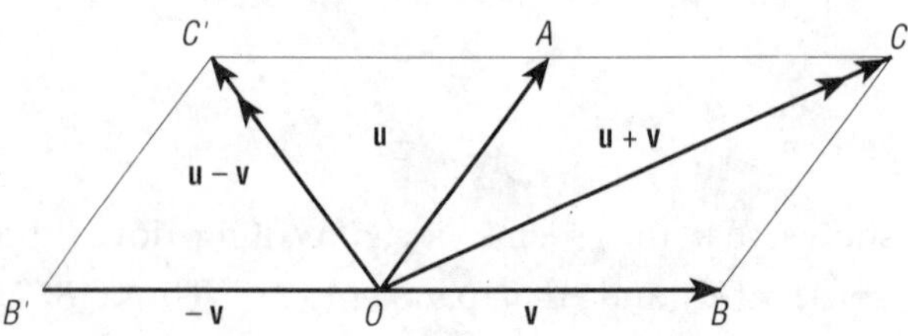

Figure 19.7

If OA represents $\mathbf{u}$ and OB represents $\mathbf{v}$, $\mathbf{u}+\mathbf{v}$ will be represented by the diagonal OC of the parallelogram $OACB$. Since $\mathbf{u}$ and $\mathbf{v}$ are unit vectors, they both have magnitude 1, and triangle OAC is isosceles. Hence $OC=2\cos 30°\approx 1.73$, and the angle between OC and OA is 30°.

If OB' represents $-\mathbf{v}$ as before, OC' represents $\mathbf{u}-\mathbf{v}$. Since $AOC'=120°$, and $OAC'B'$ is a rhombus, triangle OAC' is equilateral, the magnitude of $\mathbf{u}-\mathbf{v}=1$, and the angle it makes with the vector $\mathbf{u}$ is 60°.

Example 2. Unit vectors $\mathbf{u}$ and $\mathbf{v}$ are inclined at 60°. Find the magnitude of $3\mathbf{u}+2\mathbf{v}$, and the angle it makes with the vector $\mathbf{u}$.

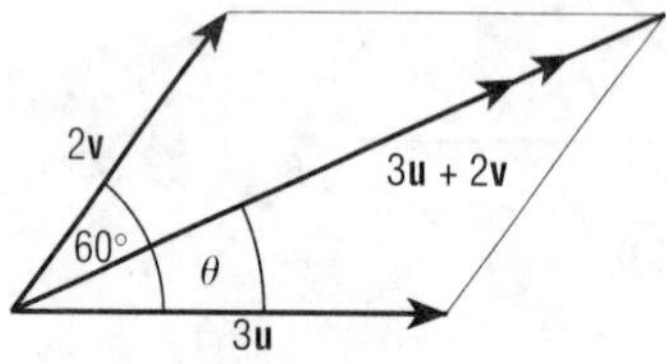

Figure 19.8

Using the cosine formula,

$$OC^2=2^2+3^2-2\times 2\times 3\times \cos 120°$$
$$=13+12\cos 60°=19,$$
$$OC\approx 4.36$$

We can check this is reasonable from the diagram, as we expect a length a little less than 5.

To find the angle required, marked θ, from the sine formula,

$$\sin\theta = \frac{2\sin 60^\circ}{\sqrt{19}}$$

$$\theta \approx 23.4^\circ$$

The problem could have been solved, with less accuracy, by scale drawing.

Section theorem

If M is the midpoint of AB, $\overrightarrow{OM} = \overrightarrow{OA} + \frac{1}{2}\overrightarrow{AB}$

$$= \mathbf{a} + \tfrac{1}{2}(\mathbf{b} - \mathbf{a})$$

$$= \tfrac{1}{2}(\mathbf{a} + \mathbf{b})$$

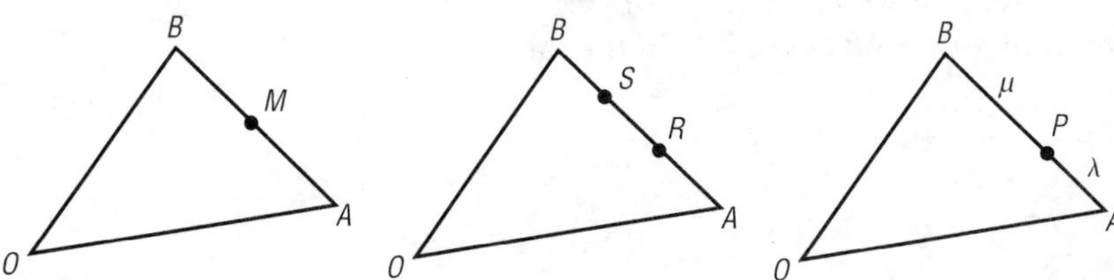

Figure 19.9

If R and S are the points of trisection of AB, $\overrightarrow{OR} = \overrightarrow{OA} + \frac{1}{3}\overrightarrow{AB}$

$$= \mathbf{a} + \tfrac{1}{3}(\mathbf{b} - \mathbf{a})$$

$$= \tfrac{2}{3}\mathbf{a} + \tfrac{1}{3}\mathbf{b}$$

and $\overrightarrow{OS} = \overrightarrow{OA} + \overrightarrow{AS}$

$$= \mathbf{a} + \tfrac{2}{3}(\mathbf{b} - \mathbf{a})$$

$$= \tfrac{1}{3}\mathbf{a} + \tfrac{2}{3}\mathbf{b}$$

More generally, if P divides AB in the ratio $\lambda{:}\mu$,

$$\overrightarrow{OP} = \overrightarrow{OA} + \overrightarrow{AP}$$

$$= \overrightarrow{OA} + \frac{\lambda}{\lambda+\mu}\overrightarrow{AB}$$

$$= \mathbf{a} + \frac{\lambda}{\lambda+\mu}(\mathbf{b} - \mathbf{a}) = \frac{\mu\mathbf{a} + \lambda\mathbf{b}}{\lambda+\mu}$$

Notice that if P divides AB in the ratio $\lambda{:}\mu$, the coefficient of $\mathbf{a}$ is μ and of $\mathbf{b}$ is λ in the numerator of $\mathbf{p}$. This can be checked by considering the extreme case 1:0.

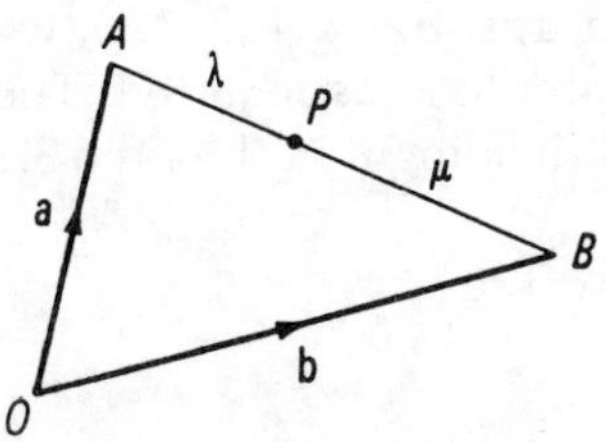

Figure 19.10

If points A, B have position vectors $\mathbf{a}, \mathbf{b}$ respectively, the position vector of the point P dividing AB in the ratio $\lambda:\mu$ is $(\mu\mathbf{a}+\lambda\mathbf{b})/(\lambda+\mu)$. As a special case, the midpoint of AB has position vector $\frac{1}{2}(\mathbf{a}+\mathbf{b})$. The general result is true whether P divides AB internally or externally in the ratio $\lambda:\mu$; in the latter case, λ or μ is negative. *Always draw a diagram, and check the signs carefully.*

Example. Points A, B have position vectors

$$\mathbf{a}=\begin{pmatrix}4\\3\\5\end{pmatrix}, \mathbf{b}=\begin{pmatrix}0\\-1\\1\end{pmatrix}$$

Find the position vector of
(a) the point R dividing AB in the ratio 1:3;
(b) the point S dividing AB in the ratio 3:1;
(c) the point T, dividing AB externally in the ratio 3:1.

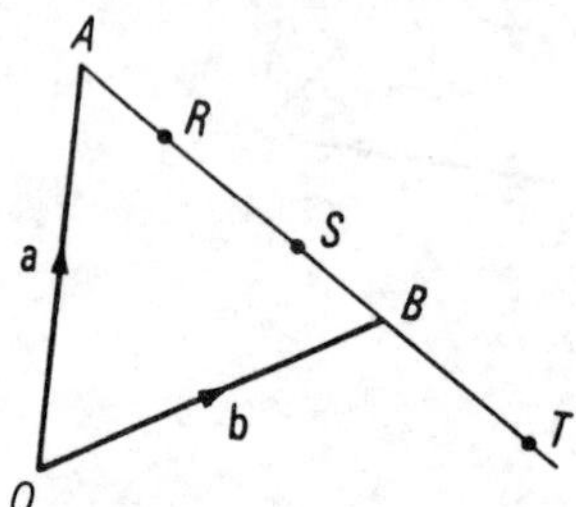

Figure 19.11

Since R divides AB in the ratio 1:3,

$$\mathbf{r}=\frac{3\mathbf{a}+\mathbf{b}}{1+3}=\tfrac{1}{4}\left[3\begin{pmatrix}4\\3\\5\end{pmatrix}+\begin{pmatrix}0\\-1\\1\end{pmatrix}\right]=\begin{pmatrix}3\\2\\4\end{pmatrix}$$

Since S divides AB in the ratio 3:1,

$$\mathbf{s}=\frac{\mathbf{a}+3\mathbf{b}}{3+1}=\tfrac{1}{4}\left[\begin{pmatrix}4\\3\\5\end{pmatrix}+3\begin{pmatrix}0\\-1\\1\end{pmatrix}\right]=\begin{pmatrix}1\\0\\2\end{pmatrix}$$

Notice that considering the first entry in each matrix $\mathbf{a}$, $\mathbf{r}$, $\mathbf{s}$, $\mathbf{b}$, i.e. 4, 3, 1, 0, we can see that R is the point nearer to A, S the point nearer to B, as required. The point dividing AB in the ratio 1:3 is $\frac{1}{4}(3\mathbf{a}+\mathbf{b})$, the point dividing it in the ratio 3:1 is $\frac{1}{4}(\mathbf{a}+3\mathbf{b})$.

To find T, since it divides AB externally in the ratio $3:-1$,

$$\mathbf{t}=\frac{1}{3-1}\left[(-1)\begin{pmatrix}4\\3\\5\end{pmatrix}+3\begin{pmatrix}0\\-1\\1\end{pmatrix}\right]=\tfrac{1}{2}\begin{pmatrix}-4\\-6\\-2\end{pmatrix}=\begin{pmatrix}-2\\-3\\-1\end{pmatrix}$$

Again, looking at Figure 19.11 shows us that we have the point we require, and that we have not inadvertently found, say, the point dividing AB in the ratio $-1{:}3$.

Geometrical theorems

Many geometrical theorems can be proved easily using vectors. Perhaps the most useful is that the medians of a triangle are concurrent.

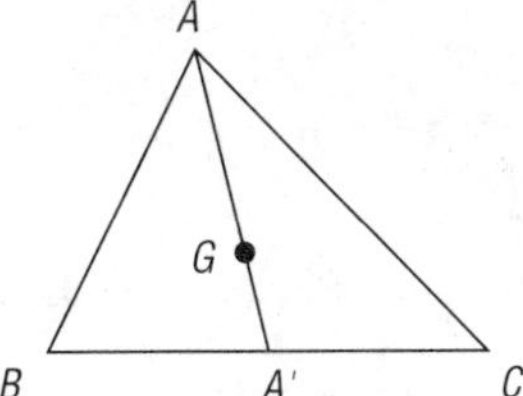

Figure 19.12

If A' is the midpoint of A, and G the point in AA' such that $AG{:}GA'=2{:}1$, the position vector of A' is $\frac{1}{2}(\mathbf{a}+\mathbf{b})$

$$\text{and } \overrightarrow{OG}\equiv\mathbf{g} = \tfrac{1}{3}\mathbf{a}+\tfrac{2}{3}[\tfrac{1}{2}(\mathbf{a}+\mathbf{b})]$$
$$= \tfrac{1}{3}(\mathbf{a}+\mathbf{b}+\mathbf{c})$$

Since this expression is symmetical in $\mathbf{a}$,$\mathbf{b}$ and $\mathbf{c}$, G must also divide BB' and CC' in the ratio 2:1, so the medians concur at a point G, where $\mathbf{g}=\frac{1}{3}(\mathbf{a}+\mathbf{b}+\mathbf{c})$.

This proof can be very easily extended into three dimensions. In a tetrahedron $ABCD$, if G_1 is the centroid of the triangle BCD, etc., we can show that AG_1, BG_2, CG_3 and DG_4 meet at the point G, the centroid of the tetrahedron, where G has position vector $\frac{1}{4}(\mathbf{a}+\mathbf{b}+\mathbf{c}+\mathbf{d})$ and G divides AG_1, BG_2, CG_3 and DG_4 in the ratio 3:1.

Exercise 19.1

1 Given $\mathbf{a}=2\mathbf{i}+3\mathbf{j}$ and $\mathbf{b}=\mathbf{i}-2\mathbf{j}$, find in terms of $\mathbf{i}$ and $\mathbf{j}$,
(a) $\mathbf{a}+\mathbf{b}$, (b) $\mathbf{a}-\mathbf{b}$, (c) $3\mathbf{a}$, (d) $\mathbf{b}-4\mathbf{a}$, (e) $2\mathbf{b}-\mathbf{a}$.

2 Find the magnitude of each of the vectors in Q.1, parts (a)–(e), and the angle each makes with the unit vector $\mathbf{i}$.

3 Given $\mathbf{a}=2\mathbf{i}+3\mathbf{j}-\mathbf{k}$ and $\mathbf{b}=\mathbf{i}+\mathbf{j}-\mathbf{k}$, find in terms of $\mathbf{i}$ and $\mathbf{j}$ and $\mathbf{k}$,
(a) $\mathbf{a}+\mathbf{b}$, (b) $\mathbf{a}-\mathbf{b}$, (c) $2\mathbf{b}$, (d) $\mathbf{a}-2\mathbf{b}$, (e) $3\mathbf{b}-\mathbf{a}$.

4 Find the magnitude of each of the vectors in Q.3, parts (a)–(e), and the angle it makes with the unit vector $\mathbf{i}$.

5 Are the points with position vectors $-4\mathbf{j}$, $\mathbf{j}$, $4\mathbf{i}+2\mathbf{j}$ and $4\mathbf{i}+\mathbf{j}$ at the vertices of a trapezium?

6 Show that the points with position vectors $\mathbf{i}+\mathbf{j}$, $3\mathbf{i}+3\mathbf{j}$, $-\mathbf{i}-\mathbf{j}$ and $-3\mathbf{i}-3\mathbf{j}$ are the vertices of a parallelogram.

7 Show that the points with position vectors $\mathbf{j}+2\mathbf{k}$, $2\mathbf{i}+3\mathbf{j}+3\mathbf{k}$, $\mathbf{j}$ and $-2\mathbf{i}-\mathbf{j}-\mathbf{k}$ are the vertices of a parallelogram.

8 Show the points position vectors $\mathbf{i}-\mathbf{j}-2\mathbf{k}$, $2\mathbf{i}+\mathbf{j}+\mathbf{k}$, $3\mathbf{i}+5\mathbf{j}+2\mathbf{k}$ and $\mathbf{i}+\mathbf{j}-4\mathbf{k}$ are the vertices of a trapezium.

9 Points A, B and C have position vectors $2\mathbf{i}+\mathbf{j}+\mathbf{k}$, $\mathbf{i}+2\mathbf{j}-3\mathbf{k}$ and $4\mathbf{i}+2\mathbf{k}$. Find the lengths of AB, BC and CA, and determine whether the largest angle of this triangle is greater than a right angle.

10 Vectors $\mathbf{a}$ and $\mathbf{b}$ are inclined at 90°. Given $|\mathbf{a}|=15$ and $|\mathbf{b}|=8$, find
(a) $|\mathbf{a}+\mathbf{b}|$, (b) $|\mathbf{a}-\mathbf{b}|$, (c) $|10\mathbf{a}+10\mathbf{b}|$, (d) $|2\mathbf{a}+5\mathbf{b}|$, (e) $|2\mathbf{a}+9\mathbf{b}|$.

11 Vectors $\mathbf{a}$ and $\mathbf{b}$ are inclined at 60°, and $|\mathbf{a}|=3$, $|\mathbf{b}|=5$. Find
(a) $|\mathbf{a}+\mathbf{b}|$, (b) $|\mathbf{a}-\mathbf{b}|$, (c) $|25\mathbf{a}+9\mathbf{b}|$.

12 Find whether A, B and C are collinear if
(a) $\mathbf{a}=\mathbf{i}+\mathbf{j}$, $\mathbf{b}=2\mathbf{i}+3\mathbf{j}$, $\mathbf{c}=3\mathbf{i}+5\mathbf{j}$, (b) $\mathbf{a}=\mathbf{i}$, $\mathbf{b}=\frac{1}{2}\mathbf{i}+\frac{1}{2}\mathbf{j}$, $\mathbf{c}=\mathbf{i}+\mathbf{j}$,
(c) $\mathbf{a}=\mathbf{i}$, $\mathbf{b}=\mathbf{i}+\frac{1}{2}\mathbf{j}$, $\mathbf{c}=\mathbf{i}+\mathbf{j}$.

13 Find the value of y if the points with position vectors $-\mathbf{i}+2\mathbf{j}$, $2\mathbf{i}+6\mathbf{j}$ and $5\mathbf{i}+y\mathbf{j}$ are collinear.

14 Find the value of y if the points with position vectors $-2\mathbf{i}$, $3\mathbf{j}$ and $\frac{1}{2}\mathbf{i}+y\mathbf{j}$ are collinear.

15 Show that the points with position vectors $\mathbf{i}+\mathbf{j}$, $4\mathbf{i}+2\mathbf{j}$, $2\mathbf{i}-2\mathbf{j}$ and $5\mathbf{i}-\mathbf{j}$ are the vertices of a square.

16 Find the position vector of the midpoint of AB if the position vectors of A and B are
(a) $\mathbf{i}+5\mathbf{j}$, $5\mathbf{i}+\mathbf{j}$, (b) $2\mathbf{i}$, $4\mathbf{j}$, (c) $-\mathbf{i}-5\mathbf{j}$, $\mathbf{i}+3\mathbf{j}$, (d) $\mathbf{i}+3\mathbf{j}+5\mathbf{k}$, $5\mathbf{i}-3\mathbf{j}+\mathbf{k}$,
(e) $2\mathbf{i}+3\mathbf{j}-4\mathbf{k}$, $4\mathbf{i}+5\mathbf{j}-4\mathbf{k}$.

17 The position vectors of points A and B are $15\mathbf{i}+2\mathbf{j}$ and $-15\mathbf{i}+17\mathbf{j}$, respectively. Find the position vector of the point that divides AB in the ratio
(a) 1:2, (b) 2:1, (c) 2:3, (d) 3:2.

18 The position vectors of points A and B are $8\mathbf{i}+7\mathbf{j}$ and $-16\mathbf{i}-5\mathbf{j}$, respectively. Find the position vector of the point that divides AB in the ratio
(a) 2:1, (b) 1:2, (c) 1:3, (d) 3:1.

19 The position vectors of points A and B are $8\mathbf{i}+7\mathbf{j}+13\mathbf{k}$ and $-4\mathbf{i}-5\mathbf{j}+\mathbf{k}$, respectively. Find the position vector of the point that divides AB in the ratio
(a) 1:2, (b) 2:1, (c) 1:3, (d) 3:1.

20 Show OAB is an isosceles triangle, where O is the origin and points A and B have position vectors $2\mathbf{i}-2\mathbf{j}+\mathbf{k}$ and $-2\mathbf{i}+2\mathbf{j}+\mathbf{k}$.

In the following questions, points A,B,C... have position vectors $\mathbf{a},\mathbf{b},\mathbf{c}$...

21 Find the condition that A is the midpoint of BC.

22 Find the condition that P and Q are the points of trisection of AB, P being nearer to A than to B.

23 The line BD is equal and parallel to AC. Find $\mathbf{d}$ in terms of $\mathbf{a},\mathbf{b}$ and $\mathbf{c}$.

24 The line CE is parallel to AD and twice AD in length. Find $\mathbf{e}$ in terms of $\mathbf{a},\mathbf{c}$ and $\mathbf{d}$.

25 Points P and Q divide OA,OB in the ratio $m{:}n$. Use vectors to prove that PQ is parallel to AB, and find the ratio $PQ{:}AB$.

26 X, Y and Z are the midpoints of the sides of a triangle ABC. Prove that $\mathbf{a}+\mathbf{b}+\mathbf{c}=\mathbf{x}+\mathbf{y}+\mathbf{z}$. Conversely, given $x+y+z=a+b+c$, prove that if X and Y are the midpoints of two sides of the triangle ABC, then Z is the midpoint of the third side.

Equation of a straight line

One and only one straight line can be drawn through a given point in a given direction. This is particularly suitable for writing in vector form, for if we have a straight line through a point position vector $\mathbf{a}$, in the direction of a vector $\mathbf{b}$, then

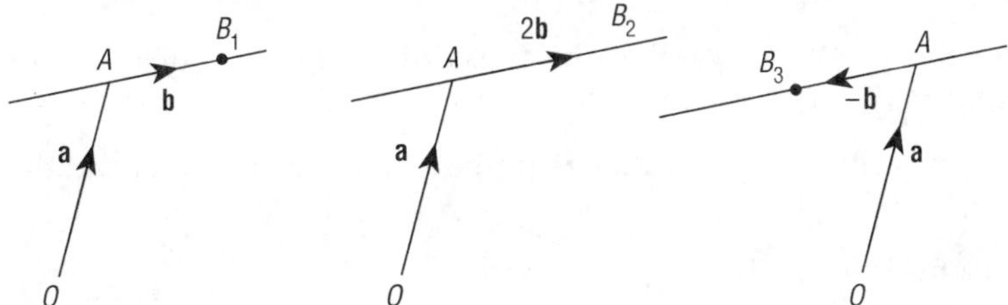

Figure 19.13

any point on that line can be reached by going to A, then a suitable multiple (positive or negative) of $\mathbf{b}$ (Figure 19.13). Thus the equation of the straight line can be written $\mathbf{r}=\mathbf{a}+t\mathbf{b}$,

i.e. $x\mathbf{i}+y\mathbf{j}=(a_1\mathbf{i}+a_2\mathbf{j})+t(b_1\mathbf{i}+b_2\mathbf{j})$, or $\begin{pmatrix}x\\y\end{pmatrix}=\begin{pmatrix}a_1\\a_2\end{pmatrix}+t\begin{pmatrix}b_1\\b_2\end{pmatrix}$

We shall find other vector forms for the equation of a straight line, but this is the simplest to understand and to use.

Example 1. Write down the vector equation of the straight line through the point position vector $2\mathbf{i}+\mathbf{j}$, in the direction of the vector $\mathbf{i}-\mathbf{j}$. Find whether the points position vectors (a) $5\mathbf{i}-2\mathbf{j}$ and (b) $7\mathbf{i}-3\mathbf{j}$ lie on this line.

The vector equation of the straight line required is

$$\mathbf{r}=(2\mathbf{i}+\mathbf{j})+t(\mathbf{i}-\mathbf{j}), \text{ i.e. } \mathbf{r}=\begin{pmatrix}2\\1\end{pmatrix}+t\begin{pmatrix}1\\-1\end{pmatrix}$$

To see whether the point $5\mathbf{i}-2\mathbf{j}$ lies on this line, we try to find a value for t so that $2\mathbf{i}+\mathbf{j}+t(\mathbf{i}-\mathbf{j})=5\mathbf{i}-2\mathbf{j}$.

Equating the $\mathbf{i}$-components, $2+t=5$;
equating the $\mathbf{j}$-components, $1-t=-2$

The value $t=3$ satisfies both these equations, and $5\mathbf{i}-2\mathbf{j}$ lies on the line $\mathbf{r}=(2\mathbf{i}+\mathbf{j})+t(\mathbf{i}-\mathbf{j})$, since $5\mathbf{i}-2\mathbf{j}=(2\mathbf{i}+\mathbf{j})+3(\mathbf{i}-\mathbf{j})$

When we consider the second point, we want a value of t such that

$$(2\mathbf{i}+\mathbf{j})+t(\mathbf{i}-\mathbf{j})=7\mathbf{i}-3\mathbf{j}$$

i.e. from the **i**-components, $2+t=7$,
and from the **j**-components, $1-t=-3$

The two equations give different values of t, so there is no one value of t that satisfies both equations, and the point $7\mathbf{i}-3\mathbf{j}$ does not lie on the given line.

Example 2. Find the equation of the straight line through the points A, B position vectors $2\mathbf{i}+3\mathbf{j}-\mathbf{k}$, $-\mathbf{i}+\mathbf{j}+\mathbf{k}$, respectively.

The direction of the straight line AB is along the vector $\mathbf{b}-\mathbf{a}$,
i.e. $-3\mathbf{i}-2\mathbf{j}+2\mathbf{k}$, so that the equation of the line is

$$\mathbf{r}=2\mathbf{i}+3\mathbf{j}-\mathbf{k}+t(-3\mathbf{i}-2\mathbf{j}+2\mathbf{k}), \text{ i.e. } \mathbf{r}=\begin{pmatrix}2\\3\\-1\end{pmatrix}+t\begin{pmatrix}-3\\-2\\2\end{pmatrix}$$

Example 3. Find the position vector of the point of intersection of the lines $\mathbf{r}=(\mathbf{i}+\mathbf{j})+t(2\mathbf{i}-\mathbf{j})$ and $\mathbf{r}=(2\mathbf{i}+5\mathbf{j})+s(\mathbf{i}-2\mathbf{j})$.

At the point where these lines intersect, the **i**-components must be equal and the **j**-components must be equal,

i.e. $1+2t=2+s$ and $1-t=5-2s$
i.e. $2t-s=1$ and $2s-t=4$
i.e. $t=2$, $s=3$

so the position vector is $\mathbf{r}=(\mathbf{i}+\mathbf{j})+2(2\mathbf{i}-\mathbf{j})$, i.e. $5\mathbf{i}-\mathbf{j}$, which of course could be obtained from $2\mathbf{i}+5\mathbf{j}+3(\mathbf{i}-2\mathbf{j})$.

Returning to the section theorem, the point which divides the straight line through P, Q in the ratio $\lambda:\mu$ is

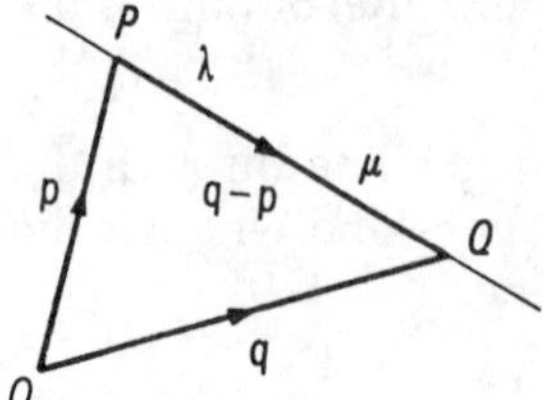

Figure 19.14

$$\mathbf{r}=\frac{\mu\mathbf{p}+\lambda\mathbf{q}}{\lambda+\mu}=\mathbf{p}+\frac{\lambda}{\lambda+\mu}(\mathbf{q}-\mathbf{p})$$

$$=\mathbf{p}+t(\mathbf{q}-\mathbf{p})$$

so that, for varying t, any point on the line through A and B can be seen to have position vector

$$\mathbf{r}=\mathbf{p}+t(\mathbf{q}-\mathbf{p})$$

as above, through the point position vector $\mathbf{p}$, in the direction of the vector $(\mathbf{q}-\mathbf{p})$.

Example 4. The vector equation of the straight line through the points position vector $\begin{pmatrix}1\\2\\3\end{pmatrix}$ parallel to the vector $\begin{pmatrix}4\\3\\2\end{pmatrix}$ is $\mathbf{r}=\begin{pmatrix}1\\2\\3\end{pmatrix}+\lambda\begin{pmatrix}4\\3\\2\end{pmatrix}$.

Example 5. The vector equation of the straight line through the point position vectors $\begin{pmatrix}2\\1\\4\end{pmatrix}$ and $\begin{pmatrix}5\\2\\3\end{pmatrix}$ is $\mathbf{r}=\begin{pmatrix}2\\1\\4\end{pmatrix}+t\begin{pmatrix}3\\1\\-1\end{pmatrix}$

Taking $\mathbf{r}=\begin{pmatrix}x\\y\\z\end{pmatrix}$, we see that this straight line has cartesian (parametric) form

$$x=2+3t,\ y=1+t,\ z=4-t$$

i.e.
$$\frac{x-2}{3}=\frac{y-1}{1}=\frac{z-4}{-1}$$

Example 6. Find the position vector of the point of intersection of straight lines

$$\mathbf{r}=\begin{pmatrix}3\\1\\2\end{pmatrix}+t\begin{pmatrix}4\\3\\1\end{pmatrix} \text{ and } \mathbf{r}=\begin{pmatrix}3\\6\\2\end{pmatrix}+s\begin{pmatrix}-2\\1\\0\end{pmatrix}$$

Any point on the first line has position vector $\begin{pmatrix}3+4t\\1+3t\\2+\ t\end{pmatrix}$, any point on the second line $\begin{pmatrix}3-2s\\6+\ s\\3\end{pmatrix}$. At the point of intersection of the straight lines, these vectors must be equal, so

$$\begin{aligned} 3-2s&=3+4t && (1)\\ 1+3t&=6+s && (2)\\ \text{and}\quad 2+t&=3 && (3)\end{aligned}$$

From (3), $t=1$; using (2), $s=-2$; these check in (1), so the point of intersection of the two lines is $\begin{pmatrix}7\\4\\3\end{pmatrix}$.

If the straight lines do not meet (skew lines) then the three equations in two unknowns are inconsistent, and there are no values of s and t that satisfy all three equations.

Exercise 19.2

1 Write down, in (i) the **i**,**j** form, (ii) the maxtrix form, the vector equations of the following straight lines: through the point position vector **a** in the direction of the vector **b**, where
(a) **a**=3**i**+**j**, **b**=**i**−**j**, (b) **a**=4**i**−**j**, **b**=−**i**−**j**, (c) **a**=**i**+2**j**+3**k**, **b**=**i**+**j**+**k**,
(d) **a**=**i**+2**j**+3**k**, **b**=**i**+2**j**+3**k**, (e) **a**=3**i**, **b**=**j**, (f) **a**=3**i**+2**j**, **b**=**k**,

(g) $\mathbf{a}=\mathbf{i}$, $\mathbf{b}=\mathbf{j}+\mathbf{k}$, (h) $\mathbf{a}=\mathbf{i}+\mathbf{j}$, $\mathbf{b}=\mathbf{k}$, (i) $\mathbf{a}=0$, $\mathbf{b}=\mathbf{i}+\mathbf{j}+\mathbf{k}$,
(j) $\mathbf{a}=2\mathbf{i}+2\mathbf{j}$, $\mathbf{b}=-\mathbf{i}-\mathbf{j}$.

2 Write down, in (i) the **i**,**j** form, (ii) the matrix form, the vector equations of the lines *AB*, where
(a) $\mathbf{a}=3\mathbf{i}+\mathbf{j}$, $\mathbf{b}=2\mathbf{i}+3\mathbf{j}$, (b) $\mathbf{a}=\mathbf{i}+\mathbf{j}$, $\mathbf{b}=3\mathbf{i}+\mathbf{j}$, (c) $\mathbf{a}=\mathbf{i}+\mathbf{j}+\mathbf{k}$, $\mathbf{b}=\mathbf{i}+\mathbf{j}+5\mathbf{k}$,
(d) $\mathbf{a}=2\mathbf{i}+3\mathbf{j}+\mathbf{k}$, $\mathbf{b}=2\mathbf{i}+\mathbf{j}+\mathbf{k}$, (e) $\mathbf{a}=3\mathbf{i}+2\mathbf{j}+\mathbf{k}$, $\mathbf{b}=2\mathbf{i}+\mathbf{j}+\mathbf{k}$.

3 Which of the straight lines in Q.1 pass through the origin?

4 Which of the straight lines in Q.2 (a) and (b) passes through the point position vector $7\mathbf{i}+\mathbf{j}$?

5 Which of the straight lines in Q.2 (c), (d) and (e) pass through the point position vector $\mathbf{i}+\mathbf{k}$?

The scalar product

If **a** and **b** are two vectors and θ is the angle between them, we define the scalar product of **a** and **b** as $ab \cos \theta$. This is usually written **a.b**, and is sometimes called the 'dot-product'.

Since $\cos (360°-\theta)=\cos \theta$, it does not matter whether we rotate from **a** to **b** or from **b** to **a**, so that $\mathbf{a.b}=\mathbf{b.a}$, the scalar product is commutative.

There may seem to be no obvious application for this definition, but we remember from Physics that the kinetic energy of a body mass m, velocity **v** is $\frac{1}{2}mv^2$; the velocity **v** is a vector, yet $\mathbf{v}^2$ here is a scalar. We shall see many other applications of the scalar product of two vectors.

Parallel and perpendicular vectors

Since $\cos 0=1$ and $\cos 90°=0$,

$$\mathbf{i.i}=\mathbf{j.j}=\mathbf{k.k}=1$$

and

$$\mathbf{i.j}=\mathbf{j.k}=\mathbf{k.i}=\mathbf{i.k}=\mathbf{k.j}=\mathbf{j.i}=0$$

This enables us to find easily the scalar product of vectors in component form.

If **a** and **b** are two parallel vectors, $\mathbf{a.b}=ab$, since the angle between them is 0; in particular, $\mathbf{a.a}=a^2$ for all **a**.

If **a** and **b** are two perpendicular vectors, $\mathbf{a.b}=ab \cos 90°=0$.

Example. If $\mathbf{a}=3\mathbf{i}+2\mathbf{j}$, $\mathbf{b}=\mathbf{i}+\mathbf{j}$, find (a) **a.b**, (b) $\mathbf{a}^2$.

(a) $\mathbf{a.b} = (3\mathbf{i}+2\mathbf{j}).(\mathbf{i}+\mathbf{j})$
$= 3\mathbf{i.i}+3\mathbf{i.j}+2\mathbf{j.i}+2\mathbf{j.j}$
$= 3+2$
$= 5$

(b) $\mathbf{a.a} = a^2 \cos 0°=a^2$
$a^2 =(3\mathbf{i}+2\mathbf{j}).(3\mathbf{i}+2\mathbf{j})$
$= 9+4$
$= 13$

The angle between two vectors

Since $\mathbf{a}.\mathbf{b}=ab\cos\theta$, we can calculate the cosine of the angle between two vectors.

Example 1. Find the angle between the vectors $\mathbf{a}=\mathbf{i}$ and $\mathbf{b}=3\mathbf{i}+4\mathbf{j}$.

Here, $|\mathbf{a}|=a=\sqrt{2}$ and $|\mathbf{b}|=b=5$.
Since $\mathbf{a}.\mathbf{b} = ab\cos\theta$, and $\mathbf{a}.\mathbf{b}=(\mathbf{i}+\mathbf{j})(3\mathbf{i}+4\mathbf{j})=7$

$$7 = 5\sqrt{2}\cos\theta,$$

$$\cos\theta = \frac{7}{5\sqrt{2}}$$

$$= 8°$$

Example 2. Show that the vectors $3\mathbf{i}+4\mathbf{j}+\mathbf{k}$ and $\mathbf{i}-\mathbf{j}+\mathbf{k}$ are perpendicular.

$$(3\mathbf{i}+4\mathbf{j}+\mathbf{k}).(\mathbf{i}-\mathbf{j}+\mathbf{k}) = 3-4+1$$
$$= 0$$

so the vectors are perpendicular.

Example 3. Find a unit vector perpendicular to $3\mathbf{i}+4\mathbf{j}+2\mathbf{k}$ and $5\mathbf{i}+4\mathbf{j}-2\mathbf{k}$.

Let the unit vector be $x\mathbf{i}+y\mathbf{j}+z\mathbf{k}$, where $x^2+y^2+z^2=1$, as it is a unit vector.

Since it is perpendicular to the two given vectors,

$$(x\mathbf{i}+y\mathbf{j}+z\mathbf{k}).(3\mathbf{i}+4\mathbf{j}+2\mathbf{k})=0$$

i.e. $3x+4y+2z=0$

and $(x\mathbf{i}+y\mathbf{j}+z\mathbf{k}).(5\mathbf{i}+4\mathbf{j}-2\mathbf{k})=0$

i.e. $5x+4y-2z=0$

Adding (1) and (2), we have $8x+8y=0$, i.e. $y=-x$.
Subtracting (1) from (2), $2x-4z=0$, $z=\frac{1}{2}x$
Substituting in $x^2+y^2+z^2=1$,

$$x^2+x^2+(\tfrac{1}{2}x)^2=1$$
$$x=\pm(2/3)$$

The two vectors are $\frac{1}{3}(2\mathbf{i}-2\mathbf{j}+\mathbf{k})$ and $-\frac{1}{3}(2\mathbf{i}-2\mathbf{j}+\mathbf{k})$
Check: $(2\mathbf{i}-2\mathbf{j}+\mathbf{k}).(3\mathbf{i}+4\mathbf{j}+2\mathbf{k})=6-8+2=0$, so these two vectors are perpendicular. We realise that if a vector $\mathbf{p}$ is perpendicular to two given vectors, then $-\mathbf{p}$ is also perpendicular to those vectors.

Equation of a straight line

In two dimensions, a straight line can be defined by saying that it goes through a fixed point, position vector $\mathbf{a}$ say, and is perpendicular to a given vector $\mathbf{n}$. Thus if $\mathbf{r}$ is the position vector of any point in this line (Figure 19.15), $\mathbf{r}-\mathbf{a}$ is perpendicular to $\mathbf{n}$, i.e. $(\mathbf{r}-\mathbf{a}).\mathbf{n}=0$, $\therefore$ $\mathbf{r}.\mathbf{n}=\mathbf{a}.\mathbf{n}$. This form is not often required, but can be compared with the equation of a plane in three dimensions.

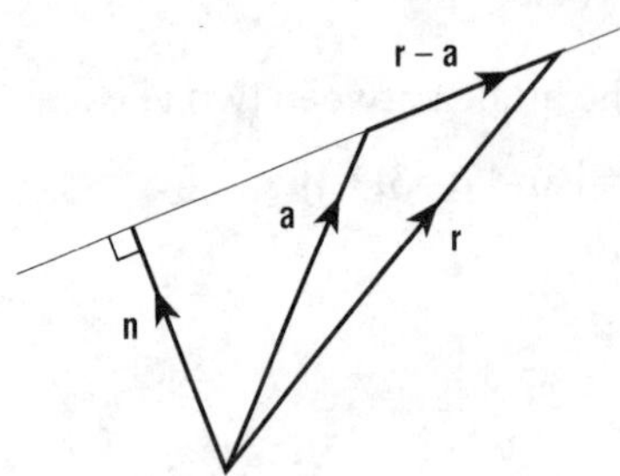

Figure 19.15

Exercise 19.3

1 Given $\mathbf{a}=\mathbf{i}-\mathbf{j}$, $\mathbf{b}=2\mathbf{i}+3\mathbf{j}$ and $\mathbf{c}=-\mathbf{i}-\mathbf{j}$, find
(a) $\mathbf{a}.\mathbf{b}$, (b) $\mathbf{a}.\mathbf{c}$, (c) $\mathbf{b}.\mathbf{c}$, (d) a^2, (e) c^2.

2 With the vectors defined in Q.1, find the cosine of the angle between
(a) **a** and **b**, (b) **b** and **c**, (c) **c** and **a**, (d) **a** and $\mathbf{b}-\mathbf{c}$, (e) **c** and $2\mathbf{a}-\mathbf{b}$.

3 Given $\mathbf{a}=\mathbf{i}+\mathbf{j}+\mathbf{k}$, $\mathbf{b}=2\mathbf{i}-\mathbf{k}$ and $\mathbf{c}=-\mathbf{j}-\mathbf{k}$, find
(a) $\mathbf{a}.\mathbf{b}$, (b) $\mathbf{a}.\mathbf{c}$, (c) $\mathbf{b}.\mathbf{c}$, (d) a^2, (e) c^2.

4 With the vectors defined in Q.3, find the cosine of the angle between
(a) **a** and **b**, (b) **b** and **c**, (c) **c** and **a**, (d) **a** and $\mathbf{b}-\mathbf{c}$, (e) **c** and $2\mathbf{a}-\mathbf{b}$.

5 Find a unit vector perpendicular to (a) $4\mathbf{i}-3\mathbf{j}$, (b) $-\mathbf{i}-\mathbf{j}$.

6 Find unit vectors perpendicular to
(a) $2\mathbf{i}$ and $3\mathbf{k}$,
(b) $\mathbf{i}+\mathbf{j}$ and $\mathbf{i}-4\mathbf{j}$,
(c) $2\mathbf{i}+\mathbf{j}+2\mathbf{k}$ and $-\mathbf{i}+7\mathbf{j}+4\mathbf{k}$,
(d) $\mathbf{i}+2\mathbf{j}+3\mathbf{k}$ and $-\mathbf{i}+\mathbf{j}+2\mathbf{k}$,
(e) $\mathbf{i}+\mathbf{j}+\mathbf{k}$ and $-2\mathbf{i}+\mathbf{j}+2\mathbf{k}$.

7 Find the equation of the straight line through the point position vector **a** perpendicular to the vector **n** where
(a) $\mathbf{a}=2\mathbf{i}-\mathbf{j}$, $\mathbf{n}=3\mathbf{i}+5\mathbf{j}$, (b) $\mathbf{a}=-5\mathbf{i}-\mathbf{j}$, $\mathbf{n}=\mathbf{i}+2\mathbf{j}$, (c) $\mathbf{a}=7\mathbf{i}+\mathbf{j}$, $\mathbf{n}=-3\mathbf{i}-2\mathbf{j}$
Compare each with the corresponding cartesian form.

Equation of a plane perpendicular to a given vector n

A plane Π is fixed if we know a point through which Π passes, and a vector perpendicular to Π. If **a** is the position vector of a point in Π, **n** a vector perpendicular to Π, and **r** is the position vector of any point in Π, then $(\mathbf{r}-\mathbf{a})$ lies in Π and so is perpendicular to **n**,

i.e. $(\mathbf{r}-\mathbf{a}).\mathbf{n}=0$

i.e. $\mathbf{r}.\mathbf{n}=\mathbf{a}.\mathbf{n}$

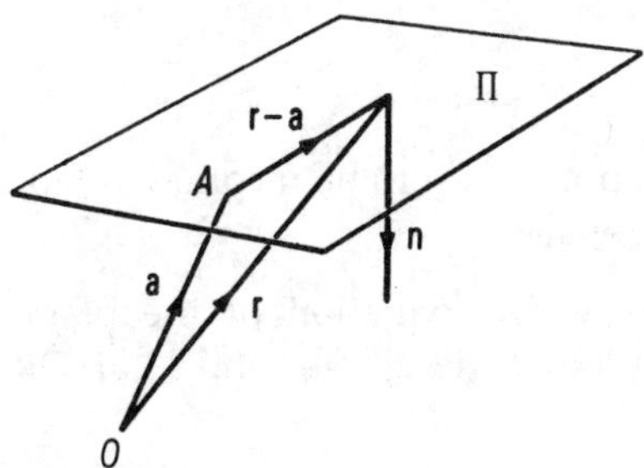

Figure 19.16

Example 1. Find the equation of the plane through the point position vector $2\mathbf{i}-3\mathbf{j}-4\mathbf{k}$, perpendicular to the vector $2\mathbf{i}-\mathbf{j}-\mathbf{k}$.

$$\mathbf{r}.\mathbf{n}=\mathbf{a}.\mathbf{n}$$

$\Rightarrow$ $$\mathbf{r}.(2\mathbf{i}-\mathbf{j}-\mathbf{k})=(2\mathbf{i}-3\mathbf{j}-4\mathbf{k}).(2\mathbf{i}-\mathbf{j}-\mathbf{k})$$

i.e. $$\mathbf{r}.(2\mathbf{i}-\mathbf{j}-\mathbf{k})=11$$

This can be written $$2x-y-z=11$$

Example 2. Find the position vector of the point in which the line $\mathbf{r}=3\mathbf{i}+2\mathbf{j}+\mathbf{k}+t(2\mathbf{i}+\mathbf{j}+2\mathbf{k})$ meets the plane $\mathbf{r}.(2\mathbf{i}+3\mathbf{j}+\mathbf{k})=4$

These intersect where

$$[3\mathbf{i}+2\mathbf{j}+\mathbf{k}+t(2\mathbf{i}+\mathbf{j}+2\mathbf{k})].(2\mathbf{i}+3\mathbf{j}+\mathbf{k})=4$$

i.e. $$13+9t=4$$

$$t=-1$$

so the position vector of their point of intersection is $\mathbf{i}+\mathbf{j}-\mathbf{k}$.

Equation of a plane through three points

If A, B and C are three points determining a plane, the position vector relative to A of any point in that plane is $\lambda\overrightarrow{AB}+\mu\overrightarrow{AC}$, so that if the position vectors of A, B, C relative to an origin O are $\mathbf{a}$, $\mathbf{b}$, $\mathbf{c}$ respectively, $\overrightarrow{AB}=(\mathbf{b}-\mathbf{a})$, $\overrightarrow{AC}=(\mathbf{c}-\mathbf{a})$ and the position vector $\mathbf{r}$ of a point P relative to O is

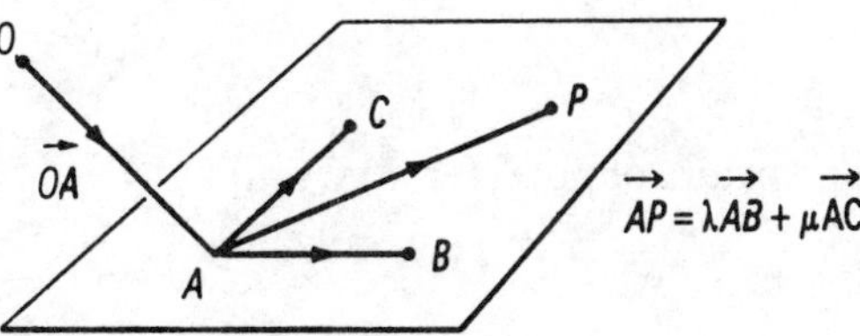

Figure 19.17

$$\mathbf{a}+\lambda\overrightarrow{AB}+\mu\overrightarrow{AC}$$

i.e. $\mathbf{a}+\lambda(\mathbf{b}-\mathbf{a})+\mu(\mathbf{c}-\mathbf{a})$,

i.e. $(1-\lambda-\mu)\mathbf{a}+\lambda\mathbf{b}+\mu\mathbf{c}$

There are two parameters in this form, and it is not a form to be recommended, but it is specified at present in some A-level syllabuses.

Example. Find, in the form $\mathbf{r}=\mathbf{a}+s\mathbf{b}+t\mathbf{c}$, the vector equation of the plane through the points A, B, C, position vectors $3\mathbf{i}+2\mathbf{j}+\mathbf{k}$, $\mathbf{i}-2\mathbf{j}-3\mathbf{k}$, and $\mathbf{i}+3\mathbf{j}+2\mathbf{k}$ respectively.

Since $\overrightarrow{AB}=-2\mathbf{i}-4\mathbf{j}-4\mathbf{k}$, $\overrightarrow{AC}=-2\mathbf{i}+\mathbf{j}+\mathbf{k}$

the position vector of any point in this plane is

$$\mathbf{r}=(3\mathbf{i}+2\mathbf{j}+\mathbf{k})+s(-2\mathbf{i}-4\mathbf{j}-4\mathbf{k})+t(-2\mathbf{i}+\mathbf{j}+\mathbf{k})$$

Alternative method

A better method of finding the equation of a plane through three points is to take the form $\mathbf{r}.\mathbf{n}=k$, for some $\mathbf{n}$ and k. Then we can divide by k, and suppose that

$$\frac{1}{k}\mathbf{n}=a\mathbf{i}+b\mathbf{j}+c\mathbf{k}$$

for some a, b, c to be found, i.e. the equation of the plane is $\mathbf{r}.(a\mathbf{i}+b\mathbf{j}+c\mathbf{k})=1$. Since this passes through the point position vector $3\mathbf{i}+2\mathbf{j}+\mathbf{k}$,

$$(3\mathbf{i}+2\mathbf{j}+\mathbf{k}).(a\mathbf{i}+b\mathbf{j}+c\mathbf{k})=1$$

i.e. $3a+2b+c=1$ (1)

Similarly, since it passes through the point $\mathbf{i}-2\mathbf{j}-3\mathbf{k}$,

$a-2b-3c=1$ (2)

and if it passes through $\mathbf{i}+3\mathbf{j}+2\mathbf{k}$,

$a+3b+2c=1$ (3)

Solving equations (1), (2) and (3) simultaneously, $a=0$, $b=1$ and $c=-1$, so the equation of the plane can be written

$$\mathbf{r}.(\mathbf{j}-\mathbf{k})=1$$

Miscellaneous exercise 19.4

In this exercise $\mathbf{a}$, $\mathbf{b}$, $\mathbf{c}$, $\mathbf{d}$ are the position vectors of points A, B, C and D.

1 Given that

$$\mathbf{a}=\begin{pmatrix}1\\2\end{pmatrix} \quad \mathbf{b}=\begin{pmatrix}3\\7\end{pmatrix} \quad \mathbf{d}=\begin{pmatrix}6\\4\end{pmatrix}$$

(a) show that AB is equal in length to AD;

(b) find the vector **c** if $ABCD$ is a rhombus;
(c) find the position vectors of M and N, the midpoints of BC and CD, respectively;
(d) find the vector $\overrightarrow{MN}$, and show $\overrightarrow{MN}=\frac{1}{2}\overrightarrow{BD}$.

2 Given

$$\mathbf{a}=\begin{pmatrix}2\\-1\end{pmatrix}\quad \mathbf{b}=\begin{pmatrix}5\\3\end{pmatrix}\quad \mathbf{c}=\begin{pmatrix}-1\\-1\end{pmatrix}$$

(a) find **d** if $ABCD$ is a parallelogram;
(b) find **d** if $ABDC$ is a parallelogram.

3 Given that

$$\mathbf{a}=\begin{pmatrix}-1\\-3\end{pmatrix}\quad \mathbf{b}=\begin{pmatrix}2\\4\end{pmatrix}\quad \mathbf{c}=\begin{pmatrix}5\\5\end{pmatrix}$$

find (a) the position vector of X, the midpoint of BC;
(b) the position vector of Y, the midpoint of CA;
(c) the position vector of G, the point that divides AX in the ratio 2:1;
(d) the position vector of G', the point that divides BY in the ratio 2:1.

4 If **a**, **b**, **c** and **d** are the position vectors of points A, B, C, D respectively,

when $\mathbf{a}=\begin{pmatrix}1\\1\\0\end{pmatrix}$, $\mathbf{b}=\begin{pmatrix}3\\2\\-1\end{pmatrix}$, $\mathbf{c}=\begin{pmatrix}-2\\-2\\0\end{pmatrix}$, $\mathbf{d}=\begin{pmatrix}4\\1\\-3\end{pmatrix}$

(a) show AB is parallel to CD,
(b) find the lengths of AB, CD and AC.

5 Points A, B, C, D have position vectors

$$\mathbf{a}=\begin{pmatrix}1\\2\\3\end{pmatrix},\quad \mathbf{b}=\begin{pmatrix}-1\\-1\\2\end{pmatrix},\quad \mathbf{c}=\begin{pmatrix}2\\4\\5\end{pmatrix}$$

Find (a) the position vector of D, if $ABCD$ is a parallelogram, (b) the position vector of E, if $ACEB$ is a parallelogram, (c) the position vector of F, if $ABCF$ is a trapezium with AB parallel to CF and $AB=\frac{1}{2}CF$.

6 Find, in the form $\mathbf{r}=\mathbf{a}+t\mathbf{b}$, the vector equation of the line

(a) through A, position vector $\begin{pmatrix}2\\1\end{pmatrix}$, parallel to the vector $\begin{pmatrix}-1\\-1\end{pmatrix}$,

(b) through A, parallel to BC, where $\mathbf{b}=\begin{pmatrix}5\\2\end{pmatrix}$, $\mathbf{c}=\begin{pmatrix}-1\\3\end{pmatrix}$

(c) through A perpendicular to the unit vector $\begin{pmatrix}1\\0\end{pmatrix}$.

7 Find which of the points A, B, C lie on the straight line

$$\mathbf{r}=\begin{pmatrix}2\\3\end{pmatrix}+t\begin{pmatrix}-1\\1\end{pmatrix}$$

given $\mathbf{a}=\begin{pmatrix}-1\\6\end{pmatrix}$ $\mathbf{b}=\begin{pmatrix}-3\\7\end{pmatrix}$ $\mathbf{c}=\begin{pmatrix}-5\\10\end{pmatrix}$

8 Find, in vector and cartesian form, the equation of the straight lines *AB*, *BC*, *CA* given that

$$\mathbf{a}=\begin{pmatrix}1\\3\end{pmatrix} \quad \mathbf{b}=\begin{pmatrix}3\\7\end{pmatrix} \quad \mathbf{c}=\begin{pmatrix}5\\-1\end{pmatrix}$$

9 Find the equation of the straight line through the point position vector $\begin{pmatrix}3\\1\\2\end{pmatrix}$ parallel to the vector $\begin{pmatrix}-1\\2\\-3\end{pmatrix}$. Show that this straight line passes through the point $\begin{pmatrix}1\\5\\-4\end{pmatrix}$.

10 Points *A*, *B* and *C* have position vectors $\begin{pmatrix}2\\1\\0\end{pmatrix}$, $\begin{pmatrix}4\\0\\-1\end{pmatrix}$, $\begin{pmatrix}5\\-1\\1\end{pmatrix}$.

Find, in vector and cartesian form, the equations of the straight lines *AB*, *BC*, *CA*.

11 Find the scalar products **a.b**, **b.c**, **c.a**, where
$\mathbf{a}=3\mathbf{i}+2\mathbf{j}$, $\mathbf{b}=2\mathbf{i}-\mathbf{j}$ and $\mathbf{c}=-2\mathbf{i}+5\mathbf{j}$

12 Show that the vectors $2\mathbf{i}+5\mathbf{j}$ and $15\mathbf{i}-6\mathbf{j}$ are perpendicular.

13 Find the cosine of the angle between the vectors $\mathbf{i}+\mathbf{j}$ and $2\mathbf{i}-\mathbf{j}$.

14 Find the cosines of the angles between the vectors **a** and **b**, **b** and **c** and **c** and **a**, when $\mathbf{a}=2\mathbf{i}-3\mathbf{j}$, $\mathbf{b}=3\mathbf{i}+4\mathbf{j}$ and $\mathbf{c}=\mathbf{i}-\mathbf{j}$.
Check that one of the angles is the sum of the other two.

15 Find a unit vector **u** in the plane of **i** and **j** perpendicular to
$\mathbf{a}=6\mathbf{i}-8\mathbf{j}$
by taking the unit vector $\mathbf{u}=x\mathbf{i}+y\mathbf{j}$, using $\mathbf{u}.\mathbf{a}=0$ and $|\mathbf{u}|=1$.

16 Find two unit vectors perpendicular to $4\mathbf{i}-7\mathbf{j}+4\mathbf{k}$ and $2\mathbf{i}-\mathbf{j}+2\mathbf{k}$.

17 Show that the vectors $2\mathbf{i}+3\mathbf{j}+\mathbf{k}$ and $4\mathbf{i}-3\mathbf{j}+\mathbf{k}$ are perpendicular.

18 Find the cosine of the angle between the vectors $2\mathbf{i}+\mathbf{j}-\mathbf{k}$ and $\mathbf{i}-3\mathbf{j}+2\mathbf{k}$.

19 Find the cosine of the angle between the vectors $3\mathbf{j}+\mathbf{k}$, $2\mathbf{i}-\mathbf{k}$.

20 Find a unit vector in the plane of **i** and **j** perpendicular to $2\mathbf{i}-\mathbf{j}$. Find also a unit vector in three dimensions perpendicular to these vectors.

21 Find the equation of the following planes:

(a) through the point position vector $3\mathbf{i}-2\mathbf{j}-\mathbf{k}$ perpendicular to the vector $\mathbf{i}-2\mathbf{j}+3\mathbf{k}$,

(b) through the point position vector $3\mathbf{i}-2\mathbf{j}+2\mathbf{k}$ perpendicular to the vector $2\mathbf{i}-3\mathbf{j}$,

(c) through the point position vector $3\mathbf{i}+2\mathbf{j}+\mathbf{k}$ perpendicular to the vector **i**.

22 Find the position vector of the point in which the line l meets the plane Π when

(a) l is $\mathbf{r}=\mathbf{i}+t(\mathbf{j}+\mathbf{k})$ and Π is $\mathbf{r}.(3\mathbf{i}+2\mathbf{j}+\mathbf{k})=9$,

(b) l is $\mathbf{r}=2\mathbf{i}+\mathbf{j}-\mathbf{k}+t(\mathbf{i}+\mathbf{k})$ and Π is $\mathbf{r}.(4\mathbf{i}+2\mathbf{j}-3\mathbf{k})=15$,
(c) l is $\mathbf{r}=\mathbf{i}+\mathbf{j}+t\mathbf{k}$ and Π is $\mathbf{r}.(3\mathbf{i}+4\mathbf{j}+5\mathbf{k})=22$.

23 (a) Write down a vector perpendicular to the plane $\Pi\equiv x+2y+2z=6$.
(b) Write down the equation of the line l through the point P position vector $3\mathbf{i}-2\mathbf{j}-\mathbf{k}$ perpendicular to Π.
(c) Find the point at which l meets the plane Π.
(d) Find the perpendicular distance of P from Π.
(e) Find the position vector of the point Q, being the reflection in Π of P.

24 Find the perpendicular distance of the point P from the plane Π and the image of P in Π when
(a) $\mathbf{p}=2\mathbf{i}+3\mathbf{j}+4\mathbf{k}$, Π is $\mathbf{r}.(2\mathbf{i}+\mathbf{j}-2\mathbf{k})=-10$,
(b) $\mathbf{p}=\mathbf{i}-2\mathbf{j}+\mathbf{k}$, Π is $\mathbf{r}.(\mathbf{i}-\mathbf{j})=6$,
(c) $\mathbf{p}=3\mathbf{i}-2\mathbf{j}-4\mathbf{k}$, Π is $\mathbf{r}.(3\mathbf{i}+\mathbf{j}+2\mathbf{k})=13$.

25 Find the cosine of the angle between straight lines perpendicular to each of the planes $\mathbf{r}.(2\mathbf{i}-\mathbf{j}-2\mathbf{k})=3$ and $\mathbf{r}.(\mathbf{i}+\mathbf{j}+\mathbf{k})=1$, and deduce the angle between the two planes.

26 Find the equation of the plane through the points position vectors $\mathbf{i}+\mathbf{j}+\mathbf{k}$, $2\mathbf{i}+\mathbf{j}$ and $3\mathbf{i}-\mathbf{j}-\mathbf{k}$,
(a) in the form $\mathbf{r}=\mathbf{a}+s\mathbf{b}+t\mathbf{c}$,
(b) in the form $\mathbf{r}.\mathbf{n}=k$.

27 Find, in the two forms given above, the equation of the plane through the points position vectors $4\mathbf{i}-3\mathbf{j}-2\mathbf{k}$, $-2\mathbf{i}+\mathbf{j}+2\mathbf{k}$ and $3\mathbf{i}-\mathbf{j}-\mathbf{k}$.

28 Find in the two forms given above the equation of the plane through the points position vectors $\mathbf{i}+2\mathbf{j}+2\mathbf{k}$, $\mathbf{i}+\mathbf{j}$, $\mathbf{j}-3\mathbf{k}$.

29 Find in the form $\mathbf{r}.\mathbf{n}=k$ the equation of the plane through the points position vectors $\mathbf{i}-\mathbf{j}+\mathbf{k}$, $\mathbf{j}$, $2\mathbf{i}+\mathbf{j}-4\mathbf{k}$. Show that it passes through the point position vector $3\mathbf{i}+3\mathbf{j}-9\mathbf{k}$.

30 Show that the points position vectors $-\mathbf{i}+\mathbf{j}$, $2\mathbf{i}-\mathbf{j}+\mathbf{k}$, $3\mathbf{i}-2\mathbf{j}+3\mathbf{k}$ and $\mathbf{i}-\mathbf{j}+4\mathbf{k}$ lie in a plane.

31 The position vectors of points A, B and C are $\mathbf{a}$, $\mathbf{b}$, $\mathbf{c}$ respectively. Find the position vector of the fourth vertex
(a) of the parallelogram $ABCD$,
(b) of the parallelogram $ABDC$.

32 Find the position vector of the point of intersection of the straight lines $\mathbf{r}=2\mathbf{i}+3\mathbf{j}+\mathbf{k}+s(\mathbf{i}-\mathbf{j}-\mathbf{k})$ and $\mathbf{r}=\mathbf{i}+2\mathbf{j}+4\mathbf{k}+t(\mathbf{i}-2\mathbf{k})$, and find the cosine of the angle between these straight lines.

33 Show that the straight lines $\mathbf{r}=3\mathbf{i}+4\mathbf{j}+\mathbf{k}+s(-\mathbf{i}+\mathbf{j}+2\mathbf{k})$ and $\mathbf{r}=\mathbf{i}+5\mathbf{j}+7\mathbf{k}+t(\mathbf{j}+\mathbf{k})$ are skew.

34 (a) Find the equation in a plane of the circle on points position vectors $\mathbf{i}+\mathbf{j}$, $3\mathbf{i}-5\mathbf{j}$ as diameter,
(b) Find the equation in space of the sphere on the points $3\mathbf{i}-4\mathbf{j}+\mathbf{k}$, $\mathbf{i}-2\mathbf{j}+3\mathbf{k}$ as diameter.

35 Points A, B have position vectors $\mathbf{a}$, $\mathbf{b}$ relative to an origin O. Show that the area of triangle $OAB=\frac{1}{2}\sqrt{[a^2b^2-(\mathbf{a}.\mathbf{b})^2]}$. Hence find
(a) the area of triangle OAB, where A, B have position vectors $\mathbf{i}-2\mathbf{j}+3\mathbf{k}$,

2i+2**j**+**k**,

(b) the area of triangle ABC, C having position vector 3**i**+**j**+2**k**.

36 (a) Find the position vector of the point of intersection of the line **r**=3**i**+2**j**+**k**+t(−**i**+**j**+**k**) and the plane **r**.(**i**+4**j**+3**k**)=2.

(b) Find the coordinates of the point of intersection of the line

$$\frac{x-3}{-1}=\frac{y-2}{1}=\frac{z-1}{1}$$

with the plane $x+4y+3z=2$.

Compare (a) with (b).

37 Find the cosine of the acute angle between the straight lines

$$\frac{x-1}{3}=\frac{y-3}{2}=\frac{z+2}{1} \text{ and } \frac{x+5}{2}=\frac{y-2}{-1}=\frac{z+4}{4}$$

38 Find the cosine of the acute angle between the planes

$$4x-3y+2z=1 \text{ and } 3x+2y-z=5$$

Differentiation 20

The gradient of a curve 221

Notation 222

Other derivatives 223

Composite functions 223

Products and quotients 224

Limit of $(\sin x)/x$ as $x \to 0$ 225

Derivative of $\sin x$ 225

Derivative of $\tan x$ 226

Derivative of $\sec x$ 226

Derivative of $\sin 2x$ 226

Derivative of logarithmic functions 227

Derivative of exponential functions 227

Derivative of a function given implicitly 228

Parametric relations 230

Notes

Learn these derivatives:

	Function F(x)	*Derivative* F′(x)
	x^n	nx^{n-1}
	$\sin(ax+b)$	$a\cos(ax+b)$
	$\cos(ax+b)$	$-a\sin(ax+b)$
	$\tan(ax+b)$	$a\sec^2(ax+b)$
	$\ln f(x)$	$\dfrac{f'(x)}{f(x)}$
	$e^{f(x)}$	$f'(x)e^{f(x)}$
Product	uv	$u\dfrac{dv}{dx}+v\dfrac{du}{dx}$
Quotient	$\dfrac{u}{v}$	$\dfrac{v\dfrac{du}{dx}-u\dfrac{dv}{dx}}{v^2}$
Function of a function If z is a function of x, f(z)		$\dfrac{df}{dz}\cdot\dfrac{dz}{dx}$

Parametric forms

If x and y are each functions of t,

$$\frac{dy}{dx}=\frac{dy}{dt}\bigg/\frac{dx}{dt}$$

$$\frac{d^2y}{dx^2}=\frac{d}{dt}\left(\frac{dy}{dx}\right)\bigg/\frac{dx}{dt}$$

NB. $\dfrac{dx}{dt}=1\bigg/\dfrac{dt}{dx}$ but $\dfrac{d^2x}{dt^2}$ is **not** equal to $1\bigg/\dfrac{d^2t}{dx^2}$ and $\dfrac{d^2y}{dx^2}$ is **not** equal to $1\bigg/\dfrac{d^2x}{dy^2}$.

The gradient of a curve

The gradient of a straight line is defined as

$$\frac{\text{increase in } y}{\text{increase in } x}$$

and is constant for any straight line (Figure 20.1). The gradient of a curve can be

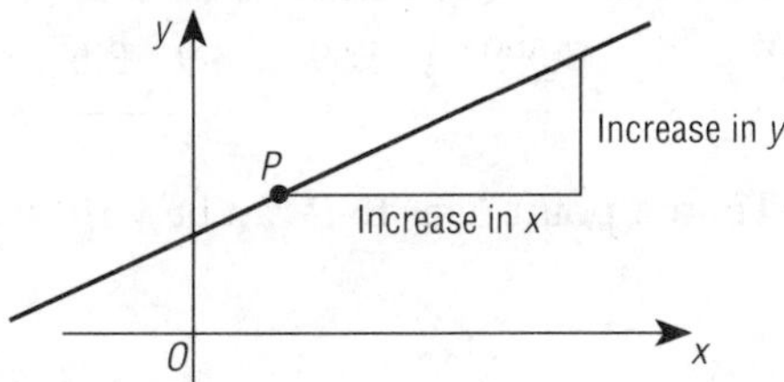

Figure 20.1

defined as the gradient of the tangent to that curve, and will vary along the curve (Figure 20.2), so that we have to define the gradient 'at a given point', which we define as the gradient of the tangent at that point.

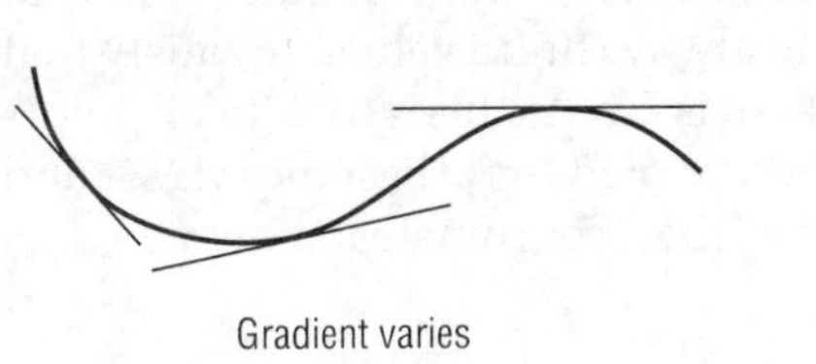

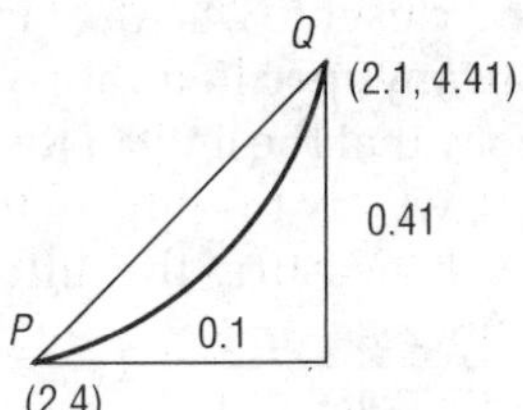

Figure 20.2

Look first at a very simple curve $y=x^2$. If P is the point whose x coordinate is 2, P has y coordinate 4, given by the equation of the curve, $y=x^2$. If Q is the point (2.1, 4.41), the gradient of PQ is

$$\frac{4.41-4}{2.1-2}$$

i.e. 4.1. Table 20.1 shows the gradient of PQ for different points Q. The nearer Q is to P, the closer the gradient is to 2. If Q is to the right of P, the gradient is greater than 2; if Q is to the left of P, the gradient is less than 2. While Q is distinct from P, the gradient will not be equal to 2, but it will be as close as we wish to 2. If we want the gradient to be between 4.01 and 4, the x coordinate of Q must be between 2 and 2.005; if we want the gradient to be between 3.99 and 4, the x coordinate of Q must be between 1.995 and 2. However close to 4 we want the gradient to be, we can always find a range of values of x that satisfies this.

Table 20.1

Coordinates of Q	x	3	2.5	2.1	2.01	2.001	2	1.999	1.99	1.9	1.5	1
	y	9	6.25	4.41	4.0401	4.004 001	4	3.996 001	3.9601	3.61	2.25	1
Increase in (for PQ)	y	5	2.25	0.41	0.0401	0.004 001	.	0.003 999	0.0399	0.39	1.75	3
	x	1	0.5	0.1	0.01	0.001	.	0.001	0.01	0.1	0.5	1
Gradient PQ		5	4.5	4.1	4.01	4.001		3.999	3.99	3.9	3.5	3

Take any point on the curve as (X, X^2). Then a point near to P can be written $(X+h, (X+h)^2)$. The gradient PQ will be

$$\frac{(X+h)^2-X^2}{(X+h)-X}$$

i.e. $$\frac{X^2+2Xh+h^2-X^2}{X+h-X}$$

i.e. $2X+h$

We can see that if h is positive, the gradient is greater than $2X$; if X is negative, the gradient is less than $2X$. As h becomes smaller and smaller, the gradient becomes closer and closer to $2X$. Most important, if we want the gradient of PQ to be closer to $2X$ than any specified value, we can always find a value h to satisfy that requirement. We say that the limit of the gradient is $2X$. As this is true for all points (x, x^2) on the curve, we say the limit of the gradient of PQ as Q becomes closer and closer to P is $2x$. As h measures the difference in the x coordinates, we say

$$\underset{h\to 0}{\text{Limit}} \quad \frac{\text{increase in } y}{\text{increase in } x} = 2x$$

We often use δx to denote a small change in x, δy to denote the corresponding small change in y, so

$$\underset{\delta x\to 0}{\text{Limit}} \; \frac{\delta y}{\delta x} = 2x, \text{ which we write } \frac{\mathrm{d}y}{\mathrm{d}x} = 2x$$

For the function x^2 (which we can write $y=x^2$) we have obtained another function $2x$, which we can call the gradient function, as it gives the gradient to the curve $y=x^2$ at any point, but which is often called the derived function or derivative. The process of finding a derived function is called differentiating.

Notation

For any function $y=\mathrm{f}(x)$, we write the derived function as $\frac{\mathrm{d}y}{\mathrm{d}x}$ or as $\mathrm{f}'(x)$. It often helps initially to think of the derived function as the gradient function, the function which gives us the gradient of the curve illustrating the original function.

Other derivatives

By considering similar small increases h in the value of x, we can show that the gradient function of x^3 is $3x^2$,

of x^4 is $4x^3$,

of x^5 is $5x^4$,

and, when n is a positive integer, of x^n is nx^{n-1}.

It can be shown that for all values of n, not just integer values,

$$\frac{d}{dx}(x^n) = nx^{n-1}$$

We can also show from first principles that a function written $f(x)+g(x)$ has derivative $f'(x)+g'(x)$, and that this is true however many functions are summed.

Example 1. If $f(x)=4x^3+5x^2+7x+8$, find $f'(x)$

It can easily be shown that the derivative of ax^n is anx^{n-1}, and of a constant is zero, as we would expect. Thus

$$f'(x)=12x^2+10x+7$$

Example 2. If $f(x)=x(3x^2+4x)$, find $f'(x)$

We first express $f(x)$ as the sum of terms like x^n, i.e.

$$f(x)=3x^3+4x^2$$

so $\quad f'(x)=9x^2+8x$

Example 3. If $f(x) = \dfrac{x+2x^2+x^4}{\sqrt{x}}$, find $f'(x)$

Writing $f(x)=x^{1/2}+2x^{3/2}+x^{7/2}$,
we see $f'(x)=\frac{1}{2}x^{-1/2}+3x^{1/2}+\frac{7}{2}x^{5/2}$

Exercise 20.1

Find the derived functions of each of the following:

1 (a) $3x+4x^2+5x^3$, (b) $3x^{1/2}+3x^{2/3}+8x^{3/4}$, (c) $x(x+2x^2+3x^3)$,

(d) $x^{1/2}(2+4x+8x^2)$, (e) $\dfrac{1+2x+3x^2}{x}$, (f) $\dfrac{2+4x+8x^2}{x^{1/2}}$,

(g) $x^2(x+4x^{1/2}+6x^{2/3})$, (h) $x^{1/4}(4x+16x^2)$, (i) $\dfrac{3x+4x^2+1}{x^3}$,

(j) $\dfrac{2+3x+4x^2}{x^{1/2}}$.

Composite functions

There are many functions that can most easily be differentiated by realising that they are composite functions, sometimes called functions of a function, e.g.

$$f(x)=\sqrt{(x^2+x+1)}$$

where we have first one function, here x^2+x+1, then a function of that function, here the square root, giving $\sqrt{(x^2+x+1)}$. Using the function notation of Chapter 1,

$$\text{if } g:x\to x^2+x+1 \text{ and } h:x\to x^{1/2},$$
$$hg=f:x\to(x^2+x+1)^{1/2}$$

Alternatively we can write

$$z=x^2+x+1,$$

so $\quad f(x)=z^{1/2}$,

and it can be shown that

$$f'(x)=\frac{d}{dx}(f(x))=\frac{df}{dz}\cdot\frac{dz}{dx}$$

so that here $\quad f'(x)=\tfrac{1}{2}(x^2+x+1)^{-1/2}(2x+1)$

since $\quad \dfrac{dz}{dx}=2x+1$,

so $\quad f'(x)=\dfrac{2x+1}{2(x^2+x+1)^{1/2}}$

Products and quotients

A function like $x^2(x+1)^{1/2}$ can be considered as the product of the two functions x^2 and $(x+1)^{1/2}$. Writing

$$y=x^2(x+1)^{1/2}$$

we have $\quad y=uv$, where $u=x^2$ and $v=(x+1)^{1/2}$.

As both u and v are functions of x, and a change δx in x produces corresponding changes δu in u and δv in v, and

$$y+\delta y=(u+\delta u)(v+\delta v)$$
$$=uv+u\delta v+v\delta u+\delta u\delta v$$

so that $\quad \delta y=u\delta v+v\delta u+\delta u\delta v$

and $\quad \dfrac{\delta y}{\delta x}=u\dfrac{\delta v}{\delta x}+v\dfrac{\delta u}{\delta x}+\dfrac{\delta u}{\delta x}\delta x$

Now as $\delta x\to 0$, $\quad \dfrac{\delta y}{\delta x}\to\dfrac{dy}{dx},\ \dfrac{\delta v}{\delta x}\to\dfrac{dv}{dx},\ \dfrac{\delta u}{\delta x}\to\dfrac{du}{dx}$

so that $\quad \dfrac{dy}{dx}=u\dfrac{dv}{dx}+v\dfrac{du}{dx}$

as $\quad \dfrac{\delta u}{\delta x}\cdot\delta x\to 0$

As a quotient, e.g. $\dfrac{(x+1)^{1/2}}{x^2}$, written $\dfrac{u}{v}$, can be considered as the product uv^{-1}, we have if $y=\dfrac{u}{v}$

$$\frac{dy}{dx}=u\frac{d}{dx}\left(\frac{1}{v}\right)+\frac{1}{v}\frac{du}{dx}$$

$$=u\left(-\frac{1}{v^2}\frac{dv}{dx}\right)+\frac{1}{v}\frac{du}{dx}$$

$$= \frac{v\dfrac{du}{dx} - u\dfrac{dv}{dx}}{v^2}$$

Limit of (sin *x*)/*x* as *x*→0

To find the derivatives of the trigonometric functions, we need to know the limit of (sin x)/x as x tends to zero. Using Figure 20.3,

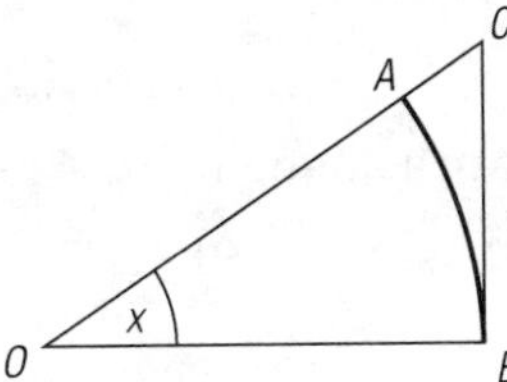

Figure 20.3

when x is measured in radians,

area triangle $OAB <$ area sector $OAB <$ area triangle OBC

i.e. $\frac{1}{2}r^2 \sin x < \frac{1}{2}r^2 x < \frac{1}{2}r^2 \tan x$

$\sin x < x < \tan x$

Dividing by $\sin x$, which is positive when x is acute

$$1 < \frac{x}{\sin x} < \sec x$$

But as $x \to 0$, $\sec x \to 1$, so $\dfrac{x}{\sin x} \to 1$ and $\dfrac{\sin x}{x} \to 1$ when $x \to 0$.

Derivative of sin *x*

Using the same idea as when finding the derivative of x^2, any point on the curve $y = \sin x$ near $P(X, \sin X)$ can be written $(X+h, \sin(X+h))$, and the gradient PQ is

$$\frac{\sin(X+h) - \sin X}{X+h-X}$$

But $\sin(X+h) - \sin X = 2\cos\frac{1}{2}(2X+h)\sin\frac{1}{2}h$

so
$$\frac{\sin(X+h) - \sin X}{h} = \frac{2\cos\frac{1}{2}(2X+h)\sin\frac{1}{2}h}{h}$$

$$= \frac{\cos\frac{1}{2}(2X+h)\sin\frac{1}{2}h}{\frac{1}{2}h}$$

$$= \cos\tfrac{1}{2}(2X+h)\frac{\sin\frac{1}{2}h}{\frac{1}{2}h}$$

We have just shown that $(\sin x)/x \to 1$ as $x \to 0$, so that

$$\frac{\sin \frac{1}{2}h}{\frac{1}{2}h} \to 1 \text{ as } h \to 0$$

and $(2X+h) \to 2X$ as $h \to 0$, so

$$\frac{\mathrm{d}}{\mathrm{d}x}(\sin x) = \cos x$$

Similarly, we can show that $\frac{\mathrm{d}}{\mathrm{d}x}(\cos x) = -\sin x$.

Derivative of tan *x*

Since $\tan x = \frac{\sin x}{\cos x}$, using the rule for finding the derivative of a quotient,

$$\begin{aligned}\frac{\mathrm{d}}{\mathrm{d}x}(\tan x) &= \frac{\cos x \cos x - \sin x(-\sin x)}{(\cos x)^2} \\ &= \frac{\cos^2 x + \sin^2 x}{\cos^2 x} \\ &= \sec^2 x\end{aligned}$$

Derivative of sec *x*

Since $\sec x = \frac{1}{\cos x} = (\cos x)^{-1}$, using the rule for composite functions,

$$\begin{aligned}\frac{\mathrm{d}}{\mathrm{d}x}(\sec x) &= -1(\cos x)^{-2}(-\sin x) \\ &= \frac{\sin x}{\cos^2 x} \\ &= \sec x \tan x\end{aligned}$$

Similarly $\quad \frac{\mathrm{d}}{\mathrm{d}x}(\cot x) = -\mathrm{cosec}^2\, x$

and $\quad \frac{\mathrm{d}}{\mathrm{d}x}(\mathrm{cosec}\, x) = -\mathrm{cosec}\, x \cot x$

Derivative of sin 2*x*

Using the rule for composite functions,

$$\frac{\mathrm{d}}{\mathrm{d}x}(\sin 2x) = 2\cos 2x$$

and in general

$$\frac{\mathrm{d}}{\mathrm{d}x}(\sin ax) = a \cos ax$$

NB. Since limit $(\sin x)/x \to 1$ is only true when x is measured in radians, we always use radian measure in problems where calculus may be appropriate, i.e.

in virtually all problems at this level, except those involving mensuration of the earth. If for any reason we have to work in degrees,

$$\underset{x\to 0}{\text{Limit}} \left(\frac{\sin (x^\circ)}{x}\right) = \frac{\pi}{180}$$

and $$\frac{\mathrm{d}}{\mathrm{d}x}(\sin x^\circ) = \frac{\pi \cos (x^\circ)}{180}, \text{ etc.}$$

The limit $\pi/180$ can be verified by using a calculator to find 180 sin $(x^\circ)/x$ for smaller and smaller x, when better and better approximations for π are easily recognised.

Examples. (a) When $f(x)=\tan 2x$, $f'(x)=2\sec^2 x$
(b) When $f(x)=\sec \frac{1}{2}x$, $f'(x)=\frac{1}{2}\sec x \tan x$
(c) When $f(x)=\sin(3x+\pi/4)$, $f'(x)=3\cos(3x+\pi/4)$
(d) When $f(x)=\cos (x^2)$, $f'(x)=-2x \sin (x^2)$
(e) When $f(x)=x \sin x$, $f'(x)=x \cos x+\sin x$

Exercise 20.2
1 Find $f'(x)$ when $f(x) =$
(a) $\cos 3x$, (b) $\tan \frac{1}{2}x$, (c) $\sin (2x+\pi/2)$, (d) $\sin(x^2)$, (e) $\cos (x-\pi/6)$.
2 Find $\mathrm{d}y/\mathrm{d}x$ when $y =$
(a) $x \sin x$, (b) $2x \cos \frac{1}{2}x$, (c) $x^2 \tan x$, (d) $\sin 2x \cos x$, (e) $\dfrac{\cos 2x}{\sin x}$.

Derivative of logarithmic functions

It can be shown that

$$\frac{\mathrm{d}}{\mathrm{d}x}(\ln x) \equiv \frac{\mathrm{d}}{\mathrm{d}x}(\log_e x) = \frac{1}{x}$$

Using the rule for composite functions, we deduce

$$\frac{\mathrm{d}}{\mathrm{d}x}(\ln (ax+b)) = \frac{a}{ax+b}$$

Derivative of exponential functions

Since $y=\mathrm{e}^x \Rightarrow \ln y = x$

Differentiating, $$\frac{1}{y}\frac{\mathrm{d}y}{\mathrm{d}x} = 1$$

i.e. $$\frac{\mathrm{d}y}{\mathrm{d}x} = y = \mathrm{e}^x$$

i.e. $$\frac{\mathrm{d}}{\mathrm{d}x}(\mathrm{e}^x) = \mathrm{e}^x$$

Again, using the rule for composite functions, $\frac{\mathrm{d}}{\mathrm{d}x}(\mathrm{e}^{ax}) = a\mathrm{e}^{ax}$

and in general, $\mathrm{e}^{f(x)} = f'(x)\,\mathrm{e}^{f(x)}$

Examples. (a) When $\mathrm{f}(x)=\mathrm{e}^{2x}$, $\mathrm{f}'(x)=2\mathrm{e}^{2x}$

(b) When $\mathrm{f}(x)=\ln(2x+3)$, $\mathrm{f}'(x)=\dfrac{2}{2x+3}$

(c) When $\mathrm{f}(x)=\ln\sin x$, $\mathrm{f}'(x)=\dfrac{\cos x}{\sin x}=\cot x$

(d) When $\mathrm{f}(x)=\mathrm{e}^{\sin x}$, $\mathrm{f}'(x)=\cos x\,\mathrm{e}^{\sin x}$

(e) When $\mathrm{f}(x)=\cos x\,\mathrm{e}^{\sin x}$

$$\mathrm{f}'(x)=\cos x(\cos x\,\mathrm{e}^{\sin x})-\sin x\,\mathrm{e}^{\sin x}$$
$$=(\cos^2 x-\sin x)\,\mathrm{e}^{\sin x}$$

Exercise 20.3

1 Differentiate with respect to x

(a) $\ln 3x$, (b) $\ln(3x+1)$, (c) $\ln\cos x$, (d) $\ln\sin(x+\frac{\pi}{3})$, (e) $\ln(x^2+1)$,

(f) e^{3x}, (g) e^{3x+1}, (h) $\mathrm{e}^{\cos x}$, (i) e^{x^2}, (j) e^{2x}

2 Find $\mathrm{f}'(x)$ when $\mathrm{f}(x) =$

(a) $x\ln x$, (b) $x\ln(2x+1)$, (c) $(1+x)\ln(1+x)$, (d) $x\mathrm{e}^x$, (e) $x^2\mathrm{e}^x$,
(f) $2x\mathrm{e}^{2x}$, (g) $\mathrm{e}^x\ln x$, (h) $x\ln\sin x$, (i) $\sin x\mathrm{e}^{\cos x}$, (j) $x\mathrm{e}^{\cos x}$.

Derivative of a function given implicitly

Given the relation $y^2x^3=1$, for any positive value of x we can see that y has one of two values; the relation $y\sin x=1$ is such that any one given value of x determines a corresponding value of y and relates y *implicitly* to x. These equations could have been rewritten $y=\pm x^{-3/2}$ and $y=1/\sin x$, respectively, in each of which y is given *explicitly* in terms of x. Many implicit relations, however, are such that they cannot easily be rewritten to give x explicitly.

For example, if $y^2x+y\sin x=1$, a certain given value of x will give corresponding values of y, yet it is awkward to try to 'make y the subject of the equation', i.e. to write the equation so that y is defined explicitly.

To differentiate an implicit function (or relation), remember that, since y is a function of x, $\frac{\mathrm{d}}{\mathrm{d}x}(y^2)=2y\frac{\mathrm{d}y}{\mathrm{d}x}$, and in general

$$\frac{\mathrm{d}}{\mathrm{d}x}\mathrm{f}(y)=\frac{\mathrm{df}}{\mathrm{d}y}\cdot\frac{\mathrm{d}y}{\mathrm{d}x}$$

e.g. $$\frac{\mathrm{d}}{\mathrm{d}x}(\cos y)=-\sin y\frac{\mathrm{d}y}{\mathrm{d}x}$$

and $$\frac{\mathrm{d}}{\mathrm{d}x}(\mathrm{e}^y)=\mathrm{e}^y\frac{\mathrm{d}y}{\mathrm{d}x}$$

Example 1. If $x^2y+y^3=2$, find $\frac{dy}{dx}$ when $x=1, y=1$.

Differentiating, $2xy+x^2\frac{dy}{dx}+3y^2\frac{dy}{dx}=0$,

i.e. $$\frac{dy}{dx}(x^2+3y^2)=-2xy,$$

$$\frac{dy}{dx}=\frac{-2xy}{(x^2+3y^2)}$$

When $x=1, y=1$ $$\frac{dy}{dx}=\frac{-2}{4}=-\tfrac{1}{2}$$

There are several useful cases where we can change an explicit relation into an implicit relation in order to find the derivative of a function we do not already know. For example, if $y=\arcsin(x/a)$, and we do not know the derivative of $\arcsin(x/a)$,

$$y=\arcsin(x/a)\Rightarrow \sin y=x/a$$

so $$\cos y\frac{dy}{dx}=\frac{1}{a}$$

$$\frac{dy}{dx}=\frac{1/a}{\cos y}$$

But since $\sin y=x/a$, $$\cos^2 y=1-\sin^2 y$$

$$=1-\left(\frac{x}{a}\right)^2$$

and $$\cos y=\pm\sqrt{\left(1-\left(\frac{x}{a}\right)^2\right)}$$

So $$\frac{dy}{dx}=\pm\frac{1/a}{\sqrt{\left(1-\left(\frac{x}{a}\right)^2\right)}}$$

$$=\pm\frac{1}{\sqrt{(a^2-x^2)}}$$

Although strictly we have to consider both signs + or −, the graph (Figure 20.4) shows that for principal values of y the gradient is positive.

We therefore usually use only that sign, and write

$$\frac{d}{dx}(\arcsin x)=\frac{1}{\sqrt{(a^2-x^2)}}$$

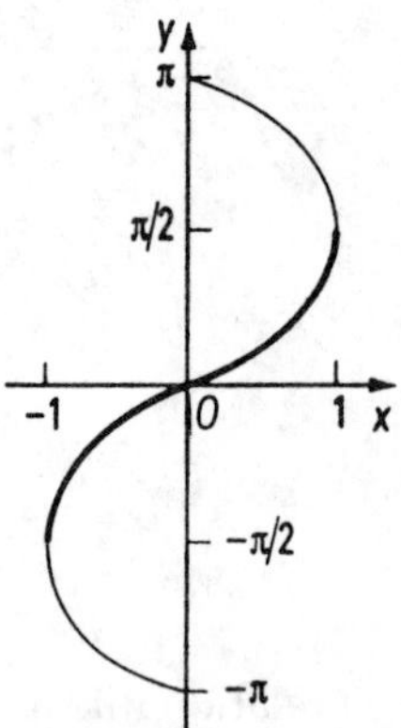

Figure 20.4

Example 2. Find the derivative with respect to x of a^x.

Writing $y=a^x$, we have $\log_a y=x$. If we do not know the derivative of $\log_a y$, we write

$$\log_a y=\frac{\log_e y}{\log_e a}$$

i.e. $$\log_a y=\frac{\ln y}{\ln a}$$

i.e. $$\ln y=x\ln a$$

$$\frac{1}{y}\frac{dy}{dx}=\ln a$$

$$\frac{dy}{dx}=y\ln a$$

$$=a^x\ln a$$

So the derivative of a^x is $a^x \ln a$. Checking by putting a=e, the derivative of $e^x=e^x \ln e=e^x$, as expected.

Parametric relations

We have seen (page 131) that a curve can be defined in terms of a single variable, say t, so that any one value of t determines one particular point on the curve. More generally, a relation between two variables x and y can be defined by describing each of x and y in terms of a third variable, a **parameter**, t, e.g. if $x=t^2$, $y=\sin t$, any one value of t determines both x and y. *When differentiating a relation given in terms of a parameter, do not attempt to eliminate that parameter.*

Example. If $x=t^2$, $y=t^3+t$, find dy/dx and d^2y/dx^2.

Since x and y are both functions of t,

$$\frac{dy}{dt}=\frac{dy}{dx}\cdot\frac{dx}{dt}$$

$$\therefore \qquad \frac{dy}{dx}=\frac{\dfrac{dy}{dt}}{\dfrac{dx}{dt}}$$

Since $y=t^3+t$, $dy/dt=3t^2+1$;
since $x=t^2$, $\quad dx/dt=2t$.

So $\quad \dfrac{dy}{dx}=\dfrac{3t^2+1}{2t}$

To find $\dfrac{d^2y}{dx^2}$, we remember that $\dfrac{d}{dt}\left(\dfrac{dy}{dx}\right)=\dfrac{d}{dx}\left(\dfrac{dy}{dx}\right)\cdot\dfrac{dx}{dt}$,

so $\quad \dfrac{d^2y}{dx^2}=\dfrac{d}{dt}\left(\dfrac{dy}{dx}\right)\Big/\dfrac{dx}{dt}$

Now $\quad \dfrac{d}{dt}\left(\dfrac{dy}{dx}\right)=\dfrac{d}{dt}\left(\dfrac{3t^2+1}{2t}\right)$

$$=\frac{d}{dt}\left(\frac{3}{2}t+\frac{1}{2t}\right)$$

$$=\frac{3}{2}-\frac{1}{2t^2}$$

so $\quad \dfrac{d^2y}{dx^2}=\left(\dfrac{3}{2}-\dfrac{1}{2t^2}\right)\Big/2t$, using $\dfrac{dx}{dt}=2t$

$$=\frac{3}{4t}-\frac{1}{4t^3}$$

NB. It is true that $\dfrac{dy}{dx}=\dfrac{dy/dt}{dx/dt}$ and $\dfrac{dx}{dt}=\dfrac{1}{dt/dx}$ but remember that $\dfrac{d^2y}{dt^2}$ is **not** equal to $\dfrac{d^2y}{dt^2}\Big/\dfrac{d^2x}{dt^2}$.

Exercise 20.4

1 Find dy/dx when

(a) $y=\text{inv}\cos x$, (b) $xy+y^2=1$, (c) $xy+e^y=1$.

2 Find dy/dx when

(a) $x=2t, y=2t^3$, (b) $x=\sin t, y=\cos t$, (c) $x=\sin^2 t, y=\cos^2 t$.

Miscellaneous exercise 20.5

1 Find dy/dx, if $y=$

(a) $\sqrt{(1+x^2)}$, (b) $\dfrac{1}{(1+2x)}$, (c) $\sin 4x$, (d) $\ln(4x)$, (e) e^{3x+2}.

2 Differentiate with respect to x,

(a) $\dfrac{1}{(3x+2)}$, (b) $\sin^2 x$, (c) $\ln(\cos x)$, (d) $e^{\sin x}$, (e) $(1+\sin x)^{1/2}$.

3 (a) If $f(x)=\ln(x^2+2x+3)$, find $f'(0)$.

(b) If $f(x)=\dfrac{1}{1+\sin x}$, find $f'(\pi/6)$.

(c) If $f(x)=e^{\tan x}$, find $f'(0)$.

Differentiate with respect to x:

4 $x \sin 3x$.

5 $x^2 \cos 2x$.

6 $x^3 \tan x$.

7 xe^{2x}.

8 x^2e^{2x+1}.

9 $x \ln x$.

10 $x^2(x+1)^{1/2}$.

11 $\dfrac{\sin x}{x}$.

12 $\dfrac{\cos x}{x^2}$.

13 $\dfrac{\sin x}{e^x}$.

14 $\dfrac{\ln x}{x^2}$.

15 $\dfrac{\cos 2x}{\sin x}$.

16 Find dy/dx in each of the following:

(a) $y+x\sin y=1$, (b) $xy+y^3=\sin x$, (c) $ye^x+y^2=x^2$.

17 If $xy^2+yx^2=2$, find dy/dx at the point $(1,1)$.

18 If $y=\text{arc}\cos(\sqrt{x})$, show that $dy/dx=-1/\sin 2y$.

19 If $y=x^x$, show that $dy/dx=y(1+\ln x)$.

20 Find dy/dx if

(a) $x=t^2, y=t^3$, (b) $x=\sin 2t, y=\cos t$, (c) $x=\sin^2 t, y=\cos^2 t$.

21 If $x=2t/(1-t^2)$ and $y=(1+t^2)/(1-t^2)$, find d^2y/dx^2 in terms of t.

22 Find dy/dx if $y=\ln(1+\cos 2x)$.

23 Differentiate with respect to x,
(a) $\ln(x^2)$, (b) $(\ln x)^2$.

24 If $f(x)=(1-x^2)^{1/2}\arcsin x$, find $f'(x)$ in its simplest form.

25 A curve is given parametrically by $x=t+\sin t$, $y=1+\cos t$. Find dy/dx, and the equation of the tangent at the point where $t=\pi/2$.

26 Differentiate with respect to x,
(a) $\dfrac{x^2-1}{x^2+1}$, (b) $\dfrac{x^2-2}{x+1}$.

27 Find the derivative with respect of x of $\ln\left(\dfrac{x}{1+x^2}\right)$.

28 If $ye^x=(1+x)^2$, find dy/dx in terms of x.

29 If $y=\ln\sin x$, prove that $\dfrac{d^2y}{dx^2}+\left(\dfrac{dy}{dx}\right)^2+1=0$.

30 If $\dfrac{1}{x}+\dfrac{1}{y}-\dfrac{1}{a}=0$, show that $\dfrac{dy}{dx}=-\dfrac{y^2}{x^2}$.

31 If $y=\tan^2 x$, show that $\dfrac{d^2y}{dx^2}=6y^2+8y+2$.

Applications of differential calculus 21

Maxima and minima 238

Use of second derivative 240

Summary 240

Maximum and minimum values 241

Rates of change 241

Small increments 242

Notes

Maxima and minima

At a **maximum** of f(x), f′(x)=0 and is decreasing;
at a **minimum of** f(x), f′(x)=0 and is increasing;
at a **point of inflexion**, f″(x)=0 and changes sign; f′(x) may or may not equal zero.

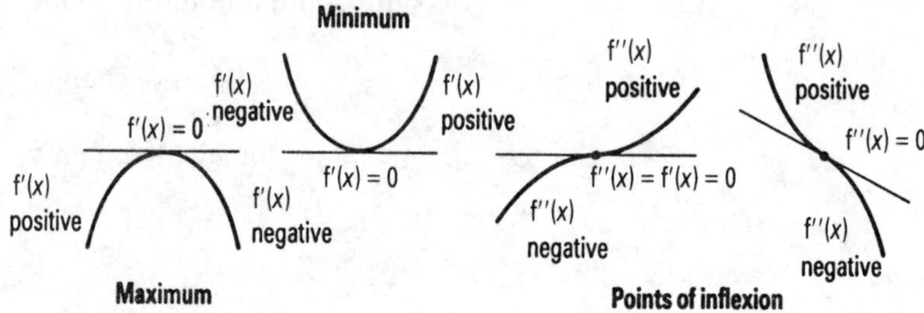

Figure 21.1

Maxima and minima are sometimes called **turning points**.

All points for which f′(x)=0 are called **stationary points**, and the corresponding values of f(x) are called **stationary values**. Thus maxima and minima are stationary points, and so are some points of inflexion.

If f(x) has a stationary value at $x=a$,

$$f'(x)=(x-a)F(x);$$

if $(x-a)$ is not a factor of F(x), $x=a$ will be a maximum if F(a) is negative, a minimum if F(a) is positive.

Rates of change

If y is a function of x, and x is a function of t,

$$\frac{dy}{dt}=\frac{dy}{dx}\cdot\frac{dx}{dt}$$

Small increments

If y is a function of x, then a small increment δx in x produces a corresponding small increment δy in y, where

$$\delta y \approx \frac{dy}{dx}\,\delta x$$

Maxima and minima

A function y of x is said to have a maximum when $x=x_1$ if the value of y when $x=x_1$ is greater than the value of y at points immediately on either side of it, i.e. $f(x_1)>f(x)$ for all values of x 'near to' x_1. Similarly, the function is said to have a minimum at $x=x_2$ if

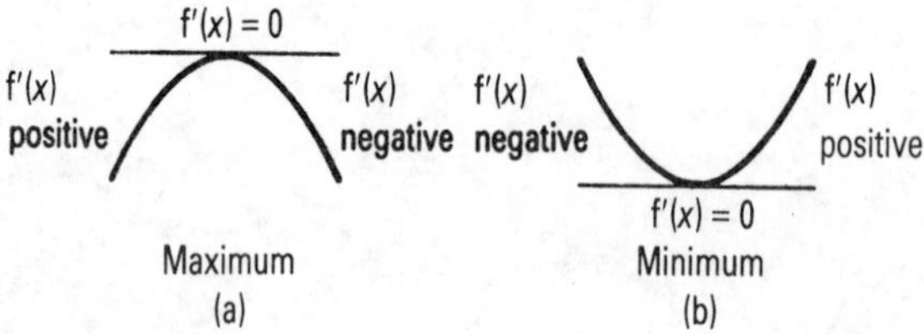

Figure 21.2

$f(x_2)<f(x)$ for all values of x 'near to' x_2. Note that the maxima and minima are not necessarily the greatest and least values in a range (Figure 21.3).

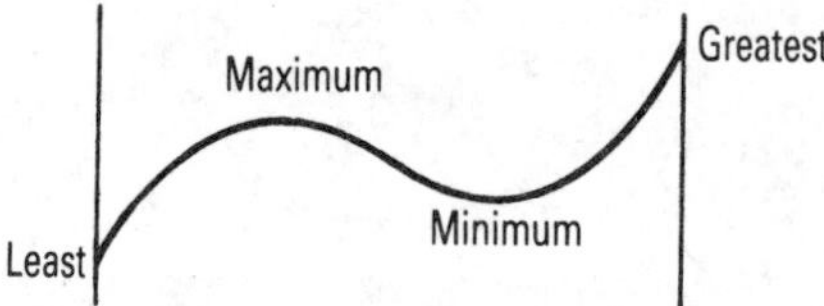

Figure 21.3

From Figure 21.2(a), we see that at $x=x_1$, $f'(x_1)=0$, and that the sign of the gradient changes from positive to negative at a maximum, whereas at a minimum the sign changes from negative to positive; this gives us a good way of distinguishing between maxima and minima. A point at which the gradient is zero, but the sign of the gradient does not change, is called a **point of inflexion**.

Example. Find the values of x which give stationary values of the function $f(x)=x^3(x+1)^2$, distinguishing between maxima, minima and points of inflexion.

All points for which $f'(x)=0$ are called **stationary points**, and the corresponding values of $f(x)$ are called **stationary values**. These include maxima, minima and points of inflexion.

Since $\quad f(x)=x^3(x+1)^2$

$$\begin{aligned} f'(x) &= 3x^2(x+1)^2+x^3[2(x+1)] \\ &= x^2(x+1)\,[3(x+1)+2x] \\ &= x^2(x+1)(5x+3) \end{aligned}$$

so that $f'(x)=0$ when $x=0$, -1 or -0.6.

To investigate the nature of the stationary point when $x=-1$, write $f'(x)=(x+1)x^2(5x+3)$.

Then when x is slightly less than -1, say -1.1, $f'(x)$ is the product of three terms, one negative, one positive, and one negative, and so $f'(x)$ must be positive,

i.e., since $\quad f'(x)=(x+1)x^2(5x+3)$
for x slightly less than -1 $\quad f'(x)=$(negative)(positive)(negative)

When x is slightly more than -1, e.g. $x=-0.9$,

$$f'(x)=\text{(positive)(positive)(negative)}$$

since $x+1$ is now positive, so that $f'(x)$ is negative. Thus around $x=-1$, $f'(x)$ is positive, then zero, and then negative, so that $x=-1$ is a maximum.
To investigate $x=-0.6$, when x is slightly less than -0.6, say -0.7,

since $\quad f'(x)=(x+1)x^2(5x+3)$
$\quad f'(x)=$(positive)(positive)(negative)

and when x is slightly more than -0.6, say -0.5,

$$f'(x)=\text{(positive)(positive)(positive)}$$

so that around $x=-0.6$, $f'(x)$ is negative, then zero, and then positive. Thus $x=-0.6$ is a maximum.
To investigate $x=0$, near $x=0$ both $x+1$ and $5x+3$ are positive. x^2 does not change sign, being a square, so that $f'(x)$ does not change sign, and $f'(x)$ is positive, then zero, and then positive. Thus $x=0$ is a point of inflexion.
The nature of these stationary points is shown in Figure 21.4.

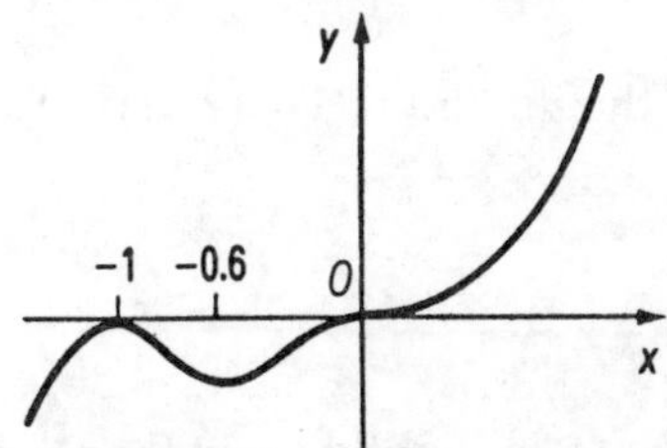

Figure 21.4

The method can be abbreviated thus:
If $f'(x)$ has a stationary value at $x=a$,

$$f'(x)=(x-a)F(x)$$

If $(x-a)$ is not a factor of $F(x)$, $F(x)$ does not change sign as x increases through $x=a$, so that if $F(a)$ is positive, $f'(x)$ is

negative zero positive

and $x=a$ is a minimum; if $F(a)$ is negative, the sign of $f'(x)$ is

positive zero negative

and $x=a$ is a maximum. If, however, $(x-a)$ is a factor of $F(x)$, this abbreviation needs modifying.

Look at the previous Example. Considering the stationary value $x=-1$,

$$f'(x)=(x+1)x^2(5x+3)$$

Here, $F(x)=x^2(5x+3)$, and $F(-1)=-2$, negative, so $x=-1$ is a maximum. Considering the stationary value $x=-0.6$,

$$f'(x)=(5x+3)x^2(x+1)$$

Now $F(x)=x^2(x+1)$ and $F(-0.6)$ is positive, so $x=-0.6$ is a minimum. When we consider $x=0$,

$$f'(x)=x^2(x+1)(5x+3)$$

If we take $F(x)=(x+1)(5x+3)$, $F(0)=3$, positive. Since x^2 is positive on either side of $x=0$, $f'(x)$ is always positive near $x=0$, and we have a point of inflexion.

NB. Write $f'(x)=(x-a)F(x)$, **not** $f'(x)=(a-x)F(x)$.

Use of second derivative

At a maximum, we have seen that $f'(x)$ is positive, then zero, and then negative, and so seems to be decreasing with its own second derivative, $f''(x)$, being negative. Similarly, it seems that at a minimum $f''(x)$ is positive. Indeed, both conclusions will often be true, but the next example shows that there are exceptions.

Example. Find the nature of the stationary point of the function $f(x)=(x-1)^4$.

Since $f(x)=(x-1)^4$

$$f'(x)=4(x-1)^3$$

so $f'(x)=0 \Rightarrow 4(x-1)^3=0$, i.e. $x=1$.

When x is slightly less than 1, $f'(x)$ is negative; when x is slightly more than 1, $f'(x)$ is positive, so that $f'(x)$ is negative, then zero, then positive, and $x=1$ is seen to be a minimum.

Notice that in this case $f''(x)=12(x-1)^2$, so $f''(1)=0$, and we cannot identify this minimum by using the test of the second derivative.

Summary

These findings can be summarized:

at a **maximum**, $f'(x)=0$ and $f''(x)$ is not positive;
at a **minimum**, $f'(x)=0$ and $f''(x)$ is not negative;

at a **point of inflexion**, $f''(x)=0$; *note that* $f'(x)$ *may or may not be zero.*

if $f'(x_1)=0$ and $f''(x_1)<0$, $x=x_1$ is a maximum;
if $f'(x_2)=0$ and $f''(x_2)>0$, $x=x_2$ is a minimum;
if $f''(x_3)=0$ and $f''(x_3)$ changes sign as x increases through the value $x=x_3$, then $x=x_3$ is a point of inflexion (Figure 21.5).

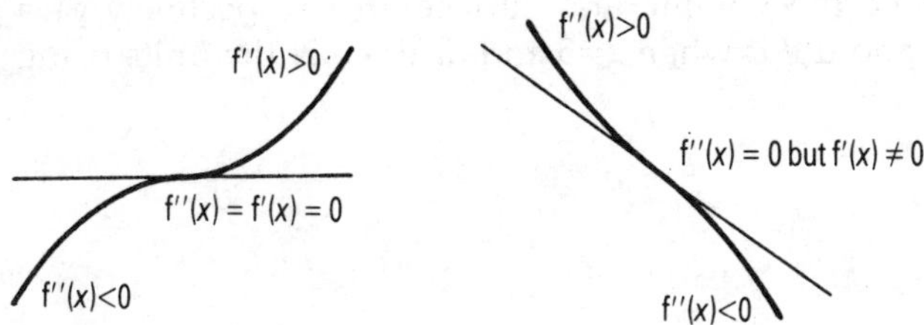

Figure 21.5

Maximum and minimum values

The function $f(x)$ has a maximum when $x=x_1$ if $f(x_1)>f(x)$ when x is 'near to' x_1; the value of $f(x_1)$ is called the **maximum value**. Similarly, if $x=x_2$ is a minimum, then $f(x_2)$ is the **minimum** value. Distinguish carefully whether an examination question requires the values of x that give maxima or minima, i.e. x_1 or x_2, or whether it requires the maximum or minimum values, i.e. $f(x_1)$ or $f(x_2)$.

Example. Find the maximum and minimum of $y=x(x-2)^2$.

We can differentiate $x(x-2)^2$ as a product, which will save expanding and then later factorisation of a quadratic.

Since $\quad y=x(x-2)^2$

$$\frac{dy}{dx}=(x-2)^2+2x(x-2)$$
$$=(x-2)(3x-2)$$

so $dy/dx=0$ when $x=\frac{2}{3}$ and when $x=2$.
Near $x=\frac{2}{3}$, dy/dx is positive, zero, then negative, so $x=\frac{2}{3}$ is a maximum.
Near $x=2$, dy/dx is positive, zero, then negative, so $x=2$ is a minimum.

When $x=\frac{2}{3}$, $y=\frac{2}{3}(-\frac{4}{3})^2=\frac{32}{27}$; when $x=2$, $y=0$,

so the maximum value is $\frac{32}{27}$, when $x=\frac{2}{3}$; the minimum value is 0, when $x=2$.

Rates of change

The radius r of a sphere determines the volume V of the sphere, for V is a function of r. If r varies with time t, then, since $\quad V=\frac{4}{3}\pi r^3$

$$\frac{dV}{dt}=4\pi r^2\frac{dr}{dt}$$

Knowing r and dr/dt, we can find dV/dt.

Example. If V and S denote the volume and surface area respectively of a sphere radius r, find dV/dt and dS/dt when $r=5$ and $dr/dt=0.2$, the units being cm and seconds.

Since $\quad V=\frac{4}{3}\pi r^3$

$$\begin{aligned}\frac{dV}{dt}&=4\pi r^2\frac{dr}{dt}\\&=4\pi(5)^2(0.2)\\&\simeq 62.8\end{aligned}$$

The rate of change of volume is about $62.8\,\text{cm}^3\,\text{s}^{-1}$.

Since $\quad S=4\pi r^2$

$$\begin{aligned}\frac{dS}{dt}&=8\pi r\frac{dr}{dt}\\&\simeq 25.1\end{aligned}$$

The rate of change of surface area is about $25.1\,\text{cm}^2\,\text{s}^{-1}$.

Small increments

Figure 21.6 illustrates that if δy is a small change in y produced by a small change δx in x, then

$$\delta y\simeq\frac{dy}{dx}\delta x$$

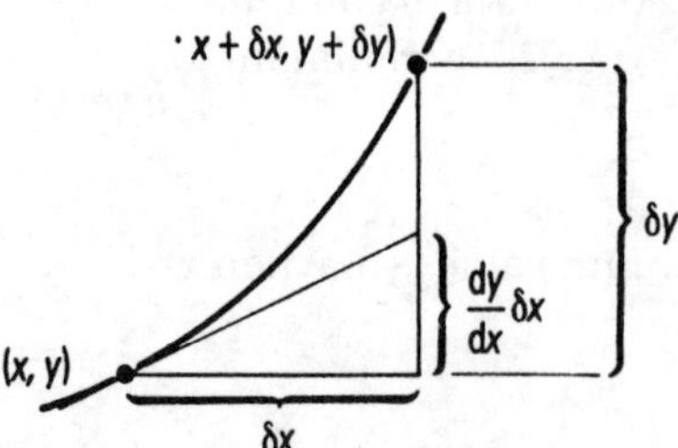

Figure 21.6

The application of this result is very similar to that of rates of change.

Example 1. Find the change in volume of a sphere, radius r, when the radius increases from 5 cm to 5.1 cm.

Since $V=\frac{4}{3}\pi r^3$

$\delta V \simeq 4\pi r^2 \delta r$

so the change in V is approximately $4\pi(5)^2(0.1)$, about 31.4 cm^3.

Example 2. The time T of oscillation of a pendulum length l is $2\pi\sqrt{(l/g)}$. Find the percentage change in T if l increases from 0.5 m to 0.52 m, g remaining constant.

The formula can be written $T=cl^{1/2}$

so $\delta T \simeq c\frac{1}{2}l^{-1/2}\delta l$

and
$$\frac{\delta T}{T}\times 100=\frac{c\frac{1}{2}l^{-1/2}}{cl^{1/2}}\,\delta l\times 100$$
$$=\frac{\delta l}{2l}\times 100$$
$$=\frac{0.02}{2\times 0.5}\times 100$$
$$=2$$

So there is approximately a 2% change in T for this change in l.

Miscellaneous exercise 21.1

1 Find the nature of the turning points of
(a) $y=x^3$, (b) $y=(x-1)^2(x+1)^2$, (c) $y=x^3(3x+1)$, (d) $y=x\sqrt{(1+x)}$.

2 Find the maxima and minima of the following functions, and the maximum and minimum values of the functions at those points:
(a) $y=(x-1)^4+3$,
(b) $y=x^2(x-1)$,
(c) $y=\sin^2 x \cos x$ for $0<x<\pi/2$,
(d) $y=xe^{-\frac{1}{2}x^2}$.

3 If x and y are both functions of t, find $\frac{dy}{dt}$ if
(a) $y=x^4$, $x=5$ and $dx/dt=0.2$,
(b) $y=\sin^2 x$, $x=\pi/4$ and $dx/dt=5$,
(c) $y=\ln \sin x$, $x=\pi/6$ and $dx/dt=4$.

4 Find the change in the surface area of a sphere when the radius increases from 10 cm to 10.1 cm.

5 Find the percentage change in the volume of a sphere when the radius increases from 8 cm to 8.1 cm. Compare this approximation with the exact percentage change, by calculating the volume of spheres radius 8 cm and 8.1 cm.

6 The surface area of a solid cylinder in which the height is twice the base-radius r is $6\pi r^2$. Find the percentage change in the surface area when the radius increases from 5 cm to 5.1 cm.

7 Find the nature of the turning points of the curve $y=\frac{x}{1+x^2}$.

8 Find the nature of the turning points of the curve $y=(1+x)^2e^{-2x}$.

9 Find the maximum value of $f(t)=2e^{-t}-3e^{-2t}$. If t is restricted so that $0\leqslant t\leqslant 1$, find the greatest value of $f(t)$.

10 Given that x and y vary so that $3x+4y=5$, write x^2+y^2 in terms of x only, and hence show that the minimum value of x^2+y^2 is 1. Interpret this result geometrically.

11 The area of a triangle is to be calculated from measurements using the formula $\Delta=\frac{1}{2}bc\sin A$. Find the percentage error in calculating the area if
(a) b and A are measured accurately, but there is an error of 1% in measuring c,
(b) b and c are measured accurately, but A is measured as 1.1 rad instead of 1 rad.

12 Points A and B lie on a circle centre O, radius a. If angle AOB is $2x$, the radius of the inscribed circle of triangle AOB is $a\tan x(1-\sin x)$. Show that this radius has a maximum value when $\sin x=\frac{1}{2}(\sqrt{5}-1)$.

13 A wire of length $2a$ is bent to form the sides of an isosceles triangle. Denoting the lengths of the sides by x, x and $2a-2x$, show that the area of the triangle is $(a-x)\sqrt{(2ax-a^2)}$ and that this area is a maximum when the triangle is equilateral.

14 Find the coordinates of the turning points of the function $f(x)=\frac{\cos x}{2-\sin x}$ in the interval $0<x<2\pi$, distinguishing between maxima and minima.

15 If $y=x^2+\frac{8}{1-x}$, show that the only turning point occurs at $x=-1$, and that there is only one point of inflexion.

16 A particle moves along the x-axis so that its displacement x metres from the origin O at time t seconds is given by $x=\sin 2t-t$. Find the greatest distance of the particle from the origin if $0<t<\pi$.

Integration 22

Integration 248

Notation 248

Trigonometric integrals 249

Logarithmic integrals 249

Partial fractions 250

Inverse trigonometric integrals 250

Integrals requiring substitution 251

Integration by parts 252

Areas of regions 254

Summary 257

Volume of solid of revolution 259

Summary 260

Mean value 261

Notes

The following integrals must be **learnt**:

$f(x)$	$\int f(x)dx$
$x^n, n \neq -1$	$\frac{x^{n+1}}{n+1}+C$
$\sin(ax+b)$	$-\frac{1}{a}\cos(ax+b)+C$
$\cos(ax+b)$	$\frac{1}{a}\sin(ax+b)+C$
$\frac{1}{ax+b}$	$\frac{1}{a}\ln(ax+b)+C$
$\frac{f'(x)}{f(x)}$	$\ln f(x)+C$
e^{ax}	$\frac{1}{a}e^{ax}+C$
$\frac{1}{\sqrt{(a^2-x^2)}}$	$\arcsin\frac{x}{a}+C$
$\frac{1}{a^2+x^2}$	$\frac{1}{a}\arctan\frac{x}{a}+C$

Trigonometric identities are often useful, e.g.

$$\int \sin^2\theta \, d\theta = \int \tfrac{1}{2}(1-\cos 2\theta)\, d\theta$$
$$= \tfrac{1}{2}\theta - \tfrac{1}{4}\sin 2\theta + C$$
$$\int \sin 3\theta \cos\theta \, d\theta = \int \tfrac{1}{2}(\sin 4\theta + \sin 2\theta)\, d\theta$$
$$= -\tfrac{1}{8}\cos 4\theta - \tfrac{1}{4}\cos 2\theta + C$$

So are partial fractions, e.g.

$$\int \frac{dx}{x(x-1)} = \int \left(\frac{-1}{x} + \frac{1}{(x-1)}\right) dx$$
$$= \ln \left|\frac{x-1}{x}\right| + C$$

If there is a product, see whether one factor is the derivative of part of the other, e.g.

$$\int (2x+1)(x^2+x+1)^{1/2}\, dx = \tfrac{2}{3}(x^2+x+1)^{3/2} + C$$

otherwise you may need to use **integration by parts**, e.g.

$$\int u\frac{dv}{dx}dx = uv - \int v\frac{du}{dx}dx$$

Areas and volumes

If the region R_1 is bounded by the x-axis, the curve $y=f(x)$ and the lines $x=a$, $x=b$, the **area** of R_1 is $\int_a^b y\, dx$; the **volume of the solid** formed when R_1 is rotated completely about the x-axis is $\pi\int_a^b y^2\, dx$.

If the region R_2 is bounded by the y-axis, the curve $x=F(y)$ and the lines $y=c$, $y=d$, the area of R_2 is $\int_c^d x\, dy$; the volume of the solid formed when R_2 is rotated completely about the y-axis is $\pi\int_c^d x^2\, dy$.

Mean value

If $y=f(x)$, the mean value $\bar{y}$ of y over the interval $a \leqslant x \leqslant b$ is

$$\frac{1}{b-a}\int_a^b y\, dx$$

We must be thoroughly familiar with the integrals listed above, even if we are taking an examination in which formula sheets are provided.

Integration

Integration should be considered as the inverse of differentiation. Since the derivative of x^2 is $2x$, the integral of $2x$ is x^2. Strictly, of course, $2x$ is also the derivative of x^2+1, of x^2+2, of x^2-1... indeed, of x^2+C, where C is any constant. Sometimes for brevity we may omit the constant C, the arbitrary constant, but we should always remember that there may be an arbitrary constant for an integral.

Notation

When we differentiate, we use the notation $f'(x)$ to denote the derivative of a function $f(x)$, or dy/dx to denote a derivative with y, if the function has been expressed in that form. We use the notation $\int f(x)\,dx$ or $\int y\,dx$ to denote the integral, where $\int$ is obtained from the old $\mathcal{S}$, the initial letter of summation. To integrate a function, we merely have to find the function whose derivative is $f(x)$.

Examples

(a) $\int(4x^3+3x^2+2x+1)dx=x^4+x^3+x^2+x+C$.

(b) $\int x^{25}\,dx = \frac{1}{26}x^{26}+C$.

(c) $\int x^n\,dx = \frac{1}{n+1}x^{n+1}+C,\ n\neq-1$.

Note this is only true if $n\neq-1$. We cannot find a power of x which, when differentiated, equals $\frac{1}{x}$.

(d) $\int\cos x\,dx = \sin x+C$.

(e) $\int\sin\frac{1}{2}x\,dx = -2\cos\frac{1}{2}x+C$.

(f) $\int\sec^2 2x\,dx = \frac{1}{2}\tan 2x+C$.

With the simplest functions, all that is needed is to spot the function, which, when differentiated, gives us the function we are trying to integrate.

Exercise 22.1

1 Integrate with respect to x:

(a) $6x^5+7x^6$, (b) $2x^3+x^2+1$, (c) $2x^{1/2}+\frac{1}{2}$, (d) $x(x^2+x+1)+1$,

(e) $x^2(x^2+x^3)$, (f) $\frac{x^2+x+1}{x^4}$, (g) $\frac{x+x^4+x^5}{x^3}$, (h) $x^{1/2}(x+2+1/x)$,

(i) x^m+ax^n, (j) ax^{m+n}.

2 Find the following integrals:

(a) $\int\sin 3x\,dx$, (b) $\int\cos\frac{1}{4}x\,dx$, (c) $\int\sec^2 4x\,dx$,

(d) $\int 2\cos 2x\,dx$, (e) $\int(1+\cos 2x)\,dx$.

Trigonometric integrals

Many trigonometric functions can be integrated using the formulae on page 162, expressing a product of two functions as the sum or difference of two functions. All of these will be fairly simple, and should avoid any very awkward algebra.

Example

(a) $\sin^2 2\theta\, d\theta \quad = \int \frac{1}{2}(1-\cos 4\theta) d\theta$
$= \frac{1}{2}\theta - \frac{1}{8}\sin 4\theta + C$

(b) $\cos 4\theta \cos\theta\, d\theta \quad = \int \frac{1}{2}(\cos 5\theta + \cos 3\theta)\, d\theta$
$= \frac{1}{10}\sin 5\theta + \frac{1}{6}\sin 3\theta + C$

But (c) $\int \sin^7\theta \cos\theta\, d\theta = \frac{1}{8}\sin^8\theta + C$,
noticing that $\cos\theta$ is the derivative of $\sin\theta$. Any attempt to use sums and products formulae here soon leads to heavy algebra.

Exercise 22.2

1 Integrate with respect to x
(a) $\sin^2 x$, (b) $\cos^2(\frac{1}{2}x)$, (c) $\sin x \cos x$, (d) $\sin 2x \cos x$, (e) $\sin 3x \cos x$,
(f) $\sin 4x \sin 2x$, (g) $\cos 5x \cos x$, (h) $\cos^5 x \sin x$, (i) $\sin 2x \cos 2x$,
(j) $\cos^4 x$ [Hint: use $\cos^4 x = (\cos^2 x)^2 = (\frac{1}{2}(1+\cos 2x))^2$.]

Logarithmic integrals

To integrate a quotient, always look to see if the numerator is the derivative of the denominator, or if by division it can be rearranged so that it is.

Example

(a) $\int \frac{x^2}{x^3+5} dx = \int \frac{\frac{1}{3}(3x^2)}{x^3+5} dx = \frac{1}{3}\ln(x^3+5) + C$

(b) $\int \frac{\cos x}{1+\sin x} dx = \ln(1+\sin x) + C.$

(c) $\int \frac{x}{x+1} dx = \int \left(\frac{x+1}{x+1} - \frac{1}{x+1}\right) dx$
$= x - \ln(x+1) + C.$

(d) $\int \frac{1}{1+e^x} dx = \int \left(\frac{1+e^x}{1+e^x} - \frac{e^x}{1+e^x}\right) dx$
$= x - \ln(1+e^x) + C.$

Strictly, of course, $\int \frac{1}{x} dx = \ln|x| + C$, but the integrand $\frac{1}{x}$ is usually positive over the interval chosen so that we can generally omit the modulus sign.

Since $\ln x + \ln A = \ln Ax$, we may find it easier to use $\ln Ax$ instead of $\ln x + C$, where $\ln A = C$.

Partial fractions

If the integrand contains a product in the denominator, then we usually need to express it in partial fractions.

Examples

(a) $\int \frac{1}{(x-1)(x+2)} \mathrm{d}x = \int \left(\frac{\frac{1}{3}}{x-1} - \frac{\frac{1}{3}}{x+2}\right) \mathrm{d}x$

$= \frac{1}{3} \ln\left(\frac{x-1}{x+2}\right) + C$

(b) $\int_1^2 \frac{x-1}{(x+1)(x^2+1)} \mathrm{d}x = \int \left(\frac{x}{x^2+1} - \frac{1}{(x+1)}\right) \mathrm{d}x$

$= \left[\frac{1}{2}\ln(x^2+1) - \ln(x+1)\right]_1^2$

$= \frac{1}{2}\ln 5 - \ln 3 - (\frac{1}{2}\ln 2 - \ln 2)$

$= \frac{1}{2}\ln(10/9) + C$

Inverse trigonometric integrals

Since $\frac{\mathrm{d}}{\mathrm{d}x}(\arcsin\left(\frac{x}{a}\right)) = \frac{1}{\sqrt{(a^2-x^2)}}$ and $\frac{\mathrm{d}}{\mathrm{d}x}(\arctan\left(\frac{x}{a}\right)) = \frac{a}{a^2+x^2}$

it follows that $\int \frac{1}{\sqrt{(a^2-x^2)}} \mathrm{d}x = \arcsin\left(\frac{x}{a}\right) + C$

and $\int \frac{1}{(a^2+x^2)} \mathrm{d}x = \frac{1}{a} \arctan\left(\frac{x}{a}\right) + C$

Examples

(a) $\int \frac{1}{\sqrt{(9-x^2)}} \mathrm{d}x = \arcsin(x/3) + C$

(b) $\int \frac{1}{\sqrt{(9-4x^2)}} \mathrm{d}x = \frac{1}{2} \int \frac{1}{\sqrt{(\frac{9}{4}-x^2)}} \mathrm{d}x$

$= \frac{1}{2} \arcsin(2x/3) + C$

(c) $\int \frac{1}{9+4x^2} \mathrm{d}x = \frac{1}{4} \int \frac{1}{(3/2)^2+x^2} \mathrm{d}x$

$= \frac{1}{4}(\frac{2}{3}) \arctan\left(\frac{x}{3/2}\right) + C$

$= \frac{1}{6} \arctan\left(\frac{2x}{3}\right) + C$

Very occasionally we may need to 'complete the square' in the denominator and we may need to make a substitution, as in the next section.

Exercise 22.3

1 Integrate with respect to x

(a) $\dfrac{2x}{x^2+3}$, (b) $\dfrac{3x^2}{x^3+2}$, (c) $\dfrac{2\cos 2x}{1+\sin 2x}$,

(d) $\dfrac{e^x+1}{e^x+x+1}$, (e) $\dfrac{1+2x}{1+x+x^2}$, (f) $\dfrac{1+\sec^2 x}{x+\tan x}$.

2 Integrate with respect to x

(a) $\dfrac{1}{x(x-1)}$, (b) $\dfrac{1}{(x-2)(x+1)}$, (c) $\dfrac{1}{x^2-1}$,

(d) $\dfrac{x}{(x-1)(x+2)}$, (e) $\dfrac{x}{x^2+3x+2}$, (f) $\dfrac{x}{x^2-1}$.

3 Integrate with respect to x

(a) $\dfrac{1}{x^2+4}$, (b) $\dfrac{1}{x^2+9}$, (c) $\dfrac{1}{\sqrt{(4-x^2)}}$,

(d) $\dfrac{1}{\sqrt{(9-x^2)}}$, (e) $\dfrac{1}{25+x^2}$, (f) $\dfrac{1}{\sqrt{(1-4x^2)}}$.

Integrals requiring substitution

The derivative of a composite function $f(g(x))$ is $g'(x)\,f'(g(x))$, e.g. of $\sin(x^2)$ is $2x\cos(x^2)$, of $(x^3+1)^{1/2}$ is $\frac{1}{2}(3x^2)(x^3+1)^{-1/2}$, so that the integrals of some products or quotients may be composite functions. Some of the easier ones we can spot, but the harder ones may be helped by the substitution $z=g(x)$.

For example, we may spot that, since $3x^2$ is the derivative of (x^3+1),

$$\int 3x^2(x^3+1)^4\,dx=\tfrac{1}{5}(x^3+1)^5+C$$

Since $\cos x$ is the derivative of $\sin x$, we may spot that

$$\int \sin^4 x\cos x\,dx=\tfrac{1}{5}\sin^5 x+C$$

It will not always be possible to spot such integrals, and a substitution may help. Recalling the function notation $f(g(x))$, the substitution to use will be $z=g(x)$, but the substitution will always be given in an examination.

To find $\displaystyle\int \frac{1}{x^2+2x+2}dx$, we write the denominator as $(x+1)^2+1$.

We can now substitute $z=x+1$, i.e. $dx/dz=1$, so that

$$\int \frac{1}{(x+1)^2+1}dx=\int \frac{1}{z^2+1}\left(\frac{dx}{dz}\right)dz$$

$$=\arctan z+C\left(\text{since}\frac{dx}{dz}=1\right)$$

$$=\arctan(x+1)+C$$

Notice that the original integral $\int dx$ must be changed into $\displaystyle\int \frac{dx}{dz}dz$.

We must take care always to write down the 'dx', otherwise it is easy to forget that the second integral must be $\int dz$.

Example. Find $\int \sqrt{(a^2-x^2)}\mathrm{d}x$, using the substitution $x=a\sin\theta$.
If $x=a\sin\theta$, $\dfrac{\mathrm{d}x}{\mathrm{d}\theta}=a\cos\theta$, so

$$\begin{aligned}\int\sqrt{(a^2-x^2)}\mathrm{d}x&=\int\sqrt{(a^2-x^2)}\frac{\mathrm{d}x}{\mathrm{d}\theta}\mathrm{d}\theta\\&=\int\sqrt{(a^2-a^2\sin^2\theta)}(a\cos\theta)\,\mathrm{d}\theta\\&=a^2\int\cos^2\theta\,\mathrm{d}\theta\\&=\tfrac{1}{2}a^2\int(1+\cos 2\theta)\,\mathrm{d}\theta\\&=\tfrac{1}{2}a^2[\theta+\tfrac{1}{2}\sin 2\theta]+C\\&=\tfrac{1}{2}a^2[\theta+\sin\theta\cos\theta]+C\\&=\tfrac{1}{2}a^2\left[\arcsin(x/a)+\left(\frac{x}{a}\right)\sqrt{\left(1-\frac{x^2}{a^2}\right)}\right]+C\\&=\tfrac{1}{2}a^2\arcsin(x/a)+\tfrac{1}{2}x\sqrt{(a^2-x^2)}+C\end{aligned}$$

When we have a definite integral, it is almost invariably best to change the limits of the integral to avoid substituting at the end. Here

$$\int_{x=0}^{x=\frac{1}{2}a}\sqrt{(a^2-x^2)}\,\mathrm{d}x=a^2\int_{\theta=0}^{\theta=\pi/6}\cos^2\theta\,\mathrm{d}\theta,$$

since when $x=\frac{1}{2}a$, $\quad\frac{1}{2}a=a\sin\theta\Rightarrow\theta=\pi/6$
and when $x=0$, $\quad 0=a\sin\theta\Rightarrow\theta=0$

$$\begin{aligned}a^2\int_0^{\pi/6}\cos^2\theta\,\mathrm{d}\theta&=\tfrac{1}{2}a^2\Big[\theta+\sin\theta\cos\theta\Big]_0^{\pi/6}\text{, as before,}\\&=\tfrac{1}{2}a^2\left[\frac{\pi}{6}+\tfrac{1}{4}\sqrt{3}\right]\end{aligned}$$

Integration by parts

Since $\quad\dfrac{\mathrm{d}}{\mathrm{d}x}(uv)=v\dfrac{\mathrm{d}u}{\mathrm{d}x}+u\dfrac{\mathrm{d}v}{\mathrm{d}x}$

$$\int u\frac{\mathrm{d}v}{\mathrm{d}x}\mathrm{d}x=uv-\int v\frac{\mathrm{d}u}{\mathrm{d}x}\mathrm{d}x \qquad (1)$$

Often we can differentiate one term of a product and make it simpler, while when we integrate the other it does not become much more difficult. For example, considering $\int x\ln x\,\mathrm{d}x$, we see that $\dfrac{\mathrm{d}}{\mathrm{d}x}(\ln x)=\dfrac{1}{x}$, whereas $\int x\,\mathrm{d}x=\frac{1}{2}x^2$, so that we *may* obtain an integral that is simpler than our initial integral.

Set out clearly which function we are differentiating, here $u=\ln x$, $\dfrac{\mathrm{d}u}{\mathrm{d}x}=\dfrac{1}{x}$, and which we are integrating, here $\dfrac{\mathrm{d}v}{\mathrm{d}x}=x$, $v=\frac{1}{2}x^2$, and substitute in (1),

$$\int x \ln x \, dx = \tfrac{1}{2}x^2 \ln x - \int (\tfrac{1}{2}x^2)\frac{1}{x} dx$$

$$= \tfrac{1}{2}x^2 \ln x - \int \tfrac{1}{2}x \, dx$$

$$= \tfrac{1}{2}x^2 \ln x - \tfrac{1}{4}x^2 + C$$

Example 1. Find $\int x \arctan x \, dx$.

Since we do not know $\int \arctan x \, dx$, we cannot integrate that, and anyway $\frac{d}{dx}(\arctan x) = \frac{1}{1+x^2}$, which may seem a little simpler, so integrate x and differentiate $\arctan x$. Thus if

$$u = \arctan x, \quad \frac{du}{dx} = \frac{1}{1+x^2}$$

and if $\frac{dv}{dx} = x$, $v = \tfrac{1}{2}x^2$

so $$\int x \arctan x \, dx = \tfrac{1}{2}x^2 \arctan x - \int \frac{\tfrac{1}{2}x^2}{1+x^2} dx$$

Now $$\int \frac{x^2}{1+x^2} dx = \int \frac{x^2+1-1}{1+x^2} dx$$

$$= \int \left(1 - \frac{1}{1+x^2}\right) dx$$

$$= x - \arctan x$$

so $$\int x \arctan x \, dx = \tfrac{1}{2}x^2 \arctan x - \tfrac{1}{2}(x - \arctan x) + C$$

$$= \tfrac{1}{2}(x^2+1) \arctan x - \tfrac{1}{2}x + C$$

Sometimes it is useful to consider a function $f(x)$ as $1 \times f(x)$, in order to differentiate $f(x)$ and integrate the 1.

Example 2. Find $\int \ln x \, dx$.

Write $\int \ln x \, dx = \int 1 \times \ln x \, dx$.

If $u = \ln x$, $\frac{du}{dx} = \frac{1}{x}$ and if $\frac{dv}{dx} = 1$, $v = x$,

so $$\int \ln x \, dx = x \ln x - \int x \frac{1}{x} dx$$

$$= x \ln x - x + C$$

Exercise 22.4

1 Integrate the following with respect to x, using the substitions given:
(a) $x(x^2+2)^{1/2}$; $z=x^2+2$,
(b) $6x\,(3x^2+1)^{1/3}$; $z=3x^2+1$,
(c) $(x+2)^5$; $z=x+2$,
(d) $(2x+1)^7$; $z=2x+1$,
(e) $\sin^4 x \cos x$; $z=\sin x$,
(f) $\cos^5 x \sin x$; $z=\cos x$,
(g) $\sec^4 x \tan x$; $z=\sec x$,
(h) $e^x(e^x+1)^3$; $z=e^x+1$.

2 Integrate the following with respect to x:
(a) $x \cos x$, (b) $x \sin 2x$, (c) $x\,e^x$, (d) $x(x+1)^5$, (e) $(x+1)\sin x$,
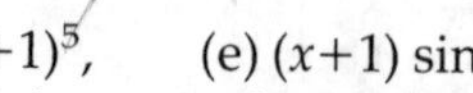
(f) $x^2 e^x$ [Hint: integrate by parts twice.] (g) $x^2 \sin x$, (h) $e^x \sin x$
[Hint: integrate by parts twice and from an equation.]

Areas of regions

Look at the region bounded by $y=x^2$, the x-axis and the straight line $x=1$. Since

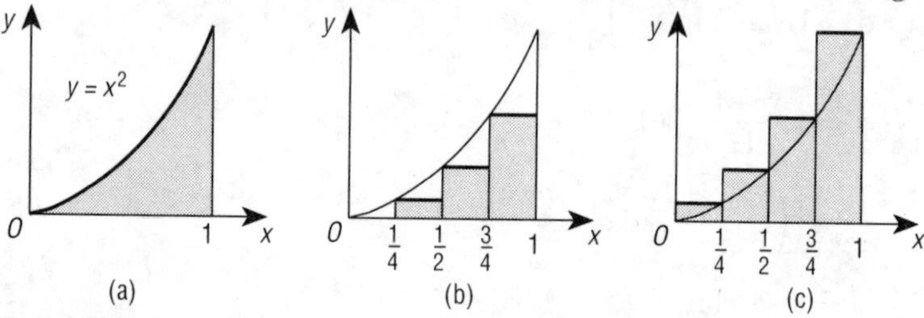

Figure 22.1

one boundary is curved, we cannot find the area by dividing the region into rectangles and summing, but we can say that the area A of the region is greater then the area of the rectangles in Figure 22.1(b), and less than the area of the rectangles in Figure 22.1(c). As these regions have been divided into four rectangles, width $\frac{1}{4}$, we have

$$\frac{1}{4}\times\left(\frac{1}{4}\right)^2+\frac{1}{4}\times\left(\frac{1}{2}\right)^2+\frac{1}{4}\times\left(\frac{3}{4}\right)^2 < A < \frac{1}{4}\times\left(\frac{1}{4}\right)^2+\frac{1}{4}\left(\frac{1}{2}\right)^2+\frac{1}{4}\times\left(\frac{3}{4}\right)^2+\frac{1}{4}\times(1)^2$$

i.e. $$\frac{7}{32} < A < \frac{15}{32}$$

If we had divided the region into 10 rectangles of equal width, we should have found a much smaller range for A, as there would have been much less space between the bounding rectangles and the curve, and

$$\frac{1}{10}\left\{\left(\frac{1}{10}\right)^2+\left(\frac{2}{10}\right)^2+\left(\frac{3}{10}\right)^2\cdots\left(\frac{9}{10}\right)^2\right\} < A < \frac{1}{10}\left\{\left(\frac{1}{10}\right)^2+\left(\frac{2}{10}\right)^2\cdots\left(\frac{10}{10}\right)^2\right\}$$

i.e. $0.285 < A < 0.385$

If we divide the region into n rectangles, the width of each rectangle is $1/n$, and the area A is such that

$$\frac{1}{n}\left\{\left(\frac{1}{n}\right)^2+\left(\frac{2}{n}\right)^2+\left(\frac{3}{n}\right)^2\ldots\left(\frac{(n-1)}{n}\right)^2\right\}<A<\left(\frac{1}{n}\right)\left\{\left(\frac{1}{n}\right)^2+\left(\frac{2}{n}\right)^2\ldots\left(\frac{n}{n}\right)^2\right\}$$

$$\frac{1}{n^3}\left\{\frac{1}{6}(n-1)n(2n-1)<A<\frac{1}{n^3}\times\frac{1}{6}n(n+1)(2n+1)\right.$$

using the formula $\sum_{r=1}^{r=n} r^2=\frac{1}{6}n(n+1)(2n+1)$

So $$\frac{1}{6n^3}\{2n^3-3n^2+n\}A<\frac{1}{6n^3}\{2n^3+3n^2+n\}$$

$$\frac{1}{3}-\frac{1}{2n}+\frac{1}{6n^2}<A<\frac{1}{3}+\frac{1}{2n}+\frac{1}{6n^2}$$

Thus, as n becomes larger and larger, the interval in which A lies becomes smaller and smaller, and the value of A is seen to be $\frac{1}{3}$. If we had used the interval from $x=0$ to $x=X$, the width of each rectangle would have been X/n, and we should have found that A became as close as we wish to $\frac{1}{3}x^3$.

We can adapt this method to find the area of the region bounded by $y=x^3$, $x=X$ and the x-axis, or by $y=x^n$, $x=X$ and the x-axis. We use a slightly different method for a general curve $y=f(x)$. Taking a point $P(x,y)$ on the curve, a 'nearby'

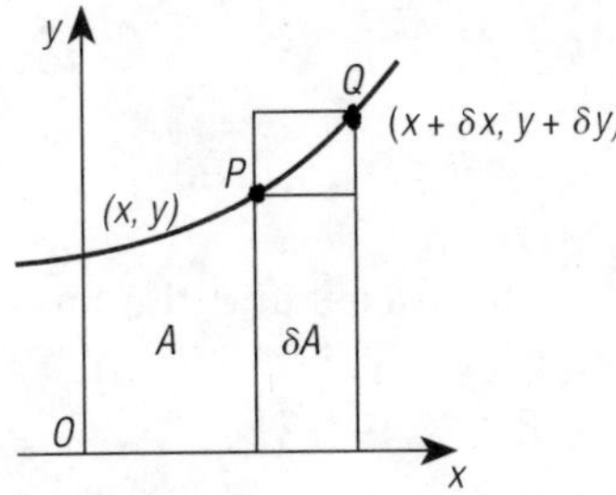

Figure 22.2

point Q $(x+\delta x,\ y+\delta y)$, and using Figure 22.2, the area δA of the shaded region lies between the area of the two rectangles,

$$y\delta x<\delta A<(y+\delta y)\delta x$$

i.e. $$y<\frac{\delta A}{\delta x}<y+\delta y$$

As $\delta x \to 0$, $\delta y \to 0$ and $y + \delta y \to y$, so that $\frac{\delta A}{\delta x}$ lies between y and something which is as close as we wish to y. Thus

$$\underset{\delta x \to 0}{\text{Limit}} \frac{\delta A}{\delta x} = y$$

i.e.

$$\frac{dA}{dx} = y$$

We saw that the area of the region bounded by $y = x^2$, $x = X$ and the x-axis was $\frac{1}{3}X^3$. If we had wanted the region bounded by $y = x^2$, the x-axis is

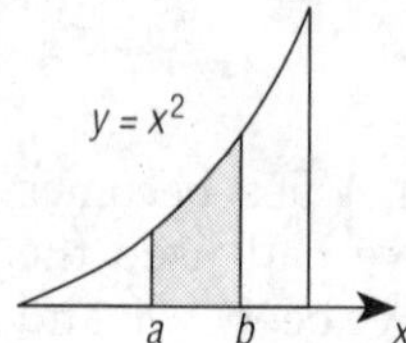

Figure 22.3

and the lines $x = a$, $x = b$, regarding it as the difference between two areas we see that it is $\frac{1}{3}a^3 - \frac{1}{3}b^3$. We write this

$$A = \int_a^b x^2 \, dx = \left[\frac{1}{3}x^3\right]_a^b$$

$$= \frac{1}{3}b^3 - \frac{1}{3}a^3$$

In general, the area of the region bounded by $y = f(x)$, the x-axis, and the lines $x = a$, $x = b$ is $\int_a^b f(x) \, dx$

Example 1. Find the area of the region bounded by $y = x^{1/2}$, the x-axis and the lines $x = 1$, $x = 4$.

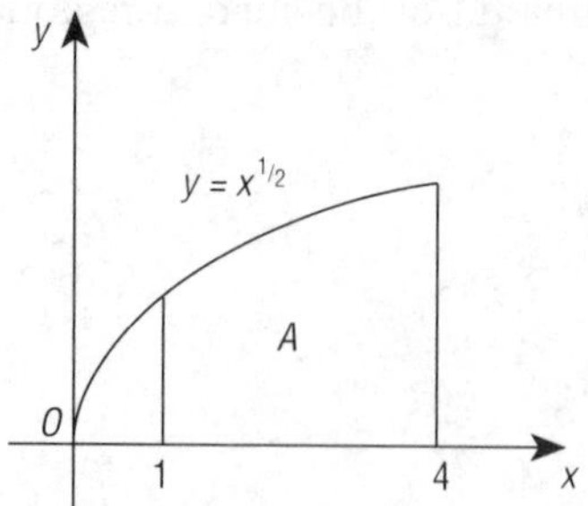

Figure 22.4

$$A=\int_1^4 x^{1/2}\,dx=\left[\tfrac{2}{3}x^{3/2}\right]_1^4=\tfrac{2}{3}\left[4^{3/2}-1^{3/2}\right]$$

$$=\frac{14}{3}$$

Notice that $y=x^{1/2}$, the integrand, is always positive and does not cross the x-axis in this interval. The area is less than that of a rectangle between (2,4) and the origin, i.e. less than 8, and quite a lot more than the triangle on (0,0), (4,0) and (4,2), and so is reasonable.

Example 2. Find the region bounded by the curve $y=\sin x$, the x-axis and the lines $x=\pi/3$, $x=\pi/2$.

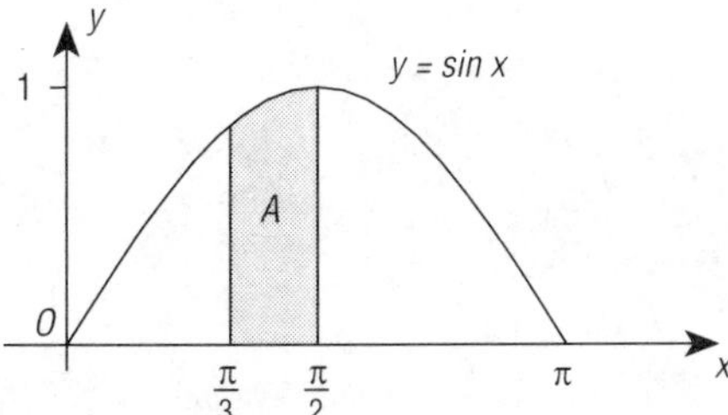

Figure 22.5

$$A=\int_{\pi/3}^{\pi/2}\sin x\,dx=\Big[-\cos x\Big]_{\pi/3}^{\pi/2}=0-\tfrac{1}{2}=\tfrac{1}{2}$$

Again, from the graph, we see that this is reasonable. The length of a complete arc of the sine curve goes from 0 to π, a distance of π units, about 3. The greatest height is 1, so that $\tfrac{1}{2}$ is a reasonable value for A.

Summary

The area of the region bounded by the curve $y=f(x)$, straight lines $x=a$, $x=b$ and the x-axis is $\int_a^b y\,dx$ (Figure 22.6a); similarly the region bounded by the curve $x=F(y)$, the lines $y=c$, $y=d$ and the y-axis is $\int_c^d x\,dy$ (Figure 22.6b). Take care that the integrand is positive throughout the interval, and where possible, always check approximately the answer.

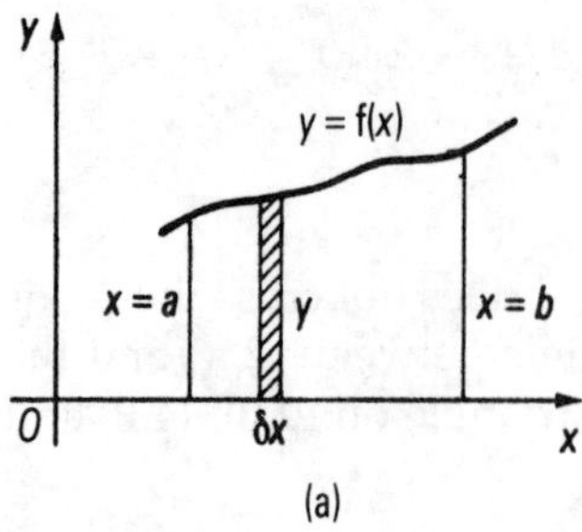

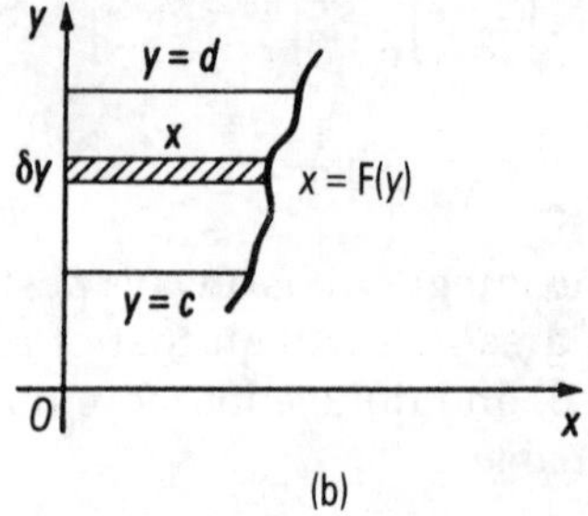

Figure 22.6

Example. Find the area of the region bounded by the curves $y=x^2$ and $x=y^2$.

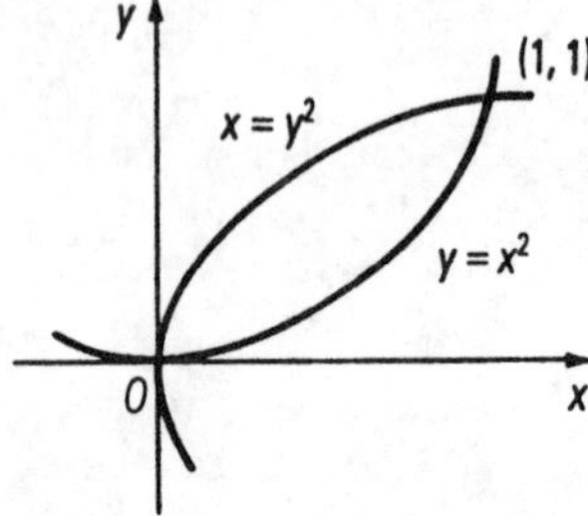

Figure 22.7

Solving simultaneously we see (Figure 22.7) that the curves meet at (0,0) and at (1,1). The area of the region bounded by $x=y^2$, $x=1$ and the x-axis is

$$\int_0^1 y\,dx=\int_0^1 x^{1/2}\,dx$$

$$=\left[\tfrac{2}{3}x^{3/2}\right]_0^1$$

$$=\tfrac{2}{3}$$

The area of the region bounded by $y=x^2$, $x=1$ and the x-axis is

$$\int_0^1 x^2\,dx=\left[\tfrac{1}{3}x^3\right]_0^1$$

$$=\tfrac{1}{3}$$

so the area of the given region is $\frac{2}{3}-\frac{1}{3}$, i.e., $\frac{1}{3}$. Checking, the area of the square bounded by the coordinate axes, $x=1$ and $y=1$ is 1, so that the area required is about $\frac{1}{3}$.

Exercise 22.5

1 Find the area of the region bounded by the x-axis and the given curves and ordinates:

(a) $y=x^3$, $x=1$,
(b) $y=x^2+1$, $x=3$,
(c) $y=x^2+2x+2$, $x=2$, $x=1$,
(d) $y=(x-1)(x+2)$, $x=\frac{1}{2}$, for $\frac{1}{2}\leqslant x\leqslant 1$,
(e) $y=\cos x$, $x=0$, $0\leqslant x\leqslant \pi/2$,
(f) $y=\sec^2 x$, $x=\pi/4$, $0\leqslant x\leqslant \pi/4$,
(g) $y=e^x$, $x=1$, $0\leqslant x\leqslant 1$,
(h) $y=\ln x$, $x=2$, $1\leqslant x\leqslant 2$,
(i) $y=x(x-1)^2$, $0\leqslant x\leqslant 1$,
(j) $y=x^{1/4}(x^2+1)$, $x=1$, $0\leqslant x\leqslant 1$.

2 Find the area of the region bounded by the y-axis and the given curves and straight lines:

(a) $y=x^2$, $y=4$,
(b) $y=x^3$, $y=1$, $y=8$,
(c) $y=\arcsin x$, $y=\pi/2$,
(d) $y=\ln x$, $y=1$,
(e) $y=e^x$, $y=e^2$.

3 Find the coordinates of the points of intersection of the following pairs of curves and the area of the region enclosed by them:

(a) $y=x^3$ and $x=y^3$,
(b) $y=x^2$, $y=8-x^2$,
(c) $y=\sin x$, $y=\cos x$, $-3\pi/4\leqslant x\leqslant \pi/4$,
(d) $y=x(x-2)$, $y=x(2-x)$,
(e) $xy=4$, $x+y=5$.

Volume of solid of revolution

When the region R is rotated completely about the x-axis, a shape is formed,

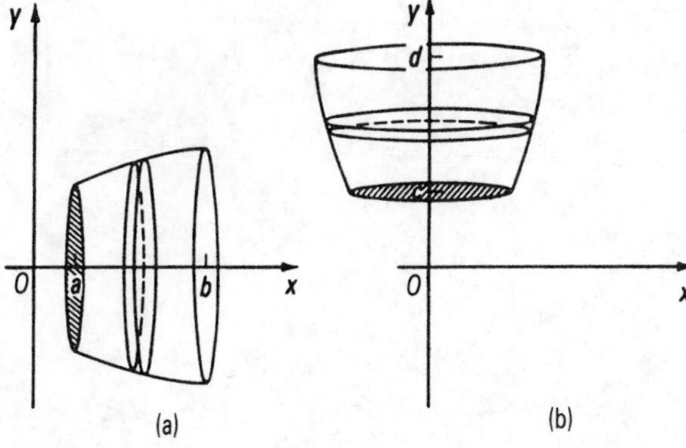

Figure 22.8

called a solid of revolution. When a small strip, thickness δx is rotated, a small solid is formed, whose volume δV satisfies the inequalities

$$\pi y^2 \delta x < \delta V < \pi(y+\delta y)^2 \delta x$$

In the limit, as $\delta x \to 0$, we have

$$\frac{dV}{dx} = \pi y^2$$

i.e. $V = \int y^2\, dx$

the integral being between the appropriate limits. Similarly, if the region is bounded by the y-axis, and is rotated about that axis, the volume of the solid of revolution is

$$\int x^2\, dy$$

Summary

If a region bounded by the x-axis, the curve $y=f(x)$, and the lines $x=a$, $x=b$ is rotated completely about the x-axis, the volume of the solid so formed is $\pi\int_a^b y^2\, dx$ (Figure 22.8a); if the region bounded by the y-axis, $x=F(y)$, $y=c$ and $y=d$ is rotated completely about the y-axis, the volume of the solid so formed is $\pi\int_c^d x^2\, dy$.

Example. The region bounded by $y=1+e^{-x}$, the x-axis, the y-axis and the line $x=1$ is rotated completely about the x-axis. Find the volume of the solid so formed (Figure 22.9).

$$V=\pi\int_0^1 y^2\, dx = \pi\int_0^1 (1+e^{-x})^2\, dx$$

$$=\pi\int_0^1 (1+2e^{-x}+e^{-2x})\, dx$$

$$=\left[x-2e^{-x}-\tfrac{1}{2}e^{-2x}\right]_0^1$$

$$=2.7\pi, \text{ about } 8.47$$

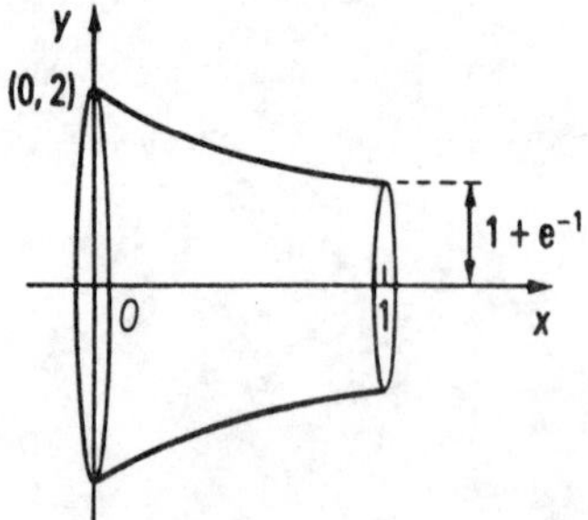

Figure 22.9

Checking, this solid is smaller than a circular cylinder radius 2, length 1, (volume $4\pi \simeq 12$); greater than a cylinder radius $1+e^{-1}$*, and $\pi \times 1.4^2$ is about 6, so the answer is reasonable.

Exercise 22.6

1 Find the volume of the solid of revolution formed by rotating about the x-axis the region R, bounded by the x-axis, the line $x=1$ and the following curves:
(a) $y=x^2$, (b) $y=x^{1/2}$, (c) $y=x^3$, (d) $y=x(x+1)^{1/2}$.

2 Find the volume of the solid of revolution formed by rotating about the x-axis the region R, bounded by the x-axis and the following curves:
(a) $y=[x(1-x)]^{1/2}$, (b) $y=[\sin x]^{1/2}$, $0 \leqslant x \leqslant \pi$, (c) $y=\sin x$, $0 \leqslant x \leqslant \pi$.

3 Find the volume of the solid of revolution formed by rotating about the y-axis the region R bounded by the y-axis, the line $y=1$ and the following curves:
(a) $y=x$, (b) $y=x^2$, (c) $y=x^{1/2}$, (d) $y=x-1$, $0 \leqslant y \leqslant 1$.

Mean value

If we have several numbers, e.g. 1,3,5,8, we can define their mean as $\frac{1}{4}(1+3+5+8)$, which gives a 'statistic' with which to describe this set of numbers. If we have a continuously-varying quantity described by $y=f(x)$, varying over an interval $a \leqslant x \leqslant b$, then we can define the mean value $\bar{y}$ of y over that interval as $\bar{y} = \dfrac{1}{b-a}\displaystyle\int_a^b y\,dx$.

Figure 22.10 illustrates the manner in which three different functions vary over the same interval. $y=x^2$ increases slowly at first; $y=x$ increases more rapidly initially, $y=\sin(\frac{1}{2}\pi x)$ increases even more rapidly initially. We should expect the corresponding values of y to have different means.

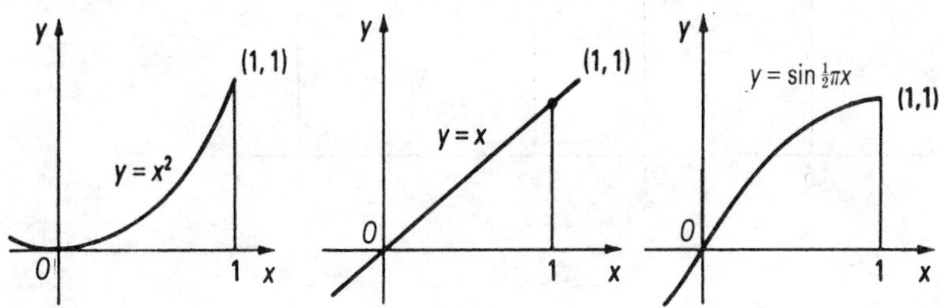

Figure 22.10

*$1+e^{-1} \simeq 1.4$.

To find the mean value $\overline{y}$ of $y=x^2$ over the interval $0\leqslant x\leqslant 1$,

$$\overline{y}=\frac{1}{1-0}\int_0^1 x^2\,dx$$

$$=\frac{1}{3}$$

the mean value of $y=x$ over the same interval is

$$\overline{y}=\int_0^1 x\,dx$$

$$=\tfrac{1}{2}$$

whereas of $y=\sin(\pi x/2)$, the mean value is

$$\int_0^1 \sin(\pi x/2)\,dx$$

$$=\left[-\frac{2}{\pi}\cos(\pi x/2)\right]_0^1$$

$$=\frac{2}{\pi}$$

greater than the others, as expected.

We can see from Figure 22.11 that the area of the region R_1 bounded by the x-axis, the ordinates $x=a$, $x=b$ and the curve $y=f(x)$ is equal to the area of the rectangle R_2, bounded by the x-axis, the ordinates $x=a$, $x=b$ and the line $y=\overline{y}$.

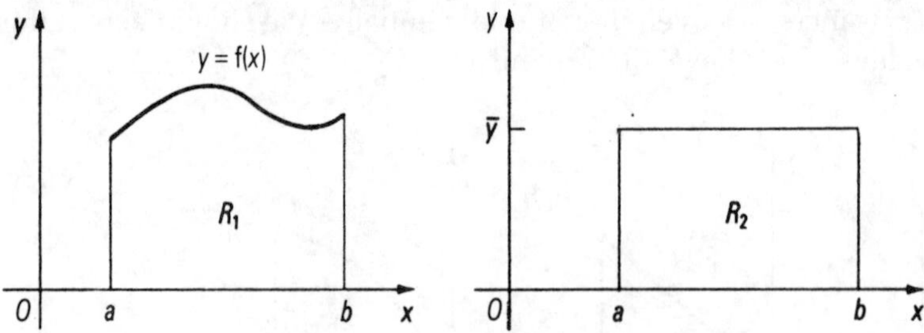

Figure 22.11

Exercise 22.7

1 Find the mean value of each of the following over the given interval:
(a) $y=x^{1/2}$, $0\leqslant x\leqslant 1$, (b) $y=x^{1/2}$, $0\leqslant x\leqslant 4$, (c) $y=x^{1/2}$, $0\leqslant x\leqslant 100$,
(d) $y=x^{1/3}$, $0\leqslant x\leqslant 1$.

2 Sketch each of the following graphs: $y=f(x)$ for $0\leqslant x\leqslant 1$. Calculate the mean value of $f(x)$ over this interval, and illustrate these on your graphs:

$$y=1-x,\quad y=1-x^2,\quad y=\cos(\tfrac{1}{2}\pi x)$$

Miscellaneous exercise 22.8

Find the integral with respect to x of:

1 $\cos^2 x$.

2 $\cos 3x \cos x$.

3 $\sin 3x \cos 2x$.

4 $\sin 5x \sin x$.

5 $\sin^2 3x$.

Evaluate the following integrals:

6 $\int_0^{\pi} \sin^2 (\frac{1}{2}x)\, dx$.

7 $\int_0^{\pi/6} \sin 2x \cos x\, dx$.

8 $\int_0^{\pi/2} \cos 2x \cos x\, dx$.

9 $\int_0^{\pi/2} \sin 3x \sin x\, dx$.

10 $\int_0^{\pi/2} \sin^4 x\, dx$.

Integrate with respect to x:

11 $\frac{1}{x+2}$.

12 $\frac{x}{x+2}$.

13 $\frac{x^2}{x+2}$.

14 $\frac{\sin x}{2-\cos x}$.

15 $\frac{e^{2x}}{1+e^{2x}}$.

Evaluate:

16 $\int_3^5 \frac{1}{(x+1)(x-2)}\, dx$.

17 $\int_1^2 \frac{1}{x(x+3)}\, dx$.

18 $\int_0^{\pi/2} \frac{\sin x}{1+\cos x}\, dx$.

19 $\int_0^{\pi/6} \frac{\sin x+\cos x}{\cos x-\sin x}\, dx$.

20 $\int_1^2 \frac{1}{x(x^2+1)}dx$.

Find the following integrals:

21 $\int \frac{1}{\sqrt{(4-x^2)}}dx$.

22 $\int \frac{1}{4+x^2}dx$.

23 $\int \frac{1}{1+4x^2}dx$.

24 $\int \frac{1}{\sqrt{(1-4x^2)}}dx$.

25 $\int \frac{1}{25+9x^2}dx$.

Evaluate:

26 $\int_0^{3/2} \frac{1}{\sqrt{(9-x^2)}}dx$.

27 $\int_0^3 \frac{1}{9+x^2}dx$.

28 $\int_0^{2/3} \frac{1}{\sqrt{(4-9x^2)}}dx$.

29 $\int_{5/4}^{5/2} \frac{1}{\sqrt{(25-4x^2)}}dx$.

30 $\int_0^{\infty} \frac{1}{25+4x^2}dx$.

Using the substitutions given, find

31 $\int \frac{1}{x^2+4x+5}dx$, $z=x+2$.

32 $\int \frac{1}{x^2+4x+3}dx$, $z=x+2$

33 $\int_0^3 x\sqrt{(1+x)}dx$, $z^2=1+x$.

34 $\int_0^{\infty} \frac{1}{(1+x^2)^2}dx$, $\tan\theta=x$.

35 $\int_0^1 \sqrt{\frac{x}{1-x}}dx$, $\sin^2\theta=x$.

Use integration by parts to find:

36 $\int x \sin x \, dx$.

37 $\int x e^x \, dx$.

38 $\int x^2 e^x \, dx$.

39 $\int x^2 \ln x \, dx$.

40 $\int \arctan x \, dx$.
41 Find the area of the region bounded by $y=x(2-x)$ and the x-axis. Find also the volume of the solid formed when this region is rotated completely about the x-axis.
42 Find the area of the finite region bounded by $y=3x-x^2$ and the straight line $y=x$. Find also the volume of the solid formed when this region is rotated completely about the x-axis.
43 The region bounded by the curve $y=\arcsin x$ and the y-axis for which $0 \leqslant y \leqslant \pi$ is rotated completely about the y-axis. Find (a) the area of this region, (b) the volume of the solid so formed.
44 The region bounded by $x^2+y^2=a^2$, the x-axis, the line $x=\frac{1}{2}a$ and that part of the x-axis for which $\frac{1}{2}a \leqslant x \leqslant a$ is rotated completely about the x-axis, to form a piece cut from a sphere. Find the volume of the solid so formed.
45 The region bounded by the y-axis, the x-axis, the curve $y=\ln x$ and the line $y=2$ is rotated completely about the y-axis. Find the volume of the solid so formed.

Find the mean value of each of the following, over the interval given.

46 $y=x^3$, $0 \leqslant x \leqslant 1$.
47 $y=x^3$, $2 \leqslant x \leqslant 4$.
48 $y=\sin x$, $0 \leqslant x \leqslant \pi/2$.
49 $y=\sin x$, $0 \leqslant x \leqslant 2\pi$.
50 $y=\sin^2 x$, $0 \leqslant x \leqslant 2\pi$.
51 Integrate

(a) $\displaystyle\int \frac{1}{\sqrt{4-x}} \, dx$,

(b) $\displaystyle\int \frac{1}{4-x} \, dx$,

(c) $\displaystyle\int \frac{1}{\sqrt{(4-x^2)}} \, dx$,

(d) $\displaystyle\int \frac{1}{4+x^2} \, dx$.

52 Use the substitution $z=e^x$ to find $\displaystyle\int \frac{e^x}{1+e^{2x}} \, dx$.

53 Using integration by parts, find $\displaystyle\int \arcsin x \, dx$.

54 Evaluate $\displaystyle\int_0^1 \frac{x^2}{(x+1)(x+3)} \, dx$.

55 The region R is bounded by the coordinate axes, the curve $y=\dfrac{1}{\sqrt{(1+x)}}$ and the straight line $x=1$. Find the area of R, and volume of the solid formed when R is rotated completely about (a) the x-axis, (b) the y-axis.

56 Show that $\displaystyle\int_0^{1/2} \frac{1}{1-x^2} \, dx = \tfrac{1}{2} \ln 3$.

57 The curves $y=1+x^3$ and $y=3x^2-3$ meet at $(-1,0)$ and at $(2,9)$. Sketch the two curves in the same diagram and show that the area of the region between the curves is 27/4.

58 Find the integral $\int \frac{1}{x(1-x^2)} dx$.

59 Find the mean value of $\sin^3 x$ over the interval $0 \leqslant x \leqslant \pi/2$.

60 The displacement x of a particle at time t is given by $x=\sin t$. The mean value of its velocity with respect to time is $\frac{1}{b-a}\int_{t=a}^{t=b} v \, dt$; the mean value of its velocity with respect to displacement is

$\frac{1}{d-c}\int_{x=c}^{x=d} v \, dx$. Calculate each of these mean values, over the interval $0 \leqslant x \leqslant \pi/2$.

Differential equations 23

Differential equations 269

Exponential functions 269

Separable variables 270

Equations requiring substitution 271

Second-order differential equations 273

Trigonometric functions 274

Second-order differential equations with a constant 275

Notes

Some differential equations can be solved by **integrating term by term** as they stand, e.g.

$$\frac{dy}{dx}=x+\cos 2x \Rightarrow y=\tfrac{1}{2}x^2+\tfrac{1}{2}\sin 2x+C$$

Some are such that the **variables are separable**, i.e. of the form $f(y)\frac{dy}{dx}=F(x)$,

e.g. $$\sin y\frac{dy}{dx}=\frac{1}{(1+x^2)} \Rightarrow \int \sin y\,dy=\int \frac{1}{1+x^2}\,dx$$

or are equations that can be reduced to this form.

When a **substitution** is given, do not forget to change $\frac{dy}{dx}$, e.g. if the substitution given is

$$y=vx, \frac{dy}{dx}=v+x\frac{dv}{dx}.$$

Second-order differential equations will probably be of the form

$$\frac{d^2y}{dx^2}-k^2y=0, \text{ solution } y=Ae^{kx}+Be^{-kx}$$

or $$\frac{d^2y}{dx^2}+k^2y=0, \text{ solution } y=A\sin kx+B\cos kx$$

or can be reduced to this form.

Differential equations

It is most desirable to be able to see that a differential equation is one of a certain type, and in some cases it is possible to see at once which function satisfies the differential equation. For example, all differential equations of the type

$$\frac{dy}{dx}=f(x), \text{ e.g. } \frac{dy}{dx}=x+x^2+\sin x$$

can be integrated term by term.

Example. Solve $\frac{dy}{dx}=2x+x^3+\sin x$.

Integrating term by term,

$$y=x^2+\tfrac{1}{4}x^4-\cos x+C.$$

Since there is no information to determine the constant C, the final expression must be left in this form.

Exponential functions

Given the equation $\frac{dy}{dx}=ky$, we know that the solution must be $y=Ce^{kx}$ for some constant C, for the exponential function is the only function f such that $\frac{d}{dx}(f)=kf$, and indeed it can be defined in that form. Similarly we shall see (page 274) that we should quote at once the form of solutions of the equation

$$\frac{d^2y}{dx^2}=ky$$

and then find the value of the arbitrary constants that satisfy any initial (or other boundary) conditions given.

Example. Solve $\frac{dy}{dx}=-4y$, given that $y=3$ when $x=0$.

We know that $\frac{dy}{dx}=-4y \Rightarrow y=Ce^{-4x}$.

But when $x=0$, $y=3$ $\therefore$ $3=Ce^0$,

$$C=3,$$

So $\quad y=3e^{-4x}$.

Separable variables

Many differential equations can be rewritten in the form

$$f(y)\frac{dy}{dx}=F(x), \text{ e.g. } \sin y\frac{dy}{dx}=e^x$$

so that each side can be integrated separately, e.g. if

$$3y^2\frac{dy}{dx}=2x$$

then $\quad y^3=x^2+C$

or if $\quad \sin y\frac{dy}{dx}=e^x$

then $\quad -\cos y=e^x+C$

Some may need rearranging before they are in a suitable form, e.g.

$$\frac{dy}{dx}=\frac{x}{(1+y^2)}$$

then $\quad (1+y^2)\frac{dy}{dx}=x$

whence

$$y+\tfrac{1}{3}y^3=\tfrac{1}{2}x^2+C$$

whereas if

$$\frac{dy}{dx}=\frac{x}{1+xy}, \text{ then } (1+xy)\frac{dy}{dx}=x$$

and we cannot solve this equation by this method, for we cannot find

$$\int xy\frac{dy}{dx}dx$$

Example. Solve $\frac{1}{y}\frac{dy}{dx}+x=xy$, given that $y=2$ when $x=0$.

Rearranging, $\quad \frac{1}{y}\frac{dy}{dx}=x(y-1)$

so that $\quad \frac{1}{y(y-1)}\frac{dy}{dx}=x$

$$\int\frac{1}{y(y-1)}dy=\int x\,dx$$

$$\therefore \qquad \int\left(-\frac{1}{y}+\frac{1}{(y-1)}\right)dy=\int x\,dx$$

$$\therefore \qquad \ln\left|\frac{y-1}{y}\right|=\tfrac{1}{2}x^2+C$$

But $y=2$ when $x=0$, so

$$\ln(\tfrac{1}{2})=C, \text{ i.e. } C=-\ln 2$$

The solution is
$$\ln\frac{(y-1)}{y}=\tfrac{1}{2}x^2-\ln 2$$

i.e.
$$\frac{2(y-1)}{y}=e^{\frac{1}{2}x^2}$$

Equations requiring substitution

Some equations can be reduced to the form in which the variables are separable by means of a substitution, which will usually be given in examinations. For example,

if $\dfrac{dy}{dx}=x-y$

the variables x and y cannot be separated as the equation stands, but if we use the substitution

$$z=x-y$$

$$\frac{dz}{dx}=1-\frac{dy}{dx}, \text{ i.e. } \frac{dy}{dx}=1-\frac{dz}{dx}$$

the equation becomes

$$1-\frac{dz}{dx}=z$$

whence
$$\frac{dz}{dx}=1-z$$

$$\int\frac{1}{1-z}dx=\int dx$$

i.e.
$$-\ln(1-z)=x+C \qquad (1)$$

whence
$$1-z=e^{-(x+C)}$$

i.e.
$$1-(x-y)=e^{-(x+C)}$$

$$y=x-1-e^{-(x+C)}$$

Equation (1) illustrates that if the equation contains many logarithmic terms the constant of integration can often be more usefully taken as $\ln A$ (where here $-\ln A=C$), then

$$-\ln(1-z)=x-\ln A,$$

$$1-z=Ae^{-x}$$

and
$$y=x-1+Ae^{-x}$$

Where it is necessary to use a substitution $z=f(x,y)$, care must always be taken to obtain $\frac{dz}{dx}$ correctly. The example below illustrates the method used when solving a homogeneous equation, one in which the terms are of the same degree in x and y, when the substitution $y=xz$ often reduces the equation to one in which the variables can be separated.

Example. Solve $xy\frac{dy}{dx}=x^2-y^2$.

Every term is of degree two (either x^2 or y^2 or x^1y^1) so we can try the substitution $y=xz$, where z is a function of x, so $\frac{dy}{dx}=z+x\frac{dz}{dx}$. The equation then becomes $x(xz)\left(z+x\frac{dz}{dx}\right)=x^2-x^2z^2$, i.e.

$$z\left(z+x\frac{dz}{dx}\right)=1-z^2$$

$$zx\frac{dz}{dx}=1-2z^2$$

$$\int\frac{-4z}{1-2z^2}dz=\int\frac{-4}{x}dx, \text{ multiplying by } -4$$

so that on the left-hand side the numerator is the derivative of the denominator,

i.e.
$$\ln(1-2z^2)=-4\ln x+\ln A$$

$$1-2z^2=Ax^{-4}$$

$$1-2\frac{y^2}{x^2}=\frac{A}{x^4}$$

$$x^4-2x^2y^2=A$$

Exercise 23.1

1 Solve $\frac{dy}{dx}=3x^2+4x^3$, given that $y=1$ when $x=1$.

2 Solve $\frac{dy}{dx}=\sin x+e^x$, given that $y=0$ when $x=0$.

3 Solve $\frac{dy}{dx}=x^2+e^{-x}$, given that $y=0$ when $x=0$.

4 Solve $\frac{dy}{dx}=\cos 2x$, given that $y=0$ when $x=\pi/4$.

5 Solve $\frac{dy}{dx}=5y$, given that $y=2$ when $x=0$.

6 Solve $\frac{dy}{dx}=3y$, given that $\frac{dy}{dx}=6$ when $x=0$.

7 Solve $\frac{dy}{dx}+4y=0$, given that $y=5$ when $x=0$.

8 Solve $\frac{dy}{dx}+y=0$, given that $y=1$ when $x=2$.

9 Solve $x\frac{dy}{dx}=y^2$, given that $y=1$ when $x=1$.

10 Solve $x\frac{dy}{dx}=\cot y$, given that $y=\frac{\pi}{2}$ when $x=1$.

11 Solve $\cot x\frac{dy}{dx}=1+y^2$, given that $y=1$ when $x=0$.

12 Solve $\cot x\frac{dy}{dx}=1-y^2$, given that $y=0$ when $x=\frac{\pi}{4}$.

13 Solve $x\frac{dy}{dx}=(1+2x^2)y^2$, given that $y=1$ when $x=1$.

14 Solve $\frac{dy}{dx}=x+y$, using the substitution $z=x+y$.

15 Solve $\frac{dy}{dx}=(x+y)^2$, given that $y=1$ when $x=0$. [Use the substitution $z=x+y$.]

16 Solve $xy\frac{dy}{dx}=x^2+y^2$, given that $y=1$ when $x=1$.

17 Solve $xy\frac{dy}{dx}=x^2-y^2$, given that $y=0$ when $x=1$.

Second-order differential equations

We saw that the exponential function e^{kx} was the only function that satisfies the equation $\frac{d}{dx}(f)=kf$. We can see that $y=e^{kx}$ satisfies $\frac{d^2y}{dx^2}=k^2y$, but $y=e^{-kx}$ also satisfies the equation, and indeed so does $y=Ae^{kx}+Be^{-kx}$ for all values of A and B. It can be shown that this is the most general form for the solution of $\frac{d^2y}{dx^2}=k^2y$, and it is often wise to proceed straight to this solution, and find the constants A and B from the given data.

Example 1. Find the solution of $\frac{d^2y}{dx^2}=4y$, given that when $x=0$, $y=3$ and $\frac{dy}{dx}=2$.

We know that the general solution of $\frac{d^2y}{dx^2}=4y$ is

$$y=Ae^{2x}+Be^{-2x}$$

Since $y=3$ when $x=0$, $3=A+B$.

Since $\frac{dy}{dx}=2$ when $x=0$, $2=2A-2B$

Solving simultaneously, $A=2$ and $B=1$, so the solution required is

$$y=2e^{2x}+e^{-2x}$$

Example 2. Find the solution of $\frac{d^2y}{dx^2}=y$, given that $y=3$ when $x=0$, and that y becomes small as x becomes large and positive.

Again, we know that the general solution of $\frac{d^2y}{dx^2}=y$ is $y=Ae^x+Be^{-x}$, k^2 being equal to 1 in this case. Since $y=3$ when $x=0$, $3=A+B$, but the condition that $y \to 0$ as $x \to +\infty$ requires that $A=0$, for otherwise $Ae^x \to \infty$ as $x \to +\infty$. Since $A=0$, $B=3$, and the required solution is

$$y=3e^{-x}$$

Trigonometric functions

The differential equation $\frac{d^2y}{dx^2}=-k^2y$ is clearly similar to $\frac{d^2y}{dx^2}=k^2y$, but here the solutions are of the form $y=A\sin kx+B\cos kx$, since $\sin kx$ and $\cos kx$ are the only functions that have the property $\frac{d^2y}{dx^2}=-k^2y$. Again, write down the general form of the solution, and fit the initial or boundary conditions.

Example 1. Solve the differential equation $\frac{d^2y}{dx^2}=-25y$, given that when $x=0$, $y=0$ and $\frac{dy}{dx}=20$.

The general solution of the differential equation is

$$y=A\sin 5x+B\cos 5x$$

since $k^2=25$

Since $y=0$ when $x=0$

$$0=B\cos 0$$

i.e. $B=0$

Since when $x=0, \dfrac{dy}{dx}=20,$

$$20=5A\cos 0$$

i.e. $A=4$

The solution is $y=4\sin 5x$.

We soon come to recognize that if the initial conditions are such that $y=0$ when $x=0$, then $B=0$ and the solution is $y=A\sin kx$;

if when $x=0, \dfrac{dy}{dx}=0$, then $A=0$ and the solution is $y=B\cos kx$.

These are expected from our knowledge of the sine and cosine functions.

Example 2. Solve the differential equation $\dfrac{d^2y}{dx^2}+16y=0$, given that $y=1$ when $x=0$ and $y=5$ when $x=\pi/8$.

Here, $k^2=16$, so the solution is of the form

$$y=A\sin 4x+B\cos 4x$$

When $x=0$, $y=1$

$$1=B$$

when $x=\pi/8$, $y=5$

$$5=A\sin(\pi/2)+B\cos(\pi/2)$$

$$5=A$$

so the solution is

$$y=5\sin 4x+\cos 4x$$

Second-order differential equations with a constant

If the differential equation is of the form

$$\frac{d^2y}{dx^2}+ky=c$$

write it as $$\frac{d^2y}{dx^2}+k\left(y-\frac{c}{k}\right)=0$$

and substitute $z=y-c/k$.

Example 1. Solve $\frac{d^2y}{dx^2}+3y=12$.

Write the equation as

$$\frac{d^2y}{dx^2}+3(y-4)=0$$

Substituting $z=y-4$, $\frac{d^2z}{dx^2}=\frac{d^2y}{dx^2}$, the equation becomes

$$\frac{d^2z}{dx^2}+3z=0$$

The solution of this is

$$z=A\sin(x\sqrt{3})+B\cos(x\sqrt{3})$$

so the solution of the original equation is

$$y=A\sin(x\sqrt{3})+B\cos(x\sqrt{3})+4$$

It is to this final equation, of course, that we must fit the initial or boundary conditions.

Example 2. Solve $\frac{d^2y}{dx^2}+4y=20$, given that $\frac{dy}{dx}=y=0$ when $x=0$.

Proceeding as before,

$$\frac{d^2y}{dx^2}+4(y-5)=0$$

i.e. $$\frac{d^2z}{dx^2}+4z=0$$

which has the solution

$$z=A\sin 2x+B\cos 2x,$$

so $$y=5+A\sin 2x+B\cos 2x$$

Since $y=0$ when $x=0$, $B=-5$; since $\frac{dy}{dx}=0$, $A=0$,

so the solution that satisfies the initial conditions is

$$y=5-5\cos 2x$$

Exercise 23.2

Solve the following differential equations:

1 $\frac{d^2y}{dx^2}-4y=0$, given $y=2$ and $\frac{dy}{dx}=0$ when $x=0$.

2 $\frac{d^2y}{dx^2}+4y=0$, given $y=2$ and $\frac{dy}{dx}=0$ when $x=0$.

3 $\frac{d^2y}{dx^2}-9y=0$, given $y=0$ and $\frac{dy}{dx}=6$ when $x=0$.

4 $\frac{d^2y}{dx^2}+9y=0$, given that $y=0$ and $\frac{dy}{dx}=6$ when $x=0$.

5 $\frac{d^2y}{dx^2}+y=0$, given that $y=3$ and $\frac{dy}{dx}=1$ when $x=0$.

6 $\frac{d^2y}{dx^2}-y=0$, given that $y=3$ and $\frac{dy}{dx}=1$ when $x=0$.

7 $4\frac{d^2y}{dx^2}+y=0$, given that $y=3$, $\frac{dy}{dx}=0$ when $x=\pi$.

8 $4\frac{d^2y}{dx^2}-y=0$, given that $y=3$, $\frac{dy}{dx}=0$ when $x=1$.

9 $25\frac{d^2y}{dx^2}+4y=0$, given that $y=5$, $\frac{dy}{dx}=1$ when $x=0$.

10 $25\frac{d^2y}{dx^2}-4y=0$, given that $y=5$, $\frac{dy}{dx}=2$ when $x=0$.

11 $\frac{d^2y}{dx^2}+4y=8$, $y=3$ and $\frac{dy}{dx}=0$ when $x=0$.

12 $\frac{d^2y}{dx^2}-4y=8$, $y=4$ and $\frac{dy}{dx}=0$ when $x=0$.

13 Solve $x\frac{dy}{dx}=(1+x)y$, given that $y=\mathrm{e}$ when $x=1$.

14 Solve $(1+2x^2)\frac{dy}{dx}=xy$, given that $y=1$ when $x=0$.

15 Solve $\frac{dy}{dx}+xy^3=y^3$, given that $y=1$ when $x=1$.

16 Solve $\frac{dy}{dx}=\frac{1}{2}xy$, given that $y=1$ when $x=2$.

17 Solve $\frac{dy}{dx}+x^2+4x^3=0$, given that $y=5$ when $x=1$.

18 Solve $\frac{d^2y}{dx^2}+4\frac{dy}{dx}=0$.

19 Solve $\frac{d^2y}{dx^2}+4\frac{dy}{dx}=8$.

20 Solve $x\frac{dy}{dx}=y(y-2)$.

21 Solve $\frac{dy}{dx}=xy(y-2)$.

22 Solve $\cos x\frac{dy}{dx}-y\sin x=y^2\sin x$.

Numerical methods 24

Approximations to integrals: trapezium rule 282

Simpson's rule 282

Maclaurin's theorem 285

Taylor's theorem 286

Newton–Raphson method for finding successive approximations to a root of an equation 286

Other iterative methods 288

Notes

Approximate integration

If $y_0, y_1, y_2, \ldots y_n$ are successive ordinates dividing a region R into n strips of equal width h, the trapezium rule says that the area A of R is approximately

$$\tfrac{1}{2}h\{y_0+2(y_1+y_2+y_3\ldots)+y_n\}$$

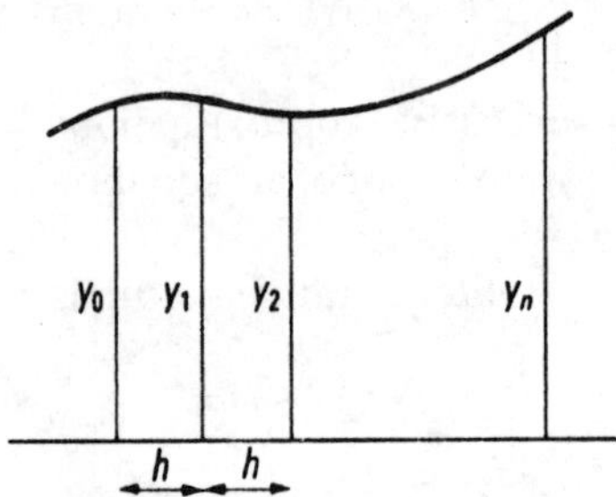

Figure 24.1

Simpson's rule says that, **when *n* is even,**

$$A\approx\tfrac{1}{3}h\{y_0+4y_1+2y_2+4y_3+2y_4\ldots+4y_{n-1}+y_n\}.$$

Maclaurin's theorem

If all derivatives of f(x) exist when $x=0$,

$$f(x)=f(0)+f'(0)+\frac{1}{2!}x^2f''(0)+\frac{1}{3!}x^3f'''(0)+\ldots$$

Taylor's theorem

If all derivatives of f(x) exist when $x=a$,

$$f(a+x)=f(a)+xf'(a)\frac{1}{2!}+x^2f''(a)+\frac{1}{3!}x^3f'''(a)+\ldots$$

Newton–Raphson formula

If x_r is a good approximation to a root of $f(x)=0$, a better approximation is x_{r+1}, where

$$x_{r+1}=x_r-\frac{f(x_r)}{f'(x_r)}$$

Other iterations

If the equation $f(x)=0$ is to be solved by an iteration

$$x_{r+1}=F(x_r)$$

the iteration will converge to the required root if $|F'(x_r)|<1$.

Approximations to integrals: trapezium rule

Considering the region bounded by the curve $y=\mathrm{f}(x)$, the straight lines $x=a$, $x=b$ and the x-axis, we see that the area of each strip into which it can be divided is approximately $\frac{1}{2}h(y_k+y_{k+1})$, h being the width of the strip and y_k and y_{k+1} the ordinates at each side of the strip (Figure 24.2). Continuing this procedure over the whole of the region, the area is approximately

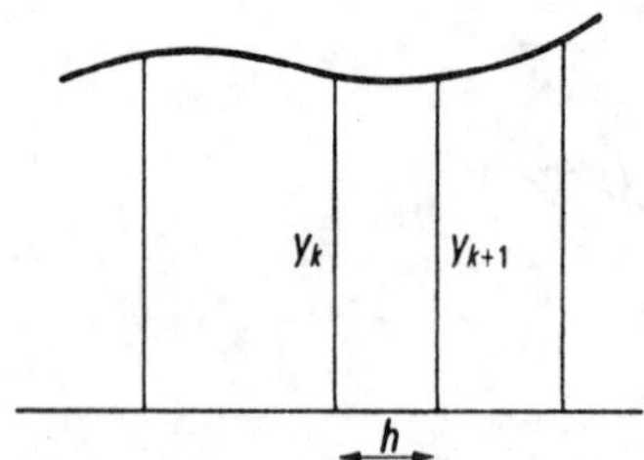

Figure 24.2

$$\tfrac{1}{2}h(y_0+2y_1+2y_2+2y_3+\ \dots\ +2y_{n-1}+y_n)$$

as we have divided the region into n trapezia. This is called the **trapezium rule**.

Simpson's rule

The equation of a parabola with axis parallel to the y-axis is $y=ax^2+bx+c$, for some a, b and c. Considering a region bounded by such a parabola, straight lines $x=-h$, $x=h$ and the x-axis, the area A is *exactly* equal to $\int_{-h}^{h}(ax^2+bx+c)\mathrm{d}x$, i.e.

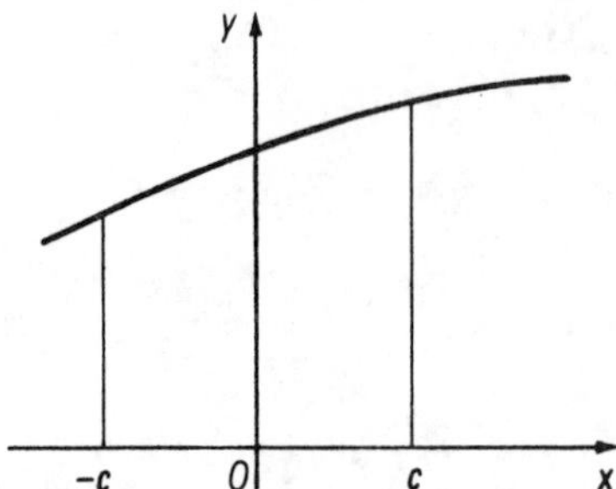

Figure 24.3

$$A=\left[\tfrac{1}{3}ax^3+\tfrac{1}{2}bx^2+cx\right]_{-h}^{h}$$
$$=\tfrac{2}{3}ah^3+2ch$$
$$=\tfrac{1}{3}h(2ah^2+6c)$$

Denoting the ordinates by y_0, y_1, y_2,

we see $\quad y_0=ah^2-bh+c,$
$\quad y_1=c$
and $\quad y_2=ah^2+bh+c,$

so that
$$y_0+4y_1+y_2=2ah^2+6c$$
i.e. $$A=\tfrac{1}{3}h(y_0+4y_1+y_2)$$

and the area of this region is exactly equal to $\tfrac{1}{3}h(y_0+4y_1+y_2)$.

It can be shown that this is true for all parabolae with axes parallel to the y-axis, so that if we divide a region into parts, each width $2h$, each approximately bounded on one side by a parabola, then the area of the region is *approximately*

$$\tfrac{1}{3}h(y_0+4y_1+2y_2+4y_3+\ldots+2y_{2n-2}+4y_{2n-1}+y_{2n})$$

Notice that we have to have an even number of ordinates, since the width of the 'parabolic strips' is $2h$.

Many calculators are now programmable so that they will carry out the required calculations for the trapezium rule or for Simpson's rule, and even those that cannot be so programmed will carry out much of the work done in detail in this example. In an examination, though, candidates are always required to show enough working for the examiner to be able to see that he or she has understood the method used.

Example. Find $\int_0^1 e^{-x^2}dx$, using (a) the trapezium rule, (b) Simpson's rule, with 10 intervals.

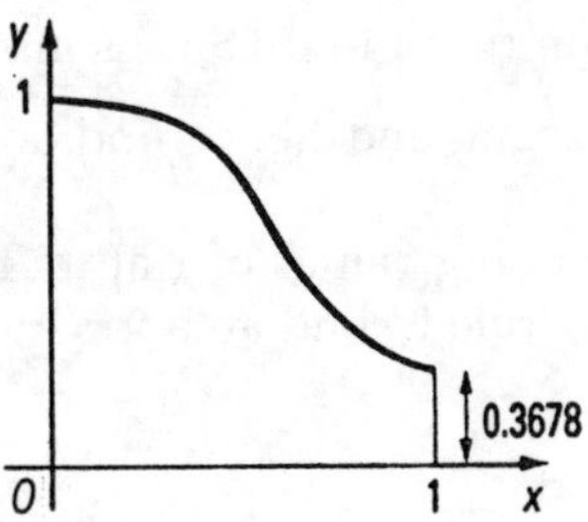

Figure 24.4

Forming a table of values, we have

x	0	0.1	0.2	0.3	0.4	0.5	0.6
e^{-x^2}	1	0.9900	0.9608	0.9139	0.8521	0.7788	0.6977
x	0.7	0.8	0.9	1.0			
e^{-x^2}	0.6126	0.5273	0.4449	0.3678			

(a) Using the trapezium rule,

$$A \approx \tfrac{1}{2}(0.1)[1+2(0.9900+0.9608+0.9139+0.8521+0.7788 +0.6977+0.6126+0.5273+0.4449)+0.3678] \approx 0.746$$

(b) Using Simpson's rule,

$$A \approx \tfrac{1}{3}(0.1)[1+4(0.9900+0.9139+0.7788+0.6126+0.4449) +2(0.9608+0.8521+0.6977+0.5273)+0.3678] \approx 0.747$$

Checking, we expect the area to be slightly greater than that of a trapezium, width 1, parallel sides 1 and 0.3678, i.e. greater than 0.6839.

These approximate methods are useful when we have a non-integrable function, as here, or in cases where we only know the ordinates, and not the function that describes the relation.

Exercise 24.1

1 Use (a) the trapezium rule and (b) Simpson's rule to find the area of the region bounded by $y=x(2-x)$ and the x-axis between 0 and 2 with 10 intervals, i.e. each interval of width 0.2. Check your answers by direct integration.

2 Use (a) the trapezium rule and (b) Simpson's rule to find the area of the region bounded by the x-axis and the curve $y=\sin x$, for $0\leqslant x\leqslant\pi$, with 6 intervals, i.e. each interval width $\pi/6$. Check your answers by direct integration.

3 Find the value of $\int_0^{\frac{1}{2}} \frac{1}{\sqrt{1-x^2}}\,dx$, using (a) the trapezium rule and (b) Simpson's rule with 4 intervals. Find the exact value by direct integration, and hence find an approximation for π.

4 Find the value of $\int_0^1 \frac{1}{1+x^2}\,dx$, using (a) the trapezium rule and (b) Simpson's rule with 10 intervals. Find the exact value of the integral and hence find an approximation for π.

5 The values of a function $f(x)$ are given for corresponding values of x at unit intervals. Use (a) the trapezium rule and (b) Simpson's rule to find an approximation to $\int_0^{10} f(x)\,dx$.

x	0	1	2	3	4	5	6	7	8	9	10
y	2	4	5	7	7	8	9	10	11	12	14

Maclaurin's theorem

We should be familiar with certain approximations that are convenient for small values of x, e.g. $\sin x \approx x$, $\cos x \approx 1-\frac{1}{2}x^2$. Maclaurin's theorem enables us to find polynomials that are good approximations to other functions when x is small.

Maclaurin's theorem states that if $f(x)$ is a function of x for which all derivatives exist and have finite values when $x=0$,

$$f(x) \equiv f(0)+xf'(0)+\frac{1}{2!}x^2f''(0)+\frac{1}{3!}x^3f'''(0)\ldots$$

To prove this, suppose that

$$f(x) \equiv a_0+a_1x+\frac{1}{2!}a_2x^2+\frac{1}{3!}a_3x^3+\ldots$$

(The working is slightly easier if we introduce the factorials in the denominators.) Then when $x=0$, $f(0)=a_0$.

Differentiating $\quad f'(x)=a_1+a_2x+\frac{a_3}{2!}x^2+\frac{a_4}{3!}x^3\ldots$

When $\quad x=0$, $f'(0)=a$

Differentiating again, $\quad f''(x)=a_2+a_3x+\frac{1}{2!}a_4x^2+\frac{1}{3!}a_5x^3+\ldots$

Again putting $x=0$, $\quad f''(0)=a_2$. Proceeding in this way we obtain $a_0=f(0)$, $a_1=f'(0)$, $a_2=f''(0)$, $a_3=f'''(0)$, ...

giving $\quad f(x)=f(0)+xf'(0)+\frac{1}{2!}x^2f''(0)+\frac{1}{3!}x^3f'''(0)+\ldots$

The need that the derivatives should exist when $x=0$ is illustrated when trying to find an expansion for $\ln x$. For if $f(x)=\ln x$, $f'(x)=\frac{1}{x}$, $f''(x)=-\frac{1}{x^2}$ ... and $f'(0)$, $f''(0)$ and all later derivatives are undefined when $x=0$.

Example. Use Maclaurin's theorem to find the expansion, up to the term in x^2, of $\ln(1+\sin x)$.

Since $f(x)=\ln(1+\sin x)$, $f(0)=\ln 1=0$.

$$f'(x)=\frac{\cos x}{1+\sin x},\ f'(0)=1$$

$$f''(x)=\frac{(1+\sin x)(-\sin x)-\cos x(\cos x)}{(1+\sin x)^2}$$

$$=\frac{-1-\sin x}{(1+\sin x^2)}=\frac{-1}{1+\sin x}$$

so $\quad f''(0)=-1$

and $\quad \ln(1+\sin x)\approx x-\frac{1}{2}x^2$

Check. When $x=0.1$ (radians, of course), $\ln(1+\sin x)=0.09516$; $x-\frac{1}{2}x^2=0.095$.

Taylor's theorem

Taylor's theorem is a more general form of Maclaurin's theorem, stating that if all derivatives of $f(x)$ exist when $x=a$,

$$f(x+a) \equiv f(a)+xf'(a)+\frac{1}{2!}x^2f''(a)+\frac{1}{3!}x^3f'''(a)+\ldots$$

It is easily seen that Maclaurin's theorem is the special case of Taylor's theorem when $a=0$. The proof is similar to that of Maclaurin's theorem.

Example. Use Taylor's theorem to find the expansion, up to and including the term in x^3, of $\sin(x+\pi/4)$ in ascending powers of x.

Since $f(x)=\sin x$, $f(\pi/4)=\frac{1}{\sqrt{2}}$; since $f'(x)=\cos x$, $f'(\pi/4)=\frac{1}{\sqrt{2}}$;

since $f''(x)=-\sin x$, $f''(\pi/4)=-\frac{1}{\sqrt{2}}$; since $f'''(x)=-\cos x$, $f'''(\pi/4) = -\frac{1}{\sqrt{2}}$.

$$\therefore \quad \sin(x+\pi/4) \approx \frac{1}{\sqrt{2}}\left(1+x-\frac{1}{2!}x^2-\frac{1}{3!}x^3\right)$$

Again, check the answer by putting $x=0.1$: $\sin(0.1+\pi/4) \approx 0.77417$; the expansion ≈ 0.77416.

Exercise 24.2

1 Use Maclaurin's theorem to find the expansion of each of the following, giving the first three non-zero terms:
(a) $\ln(1+x)$, (b) $\ln(2+x)$, (c) $(1+x)^{-2}$, (d) $\sin x$, (e) $\cos 2x$, (f) $\arctan 2x$, (g) xe^x.

2 Use Taylor's theorem to show that an approximation for $\tan(\frac{1}{4}\pi+h)$, where h is small, is $1+2h+2h^2+\frac{8}{3}h^3$.

3 Use Taylor's theorem to show that
$\sin(x+h)=\sin x+h\cos x-\frac{1}{2}h^2\sin x-\frac{1}{6}h^3\cos x$
if h is so small that powers of h greater than h^3 can be neglected.

Newton–Raphson method for finding successive approximations to a root of an equation

If $x=a$ is a good approximation to a root of an equation $f(x)=0$, the exact value of that root will be $a+\varepsilon$, where ε is small, so that $f(a+\varepsilon)=0$. By Taylor's theorem,

$$\begin{aligned} f(a+\varepsilon) &= f(a)+\varepsilon f'(a)+\ldots \\ &\approx f(a)+\varepsilon f'(a), \text{ since } \varepsilon \text{ is small.} \end{aligned}$$

Now since $f(a+\varepsilon)=0$, $\varepsilon=\dfrac{-f(a)}{f'(a)}$, so that we can deduce that, if $x=a$ is a good approximation to a root of the equation $f(x)=0$,

$$x=a-\frac{f(a)}{f'(a)} \text{ is a better approximation.}$$

This is illustrated by Figure 24.5, which assumes that $f(a)$ and $f'(a)$ are both positive. (The figure can be adapted for the cases when either or both are negative.) If R is the point where $x=a$, $PR=f(a)$, the gradient at P is $f'(a)$, so that $QR=PR/\tan\psi=f(a)/f'(a)$ and the x-coordinate of Q is $a-f(a)/f'(a)$. It can be seen that Q is nearer to the point at which the curve crosses the x-axis than R, so gives a closer approximation to the root of $f(x)=0$.

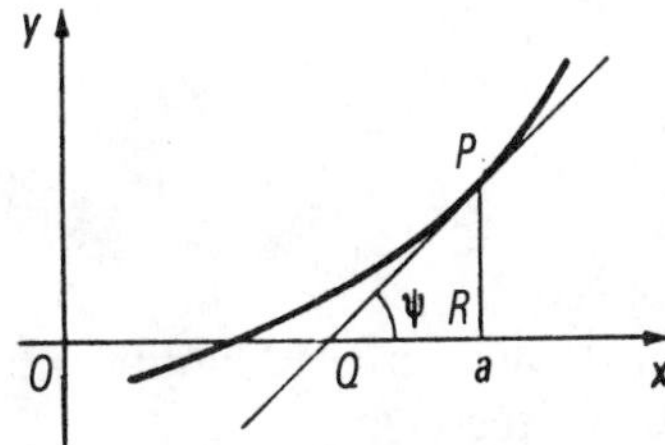

Figure 24.5

Since we can use this method to find successive approximations, we generally adopt the suffix notation, writing

if x_r is a good approximation to a root of the equation $f(x)=0$,

$$x_{r+1}=x_r-\frac{f(x_r)}{f'(x_r)} \text{ is a better approximation.}$$

To find a first approximation, we find two values of x for which $f(x)$ differ in sign; we may use linear interpolation to find a fairly good approximation with which to start.

NB. The method fails if $f'(a)$ is near to zero, or if $f''(a)$ is very large.

Example. Find the root of $x^3-3x-6=0$, correct to 3 s.f.

Tabulating the values of $f(x)$, to find a first approximation,

$$f(0)=-6,\ f(1)=-8,\ f(2)=-4,\ f(3)=12,$$

so there is a root between $x=2$ and $x=3$. Using Figure 24.6, we see that $x=2.25$ is likely to be a good approximation to the root. (Since the triangles are similar with sides in the ratio 4:12, AB:BC=4:12, giving AB=0.25.)

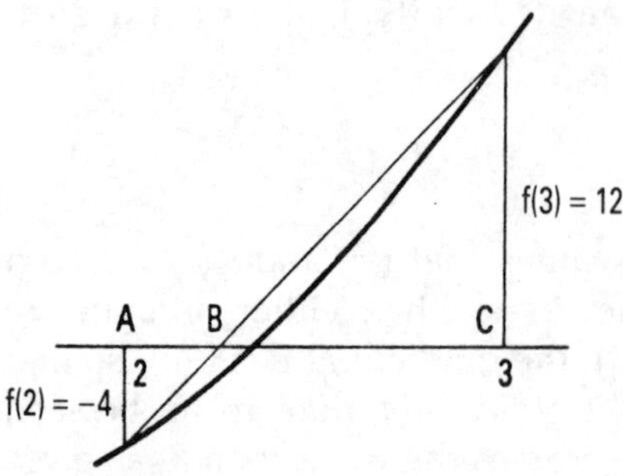

Figure 24.6

Since $f(x)=x^3-3x-6$, $f'(x)=3x^2-3$,

$$f(2.25)=-1.359\,375,\ f'(2.25)=12.187\,5,$$

a better approximation is $2.25-\dfrac{-1.359\,375}{12.187\,5}=2.361\,538.$

Repeating the procedure there is no need to work with many significant figures, because it is unlikely that the later ones will be correct.

$$f(2.361\,5)=0.084\,835,\ f'(2.361\,5)=13.730\,046,$$

so a better approximation is $2.361\,5-\dfrac{0.084\,835}{13.730\,046}=2.355\,32.$

Since each of these approximations is equal to 2.36, to 3 s.f., we know that the root has the required degree of accuracy.

The wording of the question indicated that there was only one real root of this cubic. This can be confirmed by noticing that the turning values occur where $3x^2-3=0$, i.e. $x=-1$ or 1, and that $f(-1)$ and $f(1)$ are both negative.

Other iterative methods

We can probably recall drawing graphs of say $y=1/x$ and $y=(x-1)(x+2)$ to find a solution of $x(x-1)(x+2)=1$, since the equation can be rearranged as $(x-1)(x+2)=1/x$. Many equations can be rearranged in the form $x=F(x)$, e.g. $x^3-x-2=0$ as $x=(x+2)^{1/3}$, and a method can be devised for finding successive approximations to a root of the equation.

Figure 24.7 shows the graphs of $y=x$ and $y=F(x)$, intersecting at a point X, whose x-coordinate is the root of the equation $x=F(x)$. If x_r is a good approximation to the root we see that by following the lines marked $\rightarrow$ we can proceed to the point X. The y-coordinate of P is $F(x_r)$ and since Q lies on the line $y=x$, the x-coordinate of Q is $f(x_r)$, which is a better approximation to the root of the equation than x_r. Thus we can say that, under certain circumstances,

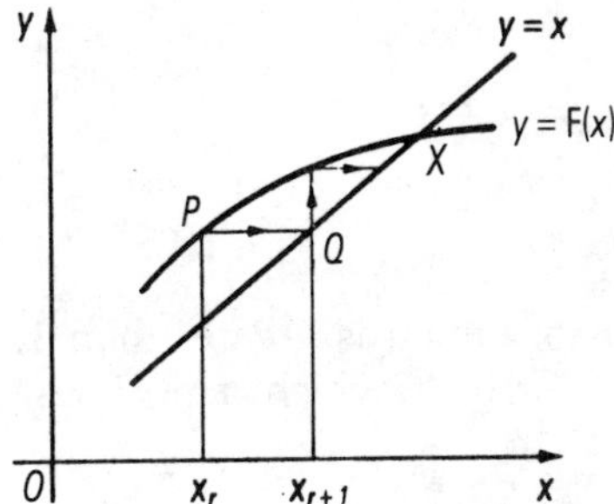

Figure 24.7

if x_r is a good approximation of a root of the equation $x=\mathrm{F}(x)$, then $\mathrm{F}(x_r)$ is a better approximation,
which can be written as an algorithm

$$x_{r+1}=\mathrm{F}(x_r)$$

By drawing various curves $y=\mathrm{F}(x)$ we can see that in many cases lines like —>— will not approach the point of intersection (Figure 24.8), and it can be shown that the condition that an iteration of this form converges to a root is that $|\mathrm{F}'(x_0)|<1$; the smaller $|\mathrm{F}'(x_0)|$, the more rapid the convergence.

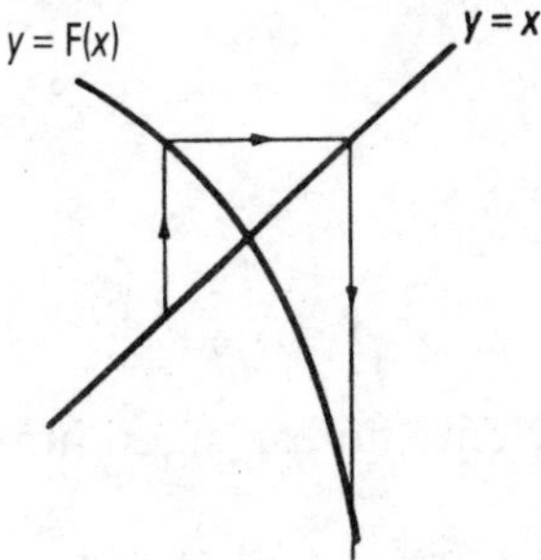

Figure 24.8

Example. The equation $x^3-2x-3=0$ has a root near to $x=2$. The equation can be rearranged as

$$x=\tfrac{1}{2}(x^3-3) \text{ or as } x=\sqrt[3]{(2x+3)}.$$

By carrying out two iterations in each case show that $x_{r+1}=\frac{1}{2}(x_r^3-3)$ does not approach the root, but that $x_{r+1}=\sqrt[3]{(2x_r+3)}$ does.

Using $\quad x_{r+1}=\frac{1}{2}(x_r^3-3)$,
if $x_0=2$, $\quad x_1=\frac{1}{2}(2^3-3)=2.5$
$\quad x_2=\frac{1}{2}(2.5^3-3)=6.3215$

which is not approaching the root.

Using $\qquad x_{r+1}=\sqrt[3]{(2x_r+3)}$,

if $x_0=2$, $\qquad x_1=\sqrt[3]{7}\approx 1.913$

$x_2\approx 1.897$

$x_3\approx 1.894$

and clearly $x=1.89$ will be the value of the root to 3 s.f.

Notice that if $F(x)=\frac{1}{2}(x^3-3)$, $F'(x)=\frac{3}{2}x^2$ and $F'(2)=6$, which is greater than 1, whereas if $F(x)=(2x+3)^{1/3}$, $F'(x)=\frac{2}{3}(2x+3)^{-2/3}$, and $F'(2)\approx 0.18$, which is much less than 1.

Exercise 24.3

1 Show there is a root of $x^2-5x+1=0$ between 0 and 1, and find an approximation to this root, correct to 2 d.p., (a) using Newton's method, (b) using a suitable iterative formula. Check your approximations by solving the equation exactly.

2 Show there is a root of $x^3-5x+1=0$ between 0 and 1, and find an approximation to this root, correct to 3 d.p., (a) using Newton's method, (b) using a suitable iterative formula.

3 Show there is a root of $x^3-4x-1=0$ between 2 and 3, and find an approximation to this root, correct to 2 d.p., using (a) Newton's method, (b) a suitable iterative formula.

4 The equation $x^3-2x-6=0$ can be rearranged as $x=F(x)$, where

$$F(x)=\tfrac{1}{2}(x^3-6)$$

or $\qquad F(x)=(2x+6)^{1/3}$

or $\qquad F(x)=\dfrac{2x+6}{x^2}$

or $\qquad F(x)=\dfrac{6}{x^2-2}$

Given there is a root near to $x=2$, find $F'(2)$ in each case. Hence find an algorithm and find the root correct to 3 s.f.

5 Given that $3\sin x=2x$ has a root near to $x=1.5$, find that root correct to 5 s.f.

Miscellaneous exercise 24.4

1 Using (a) the trapezium rule, (b) Simpson's rule, in each case with 10 intervals, find approximations to

$$\int_0^1 \frac{1}{1+x}\,dx$$

and check your answers by direct integration.

2 Using (a) the trapezium rule, (b) Simpson's rule, in each case with 10 intervals, find approximations to

$$\int_0^{\pi/2} \sqrt{\sin x}\,dx.$$

3 Given that $y=f(x)$, and the values of y at equal intervals of x as below, find (a) using the trapezium rule, (b) using Simpson's rule, the approximate area of the region bounded by the x-axis, the y-axis, the line $x=10$ and the curve $y=f(x)$.

x	0	1	2	3	4	5	6	7	8	9	10
y	0	3	7	9	5	6	7	7	8	2	1

4 Use Maclaurin's theorem to find the expansions of sin x and cos x, giving the first two non-zero terms in each case.
Deduce $(x+\sin x)\cos x=2x+\frac{5}{6}x^3$, if powers of x higher than x^3 are neglected.
5 Use Maclaurin's theorem to find the expansion of $\ln(1+x)$ up to and including the term in x^4, and deduce that

$$(1+x)^2\ln(1+x)=x+\tfrac{3}{2}x^2+\tfrac{1}{3}x^3-\tfrac{1}{12}x^4$$

if powers of x higher than x^4 are neglected.
6 Find the expansion, up to and including the term in x^4, of $e^{\sin x}$.
7 Find the first three non-zero terms in the expansion of $e^x\sin x$.
8 By finding the expansions of $(1-x^2)^{1/2}$ and arcsin x, show that $(1-x^2)^{1/2}\arcsin x\approx x-\frac{1}{3}x^3$.
9 Show that there is a root between 0 and 1 of

$$x^3-5x+2=0$$

and find this root correct to 3 d.p.
10 Show that there is a root between 0 and 1 of

$$x^3-6x=-1$$

and find this root correct to 3 d.p.
11 Find the root between $x=2$ and $x=3$ of the equation $x^3-3x-4=0$, starting with one linear interpolation and then using two iterations of Newton's formula.
12 Find an approximation to the positive root of $x^4+x^2-19=0$, correct to 4 s.f.
13 Find, correct to 3 s.f., the root near to $x=1.2$ of $\sin x+3\cos x=2$.
14 Use the iteration

$$x_{r+1}=5-2/x_r$$

to find the root near to 4 of the equation

$$x^2-5x+2=0,$$

giving this root correct to 3 d.p.
15 Use the iteration

$$x_{r+1}=(1/6)(x_r^3+2)$$

to find the solution of

$$x^3-6x+2=0$$

near to 0.5, giving the root correct to 4 d.p. Why will this iteration not give the root near to 2? Find an iteration to obtain this root correct to 2 d.p.

16 The equation $x^3-10x+1=0$ has roots near to -3, near to 0 and near to $+3$. Find algorithms to obtain these roots, and calculate approximations to these roots, correct to 2 d.p.

17 The equation $\tan x=2x$ has a root near to $x=1$. Show that $x_{r+1}=\frac{1}{2}\tan x_r$ will not obtain that root, but that $x_{r+1}=\arctan 2x_r$ will. Use this iteration to obtain that root, correct to 2 d.p. Compare this method with Newton's method by also solving the equation using Newton's method.

18 The equation $xe^x=6$ has a root close to 1.5. Show that $x_{r+1}=6e^{-x_r}$ is not a suitable algorithm, and find one that can be used to obtain this root. Use the algorithm to find the root correct to 3 s.f.

Displacement, velocity, acceleration 25

Displacement and distance 295

Velocity and speed 295

Acceleration 295

Constant acceleration formulae 295

Graphical illustrations 296

Variable acceleration 298

Force as a function of displacement 299

Displacement as a function of velocity 300

Power 301

Notes

Displacement describes the position of a particle relative to an origin O; the **distance** from O is the magnitude of the displacement.
Velocity is rate of change of displacement with respect to time.
Acceleration is rate of change of velocity with respect to time.

Constant acceleration formulae

$$v=u+at$$
$$s=ut+\tfrac{1}{2}at^2$$
$$s=\tfrac{1}{2}(u+v)t$$
$$v^2=u^2+2as$$

Variable acceleration

If the force (or acceleration) is a function of **time** t, use $\frac{dv}{dt}=f(t)$, $v=\frac{ds}{dt}=\int f(t)dt$ and integrate term by term.

If the force is a function of the **velocity**, use $\frac{dv}{dt}=F(v)$ and separate the variables to find v in terms of t; to find x in terms of t, integrate again. To find v in terms of x, use $v\frac{dv}{dx}=F(v)$ and separate the variables.

If the force is a function of the **displacement** x, use $v\frac{dv}{dx}=G(x)$ and separate the variables.

Displacement and distance

The **displacement** of a particle describes its position relative to a fixed origin O. In two or more dimensions, we use $\mathbf{r}$ to describe the displacement. In one dimension, if the x-axis is taken along the line of motion of the particle, x is the displacement of the particle from O, $|x|$ is the distance of the particle from O.

Velocity and speed

The velocity $\mathbf{v}$ of a particle is the rate of change of displacement; i.e., $\mathbf{v}=\frac{\mathrm{d}}{\mathrm{d}t}(\mathbf{r})$; the speed v of a particle is $|\mathbf{v}|$.

Acceleration

The acceleration $\mathbf{a}$ of a particle is the rate of change of velocity, i.e. $\mathbf{a}=\frac{\mathrm{d}}{\mathrm{d}t}(\mathbf{v})$.

Constant acceleration formulae

If a particle is moving in a straight line with constant acceleration a, $\frac{\mathrm{d}v}{\mathrm{d}t}=a \Rightarrow v=at+C$. If the velocity is u when $t=0$, $u=C$ and the equation is

$$v=u+at \qquad (1)$$

Writing s to denote the displacement of the particle,

$$\frac{\mathrm{d}s}{\mathrm{d}t}=u+at \Rightarrow s=ut+\tfrac{1}{2}at^2+C$$

If we measure $s=0$ when $t=0$, $C=0$ and the equation becomes

$$s=ut+\tfrac{1}{2}at^2 \qquad (2)$$

Equation (2) can be rewritten

$$\begin{aligned} s&=\tfrac{1}{2}(2u+at)t \\ &=\tfrac{1}{2}[u+(u+at)]t \end{aligned}$$

Since $v=u+at$,

$$s=\tfrac{1}{2}(u+v)t \qquad (3)$$

From (1), $t=\frac{v-u}{a}$, so that, from (3),

$$s=\tfrac{1}{2}(u+v)\frac{(v-u)}{a}$$

i.e. $2as = v^2 - u^2,$

$$v^2 = u^2 + 2as \quad (4)$$

NB. *These equations are only true if the particle is moving in a straight line with constant acceleration.*

When solving problems using these equations, always tabulate the data to see which quantities we know; we need to know three quantities, then we can always find the other two.

Example. A particle is moving in a straight line with constant acceleration. If the initial velocity is $7\,\text{m s}^{-1}$ and the velocity after 10 s is $12\,\text{m s}^{-1}$, find the acceleration, and the displacement of the particle after 100 s.

Here $u=7 \quad v=12 \quad s=? \quad a=? \quad t=10$

To find a, use $v=u+at$, i.e. $12=7+10a$, $a=0.5$, the acceleration is $0.5\,\text{m s}^{-2}$.
To find s when $t=100$,

we have $u=7 \quad v=? \quad s=? \quad a=0.5 \quad t=100$

so use $s=ut+\frac{1}{2}at^2$, i.e. $s=700+\frac{1}{2}(0.5)100^2=3200$

the displacement is 3200 m.

Graphical illustrations

Since $v=\frac{\text{d}s}{\text{d}t}$, the gradient at a point on a displacement–time curve gives the velocity at that time t.

Since $a=\frac{\text{d}v}{\text{d}t}$ and $s=\int\frac{\text{d}s}{\text{d}t}\text{d}t=\int v\text{d}t$ a velocity–time curve is often much more useful, for the gradient at any point (time t_1) gives the velocity at time t_1; the area between $t=t_1$ and $t=t_2$ gives the displacement s in the interval in which t has changed from t_1 to t_2 (Figure 25.1).

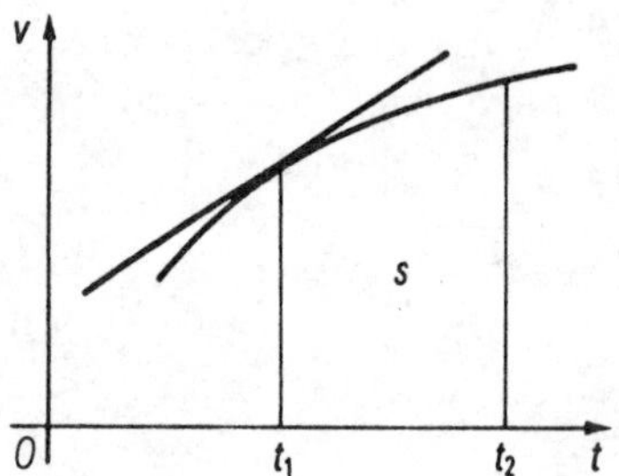

Figure 25.1

Example. A car travels 4 km in 2 minutes, from rest to rest. It accelerates with constant acceleration to its maximum velocity of 40 m s^{-1}, which it holds until it slows down with constant deceleration. The time accelerating is three times that decelerating. Find for how long the car is accelerating.

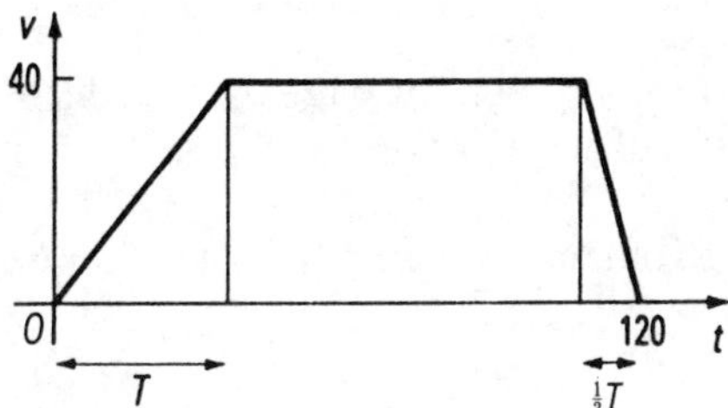

Figure 25.2

If the time spent accelerating is T seconds, the time decelerating is $\frac{1}{3}T$ seconds and the time at constant velocity is $(120-\frac{4}{3}T)$s. Considering the area under the velocity–time graph,

$$\tfrac{1}{2}\times 40T+40(120-\tfrac{4}{3}T)+\tfrac{1}{2}\times 40\times\tfrac{1}{3}T=4000$$
$$120-\tfrac{2}{3}T=100$$
$$T=30$$

The time taken accelerating is 30 s.

Exercise 25.1

1 A car is travelling with constant acceleration 0.8 m s^{-2}. If initially its velocity is 10 m s^{-1}, find its velocity 5 s later and the distance travelled in that time.

2 A car travelling with constant acceleration covers a certain distance in 2 minutes. Its average speed over the distance is 60 km h^{-1}, and during the second minute it travels 1200 m. Find the speed at the beginning of the interval and the acceleration.

3 A train starting from rest is uniformly accelerated until its speed is 45 km h^{-1}. The brakes are then applied to give a retardation twice as great as the acceleration, until its speed is 30 km h^{-1}. If the distance travelled during the retardation is 1 km, find the distance travelled while accelerating.

4 A stone is projected vertically upwards with a velocity of 24.5 m s^{-1} from a point 49 m above the ground. Taking the acceleration due to gravity as 9.8 m s^{-2}, find how long it takes to reach the ground.

5 A train starting from rest at station A accelerates uniformly until it reaches its maximum velocity of 120 km h^{-1}. It moves at this constant velocity for some time, then retards uniformly until it comes to rest at station B. Given that the acceleration and retardation are numerically equal, that the distance AB is 10 km and that the times of acceleration, constant velocity and retardation are numerically equal, find the time taken to go from station to station.

Variable acceleration

If a particle of constant mass is acted on by a force that varies, then since the relation between force and acceleration is described by Newton's second law, i.e.

force=mass×acceleration,

the acceleration varies, and the equations (1) to (4) given on pages 295 and 296 are not true. We have to return to our definition of acceleration.

If **the force is a function of time**, use $a=\frac{dv}{dt}$ to obtain v as a function of t, then $v=\frac{ds}{dt}$ to obtain s in terms of t.

Example 1. A body mass 10 kg is acted on by a force $5(1-e)^{-t/10}$ N. If the body initially has velocity of 2 m s^{-1} in the direction of the force, find the velocity after 5 s, and the displacement of the body at the end of the 5 s.

Since $F=ma$

$$5(1-e^{-t/10})=10\frac{dv}{dt}$$

i.e.

$$2\frac{dv}{dt}=1-e^{-t/10}$$

$$v=\tfrac{1}{2}(t+10e^{-t/10})+C$$

But $v=2$ when $t=0$, so $2=\tfrac{1}{2}(10)+C\Rightarrow C=-3$

$$v=\tfrac{1}{2}(t+10e^{-t/10}-3),$$

and the velocity after 5 s is $\tfrac{1}{2}(2+10e^{-\frac{1}{2}})$ m s^{-1}, about 4.03 m s^{-1}.

If the force is a function of the velocity, we still use $a=\frac{dv}{dt}$ but probably have to solve a differential equation with separable variables.

Example 2. A body mass 2 kg is acted on by a force $(8-v)$ N, where v m s^{-1} is the velocity of the body. If the body is initially at rest, find its velocity and the displacement after (a) 1 s, (b) 10 s.

Using $F=ma$ again,

$$8-v=2\frac{dv}{dt}$$

$$\frac{1}{8-v}\frac{dv}{dt}=\tfrac{1}{2}$$

$$-\ln(8-v)+C=\tfrac{1}{2}t$$

But when $t=0$, $v=0$ so $C=\ln 8$, and the equation of motion is

$$\ln 8-\ln (8-v)=\tfrac{1}{2}t$$
$$\ln\left(\frac{8}{8-v}\right)=\tfrac{1}{2}t$$
$$\frac{8}{8-v}=e^{\frac{1}{2}t}$$
$$8=(8-v)e^{\frac{1}{2}t}$$
$$v=8(1-e^{-\frac{1}{2}t})$$

After 1 s, the velocity is $8\ (1-e^{-\frac{1}{2}})$ m s^{-1}, about 3.1 m s^{-1}; after 10 s, the velocity is $8\ (1-e^{-5})$ m s^{-1}, very close to 8 m s^{-1}, and we can see that the velocity approaches 8 m s^{-1} as t becomes large. This is called the **limiting velocity**.

To find s, use $v=\dfrac{ds}{dt}$

So $$\frac{ds}{dt}=8\ (1-e^{-\frac{1}{2}t})$$
$$s=8t+16e^{-\frac{1}{2}t}+C$$

When $t=0$, $s=0$ since we almost always measure s from the point where $t=0$, so $0=16+C$, $C=-16$, and the displacement s is given by

$$s=8t+16e^{-\frac{1}{2}t}+C$$

Now when $t=1$, $s=8-16\ (1-e^{-\frac{1}{2}})$, about 1.7, so the displacement after 1 s is about 1.7 m; when $t=10$, $s=80-16\ (1-e^{-5})$, about 64, and the displacement is about 64 m. Notice that of course this is less than if the body was travelling all the time at its limiting velocity.

Force as a function of displacement

If the force acting on a body is a function of the displacement x, the acceleration and the velocity will also be functions of x. Then $\dfrac{dv}{dt}=\dfrac{dv}{dx}\cdot\dfrac{dx}{dt}=v\dfrac{dv}{dx}$, and this is the form that we have to use for the acceleration.

Example. The acceleration of a particle moving in a straight line is $(-4x)$ m s^{-2}, where the displacement is x m and the force is directed towards the origin. If initially the particle is at rest a distance 10 m from O, find the velocity with which it passes through O.

Taking the acceleration as $v\dfrac{dv}{dx}$,

$$v\frac{dv}{dx}=-4x,$$
$$\tfrac{1}{2}v^2=-2x^2+C$$

But $v=0$ when $x=10$, so $C=200$. The equation is

$$v^2=4\,(100-x^2)$$

and $v=20$ when $x=0$, so the particle passes through O with velocity 20 m s^{-1}.

If we wish to find a relation between x and t, write $v=\frac{dx}{dt}$, then $\frac{dx}{dt}=-2\sqrt{(100-x^2)}$, taking the negative square root since the particle is moving towards O.

Then $$\int\frac{-1}{\sqrt{(100-x^2)}}\,dx=2dt$$

$$\arccos\left(\frac{x}{10}\right)=2t+C.$$

But when $t=0$, $x=10$, so $C=0$, and the relation is

$$x=10\cos 2t.$$

Notice that we use $\int\frac{-1}{\sqrt{(100-x^2)}}\,dx=\arccos(x/10)$. Taking the principal value, the graph shows that $\frac{d}{dx}(\arccos x)$ is negative, whereas $\frac{d}{dx}(\arcsin x)$ is positive.

Displacement as a function of velocity

The form $v\frac{dv}{dx}$ is useful when we are given the acceleration as a function of the velocity, and wish to relate displacement and velocity.

Example (see page 298). A body mass 2 kg is acted on by a force $(8-v)$ N, where v m s^{-1} is the velocity of the body. Find the displacement of the body when the velocity is 4 m s^{-1} if the body was initially at rest.

Using acceleration as $v\frac{dv}{dx}$, $8-v=2v\frac{dv}{dx}$

$$x=\int\frac{2v}{8-v}dv$$

$$=\int\left(-2+\frac{16}{8-v}\right)dv$$

$$x=-2v-16\ln(8-v)+C.$$

When $x=0$, $v=0$, so $C=16\ln 8$ and $x=16\ln\left\{\frac{8}{(8-v)}\right\}-2v$

The displacement when $v=4$ is $16\ln 2-8$, about 3.1m.

Power

When a body is travelling in a straight line with velocity v under a force F, the power exerted (or developed) by the force is Fv. We are probably most familiar with this term when considering cars, where we know the power P, and can deduce that the propulsive force is P/v. In practice, the power produced by the engine of a car depends on the gearing, and also on the speed of the car at that instant, but may be nearly constant over a certain range of velocities. The SI unit of power is the watt (W), which is inconveniently small, so that the kilowatt (kW) is generally used. Note carefully whether W or kW is used in examinations.

Example 1. A particle mass m, initially at rest, is acted on by a force F, constant in direction, whose magnitude at time t is $k\left(1+\frac{t}{T}\right)$, $0\leqslant t\leqslant T$. Find the power developed by F at any time t, $t\leqslant T$.

Since $F=ma$,

$$a=\frac{k}{m}\left(1+\frac{t}{T}\right)$$

$$v=\frac{k}{m}\left(t+\frac{t^2}{2T}\right),$$

the constant of integration being 0 since $v=0$ when $t=0$.

The power is Fv, i.e.

$$=\frac{k^2}{m}\left(1+\frac{t}{T}\right)\left(t+\frac{t^2}{2T}\right)$$

$$=\frac{k^2t}{m}\left(1+\frac{3t}{2T}+\frac{t^2}{2T^2}\right)$$

Example 2. A car mass 500 kg has an engine that works at a constant rate of 40 kW. If there is a constant resistance to motion of 1000 N, find the time taken accelerating from 20 to 30 m s^{-1}.

The propulsive force produced by the engine is $\frac{40\,000}{v}$ N, so that $F=ma$ gives

$$\frac{40\,000}{v}-1000=500\frac{dv}{dt}$$

i.e. $$\frac{80-2v}{v}=\frac{dv}{dt}$$

$$2t=\int_{20}^{30}\frac{v\,dv}{40-v}$$

$$=\int_{20}^{30}\left(-1+\frac{40}{40-v}\right)dv$$

$$=\int_{20}^{30}(-v-40\ln(40-v))dv$$

$$=40\ln 2-10,$$
$$\simeq 17.7\text{ s}$$

Exercise 25.2

1 A body mass 1 kg initially at rest is acted on at time t seconds by a force $(40-12t^2)$ N. Find the velocity of the body after 2 s, and the displacement at that time. Find also how far the body moves in the third second of motion.

2 A lorry mass 6000 kg is travelling on level road. There is a constant resistance to motion of 2000 N, and the engine of the lorry exerts a force in the first minute of $50(100-t)$ N, where t seconds is the time since the motion started. Find the velocity after the lorry has been travelling for 30 s, and the displacement of the lorry at that time.

3 A particle moves in a straight line so that the acceleration, at time t seconds, is $(4+6t)$ m s^{-2}. If the particle travels 15 m between $t=1$ and $t=2$, find the initial velocity.

4 The acceleration of a particle moving in a straight line is $(2-v)$ m s^{-2}, where v m s^{-1} is the velocity of the particle. If the particle is initially at rest, find the velocity and the displacement after 1 s.

5 A particle mass 4 kg initially at rest is acted on by a force $(16-v^2)$ N, where v m s^{-1} is the velocity of the particle. Find the velocity of the particle after 1 s, and the limiting velocity.

6 A particle mass 4 kg initially at rest is acted on by a force $(16-v^2)$ N, where v m s^{-1} is the velocity of the particle. Find the displacement when the velocity is (a) 2 m s^{-1}, (b) 3.9 m s^{-1}.

7 A particle at rest is acted on by a force that produces an acceleration in a constant direction of $2(1+x)$ m s^{-2}, x m being the displacement from O. Find
(a) the velocity when the particle is 8 m from O,
(b) the displacement when the velocity is 4 m s^{-1}.

8 A particle unit mass is thrown vertically upwards with initial velocity u. The air exerts a resistance kv^2, where v is the velocity of the particle. Show that the greatest height reached by the particle is $\frac{1}{2k}\ln\left(1+\frac{ku^2}{g}\right)$.

9 A body mass 4 kg initially at rest is acted on by a force F which increases uniformly from 20 N to 40 N in 10 s, the direction of F remaining constant. Find the velocity attained by the body after 5 s and after 10 s, and the power developed by F at each of those times.
10 A car's engine exerts a constant power of 40 kW, which gives the car a maximum speed on level ground of 50 m s^{-1}. If the resistances to motion are proportional to the square of the speed, find the resistance when the speed is 25 m s^{-1}.
11 If the mass of the car in question 10 is 800 kg, show that the maximum speed the car can attain up a hill of 1 in 10 is about 10 m s^{-1}.
12 A car mass 800 kg has a maximum speed of 40 m s^{-1} when moving along a level road, with the engine working at 60 kW. Find the resistance to motion of the car.

If the resistance varies as the square of the speed at which the car is travelling, find the power developed by the engine when the car is
(a) travelling along a level road at a constant speed of 30 m s^{-1};
(b) travelling along the same road at 20 m s^{-1}, and accelerating at 0.5 m s^{-2},
(c) travelling at a constant speed of 20 m s^{-1} up an incline of 1 in 100.
13 A car has a maximum speed on level road of 60 m s^{-1} when the engine exerts P watts, and it can coast (i.e. run down at constant speed without power) down an incline of 1 in 20 at the same speed. If the engine exerts the same constant power P watts, how far would the car travel while accelerating on level ground from 30 m s^{-1} to 45 m s^{-1}, the resistance to motion being proportional to the square of the speed?

Use of vector notation 26

Displacement, velocity, acceleration 307

Relative velocity 308

Forces 309

Application of scalar product 309

Momentum and impulse 310

Kinetic energy 310

Work and power 310

Notes

If **r** is the displacement vector of a point P relative to an origin O,

the **velocity v** of P is $\frac{d\mathbf{r}}{dt}$,

the **acceleration a** of P is $\frac{d\mathbf{v}}{dt}$.

If $\mathbf{v}_A$ is the velocity of A, $\mathbf{v}_B$ the velocity of B, the **velocity of B relative to A** is $\mathbf{v}_B - \mathbf{v}_A$.

The **momentum** of a body mass m, velocity **v** is $m\mathbf{v}$;

the **impulse** exerted by a force **F** acting over the interval $t=0$ to $t=T$ is $\int_0^T \mathbf{F}\,dt$;

the **kinetic energy** of the body is $\frac{1}{2}mv^2$, and the **work done** by the force **F** is $\int_0^T \mathbf{F}.\mathbf{v}\,dt$, which is equal to $\frac{1}{2}mv^2 - \frac{1}{2}mu^2$. The **power** exerted by the force is **F.v.**

Units

The SI unit of **momentum** is newton seconds (Ns),
of **kinetic energy** and **work** is joules (J),
of **power** is watts (W).

Displacement, velocity, acceleration

When considering the displacement of a particle in two or three dimensions, the great advantage of vector algebra is apparent. If a particle is at a point P, coordinates (x, y), then its position vector $\mathbf{r}$ relative to the origin O can be written $x\mathbf{i}+y\mathbf{j}$ or $\begin{pmatrix}x\\y\end{pmatrix}$ if we are working in two dimensions, $x\mathbf{i}+y\mathbf{j}+z\mathbf{k}$ or $\begin{pmatrix}x\\y\\z\end{pmatrix}$ in three dimensions.

The velocity of a particle is merely $\frac{d\mathbf{r}}{dt}$, from the definition, and the acceleration likewise is $\frac{d\mathbf{v}}{dt}$. If $\mathbf{r}$ is a function of t, we can obtain the velocity of the particle and its acceleration.

Example 1. A particle moves in a plane so that its position vector $\mathbf{r}$ at time t is $t^3\mathbf{i}+t^2\mathbf{j}$. Find the velocity and acceleration of the particle at time t, and the speed after 5 s.

Since $\mathbf{r}=t^3\mathbf{i}+t^2\mathbf{j}$

$$\mathbf{v}\equiv\frac{d\mathbf{r}}{dt}=3t^2\mathbf{i}+2t\mathbf{j},$$

$$\mathbf{a}\equiv\frac{d\mathbf{v}}{dt}=6t\mathbf{i}+2\mathbf{j}.$$

The speed v is the magnitude of the velocity, so after 5 s, $\mathbf{v}=75\mathbf{i}+10\mathbf{j}$, and the speed is $\sqrt{(75^2+10^2)}$, about 75.7. The units are almost invariably the SI units, metres, seconds, newtons etc., so the speed is 75.7 m s^{-1}.

Example 2. A particle mass 2 kg has position vector $\mathbf{r}$ at time t seconds given in metres by $\mathbf{r}=t^4\mathbf{i}+6t\mathbf{j}$. Find the force acting on the particle after 10 s.

Since $\mathbf{v}\equiv\frac{d\mathbf{r}}{dt}$, $\quad \mathbf{v}=4t^3\mathbf{i}+6\mathbf{j}$

Since $\mathbf{a}\equiv\frac{d\mathbf{v}}{dt}$, $\quad \mathbf{a}=12t^2\mathbf{i}$

Since $\mathbf{F}=m\mathbf{a}$, $\quad \mathbf{F}=m(12t^2)\mathbf{i}$

$$=2400\mathbf{i}$$

The force is 2400 N, along the x-axis.

Many examination boards at present restrict their applications of vectors to two dimensions, but really three dimensions present no extra difficulty.

Example 3. A particle moves so that its displacement $\mathbf{r}$ at time t is given in metres by $\frac{1}{3}t^3\mathbf{i}+5t^2\mathbf{j}+22t\mathbf{k}$. Find the acceleration of the particle at time t, and the speed of the particle after 2 seconds.

Since $\mathbf{r}=\frac{1}{3}t^3\mathbf{i}+5t^2\mathbf{j}+22\mathbf{k}$,
$\mathbf{v}=t^2\mathbf{i}+10t\mathbf{j}+22\mathbf{k}$
$\mathbf{a}=2t\mathbf{i}+10\mathbf{j}$

Since $v=|\mathbf{v}|$, and the velocity after 2 s is $4\mathbf{i}+20\mathbf{j}+22\mathbf{k}$, the speed is $\sqrt{(4^2+20^2+22^2)}$, i.e. 30 m s^{-1}.

Relative velocity

All displacements determine the position of a particle relative to some one other point, so that if $\mathbf{r}_A$ is the displacement of a particle A relative to an origin, and $\mathbf{r}_B$ is the displacement of a particle B relative to that origin, the displacement of B relative to A is $\mathbf{r}_B-\mathbf{r}_A$, hence the velocity of B relative to A is

$$\frac{\mathrm{d}}{\mathrm{d}t}(\mathbf{r}_B-\mathbf{r}_A), \text{ i.e. } \mathbf{v}_B-\mathbf{v}_A$$

Example. Particles A and B are initially at points with position vectors $2\mathbf{i}$ and $\mathbf{j}$, respectively. A moves with constant velocity $(\mathbf{i}+\mathbf{j})$; B with constant velocity $(2\mathbf{i}-\mathbf{j})$. Find the velocity of B relative to A, and find also the least distance apart of the particles.

$$\mathbf{v}_A=\mathbf{i}+\mathbf{j},\ \mathbf{v}_B=2\mathbf{i}-\mathbf{j},$$

so the velocity of B relative to A is $\mathbf{v}_B-\mathbf{v}_A$, i.e. $(\mathbf{i}-2\mathbf{j})$.

At time t, $\mathbf{r}_A=2\mathbf{i}+t(\mathbf{i}+\mathbf{j})$, $\mathbf{r}_B=\mathbf{j}+t(2\mathbf{i}-\mathbf{j})$, so that the displacement of B relative to A is $(-2\mathbf{i}+\mathbf{j})+t(\mathbf{i}-2\mathbf{j})$, i.e. $(-2+t)\mathbf{i}+(1-2t)\mathbf{j}$. If the distance apart is d,

$$\begin{aligned} d^2&=(2-t)^2+(1-2t)^2\\ &=5-8t+5t^2\\ &=5(t^2-\tfrac{8}{5}t+\tfrac{16}{25})+\tfrac{9}{5}\\ &=5(t-\tfrac{4}{5})^2+\tfrac{9}{5}\end{aligned}$$

Therefore the least distance apart is $\sqrt{\frac{9}{5}}$. If we prefer, of course, we can use calculus to find the least value of d^2, but notice that d^2 is much easier to minimize than d.

Exercise 26.1

1 A particle P moves so that its position vector $\mathbf{r}$ metres at time $\mathbf{t}$ seconds, is given by

$$\mathbf{r}=t^2\mathbf{i}+2t\mathbf{j}$$

Find (a) its velocity, (b) its speed, when $t=1$.

Q.1 for each of the following expressions for $\mathbf{r}$:

$+t^2\,\mathbf{j}$, (b) $3t^2\,\mathbf{i}+2t^3\,\mathbf{j}$, (c) $(t^2+2)\,\mathbf{i}+t\,\mathbf{j}$.

le mass 2 kg has position vector $\mathbf{r}$ metres. Find the force $\mathbf{F}$ acting on

when $\mathbf{r}=$

(b) $2t\mathbf{i}+4\mathbf{j}$, (c) $t^3\mathbf{i}+3t^2\mathbf{j}$.

4 A particle mass 0.5 kg has velocity $\mathbf{v}$ m s^{-1}. Find the force $\mathbf{F}$ acting on the particle when $t=4$ given $v=$
(a) $t^2\mathbf{i}+2t\mathbf{j}$, (b) $t\mathbf{i}+t^3\mathbf{j}$, (c) $(t^2+t)\mathbf{i}+t^3\mathbf{j}$.
5 Points A and B have position vectors $\mathbf{r}_A$ and $\mathbf{r}_B$, respectively. Find the velocity of A relative to B when
(a) $\mathbf{r}_A=t^2\mathbf{i}+2t\mathbf{j}$, $\mathbf{r}_B=2t^2\mathbf{i}+t^3\mathbf{j}$, (b) $\mathbf{r}_A=2t\mathbf{i}+t^2\mathbf{j}$, $\mathbf{r}_B=t^3\mathbf{i}$.

Forces

We have seen above that a force can easily be described in two or three dimensions by its components. Forces can be added by adding components, so that if forces $\mathbf{F}_1$, $\mathbf{F}_2$ are such that $\mathbf{F}_1=3\mathbf{i}+2\mathbf{j}$, $\mathbf{F}_2=5\mathbf{i}-\mathbf{j}$, $\mathbf{F}_1+\mathbf{F}_2=8\mathbf{i}+\mathbf{j}$. Forces $\mathbf{F}_1$, $\mathbf{F}_2$, $\mathbf{F}_3$ passing through a point, are in equilibrium if and only if their sum is zero, so that if $\mathbf{F}_1+\mathbf{F}_2+\mathbf{F}_3=0$, $(3\mathbf{i}+2\mathbf{j})+(5\mathbf{i}-\mathbf{j})+\mathbf{F}_3=0$, $\mathbf{F}_3=-8\mathbf{i}-\mathbf{j}$.

Example. Forces $\mathbf{F}_1$, $\mathbf{F}_2$ are such that the magnitude of $\mathbf{F}_1$ is 14 N, and it acts in the direction of the vector $3\mathbf{i}+2\mathbf{j}-6\mathbf{k}$; $\mathbf{F}_2$ is of magnitude 30 N, and acts in the direction of the vector $2\mathbf{i}+10\mathbf{j}+11\mathbf{k}$. Find the magnitude of $\mathbf{F}_1+\mathbf{F}_2$.

The magnitude of the vector $3\mathbf{i}+2\mathbf{j}-6\mathbf{k}$ is $\sqrt{(3^2+2^2+(-6)^2)}$, i.e. 7, so that

$$\begin{aligned}\mathbf{F}_1&=2(3\mathbf{i}+2\mathbf{j}-6\mathbf{k})\\&=6\mathbf{i}+4\mathbf{j}-12\mathbf{k};\end{aligned}$$

the magnitude of $2\mathbf{i}+10\mathbf{j}+11\mathbf{k}$ is $\sqrt{(2^2+10^2+11^2)}$, i.e. 15, so that

$$\begin{aligned}\mathbf{F}_2&=2(2\mathbf{i}+10\mathbf{j}+11\mathbf{k})\\&=4\mathbf{i}+20\mathbf{j}+22\mathbf{k}\end{aligned}$$

and $\mathbf{F}_1+\mathbf{F}_2=10\mathbf{i}+24\mathbf{j}+10\mathbf{k}$, so the magnitude of $\mathbf{F}_1+\mathbf{F}_2$ is $\sqrt{(10^2+24^2+10^2)}$, i.e. 776; about 27.9 N.

Application of scalar product

The scalar product enables us to find the angle between two vectors, and this now allows us to compare directions of vectors.

Example. The position vector $\mathbf{r}$ of a particle at time t is $\sin t\mathbf{i}+\cos t\mathbf{j}$. Show that its acceleration is always perpendicular to its velocity.

Since $\mathbf{r}=\sin t\mathbf{i}+\cos t\mathbf{j}$,
$\mathbf{v}=\cos t\mathbf{i}-\sin t\mathbf{j}$
and $\mathbf{a}=-\sin t\mathbf{i}-\cos t\mathbf{j}$

Two vectors are perpendicular if their scalar product is zero, and

$$\begin{aligned}\mathbf{v}.\mathbf{a}.&=(\cos t\mathbf{i}-\sin t\mathbf{j}).(-\sin t\mathbf{i}-\cos t\mathbf{j})\\&=0\end{aligned}$$

so the velocity and acceleration are always perpendicular. We recognize that the particle is moving in a circle, centre the origin, radius 1.

Momentum and impulse

The momentum of a body mass m, velocity $\mathbf{v}$ is $m\mathbf{v}$; the impulse $\mathbf{I}$ produced by a force $\mathbf{F}$ acting for a time T is defined as

$$\mathbf{I}=\int_0^T \mathbf{F}\mathrm{d}t$$

Since $\mathbf{F}=m\mathbf{a}$

$$\mathbf{I}=\mathbf{F}\int_0^T m\mathbf{a}\mathrm{d}t=m\int_0^T \frac{\mathrm{d}\mathbf{v}}{\mathrm{d}t}\mathrm{d}t$$

$$=m(\mathbf{v}-\mathbf{u})$$

so that the impulse is equal to the change in momentum.

Kinetic energy

The kinetic energy of a particle mass m, velocity $\mathbf{v}$ is $\frac{1}{2}mv^2$, i.e. $\frac{1}{2}m\mathbf{v}.\mathbf{v}$. For example, the kinetic energy of a body mass 5 kg, velocity $(6\mathbf{i}-8\mathbf{j})$ m s^{-1} is $\frac{1}{2}(5)(6\mathbf{i}-8\mathbf{j}).(6\mathbf{i}-8\mathbf{j})=250$ joules.

Work and power

The work done by a force $\mathbf{F}$ is defined as $\int \mathbf{F}.\mathbf{v}\mathrm{d}t$. Since $\mathbf{F}=m\frac{\mathrm{d}\mathbf{v}}{\mathrm{d}t}$, the work done is

$$m\int \mathbf{v}.\frac{\mathrm{d}\mathbf{v}}{\mathrm{d}t}\mathrm{d}t=m(\tfrac{1}{2}v^2-\tfrac{1}{2}u^2)$$

which is the increase in kinetic energy.

The power exerted by a force $\mathbf{F}$ is the rate of doing work, i.e. $\frac{\mathrm{d}}{\mathrm{d}T}\int_0^T \mathbf{F}.\mathbf{v}\mathrm{d}t=\mathbf{F}.\mathbf{v}$.

Example. A particle mass 5 kg moves so that its position vector $\mathbf{r}$ at time t is $\mathbf{r}=\sin 2t\mathbf{i}+\cos 2t\mathbf{j}+2t\mathbf{k}$. Find (a) the momentum at time t, (b) the kinetic energy, (c) the work done on the particle in the time interval $t=0$ to $t=2$, (d) the force acting on the particle at time t, (e) the power exerted by this force.

Since $\mathbf{r}=\sin 2t\mathbf{i}+\cos 2t\mathbf{j}+2t\mathbf{k}$,

$\mathbf{v}=2\cos 2t\mathbf{i}-2\sin 2t\mathbf{j}+2\mathbf{k}$

$\mathbf{a}=-4\sin 2t\mathbf{i}-4\cos 2t\mathbf{j}$

The momentum is $m\mathbf{v}$, so the momentum is

$$5(2\cos 2t\mathbf{i}+-2\sin 2t\mathbf{j}+2\mathbf{k})$$
$$=10(\cos 2t\mathbf{i}-\sin 2t\mathbf{j}+\mathbf{k})\text{N s}$$

The kinetic energy is $\frac{1}{2}mv^2$, so this is

$$\tfrac{1}{2}(5)(2\cos 2t\mathbf{i}-2\sin 2t\mathbf{j}+2\mathbf{k}).(2\cos 2t\mathbf{i}-2\sin 2t\mathbf{j}+2\mathbf{k})$$
$$=20 \text{ joules, which is constant.}$$

The work done on the particle is $\int \mathbf{F}.\mathbf{v}dt$, i.e.

$$\int(5)(-4\sin 2t\mathbf{i}-4\cos 2t\mathbf{j}).(2\cos 2t\mathbf{i}-2\sin 2t\mathbf{j}+2\mathbf{k})dt=0,$$

as expected, since the kinetic energy is not changed.

The force acting on the particle we have already used,

$$\mathbf{F}=-20(\sin 2t\mathbf{i}+\cos 2t\mathbf{j})\text{N}$$

and the power exerted by this force is clearly zero, since no work is being done. We can see that $\mathbf{F}.\mathbf{v}=0$, as above. The particle is describing a helix.

Exercise 26.2

1 Forces $\mathbf{F}_1$ and $\mathbf{F}_2$ are defined by $\mathbf{F}_1=2\mathbf{i}+3\mathbf{j}$, $\mathbf{F}_2=3\mathbf{i}-\mathbf{j}$.
(a) Find in vector form their resultant $\mathbf{F}_1+\mathbf{F}_2$.
(b) Find the magnitude of $2\mathbf{F}_1+3\mathbf{F}_2$.
(c) Find the force $\mathbf{F}_3$ such that $\mathbf{F}_1$,$\mathbf{F}_2$ and $\mathbf{F}_3$ are in equilibrium.
(d) Find scalars λ and μ such that $\lambda\mathbf{F}_1+\mu\mathbf{F}_2=7\mathbf{i}+5\mathbf{j}$.
(e) Find the ratio $\alpha:\beta$ if $\alpha\mathbf{F}_1+\beta\mathbf{F}_2$ acts in the direction $\mathbf{j}$.
2 Find the kinetic energy of a mass 5 kg with velocity $\mathbf{v}$ m s^{-1} where
(a) $\mathbf{v}=3\mathbf{i}-4\mathbf{j}$, (b) $5\mathbf{i}+5\mathbf{j}$, (c) $\mathbf{i}+7\mathbf{j}$.
3 A body mass 4 kg strikes a fixed object with velocity $(3\mathbf{i}-5\mathbf{j})$ m s^{-1} and rebounds with velocity $(-2\mathbf{i}+4\mathbf{j})$ m s^{-1}. Find the impulse given to the moving body.

Miscellaneous exercise 26.3

In all the questions in this exercise, the standard notation $\mathbf{r}$, $\mathbf{v}$, etc., is used, and the units are kg, metres and seconds.
1 A body mass 4 kg has position vector $t^2\mathbf{i}+t^3\mathbf{j}$. Find its velocity and acceleration at time t, the speed after 2 s and the force acting on the body after 10 s.
2 A body mass m has position vector $\sin t\mathbf{i}+\cos t\mathbf{j}$. Show that the body moves with constant speed under the action of a force of constant magnitude.
3 A body mass 2 kg has position vector $e^{-t}\mathbf{i}+t^2\mathbf{j}+2\mathbf{k}$. Find the velocity and acceleration of the body at time t, and the force acting on the body.
4 A body mass 5 kg is acted on by a force 15 N in the direction of the vector $2\mathbf{i}-2\mathbf{j}+\mathbf{k}$. If the body is initially at the origin and has velocity $4\mathbf{k}$, find the displacement of the body after 2 s.
5 A body mass 3 kg is acted on by a force $6t\mathbf{i}-36t^2\mathbf{j}$. If the body is initially at rest, find its velocity and displacement at time t.

6 Particles A and B have constant velocities $(\mathbf{i}+\mathbf{j})$ and $(2\mathbf{i}-\mathbf{j})$, respectively. If they are initially at points position vectors $\mathbf{i}$ and $k\mathbf{j}$, respectively, find the displacement of B relative to A at time t, and find the value of k if the particles collide.

7 Particles A and B, initially at points with position vectors $2\mathbf{i}$ and $3\mathbf{j}$, have constant velocities of $(\mathbf{i}+\mathbf{j})$ and $(2\mathbf{i}-\mathbf{j})$, respectively. Find the distance apart of A and B at time t, and when this distance is least.

8 Concurrent forces $\mathbf{F}_1$, $\mathbf{F}_2$, $\mathbf{F}_3$ are described by the vectors $2\mathbf{i}+3\mathbf{j}$, $4\mathbf{i}-5\mathbf{j}$ and $6\mathbf{i}+2\mathbf{j}$, respectively. Find the magnitude of
(a) $\mathbf{F}_1+\mathbf{F}_2$, (b) $\mathbf{F}_1+\mathbf{F}_2+\mathbf{F}_3$, (c) $2\mathbf{F}_1+\mathbf{F}_2-3\mathbf{F}_3$.

9 Concurrent forces $\mathbf{F}_1$, $\mathbf{F}_2$ and $\mathbf{F}_3$ are such that $\mathbf{F}_1=6\mathbf{i}+5\mathbf{j}$, $\mathbf{F}_2$ is in the direction of the vector $-3\mathbf{i}-4\mathbf{j}$ and $\mathbf{F}_3$ is in the direction of the vector $\mathbf{j}$. If the system of forces is in equilibrium, find the magnitude of each of the three forces.

10 A particle mass m moves under the action of a force so that its position vector $\mathbf{r}$ is $(\frac{1}{3}t^3\mathbf{i}+\frac{1}{2}t^2\mathbf{j}+t\mathbf{k})$. Find, at time t,
(a) the momentum of the particle,
(b) the kinetic energy of the particle,
(c) the force acting on the particle,
(d) the power exerted by this force.

11 A force $(-\mathbf{i}+3\mathbf{j})$ N acts on a body mass 5 kg. If the body initially has a velocity of $(2\mathbf{i}-\mathbf{j})$ m s^{-1}, show, by considering the impulse of the force, that 5 s later the body is moving at right angles to its initial direction.

12 A body mass 3 kg, velocity $(4\mathbf{i}+5\mathbf{j})$m s^{-1}, receives an impulse of $(6\mathbf{i}-9\mathbf{j})$ Ns. Find the cosine of the angle through which the body is deflected.

13 A body mass 2 kg is acted on by a force $\mathbf{F}$, where $\mathbf{F}=12(t\mathbf{i}+\mathbf{j})$ N. If the body is initially at rest, find its velocity when $t=2$, and its momentum and kinetic energy then.

14 Particles A, B and C are such that the velocity of A is $(3\mathbf{i}+8\mathbf{j})$, of B is $(-4\mathbf{i}-\mathbf{j})$. The velocity of C relative to A is in the direction $\mathbf{i}-3\mathbf{j}$; the velocity of C relative to B is at right angles to this. Find the velocity of C.

15 Forces $\mathbf{i}+\mathbf{j}-\mathbf{k}$ and $2\mathbf{i}+3\mathbf{j}-2\mathbf{k}$ act at points $\mathbf{i}$ and $\mathbf{i}+3\mathbf{j}$, respectively. Show that the lines of action of these forces intersect, and find the single force to which they are equivalent.

16 When a motorist is driving with velocity $4\mathbf{i}+3\mathbf{j}$ the wind appears to come from the direction of $-\mathbf{j}$; when he doubles his velocity the wind appears to come from the direction $(-\mathbf{i}-\mathbf{j})$. Find the true velocity of the wind.

17 Find the cosine of the angle between the forces $\mathbf{F}_1=\mathbf{i}+\mathbf{j}-3\mathbf{k}$ and $\mathbf{F}_2=\mathbf{i}-3\mathbf{j}-\mathbf{k}$.

18 The force $\mathbf{F}=4\mathbf{i}+2\mathbf{j}+3\mathbf{k}$ moves a particle along the line from the origin to the point $5\mathbf{i}+10\mathbf{j}+20\mathbf{k}$. Find the work done by this force.

19 A particle mass 4 kg moves from rest at the origin under the action of two forces, each magnitude 10 N. One force is parallel to $3\mathbf{i}-4\mathbf{j}$; the other is parallel to $4\mathbf{i}+3\mathbf{j}$. Find
(a) the acceleration of the particle,
(b) the velocity of the particle after 5 s,
(c) the increase in kinetic energy during the fifth second of motion,
(d) the power exerted by the forces after 5 s.

20 A body mass 1 kg, velocity $(6\mathbf{i}-12\mathbf{j})$ m s^{-1} embeds itself in a body mass 5 kg, initially at rest, so that they move away together. Assuming that momentum is conserved, find the loss of kinetic energy due to the impact.

21 The position vector $\mathbf{r}$ of a point $\mathbf{P}$ at time t is $\mathbf{i}+t\mathbf{j}$. Find an expression in terms of t for θ, the angle between OP and $\mathbf{i}$, and hence obtain an expression for the angular speed of OP.

22 A particle mass 2 kg is initially at rest. It is then acted on by a force $3t^2\mathbf{i}+4t^3\mathbf{j}$ for 2 s. Find

(a) the final momentum,

(b) the final kinetic energy of the body,

(c) the power exerted by the force at the end of 2 s.

Direct impact 27

Newton's experimental law 318

Notes

Always draw a diagram, as in Figure 27.1, marking the directions of the velocities

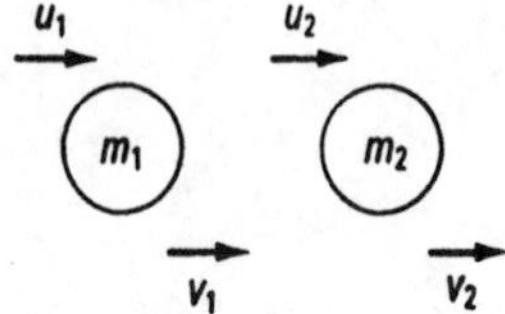

Figure 27.1

Momentum is conserved, i.e.

$$m_1\mathbf{u}_1+m_2\mathbf{u}_2=m_1\mathbf{v}_1+m_2\mathbf{v}_2$$

Newton's experimental law

velocity of separation $= e \times$ velocity of approach

i.e. $v_2-v_1=e(u_1-u_2)$ *Note the signs.*

For **impact with a wall** (Figure 27.2), this becomes

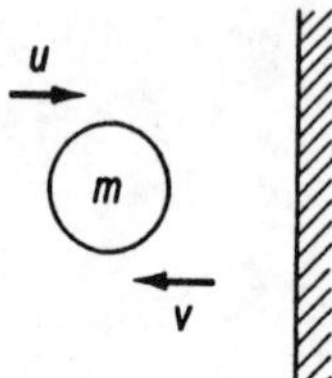

Figure 27.2

and the **impulse** given to the wall is $m(1+e)\mathbf{u}$.

The momentum of the body parallel to the wall is not altered by the impact.

If two bodies A and B collide, then by Newton's third law, the force exerted by A on B is equal and opposite to the force exerted by B on A, while the two bodies are in contact. Since momentum is $\int_{t_1}^{t_2} \mathbf{F} dt$, the vector sum of the change in momentum of the two bodies is zero, i.e.

the momentum of the two bodies is conserved.

If the bodies have mass m_1, m_2, initial velocities $\mathbf{u}_1$, $\mathbf{u}_2$ and final velocities $\mathbf{v}_1$, $\mathbf{v}_2$, respectively (Figure 27.3), then

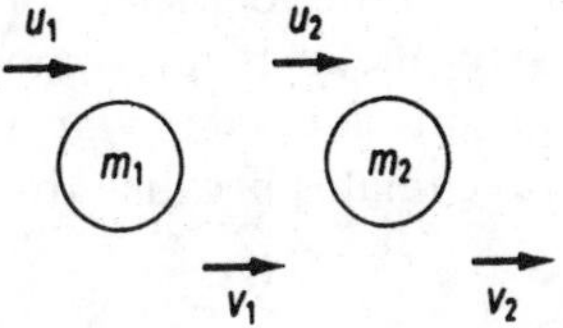

Figure 27.3

$$m_1\mathbf{u}_1+m_2\mathbf{u}_2=m_1\mathbf{v}_1+m_2\mathbf{v}_2.$$

It almost invariably helps to draw a diagram and to insert the given velocities.

Newton's experimental law

Newton found by experiment that when two small spheres collide, the ratio

$$\frac{\text{velocity of separation}}{\text{velocity of approach}}$$

is independent of the velocities of the spheres before impact, provided that these velocities are neither too large nor too small. This ratio is called the coefficient of restitution and denoted by e. It is an interesting property of e that for some substances e varies considerably with temperature, so that squash players warm the ball before a match, and golfers prefer to play in warm climates because the ball travels much further after impact.

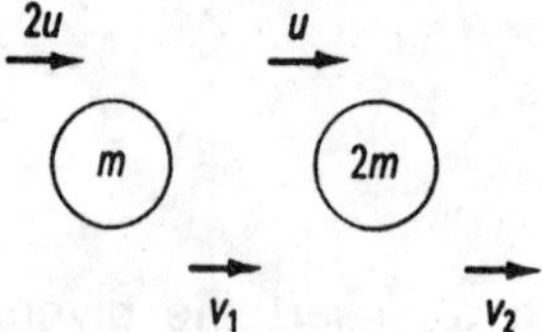

Figure 27.4

Example 1. Two small spheres, mass m, $2m$ are travelling in the same straight line with velocities $2\mathbf{u}$ and $\mathbf{u}$, respectively. If $e=\frac{1}{3}$, find the velocity of each sphere after the impact.

Since momentum is conserved, $2m\mathbf{u}+2m\mathbf{u}=m\mathbf{v}_1+2m\mathbf{v}_2$, $\mathbf{v}_1$ and $\mathbf{v}_2$ being the velocity of each sphere after the impact.

From Newton's experimental law,

$$\mathbf{v}_2-\mathbf{v}_1=\tfrac{1}{3}(2\mathbf{u}-\mathbf{u}) \qquad (1)$$

Solving simultaneously, $\mathbf{v}_1=\frac{10}{9}\,\mathbf{u}$ and $\mathbf{v}_2=\frac{13}{9}\,\mathbf{u}$.

Always take care that the quantitites equated in equation (1) are of the same sign; the diagram should help to ensure that you have been consistent in the directions in which you suppose the bodies to be travelling after the impact; if $\mathbf{v}_1$ is negative, it merely means the body is travelling in the opposite direction.

Example 2. A small body mass $3m$ moving with velocity $u\mathbf{i}$ strikes directly another small body mass $4m$, velocity $-3u\mathbf{i}$; as a result of the impact the body mass $4m$ is brought to rest. Find the coefficient of restitution e.

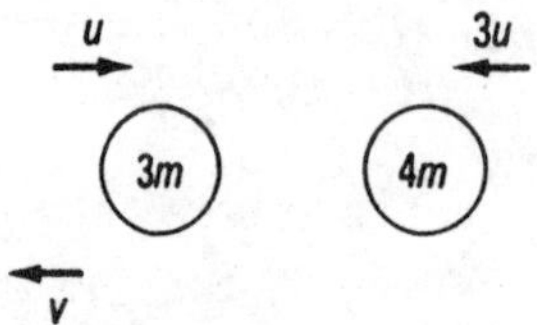

Figure 27.5

From the conservation of momentum,

$$3mu - 12mu = -3mv$$

i.e. $$v = 3u$$

From Newton's law,

$$e(4u) = v$$
$$e = \tfrac{3}{4}$$

Exercise 27.1

1 Two small spheres, masses m and $2m$, moving in the same straight line with velocities u and $4u$, meet and coalesce. Find their common velocity.

2 Two small spheres, masses m, $2m$, are moving in the direction $\mathbf{i}$, with velocities $\mathbf{u}_1, \mathbf{u}_2$; the coefficient of restitution between the spheres is 0.6. Find their velocities after the collision if

(a) $\mathbf{u}_1 = 4\mathbf{i}$, $\mathbf{u}_2 = \mathbf{i}$, (b) $\mathbf{u}_1 = 4\mathbf{i}$, $\mathbf{u}_2 = -\mathbf{i}$, (c) $\mathbf{u}_1 = 3\mathbf{i}$, $\mathbf{u}_2 = -2\mathbf{i}$.

3 A small sphere mass m_1, velocity $9\ \mathrm{m\ s^{-1}}$ overtakes and collides with a similar sphere mass m_2, velocity $3\ \mathrm{m\ s^{-1}}$. After the impact the spheres continue in the same direction with velocities $5\ \mathrm{m\ s^{-1}}$ and $7\ \mathrm{m\ s^{-1}}$, respectively. Show that $m_1 = m_2$ and find e.

4 A particle mass $2m$, velocity $4u$ coalesces with a particle mass m, moving in the same direction with velocity u. Find the kinetic energy lost in the collision.

If instead of coalescing, the bodies are such that $e = \tfrac{1}{2}$, find now the loss of kinetic energy.

5 Two particles A and B, each of mass m, moving in opposite directions with speeds $2u$ and u, respectively, collide directly. As a result of the collision, the velocity of B is reversed but its speed is not altered. Find e and the final velocity of A.

6 A small sphere A, mass m, velocity $4u$, strikes directly another identical small sphere B moving in the same direction with velocity $2u$. After the impact the velocity of B is $3u$. Find the coefficient of restitution between A and B.

The sphere B continues with constant velocity $3u$ until striking at right angles a smooth vertical wall, from which it rebounds and is later brought to rest by a second impact with sphere A. Find the coefficient of restitution between B and the wall.

7 Two small spheres mass m and $2m$ are moving in opposite directions with speeds $2u$ and u. When they collide, one-third of their kinetic energy is lost. Find the coefficient of restitution.

8 A small sphere mass m, velocity $3u$, strikes an identical sphere moving in the same direction with velocity u. Find the impulse of one sphere on the other, in terms of m, e and u.

9 A small sphere, mass 1 kg, velocity $4\mathbf{i}\ \mathrm{m\ s^{-1}}$, strikes a similar sphere, mass 2 kg, velocity $\mathbf{i}\ \mathrm{m\ s^{-1}}$. If $e = 0.4$, find the velocity of each sphere after the impact, the impulse exerted by each sphere on the other, and the loss of kinetic energy in the impact.

10 Two small spheres, masses m, $2m$, are fixed one to each end of a light inextensible string. The string is held taut and horizontal, with its mid-point fixed, then the spheres are released from rest. If $e=\frac{1}{2}$, show that one sphere is brought to rest by the first impact, and the other by the second impact.

Projectiles 28

Time of flight 323

Range on a horizontal plane 323

Maximum range on a horizontal plane 323

Greatest height 324

Impact with a vertical wall 326

Range on an inclined plane 326

Particle bouncing on an inclined plane 327

Equation of the trajectory 329

Direction of motion 329

Notes

If a particle is projected from a point O with velocity U at an angle θ above the horizontal,

the **time** taken to return to the horizontal level of O is $\dfrac{2U\sin\theta}{g}$

the **range** on the horizontal plane through O is $\dfrac{U^2\sin 2\theta}{g}$

the **greatest height** attained is $\dfrac{U^2\sin^2\theta}{2g}$

The **range** on the horizontal plane through O **is a maximum** if $\theta=\pi/4$.
The range on a **plane through O inclined at angle** α above the horizontal is

$$\frac{U^2}{g\cos^2\alpha}[\sin(2\theta+\alpha)-\sin\alpha]$$

the **greatest range** on this plane is

$$\frac{U^2}{g\cos^2\alpha}(1-\sin\alpha)$$

Referred to axes through O, the equation of the **trajectory** is

$$y=x\tan\theta-\frac{1}{2}\left(\frac{gx^2\sec^2\theta}{U^2}\right)$$

Time of flight

If a particle is projected from a point O with velocity U at an angle θ above the horizontal, the vertical component of the velocity is $U \sin \theta$; the rate of change of velocity is $-g$, the acceleration due to gravity, so the time taken to reach the highest point on the path is $U \sin \theta/g$, and the time taken to return to the horizontal level of O is $2U \sin \theta/g$.

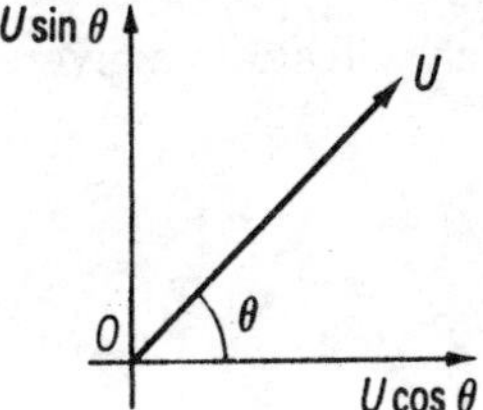

Figure 28.1

Range on a horizontal plane

Since the horizontal component of the velocity is constant, $U \cos \theta$, the horizontal distance travelled is

$$\left\{\frac{2U \sin \theta}{g}\right\} U \cos \theta = \frac{U^2 \sin 2\theta}{g}$$

Maximum range on a horizontal plane

The greatest value of $\sin 2\theta$ is 1, when θ is 45° or $\pi/4$ rad, so that the greatest range on a horizontal plane is U^2/g.

To find the angle of elevation required to attain a given horizontal range less than the maximum, say a range of kU^2/g.

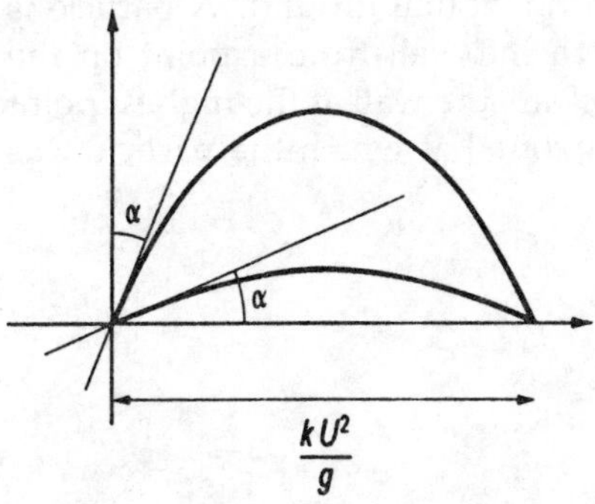

Figure 28.2

$$\frac{kU^2}{g}=\frac{U^2 \sin 2\theta}{g}$$

$\therefore \quad \sin 2\theta=k$

$$2\theta=\alpha \text{ or } \pi-\alpha, \text{ where } \sin \alpha=k$$

Thus $\quad \theta=\frac{\alpha}{2} \text{ or } \frac{\pi}{2}-\frac{\alpha}{2}.$

We see that there are two angles of elevation either of which will attain a given range.

Greatest height

Since the vertical component of the initial velocity is $U \sin \theta$, the greatest height attained is $U^2 \sin^2 \theta/2g$. This can be found by using the constant acceleration formula,

$$v^2=u^2+2as$$
$$0=(U \sin \theta)^2-2gs$$
$$\therefore \quad s=U^2 \sin^2 \theta/2g$$

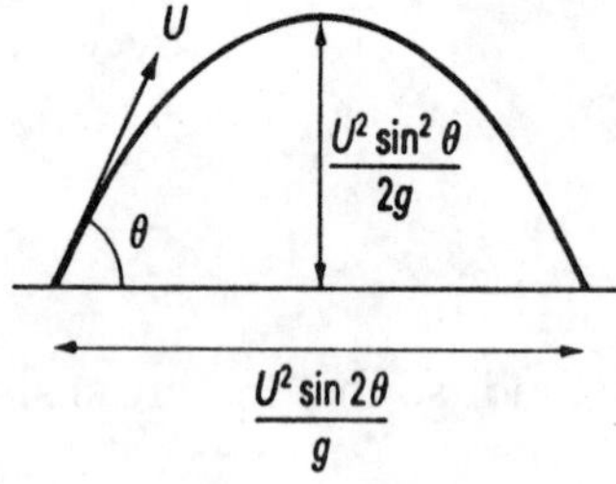

Figure 28.3

Example. A vertical wall height h stands on horizontal ground. A particle is projected in a vertical plane at right angles to the wall from a point on the ground distance d from the wall so that it just clears the wall at the highest point of its trajectory. Find the angle above the horizontal at which the particle was projected and the velocity of projection.

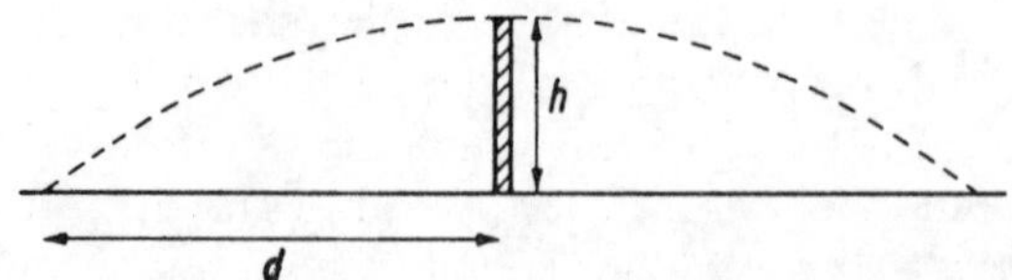

Figure 28.4

Since the particle just clears the wall at the highest point on its path, d is half the range on the horizontal plane,

$$d=\frac{V^2}{2g}\sin 2\theta$$

$$gd=V^2\sin\theta\cos\theta \tag{1}$$

Since h is the greatest height attained,

$$2gh=V^2\sin^2\theta \tag{2}$$

Dividing (2) by (1) gives $\tan\theta=2h/d$, so the angle above the horizontal is $\arctan(h/2d)$.

To find V, use a right-angled triangle as shown in Figure 28.5 to find $\sin\theta=\dfrac{2h}{\sqrt{(4h^2+d^2)}}$, so

$$V^2=2gh\,\frac{(4h^2+d^2)}{4h^2}$$

$$\therefore \qquad V=\sqrt{\left(\frac{g(4h^2+d^2)}{2h}\right)}$$

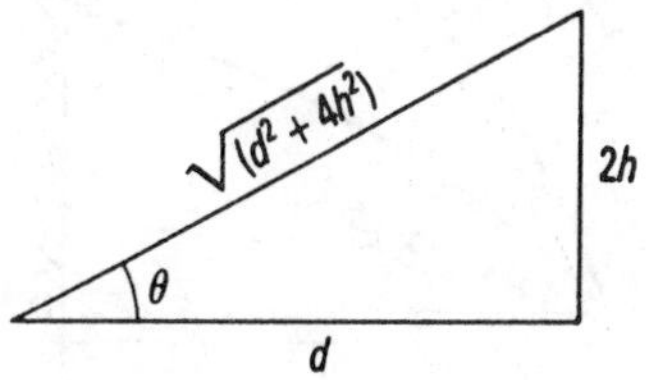

$\sqrt{(d^2+4h^2)}$ $2h$ θ d

Figure 28.5

Exercise 28.1 (Take $g=10\text{ m s}^{-2}$)

1 A ball is thrown from point O with velocity 25 m s^{-1} at 30° above the horizontal. Find
(a) the time before the ball reaches the highest point P in its path,
(b) the height of P above the horizontal plane through O,
(c) the time which elapses after projection before the ball returns to the horizontal plane,
(d) the range on the horizontal plane.

2 Find the vertical velocity with which a ball must be thrown to reach a window 10 metres above the ground. If the ball passes through this window with velocity of 5 m s^{-1}, with what velocity was it thrown?

3 A cricketer strikes a ball just above the ground so that it leaves the bat with velocity 25 m s^{-1} at 60° above the horizontal. Find how far above the ground it is when it passes over a fielder 50 m from the bat.

4 A cricketer scores 6 runs if the ball passes over the boundary before it touches the ground. If the boundary is 60 metres from the cricketer, find the least velocity he must give to the ball to score a '6'. If the cricketer strikes the ball at 30° above the horizontal, what is then the least velocity he must give to the ball?

5 An aircraft flying horizontally at 360 km h^{-1} releases a bomb (with no velocity relative to the aircraft) at a stationary target 2 km ahead of the aircraft. What must be the height of the aircraft above the horizontal plane through the target if the bomb hits the target?

Impact with a vertical wall

If a particle is projected so that it bounces off a smooth vertical wall, the vertical velocity of the particle is unaltered, so that the time of flight is not affected by the impact. This of course is true however many impacts there are with vertical surfaces. The horizontal component of velocity is reversed and reduced by a factor e.

Example. A particle is projected with speed U from a point O distance d from a smooth vertical wall. The particle returns to O after bouncing on the wall. Find the angle α above the horizontal at which the particle was projected.

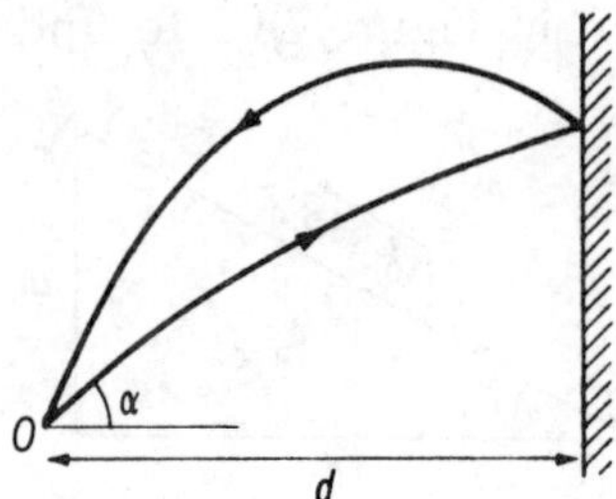

Figure 28.6

The vertical motion is not affected by the impact with the wall so the time of flight is $2U \sin \alpha/g$. The time to reach the wall is $d/(U \cos \alpha)$, and the time to return to O from the wall is $d/(eU \cos \alpha)$, so that if it returns to O,

$$\frac{2U \sin \alpha}{g} = \frac{d}{U \cos \alpha} + \frac{d}{eU \cos \alpha}$$

i.e. $$2U \sin \alpha \cos \alpha = \frac{gd}{U}\left(1 + \frac{1}{e}\right)$$

$\therefore$ $$\sin 2\alpha = \frac{gd}{U^2}\left(1 + \frac{1}{e}\right)$$

i.e. $$\alpha = \frac{1}{2} \arcsin \left[\frac{gd}{U^2}\left(1 + \frac{1}{e}\right)\right]$$

There will, of course, be two possible values for α.

Range on an inclined plane

When considering motion relative to an inclined plane it is usually advisable to consider the velocity and acceleration along and at right angles to the plane.

Considering motion perpendicular to the plane, the initial velocity in that direction is $U \sin \theta$, the acceleration is $-g \cos \alpha$, so that the time until the velocity

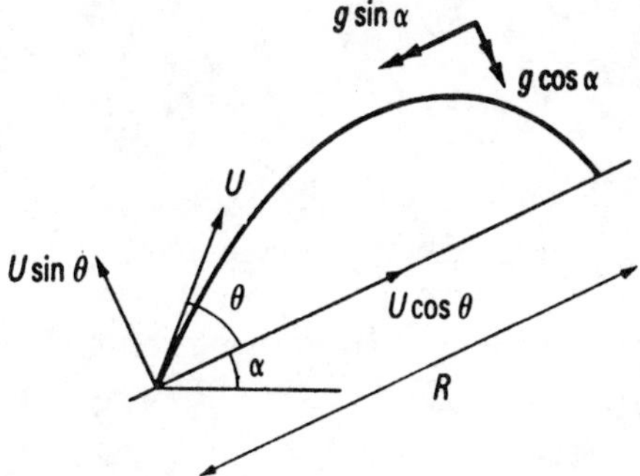

Figure 28.7

perpendicular to the plane is zero is $U \sin \theta / g \cos \alpha$, and the time of flight until the particle returns to the plane is $2U \sin \theta / (g \cos \alpha)$. Since $s = ut + \frac{1}{2}at^2$, as the acceleration is constant, the range R along the plane is

$$U \cos \theta \times \frac{2U \sin \theta}{g \cos \alpha} - \tfrac{1}{2}(g \sin \alpha)\frac{4U^2 \sin^2 \theta}{g^2 \cos^2 \alpha}$$

i.e.

$$R = \frac{2U^2 \sin \theta (\cos \theta \cos \alpha - \sin \theta \sin \alpha)}{g \cos^2 \alpha}$$

$$= \frac{2U^2 \sin \theta \cos (\theta + \alpha)}{g \cos^2 \alpha}$$

$$= \frac{U^2}{g \cos^2 \alpha}[\sin (2\theta + \alpha) - \sin \alpha]$$

As θ varies, the greatest value of $\sin 2\theta$ is 1, so that the greatest range on a plane inclined at an angle above the horizontal is

$$\frac{U^2}{g \cos^2 \alpha}(1 - \sin \alpha)$$

Replacing α by $-\alpha$, the greatest range down a plane inclined at angle α to the horizontal is

$$\frac{U^2}{g \cos^2 \alpha}(1 + \sin \alpha)$$

Particle bouncing on an inclined plane

If an elastic particle is projected so that it bounces on an inclined plane (Figure 28.8), the velocity along the line of the plane is unaltered by the impact with the plane; the velocity perpendicular to the plane is reversed and reduced by a factor e, so that the time of flight between successive bounces is reduced by a factor e.

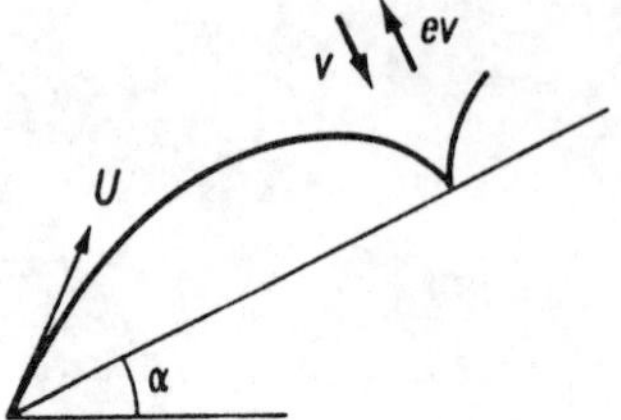

Figure 28.8

Example. A ball is projected with speed U from a point O on a smooth plane inclined at an angle α above the horizontal, so that it bounces on the plane and returns to O on the *nth* bounce. Find the tangent of the angle made by the initial velocity of the ball and the plane.

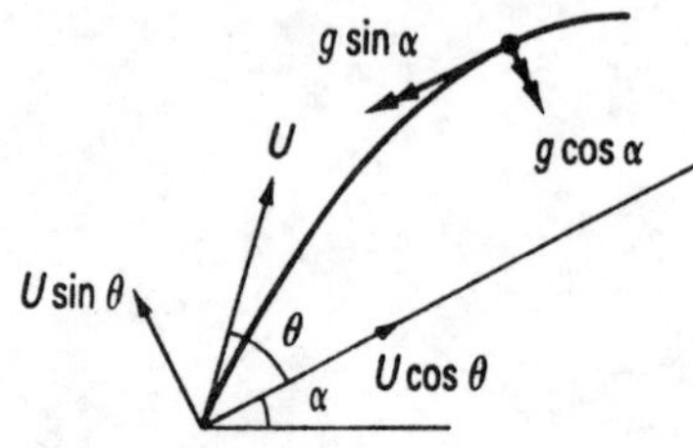

Figure 28.9

If θ is the angle between the direction of projection and the plane, the time until the first bounce is $2U \sin \theta / g \cos \alpha$, so the time until the nth bounce is

$$\frac{2U \sin \theta}{g \cos \alpha} + \frac{2eU \sin \theta}{g \cos \alpha} + \frac{2e^2U \sin \theta}{g \cos \alpha} \dots$$

$$= \frac{2U \sin \theta}{g \cos \alpha} (1+e+e^2 \dots e^{n-1})$$

$$= \frac{2U \sin \theta}{g \cos \alpha} \left(\frac{1-e^n}{1-e}\right)$$

In this time the ball must have returned to O, and we could use $s=ut+\frac{1}{2}at^2$ to find an equation relating u to t. It is easier though to see that if $s=0$, $t=2u/(-a)$, so that since along the plane $u=U \cos \theta$ and $a=-g \sin \alpha$, $t=2U \cos \theta / g \sin \alpha$ thus

$$\frac{2U \cos \theta}{g \sin \alpha} = \frac{2U \sin \theta}{g \cos \alpha} \left(\frac{1-e^n}{1-e}\right)$$

$$\therefore \qquad \tan \theta = \cot \alpha \left(\frac{1-e}{1-e^n}\right)$$

Equation of the trajectory

Taking the point of projection as the origin of coordinates, considering the horizontal distance at time t, $x=U\cos\theta t$, and considering the vertical distance, $y=U\sin\theta t-\frac{1}{2}gt^2$. Eliminating t between these equations we have

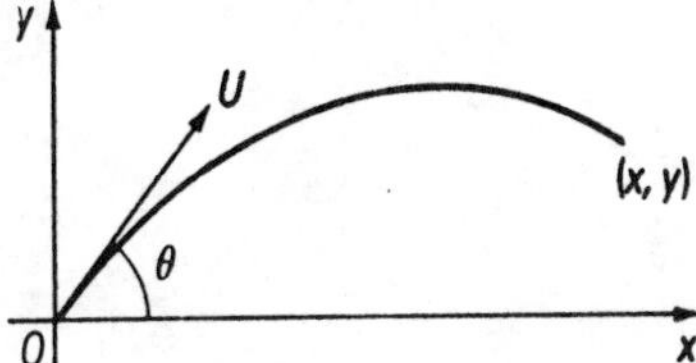

Figure 28.10

$$y=x\tan\theta-\frac{1}{2}\frac{gx^2}{U^2}\sec^2\theta$$

which is the equation of the path of the particle, called the **trajectory**.

If the origin O is taken at the highest point on the path, $\theta=0$ and the equation is $y=-\frac{1}{2}\frac{gx^2}{U^2}$.

Direction of motion

The gradient of a curve is dy/dx, and since at any instant the particle is travelling along the tangent to the curve at that instant, the direction of motion is given by dy/dx.

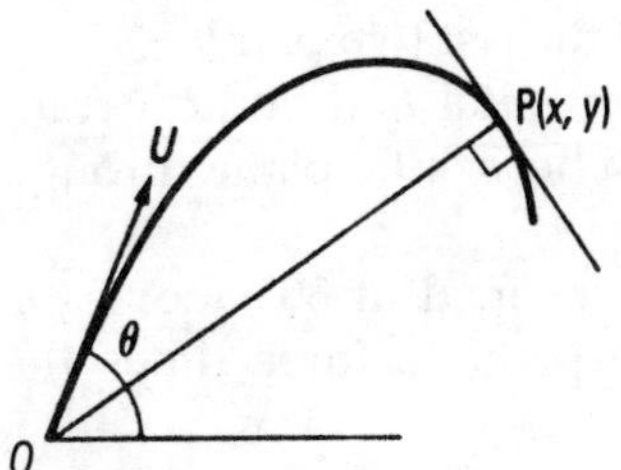

Figure 28.11

Example. A cricket ball is hit from a point O at an angle of elevation θ above the horizontal. Prove that there are two points P on the trajectory at which the direction of motion of the ball is perpendicular to OP, if and only if $\tan\theta>2\sqrt{2}$.

The equation of the trajectory is $y = x\tan\theta - \dfrac{gx^2}{2V^2}\sec^2\theta$

$$\therefore \qquad \frac{dy}{dx} = \tan\theta - \frac{gx}{V^2}\sec^2\theta$$

The gradient of OP is $\dfrac{y}{x}$, i.e. $\tan\theta - \dfrac{gx}{2V^2}\sec^2\theta$.

If the direction of motion is perpendicular to OP,

$$\left(\tan\theta - \frac{gx}{V^2}\sec^2\theta\right)\left(\tan\theta - \frac{gx}{2V^2}\sec^2\theta\right) = -1$$

i.e. $$\tan^2\theta - \frac{3gx}{2V^2}\sec^2\theta\tan\theta + \frac{g^2x^2}{2V^4}\sec^4\theta = -1$$

i.e. $$\frac{g^2x^2}{2V^4}\sec^2\theta - \frac{3gx}{2V^2}\tan\theta + 1 = 0,$$

using $\tan^2\theta + 1 = \sec^2\theta$ and dividing by $\sec^2\theta$. This is a quadratic in x, with two real distinct roots if

$$\frac{9g^2}{4V^2}\tan^2\theta > 4\frac{g^2\sec^2\theta}{2V^4}$$

i.e. $$9\tan^2\theta > 8(\tan^2\theta + 1)$$

i.e. $$\tan\theta > 2\sqrt{2}.$$

Exercise 28.2

1 A golfer drives a ball over a flat horizontal course, giving it a velocity of 35 m s^{-1} when it leaves the club. What is the greatest distance he can drive the ball? At what angle to the horizontal should he strike the ball if it is to have a range of 100 m, the velocity with which it leaves the club still being 35 m s^{-1}? Find the greatest height attained by the ball on each of the last two paths.

2 A particle is projected with a velocity whose horizontal and vertical components are u and v, respectively. Find the range on a horizontal plane through the point of projection.

3 A particle is projected from a point on a plane inclined at 30° above the horizontal. Prove that the greatest range down the plane is three times the greatest range up the plane.

4 A particle is projected with velocity V at an angle $(\alpha + \theta)$ above the horizontal from a point in a plane inclined at angle θ above the horizontal. Show that the particle strikes the plane at right angles if $2\tan\alpha = \cot\theta$.

5 A ball is thrown with speed 14 m s^{-1} from a window 25 m above a level horizontal playground and lands 10 m from the point vertically below the point of projection. Find the tangent of the angle, the direction of motion the ball made initially with the horizontal, and the direction of motion, 1 s later, of the ball along each of the two possible paths. Find also the ratio of the times of flight of the ball along the two possible trajectories.

6 A ball is thrown from a point P on smooth horizontal ground towards a smooth vertical wall, distance d from P. The ball returns to P, having bounced on the wall and having bounced once on the ground. The coefficient of restitution between the ball and the wall, and between the ball and the ground is e. If the speed of projection is $\sqrt{(2gd/e)}$, find the angle above the horizontal at which the ball was projected. Sketch the two possible paths of the ball.

Motion in a circle 29

Acceleration towards the centre 336

Use of parameters 336

Motion in a horizontal circle 337

Motion in a vertical circle 339

Notes

A particle will not describe a circle unless it has an acceleration towards the centre of the circle of $\mathbf{v}^2/r$, or $r\omega^2$. Therefore there must be a central force of $m\mathbf{v}^2/r$.

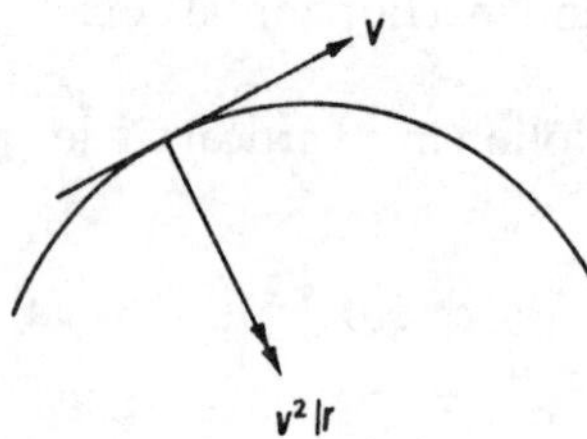

Figure 29.1

Conical pendulum

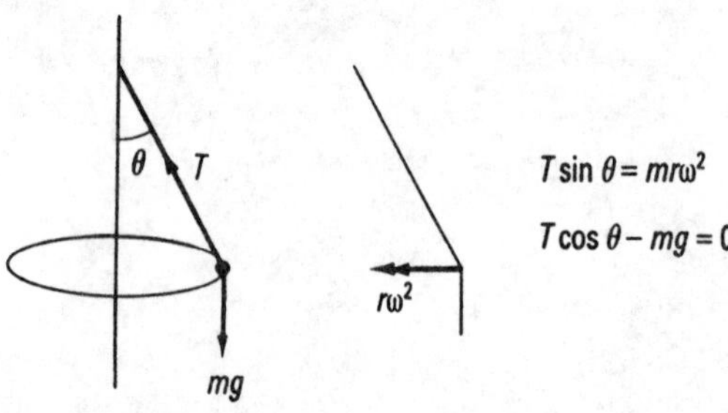

Figure 29.2

Motion in a vertical circle

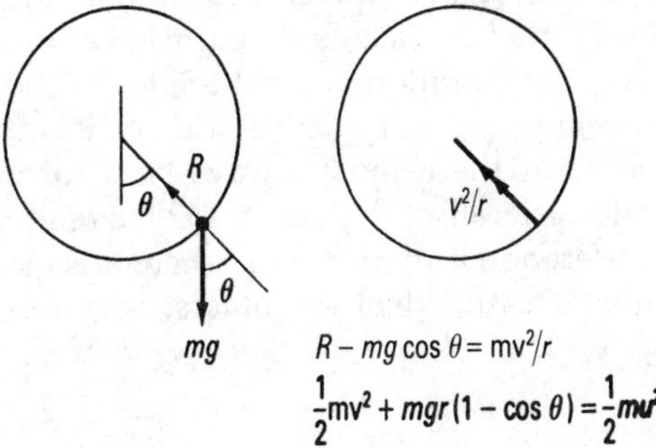

Figure 29.3

Acceleration towards the centre

Newton's first law observes that a particle stays at rest or travels in a straight line with constant velocity unless a force acts on that particle, so a particle cannot travel in any curved path unless there is an acceleration at right angles to the direction of motion. If the particle is travelling around a circle with constant speed there will not be a tangential force but there must always be a force towards the centre to produce the central acceleration (Figure 29.4). There are many ways of proving that this central acceleration is v^2/r (or $r\omega^2$), where ω is the angular speed. The one below is often found easier than the others, and uses parameters to describe the circular path.

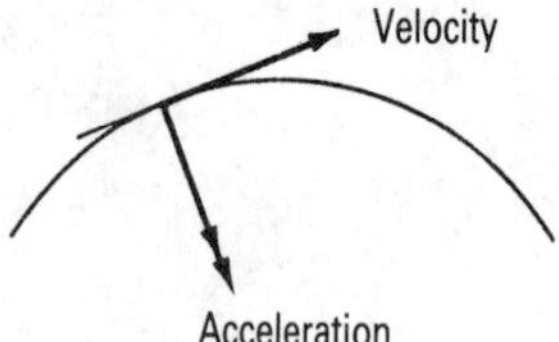

Figure 29.4

Use of parameters

The position of any particle travelling round a circle centre the origin radius r, is given by

$$x=r\cos\theta,\ y=r\sin\theta$$

Differentiating with respect to time,

$$\dot{x}=-r\sin\theta\dot{\theta},\text{ and }\dot{y}=r\cos\theta\dot{\theta}$$

$$\ddot{x}=-r\cos\theta\dot{\theta}^2-r\sin\theta\ddot{\theta}$$

and $$\ddot{y}=-r\sin\theta\dot{\theta}^2+r\cos\theta\ddot{\theta}$$

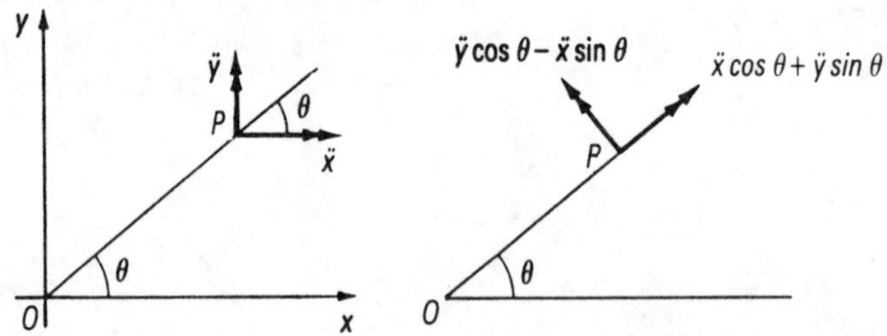

Figure 29.5

The components of acceleration outwards in the direction of OP (Figure 29.5) are

$$\ddot{x}\cos\theta+\ddot{y}\sin\theta$$

i.e. $(-r\cos\theta\dot{\theta}^2-r\sin\theta\ddot{\theta})\cos\theta+(-r\sin\theta\dot{\theta}^2+r\cos\theta\ddot{\theta})\sin\theta$

i.e. $-r\dot{\theta}^2$

so the acceleration is $r\dot{\theta}^2$ or $r\omega^2$ towards the centre.

The components of acceleration along the tangent in the direction of θ increasing are

$$\ddot{y}\cos\theta-\ddot{x}\sin\theta$$

i.e. $(-r\sin\theta\dot{\theta}^2+r\cos\theta\ddot{\theta})\cos\theta-(-r\cos\theta\dot{\theta}^2-r\sin\theta\ddot{\theta})\sin\theta$

i.e. $r\ddot{\theta}$

so that the acceleration along the tangent is $r\ddot{\theta}$ or $r\dfrac{d\omega}{dt}$.

If the particle is describing a circle with constant angular speed ω, the acceleration along the tangent is zero, as we expect.

Motion in a horizontal circle

If a particle mass m is to move in a horizontal circle, there must be a force towards the centre mv^2/r. This force may be provided by a string, a rod, or by friction or other forces.

Example 1. A toffee mass 12 g is placed on a rough turntable. When the turntable is rotating at 45 rpm the toffee describes a circle radius 15 cm. Find the frictional force exerted by the turntable on the toffee.

Since the toffee describes a circle, there must be a force towards the centre $mr\omega^2$. Express all the quantities in SI units. 15 cm=0.15 m, 45 rpm=1.5 rad s^{-1}, 12 g=0.012 kg, so that the frictional force $mr\omega^2$ is

$$(0.012)(0.15)(1.5\pi)^2 \text{ newtons, about } 0.04 \text{ N}$$

Example 2. A particle is suspended by a string, length 30 cm, one end of which is attached to a fixed point O. The particle describes a circle in a horizontal plane, with constant angular speed ω. Find the distance of the plane of the circle below O if (a) $\omega=10$ rad s^{-1}, (b) $\omega=150$ rad s^{-1}.

Since the particle, mass m, describes a circle in a horizontal plane, there is no vertical acceleration,

$$T\cos\theta-mg=0 \qquad (1)$$

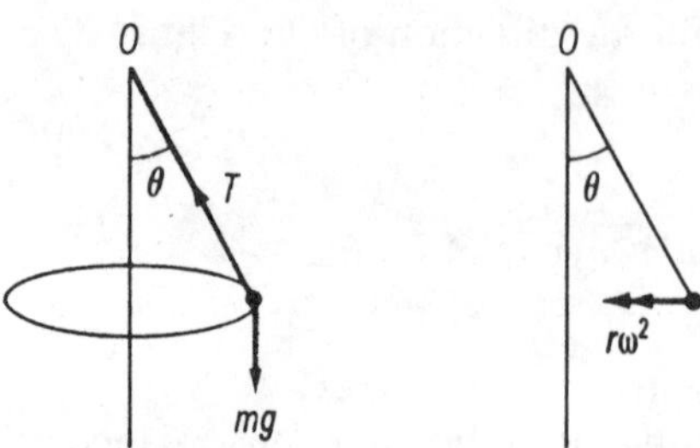

Figure 29.6

Since it describes a horizontal circle, there is an acceleration towards the centre of $(0.3 \sin \theta)\ \omega^2$

$$T \sin \theta = m\ (0.3 \sin \theta)\ \omega^2 \qquad (2)$$

Dividing (1) by (2),

$$\cos \theta = \frac{g}{0.3\omega^2}$$

When $\omega=10$, $\cos \theta = g/30$, and the distance below O is $0.3 \times g/30$ m, about 10 cm, whereas when $\omega=50$, $\cos \theta = g/750$, and the distance below O is $0.3 \times g/750$ m, about 0.4 cm.

Thus as the angular speed increases, the plane of the circle rises closer to the level of the fixed point O.

Exercise 29.1

1 A small body mass m kg is describing a circle radius r m with angular speed of ω rad s^{-1}. Find the force towards the centre if
(a) $m=0.5$, $r=0.4$, $\omega=20$, (b) $m=0.8$, $r=1.2$, $\omega=50$.

2 A small body mass 0.5 kg is describing a circle radius 0.8 m with a force F towards the centre. Find the angular speed in rad s^{-1} if F = (a) 40 N, (b) 160 N, (c) 10 N.

3 Find the central force required if a body mass 5 kg is to describe a circle radius 1.2 m at 200 rpm.

4 A bead mass 40 g is travelling with velocity 5 ms^{-1} along a smooth circular tube radius 0.4 m, which is fixed in a horizontal plane. Calculate
(a) the horizontal force exerted by the tube on the bead,
(b) the vertical force exerted by the tube on the bead,
(c) the total force exerted by the tube on the bead.

5 One end of a light string length 0.8 m is fixed at a point A. To the other end is attached a body mass 3 kg, which is made to describe a horizontal circle with angular speed 10 rad s^{-1}. Find the inclination of the string to the vertical and the tension in the string.

If the tension in the string must not exceed 200 N, what is the greatest angular speed possible for this body?

6 A car mass 700 kg is travelling along a road in an arc of a circle radius 80 m. Find the component towards the centre of the horizontal force exerted by the road on the car if the car is travelling at
(a) 10 m s^{-1}, (b) 20 m s^{-1}.
7 Part of a railway track is in an arc of a circle radius 250 m. At what angle to the horizontal is the track banked if there is no sideways thrust on the rails when trains are travelling at 20 m s^{-1}?
8 In a machine at a funfair, a man stands against the wall of a circular room, radius 3 m. The room rotates about a vertical axis through the centre of the floor at 2.5 rad s^{-1}. The floor is then lowered. If the man does not slip vertically downwards, what is the least value of the coefficient of friction between the man and the wall of the room?

If the coefficient of friction is only 0.2, at what angular speed must the room rotate if the man is not to slip down the side of the room?

Motion in a vertical circle

A particle is attached to one end of a string length r, the other end of which is attached at a fixed point O, and the particle is made to describe a circle in a horizontal plane by being given a horizontal velocity u when hanging with the string vertical. If subsequently the string makes an angle θ with the vertical and the velocity of the particle then is v, the force towards the centre now is $T-mg\cos\theta$, so $T-mg\cos\theta=mv^2/r$. But by the conservation of energy,

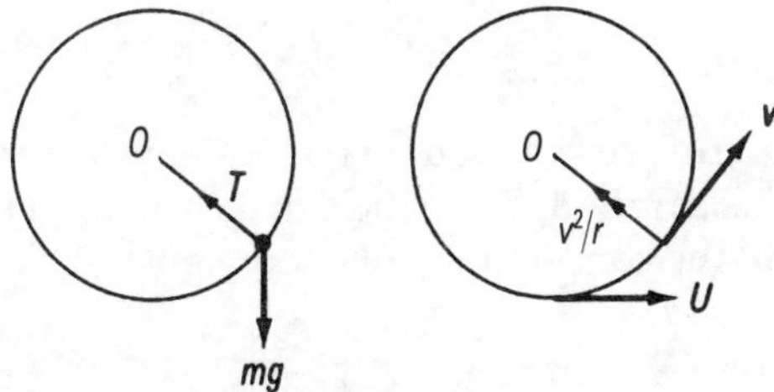

Figure 29.7

$$\tfrac{1}{2}mu^2=\tfrac{1}{2}mv^2+mgr\,(1-\cos\theta)$$

i.e. $$v^2=u^2-2gr\,(1-\cos\theta)$$

so that $$T-mg\cos\theta=\frac{mu^2}{r}-2mg\,(1-\cos\theta)$$

i.e. $$T=\frac{mu^2}{r}-mg\,(2-3\cos\theta)$$

As θ increases, T decreases, and the least value of T occurs when $\theta=\pi$, and is

$mu^2/r - 5mg$. If the particle is to describe a complete circle at the end of a string, T must never be zero, so that $u^2 \geqslant 5gr$.

It may be that the initial velocity u is small, and then the particle will only rise above the horizontal level of O if $\frac{1}{2}mu^2 > mgr$, i.e. $u^2 > 2gr$. Otherwise it will oscillate about the vertical position through O. Thus we have

(1) $u^2 \leqslant 2gr$, the particle oscillates in a vertical plane,
(2) $2gr < u^2 < 5gr$, the particle rises above the level of O, the string becomes slack, then the particle travels in a parabola until the string is taut again, or
(3) $5gr \leqslant u^2$, the particle describes a vertical circle, centre O.

If the particle is attached to a rod, so that T can be both positive and negative, then u need only be sufficiently large for there to be enough kinetic energy for the particle to rise a vertical distance of $2r$, i.e. $\frac{1}{2}mu^2 \geqslant 2mgr$, $u^2 \geqslant 4gr$ for the particle to describe a circle.

Example. A smooth circular tube is fixed in a vertical plane. A small bead, mass m, is released from the highest point in the tube and slides around the tube. Find where the contact force between the bead and the tube vanishes.

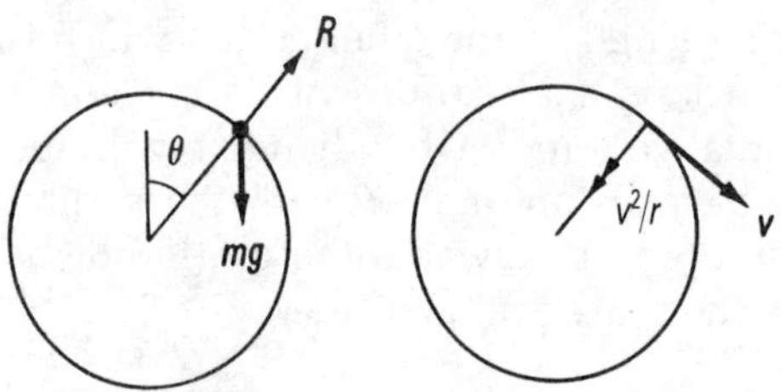

Figure 29.8

Since the bead is 'released' at the top point, we can assume the initial velocity is zero. If V is the velocity when the radius through the particle makes an angle of θ with the upward vertical (Figure 29.8), the conservation of energy gives

$$mga = \frac{1}{2}mV^2 + mga\cos\theta,$$

a being the radius of the circle

i.e. $$V^2 = 2ga(1 - \cos\theta) \qquad (1)$$

Considering the forces along the radius

$$mg\cos\theta - R = mV^2/a$$

so that when $R=0$, $V^2 = ga\cos\theta$.
Substituting in (1),

$$ga\cos\theta = 2ga(1 - \cos\theta)$$

$$\theta = \arccos\left(\tfrac{2}{3}\right)$$

Exercise 29.2

1 A bead mass 0.01 kg is suspended by a string so that it can describe a vertical circle radius 0.5 m. The bead is projected from the lowest point in its path with a velocity of 10 m s^{-1}. Find the tension when the string is
(a) vertical (two possible positions),
(b) horizontal (two possible positions),
(c) inclined at 60° to the vertical.

2 A smooth circular tube is fixed in a vertical plane. A bead mass m, which can slide in the tube, is released from rest at the highest point in the tube. Find the force exerted by the tube on the bead when the bead is at the lowest point.

3 A small bead mass m attached to an inextensible string length r can describe a vertical circle in the plane of the string. The bead is projected from the lowest point of the circle with velocity U, where $U^2=25r$. Find the angle the string makes with the upward vertical when the string becomes slack.

If instead the bead had been projected with velocity $\sqrt{10r}$, show that it would come momentarily to rest with the string at 60° to the downward vertical and that the string never becomes slack.

4 A small stone mass 0.02 kg is placed on top of a smooth sphere radius 10 cm. The stone is given an impulse 0.01 Ns, and starts to describe a circle on the outside of the sphere. Find the angle made with the vertical by the line through the stone and the centre of the sphere when the stone leaves the surface of the sphere.

Exercise 29.3

1 A particle mass M is attached to one end of a light inextensible string length l, the other end of which is fixed. The particle describes a horizontal circle with constant speed at m revolutions per second. Find the tension in the string and the angle the string makes with the vertical.

2 A particle mass m is suspended from a point O by a light inextensible string length $5a$, and is made to describe a horizontal circle radius $3a$ on a smooth horizontal table with a constant speed of $\sqrt{(2ga)}$. Find the reaction between the table and the particle.

If the speed of the particle is increased slowly until the particle is about to leave the surface of the table, what is then the speed of the particle?

3 A string length 0.4 m passes through a fixed smooth ring, and joins two bodies mass m and $2m$. The heavier mass hangs vertically below the ring, and the lighter describes a horizontal circle 0.1 m below the ring. Find the distance below the ring of the heavier of the two masses.

4 A particle P, mass m, is suspended from a fixed point O by a light inextensible string length l. The particle hangs freely in equilibrium, and is then given a horizontal speed of $\sqrt{(3lg)}$. Find the height of P above O when the string becomes slack.

5 A particle is suspended from a fixed point O by a string length 1 m. It is hit by an identical particle with horizontal velocity 10.5 m s^{-1}, and receives just enough velocity for it to describe a vertical circle centre O. Find the coefficient of restitution between the two particles.

Elasticity 30

Hooke's law 345

Energy in a stretched spring 345

Springs and strings 345

Further examples 345

Notes

Hooke's law

Tension is proportional to extension,

i.e. $T=kx$,

where k is the **spring constant** (units $\mathrm{N\,m^{-1}}$)

or $T=\frac{\lambda}{a}x$,

where λ is the **modulus of elasticity** (units N)

The **work done** in stretching an elastic string so that the extension increases from x_1 to x_2 is $\int_{x_1}^{x_2} kx\,\mathrm{d}x$

$$=\tfrac{1}{2}k(x_2^2-x_1^2)$$

or $\frac{1}{2}\frac{\lambda}{a}(x_2^2-x_1^2)$.

This is sometimes called the **elastic energy** in the string.

When a particle is oscillating while fixed to an elastic string, the equation of motion is of the form

$$\frac{\mathrm{d}^2x}{\mathrm{d}t^2}=-n^2x$$

for some n. This is **simple harmonic motion**, period $2\pi/n$.

Hooke's law

It can be shown by experiment that for any given spring the tension T is proportional to the extension x, i.e.

$$T=kx$$

where the constant k is called the spring constant. The law holds for a range of values of x, and for an elastic spring is also true when the spring is compressed, i.e. when x is negative. Spring constant is measured in newtons/metre, dimensions MT^{-2}.

For differing lengths of the same type of spring (or elastic string) then it can be shown by experiment that if we double the unstretched length a, a given force T will produce twice as much extension, so that the law can be written

$$T=\frac{\lambda}{a}x$$

where a is the unstretched length and λ is constant for that length of elastic. λ is called the **modulus of elasticity**. Notice by checking the dimensions that λ has the units of force (dimensions MLT^{-2}), and is measured in newtons.

Energy in a stretched spring

If a spring, spring constant k, is stretched so that its extension increases from x_1 to x_2, the work done is $\int_{x_1}^{x^2} T\mathrm{d}x$. But $T=kx$, so the work done is $\int_{x_1}^{x_2} kx\mathrm{d}x$, i.e.

$$\text{work done}=\tfrac{1}{2}kx_2^2-\tfrac{1}{2}kx_1^2=\tfrac{1}{2}k(x_2+x_1)(x_2-x_1)$$

But the initial and final tensions T_1 and T_2 are kx_1 and kx_2, so that the work done is $\tfrac{1}{2}(T_1+T_2)(x_2-x_1)$, the product of the mean tension and the extra extension. This work is stored in the spring as elastic energy.

Springs and strings

Take care to distinguish between elastic springs, in which $T=kx$ whether x is positive or negative, and elastic strings, which become slack (and so $T=0$) when they are not extended.

Further examples

Example 1. An elastic string natural length $2a$, spring constant k has its ends fixed at points A, B, a distance $4a$ apart, on a smooth horizontal table. A particle mass m is attached to the string at C, the midpoint of the string. The particle is then displaced from X to Y a distance a towards A, and released from rest. Show that in the subsequent motion the time taken for the particle first to reach the midpoint of AB is $(\pi/2)\sqrt{(m/2k)}$, and its greatest speed is $a\sqrt{(2k/m)}$.

Draw a diagram, as in Figure 30.1, mark clearly the extension in each part of the spring and the appropriate force when the particle is at a distance x from the equilibrium position, the midpoint of AB.

The extension in the right-hand half of the string is $(a-x)$, so the tension is $k(a-x)$ in the direction of x increasing; the tension in the left-hand half is $(a+x)$,

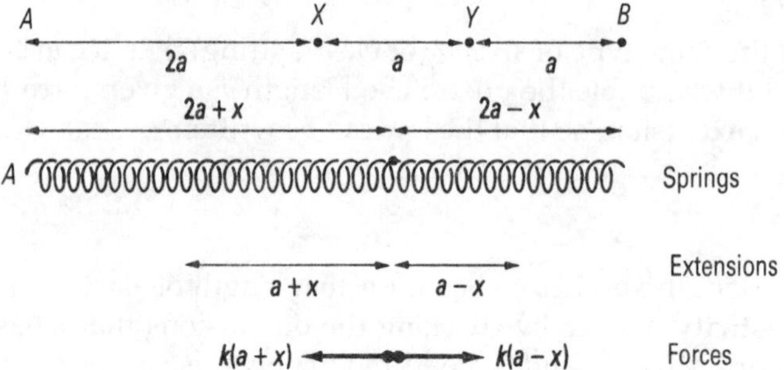

Figure 30.1

so the tension is $k(a+x)$ in the direction of x decreasing. Using $F=ma$,

$$k(a-x)-k(a+x)=m\ddot{x}$$

$$\ddot{x}+\frac{2k}{m}x=0$$

This is an example of **simple harmonic motion**, and we can write down (see page 274) the solution of this differential equation that has the initial condition $x=a$, $\dot{x}=0$ (since the particle is released from rest),

$$x=a\cos\left(t\sqrt{\frac{2k}{m}}\right)$$

The time that elapses before the particle first reaches the midpoint of AB is one-quarter of that for a complete oscillation, i.e. $\frac{1}{4}(2\pi)/\sqrt{(2k/m)}$.

i.e. $\quad \dfrac{\pi}{2}\sqrt{\dfrac{m}{2k}}$

To find the greatest velocity,

$$v=\mathrm{d}x/\mathrm{d}t=a\sqrt{(2k/m)}\sin t\sqrt{(2k/m)}$$

and the greatest value of this is $a\sqrt{(2k/m)}$.

If we had wanted to find the time before the particle reached any other point, say that point halfway between X and Y, then using $x=a\cos t\sqrt{(2k/m)}$ we have

$$\tfrac{1}{2}a = a \cos t\sqrt{\frac{2k}{m}}$$

$$t\sqrt{\frac{2k}{m}} = \arccos\left(\tfrac{1}{2}\right)$$

$$t = \frac{\pi}{3}\sqrt{\frac{m}{2k}}$$

NB. Note the dimensions of $\sqrt{(2k/m)}$ are T^{-1}, since k has dimensions MT^{-2}, so the dimensions of $a\sqrt{(2k/m)}$ are LT^{-1}, velocity, and of $(\pi/3)\sqrt{(m/2k)}$ are T.

Example 2. A particle mass m is attached to one end of a light elastic string, the other end of which is attached at a fixed point O. The natural length of the string is a and the modulus of elasticity is $4mg$. If the particle is released from rest at O, show that it first comes to rest a distance $2a$ below O.

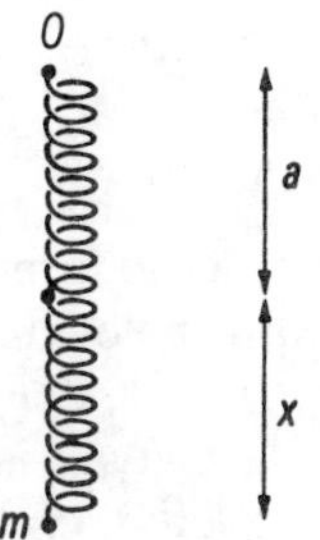

Figure 30.2

Since the velocity of the particle is 0 when it is released, and 0 when it first comes to rest, we see that the kinetic energy of the particle is zero at both instants, so that the potential energy lost is equal to the work done in stretching the string, i.e. if the particle first comes to rest when the extension is x,

$$mg(a+x) = \frac{1}{2}\frac{4mg}{a}x^2$$

$$2x^2 - ax - a^2 = 0$$

$$x = a \text{ or } -\tfrac{1}{2}a$$

The particle first comes to rest when the extension is a, i.e. at a distance $2a$ below O.

Exercise 30.1

1 Find the spring constant k if

(a) a force of 40 N produces an extension of 0.5 m,

(b) a force of 4×10^3 N produces an extension of 2.5 m.

2 Find the modulus of elasticity λ if
(a) a force of 40 N produces an extension of 0.5 m in an elastic spring, unstretched length 2 m,
(b) a force of 40 N produces an extension of 0.5 m in an elastic spring, unstretched length 5 m.
3 Find the force needed to stretch a spring, elastic constant 25 Nm^{-1}, by 4 cm.
4 Find the force needed to stretch a spring, unstretched length 2 m, modulus of elasticity 25 N, by 4 cm.
5 A light elastic string, natural length c, is attached at one end to a fixed point O. A particle mass m is attached to the other end of the string and allowed to hang freely. Find the extension in the string if the modulus of elasticity is
(a) mg, (b) $2mg$, (c) $\frac{1}{2}mg$.
6 An elastic spring, natural length 0.2 m, spring constant 160 Nm^{-1}, is placed on a smooth horizontal table. One end of the spring is fixed at a point on the table. Find the work done when the string is stretched so that the total length increases
(a) from 0.2 m to 0.25 m,
(b) from 0.25 m to 0.3 m,
(c) from 0.25 m to 0.5 m.
7 Using the data of Example 2, write down the equation of motion in the form $m\ddot{x}=f(x)$, and show that the particle is executing s.h.m. about a point $\frac{5}{4}a$ below 0. Find the period of this motion.
8 One end of a light elastic string, natural length a, modulus of elasticity λ, is attached at a fixed point A, and a small pan, mass M, is attached to the other end so that it hangs freely in equilibrium. A small piece of putty, mass m, is then fixed underneath the pan.

Show that the pan can now rest in equilibrium a distance $a(1+(m+M)g/\lambda)$, below A.

If the pan is slightly displaced a distance d vertically downwards from this position, find the greatest speed of the pan in the ensuing motion, and the greatest force between the putty and the pan.
9 A light elastic string, spring constant k, natural length $3a$, has its ends fixed at points A and D, a distance $3a$ apart and on the same horizontal level. Two particles, each mass m, are fixed one at each of B and C, the points of trisection of AD, and hang freely in equilibrium. Show that, if θ is the angle made by AB and CD with the horizontal, $2ka(\tan\theta-\sin\theta)=3mg$.

Friction 31

Laws of friction 351

Notes

The **laws of friction** required now are:
(a) Friction always opposes **relative** motion.
(b) The frictional force is **just sufficient** to prevent relative motion, up to a certain maximum. This maximum frictional force is called **limiting friction**.
(c) The limiting frictional force is proportional to the **normal reaction** between the two bodies in contact.

Laws of friction

Experiments and observations lead us to formulate certain laws to describe the nature of the forces due to friction. The ones we need to know now are:

(a) Friction always opposes **relative** motion.
(b) The frictional force is just sufficient to prevent relative motion, up to a certain maximum value, called **limiting friction**.
(c) The limiting frictional force is proportional to the **normal reaction** between the bodies in contact.

NB. *Law (a):* Friction opposes relative motion, and so can produce motion. A parcel on the back shelf of a car will not slip backwards when the car accelerates slowly if the frictional force can keep it in place. If, however, the frictional force is not sufficient to make the parcel accelerate as rapidly as the car, the parcel will slip backwards relative to the car.

Law (c): The frictional force is proportional to the normal reaction, *not* to the weight of the body.

Example 1. A body mass 4 kg is at rest on a rough horizontal surface, which can exert a limiting frictional force of 2 N. A horizontal force F N is applied, given at time t seconds by

$$F=\tfrac{1}{10}t$$

Find when the body starts to slip, and how far it has moved 10 seconds later.

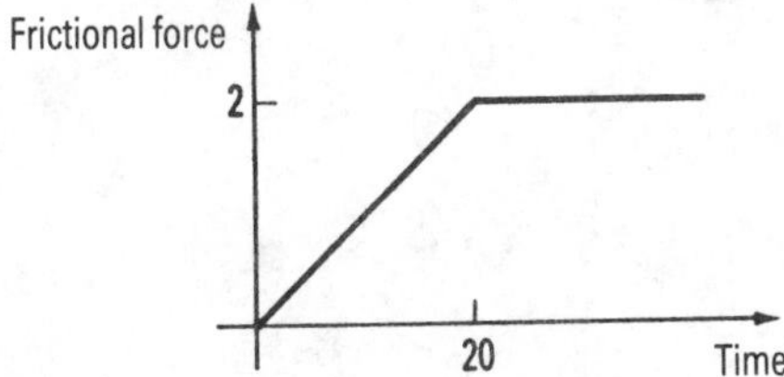

Figure 31.1

Since the maximum frictional force is 2 N, for the first 20 s, i.e. until $F=2$, the frictional force is just sufficient to balance F, as shown in Figure 31.1. When $t\geqslant 20$, however, using Newton's law,

$$4\frac{dv}{dt}=\tfrac{1}{10}t-2$$

Integrating $v=\frac{1}{80}t^2-\frac{1}{2}t+C$

When $t=20$, $v=0$, so $C=5$,

$$v=\tfrac{1}{80}t^2-\tfrac{1}{2}t+5$$

Since $s=\int v dt$, $s=\frac{1}{240}t^3-\frac{1}{4}t^2+5t+C$. When $t=20$, $s=0$, so $C=-\frac{100}{3}$ and

$$s=\frac{1}{240}t^3-\frac{1}{4}t^2+5t-\frac{100}{3}$$

When $t=30$, the distance travelled is 4.17 m. We can check this is reasonable, for the force 'to spare' to accelerate increases from zero to 1 N over 10 s, so the acceleration increases from 0 to 0.25 m s^{-2} over 10 s. At a constant acceleration of 0.1m s^{-2} for 10 s, the distance travelled would be 5 m.

Example 2. A body weight 20 N is at rest on a rough horizontal surface. A force F acts on the body. If the body is about to move under the action of a force F, magnitude 10 N, find the coefficient of friction in each of the following cases: (a) F acts horizontally, (b) F acts at an angle of 30° above the horizontal, (c) F acts at an angle 30° below the horizontal.

(a) Considering the vertical forces on the body, the normal reaction X_1 is equal to the weight of the body, 20 N, so that if μ_1 is the coefficient of friction,

$$10=20\mu_1,$$
$$\mu_1=0.5$$

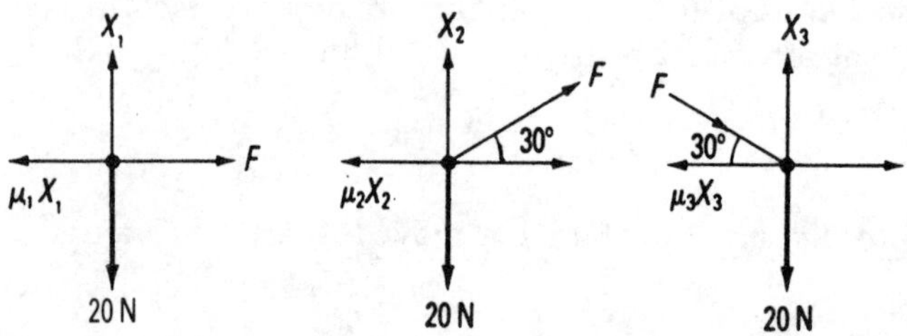

Figure 31.2

(b) Considering now the vertical forces,

$$X_2+F\sin 30°=20,$$
$$X_2=20-10\times 0.5$$
$$=15$$

so $$10\cos 30°=15\mu_2,$$
$$\mu_2=0.577$$

(c) Considering in this third case the vertical forces,

$$X_3=20+10\sin 30°$$
$$=25$$

so $$10\cos 30°=25\mu_3$$
$$\mu_3=0.346$$

Notice that in parts (b) and (c), the greater the normal reaction, the smaller the coefficient of friction necessary to produce a given horizontal force.

Example 3. A body mass m is at rest on a rough plane inclined at an angle α above the horizontal. Find the force F that will just move the body up the plane if (a) F acts along a line of greatest slope of the plane, (b) F acts horizontally, (c) we require the least force F, in any direction.

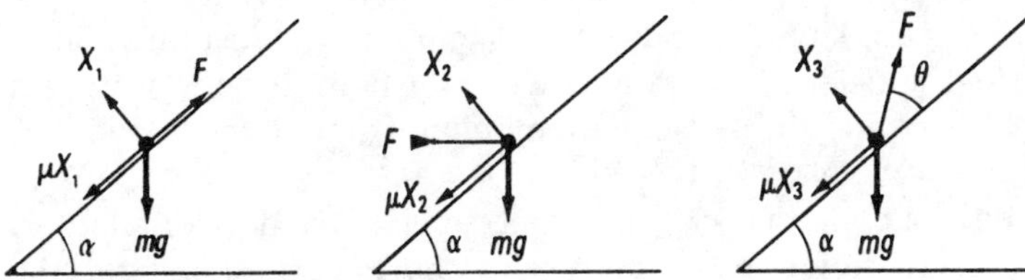

Figure 31.3

(a) The normal reaction X_1 is $mg \cos \alpha$, so the frictional force is $\mu mg \cos \alpha$. That will oppose relative motion, so will act *down* the plane. Considering then the forces along a line of greatest slope of the plane,

$$F = mg \sin \alpha + \mu mg \cos \alpha$$

i.e. $$F = mg(\sin \alpha + \mu \cos \alpha)$$

(b) Considering the forces normal to the plane,

$$X_2 = F \sin \alpha + mg \cos \alpha$$

so the frictional force is $\mu(F \sin \alpha + mg \cos \alpha)$, and considering the forces along a line of greatest slope of the plane,

$$F \cos \alpha = \mu(F \sin \alpha + mg \cos \alpha) + mg \sin \alpha$$

$$F(\cos \alpha - \mu \sin \alpha) = \mu mg \cos \alpha + mg \sin \alpha$$

$$F = \frac{mg(\mu \cos \alpha + \sin \alpha)}{\cos \alpha - \mu \sin \alpha}$$

(c) Suppose the force F acts at an angle of θ above the plane. Then considering the components of forces normal to the plane,

$$X_3 + F \sin \theta = mg \cos \alpha$$

so the frictional force is $\mu(mg \cos \alpha - F \sin \theta)$. Considering the forces along a line of greatest slope of the plane,

$$F \cos \theta = \mu(mg \cos \alpha - F \sin \theta) + mg \sin \alpha$$

$$F = \frac{mg(\mu \cos \alpha + \sin \alpha)}{\cos \theta + \mu \sin \theta}$$

The only variable in this expression is θ in the denominator, so that the least value of F occurs at the greatest value of $\cos\theta+\mu\sin\theta$, i.e. $\sqrt{(1+\mu^2)}$,* the least value of F is

$$\frac{mg}{\sqrt{(1+\mu^2)}}(\mu\cos\alpha+\sin\alpha)$$

Exercise 31.1

In this exercise, take $g=10\text{ m s}^{-2}$, so that a body mass 1 kg has weight 10 N.

1 A horizontal force F is applied to a body mass 3 kg initially at rest on a rough horizontal surface. The coefficient of friction between the body and the surface is 0.4. Find the frictional force and the subsequent motion, if any, of the body if $F=$
(a) 1 N, (b) 10 N, (c) 15 N, (d) 18 N.

2 A force **F** is applied to a body mass 30 kg initially at rest on a horizontal floor. The coefficient of friction between the body and the floor is 0.6. Find the frictional force and the acceleration of the body when **F** =
(a) 150**i** N, (b) 200**j** N, (c) (150**i**+200**j**) N.

3 A car 700 kg accelerates from rest at 1.5**i** m s^{-2}. Find the frictional force exerted by (a) the tyres on the road and (b) the road on the tyres.

4 A parcel mass 2 kg is at rest on the floor of a car. The coefficient of friction between the parcel and the car is 0.7. Find the frictional force exerted by the car on the parcel when the car accelerates at
(a) 1 m s^{-2}, (b) 3 m s^{-2}, (c) 7 m s^{-2}, (d) 8 m s^{-2}, (e) 10 m s^{-2}.

5 A body M mass 10 kg is at rest on a rough horizontal floor. Find the normal reaction R between the floor and the body if
(a) its weight is the only force acting on M,
(b) a vertical force 50 N upwards also acts on M,
(c) a horizontal force 50 N also acts on M,
(d) a force of 30 N at 36° above the floor is the only force other than the weight acting on M.

Find in each case the frictional force F which prevents motion. Find also the ratio $F{:}R$, and deduce the minimum of the coefficient of friction.

Exercise 31.2

1 A body mass 2 kg is at rest on a rough horizontal surface, which can exert a limiting frictional force of 5 N. A horizontal force F N is now applied, given at time t by $F=10\sin(\pi t/6)$. Find when the body starts to slip, and its velocity 2 s later.

2 A rough horizontal platform is oscillating along a horizontal straight line so that its displacement x at time t is given by $x=a\cos t$. A particle is placed on the platform when it is at the position $x=a$. Show that the particle slips immediately if $g\mu<a$.

3 A particle is projected with velocity u from a point P up a line of greatest slope of a rough plane inclined at an angle α above the horizontal. If μ is the

*See page 169.

coefficient of friction between the particle and the plane, find in terms of a, g and μ how long elapses before the particle comes momentarily to rest, how far up the plane the particle travels, and how much longer elapses before the particle returns to P if $\mu<\tan \alpha$.

(More questions requiring knowledge of the laws of friction are in Exercise 32.3 (page 364).

Composition and resolution of forces, moments of a force 32

Addition of forces 360

Composition of forces 360

Moment of a force 361

Rigid bodies in equilibrium 362

Notes

Forces are added by the **parallelogram law**, so that the resultant **R**

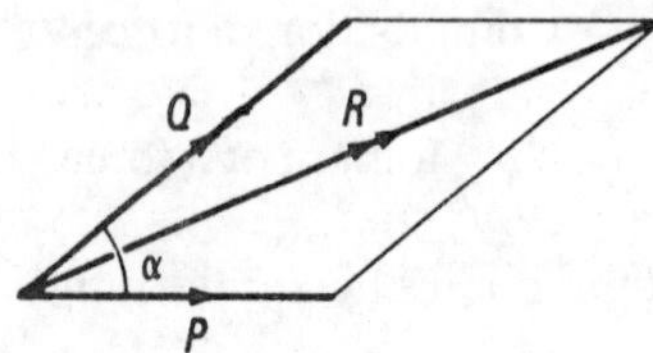

Figure 32.1

of forces **P** and **Q** inclined at an angle α has magnitude

$$\sqrt{(P^2+Q^2+2PQ\cos\alpha)}$$

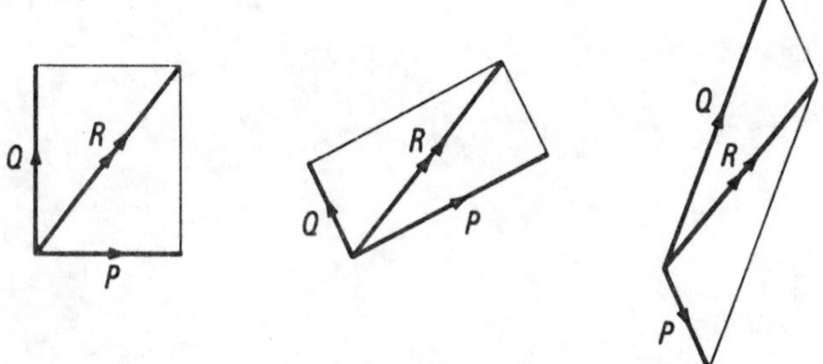

Figure 32.2

Any two forces **P** and **Q** whose vector sum is **R** can be called **components** of **R**. When these two forces are at right angles, e.g. **X** and **Y** (Figure 32.3), they are called the **resolved parts** along Ox and Oy respectively.

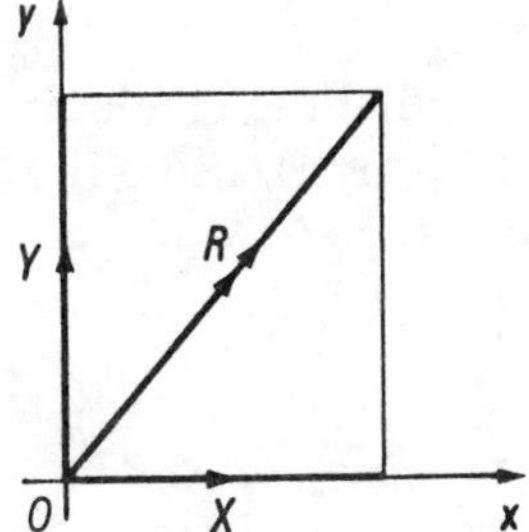

Figure 32.3

The moment of a force **F** about an axis through a point *O* perpendicular to the plane of **F** and *O* is the product of the magnitude of **F** and the perpendicular distance on to the line of action of **F**, here pF. In SI units, it is measured in newton-metres (dimensions $ML^2 T^{-2}$).

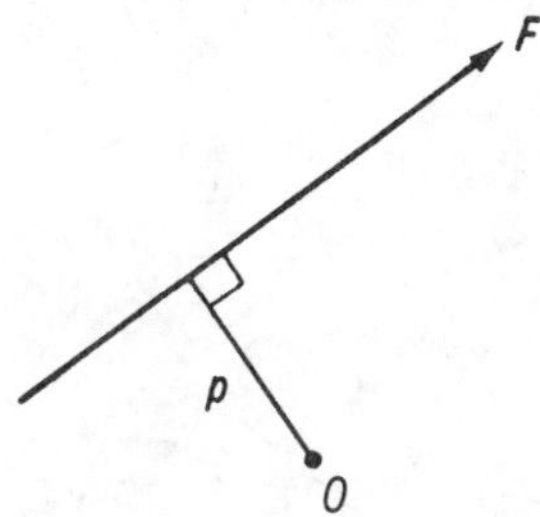

Figure 32.4

Addition of forces

Forces, being vectors, are added by the parallelogram law, so that the resultant of two forces **P** and **Q** inclined at an angle α is $\sqrt{(P^2+Q^2+2PQ\cos\alpha)}$, using the cosine formula to find the length of magnitude of their resultant.

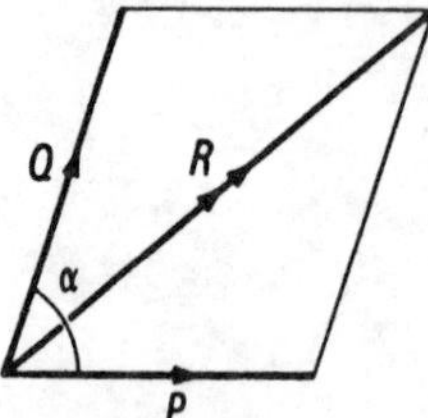

Figure 32.5

Example. Find the magnitude of the resultant forces 2 N and 3 N, inclined at an angle 30°.

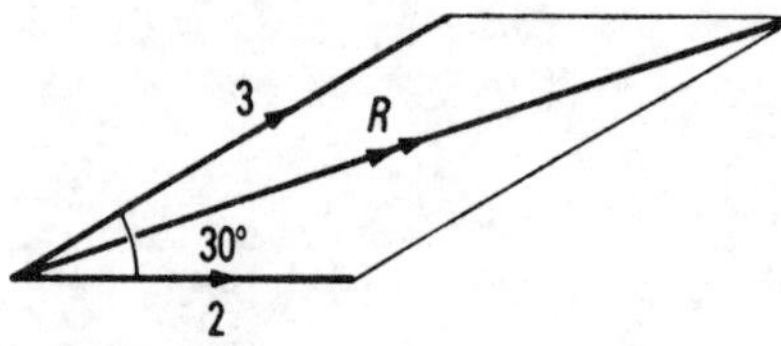

Figure 32.6

Using Figure 32.6, the magnitude of the resultant is

$$\sqrt{(2^2+3^2+2\times2\times3\cos 30°)}, \text{ about } 4.8\text{ N}.$$

Composition of forces

Often, instead of adding two forces, we find it convenient to express a single force as two forces, so that a force 4 N acting at 60° to the x-axis has a component $4\cos 60°$ along the x-axis, $4\sin 60°$ at right angles to it. This is particularly useful when we are familiar with vector notation.

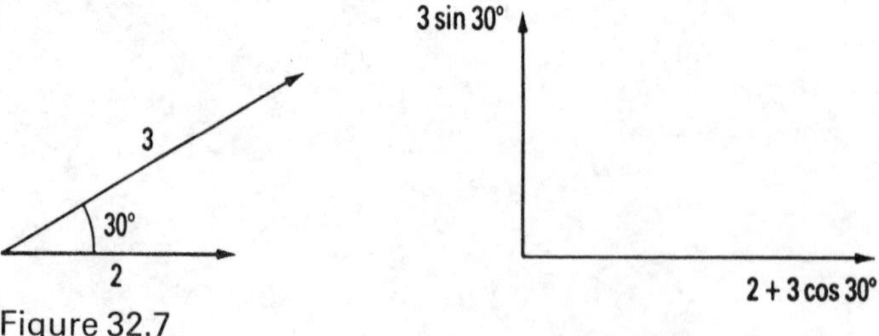

Figure 32.7

Example. Find the magnitude of the resultant of two forces 2 N, 3 N inclined at 30°.

Take **i** as a unit vector along the line of action of the force 2 N, which can then be written 2**i** N. The other force **F** can be written (3 cos 30**i**+3 sin 30**j**) N, about (2.6**i**+1.5**j**) N. The resultant of the two forces is (4.6**i**+1.5**j**) N, and its magnitude is $\sqrt{[(4.6)^2+(1.5)^2]}$, about 4.8 N as before.

Exercise 32.1

1 The force **R** is the resultant of two forces **P** and **Q**. The angle between **P** and **Q** is denoted by α. Find the magnitude of **R** and the angle between **P** and **R** when
(a) $P=12$ N, $Q=9$ N, $\alpha=90°$,
(b) $P=12$ N, $Q=10$ N, $\alpha=90°$,
(c) $P=12$ N, $Q=9$ N, $\alpha=60°$,
(d) $P=12$ N, $Q=9$ N, $\alpha=120°$,
(e) $P=12$ N, $Q=18$ N, $\alpha=50°$.

2 The force **X** is the resultant of forces **P**, **Q** and **R**. Force **P** acts along a line Ox, force **Q** along Oy perpendicular to OX, force **R** through O inclined at an angle θ to Ox and at $(90-\theta)°$ to Oy. Find the magnitude of **X** and the angle it makes with the line of action of **P** when
(a) $P=3$ N, $Q=4$ N, $R=5$ N and $\theta=30°$,
(b) $P=3$ N, $Q=4$ N, $R=5$ N and $\theta=60°$,
(c) $P=3$ N, $Q=2$ N, $R=1$ N and $\theta=45°$,
(d) $P=3$ N, $Q=2$ N, $R=1$ N and $\theta=120°$,
(e) $P=2$ N, $Q=3$ N, $R=3$ N and $\theta=150°$.

Moment of a force

The moment of a force **F** acting about an axis through a point O perpendicular to the plane of O and **F** is defined as the product of the magnitude of **F** and the perpendicular distance p of the line of action of **F** from O, i.e. Fp, using the data in Figure 32.8. The moment measures the turning effect of the force **F** about the axis through O.

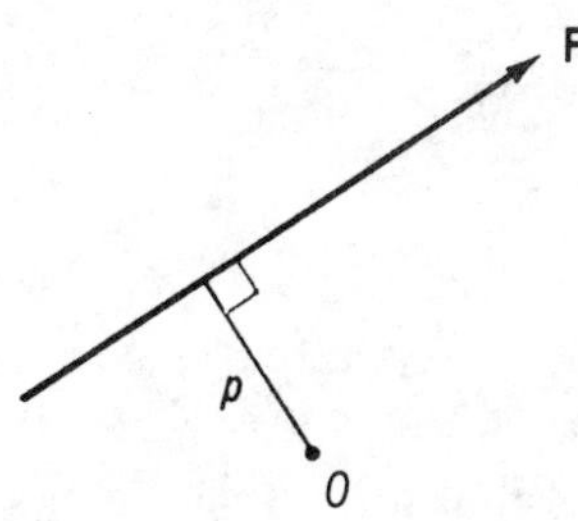

Figure 32.8

Exercise 32.2

1 Forces $\mathbf{F}_1, \mathbf{F}_2, \mathbf{F}_3$ act at points position vectors $\mathbf{r}_1, \mathbf{r}_2, \mathbf{r}_3$, respectively. Find the moment about the origin O of each of these systems of forces:
(a) $\mathbf{F}_1=2\mathbf{i}$, $\mathbf{F}_2=3\mathbf{j}$, $\mathbf{r}_1=2\mathbf{j}$, $\mathbf{r}_2=4\mathbf{i}$,
(b) $\mathbf{F}_1=2\mathbf{i}$, $\mathbf{F}_2=3\mathbf{j}$, $\mathbf{F}_3=-\mathbf{i}$, $\mathbf{r}_1=\mathbf{j}$, $\mathbf{r}_2=2\mathbf{i}$, $\mathbf{r}_3=\mathbf{i}+\mathbf{j}$,
(c) $\mathbf{F}_1=2\mathbf{i}$, $\mathbf{F}_2=2\mathbf{i}+\mathbf{j}$, $\mathbf{F}_3=\mathbf{i}-2\mathbf{j}$, $\mathbf{r}_1=3\mathbf{i}$, $\mathbf{r}_2=2\mathbf{i}+3\mathbf{j}$, $\mathbf{r}_3=-\mathbf{i}-\mathbf{j}$.

2 Find the moment about the point $-\mathbf{i}-2\mathbf{j}$ of each of the systems of forces given in Q.1.

3 Forces $\mathbf{F}_1, \mathbf{F}_2, \mathbf{F}_3, \mathbf{F}_4$ act along the sides AB, BC, CD, DA of a rectangle $ABCD$, where length $AB=2a$, length $BC=a$. Find the moments about A of each of the following systems of forces, where the anticlockwise sense is positive:
(a) $\mathbf{F}_1=2$ N, $\mathbf{F}_2=3$ N, $\mathbf{F}_3=4$ N, $\mathbf{F}_4=3$ N,
(b) $\mathbf{F}_1=3$ N, $\mathbf{F}_2=-2$ N, $\mathbf{F}_3=4$ N, $\mathbf{F}_4=-5$ N,
(c) $\mathbf{F}_1=2$ N, $\mathbf{F}_2=4$ N, $\mathbf{F}_3=-4$ N, $\mathbf{F}_4=2$ N,
(d) $\mathbf{F}_1=\mathbf{F}_2=\mathbf{F}_3=\mathbf{F}_4=2$ N.

Rigid bodies in equilibrium

A rigid body will only be in equilibrium if the vector sum of the forces acting on the body is zero, so that there is no acceleration of the body, and if the sum of the moments of the forces acting on the body is zero, so that there is no turning effect of those forces and the body does not rotate. Many of the examples testing understanding of this idea use a rod with one end on rough ground and the other end resting against a wall.

Example. A uniform straight rod, weight 20 N, rests with one end on rough horizontal ground, the other end being against a smooth vertical wall. If the rod is inclined at 60° to the horizontal, find the force exerted by the wall on the rod.

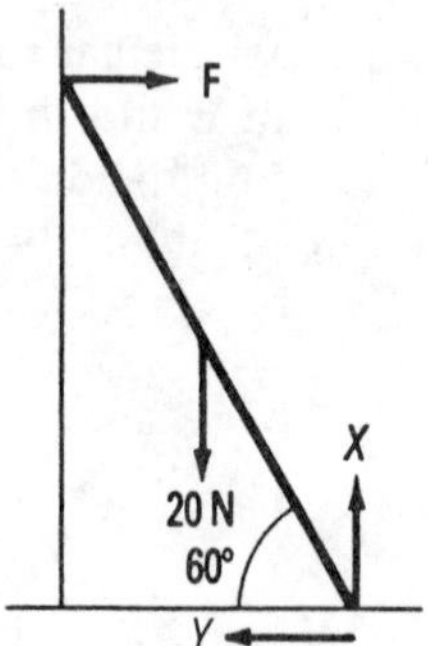

Figure 32.9

If the length of the rod is $2l$, the moment of the horizontal force $\mathbf{F}$ about the foot of the ladder is $2l \sin 60° F$ and the moment of the weight of the rod is $l \cos 60° \times 20$ in the opposite sense, both being in newton-metres. Since the rod is in equilibrium,

$$2l \sin 60° F = l \cos 60° \times 20$$

$$F = 10 \cos 60°$$

$$\simeq 5.77$$

The force between the wall and the rod is 5.77 N.

Considering the horizontal forces on the rod, we see that the frictional force exerted by the ground must be 5.77 N, so that the rod does not move horizontally, and the normal reaction between the rod and the ground is 20 N. Since the rod does not slip,

$$5.77 \leqslant 20\mu$$

The coefficient of friction must be at least 0.289.

Example. A uniform rod *AB*, length 2*a*, weight 3 N, has a light ring at one end A, which is free to slide on a rough horizontal wire. One end of a light string length *a* is fixed to the point *B* of the rod and the other end is attached at a fixed point *C* along the wire. Find the tension in the string, if the rod is inclined at an angle of 20° to the horizontal.

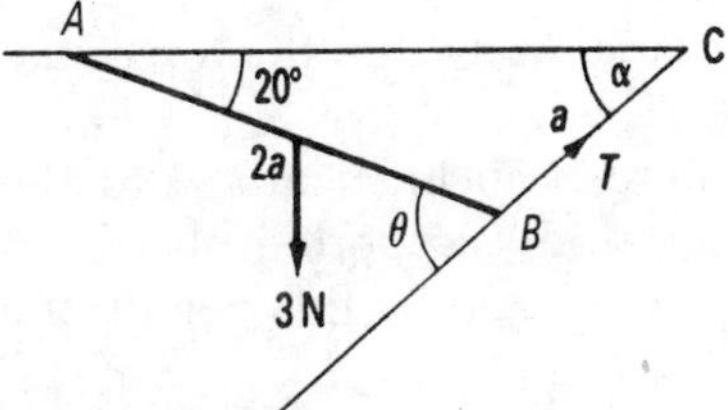

Figure 32.10

Since we do not wish to find the forces on the rod through *A*, take moments about *A*,

$$3(a \cos 20°) = T \times 2a \sin \theta$$

To find θ, we need to know angle $ACB = \alpha$. Using the sine formula,

$$\frac{a}{\sin 20°} = \frac{2a}{\sin \alpha}$$

$$\sin \alpha = 2 \sin 20°$$

$$\alpha \simeq 43.2°$$

Thus $\theta = 63.2°$, and

$$3 \cos 20° = T(2 \sin 63.2°)$$

$$T = 1.58$$

The tension is about 1.58 N.

Exercise 32.3

Using each of the two methods above, find the magnitude of the resultant of the following forces:

1 Forces 4 N, 5 N inclined at 70°.

2 Forces 4 N, 5 N inclined at 110°.

3 Forces 4 N, 5 N inclined at 20°.

4 The foot of a uniform ladder, weight 400 N, rests on rough horizontal ground and the top of the ladder rests against a smooth vertical wall. A man, weight 800 N, can stand on the top of the ladder when the ladder makes an angle of 70° with the horizontal. Find the force exerted by the wall on the ladder, and the least value of the coefficient of friction between the ladder and the ground.

5 A uniform ladder, length l, weight 80 N, rests inclined at 70° to the horizontal with one end on rough horizontal ground, the other end against a smooth vertical wall. The coefficient of friction between the ladder and the ground is 0.3. A man, weight 800 N, starts to climb the ladder slowly.
(a) Write down the normal reaction exerted by the ground on the ladder, and deduce the greatest frictional force exerted by the ground on the ladder.
(b) Find the horizontal force exerted by the wall on the ladder when the man has ascended a length kl of the ladder.
(c) Show that the ladder starts to slip just before the man reaches the top of the ladder.

6 A uniform rod, weight 100 N, length 1.6 m, rests inclined at 70° to the horizontal with one end on rough horizontal ground, supported also by a smooth peg 0.6 m above the ground. Find the force exerted by this peg on the rod.

7 A uniform rod AB, length 1 m, weight 40 N, is smoothly hinged to a vertical wall at A. It is held at rest in a horizontal position by a light inextensible string attached at B and at a point C on the wall a distance 0.3 m above A. Find the tension in the string.

8 A uniform rod AB, length 1.6 m, weight 30 N, is freely pivoted at a fixed point A. A light elastic string BC, modulus of elasticity 60 N has one end fixed at B, the other end fixed at a point C on the same horizontal level as A, AC being 2 m. The system is in equilibrium with the length BC=1.2 m. Calculate the tension in the string, and the unstretched length of the string.

Centre of mass 33

Centre of gravity 368

Centre of mass 368

Centroid 368

Centre of mass of a rod 369

Use of symmetry 371

Notes

The centre of mass $(\bar{x},\bar{y})$ of particles mass $m_1, m_2, m_3, \ldots$ at points coordinates $(x_1,y_1), (x_2,y_2), \ldots$ is given by

$$\bar{x}=\frac{m_1x_1+m_2x_2+m_3x_3+\ldots}{m_1+m_2+m_3+\ldots}$$

i.e. $$\bar{x}=\frac{\Sigma m_i x_i}{\Sigma m_i},$$

and $$\bar{y}=\frac{m_1y_1+m_2y_2+m_3y_3+\ldots}{m_1+m_2+m_3+\ldots}$$

i.e. $$\bar{y}=\frac{\Sigma m_i y_i}{\Sigma m_i}$$

This can be written

the centre of mass of particles mass m_i at points with position vectors $x_i\mathbf{i}+y_i\mathbf{j}$ is given by

$$(\bar{x}\mathbf{i}+\bar{y}\mathbf{j})\Sigma m_i=\Sigma m_i(x_i\mathbf{i}+y_i\mathbf{j})$$

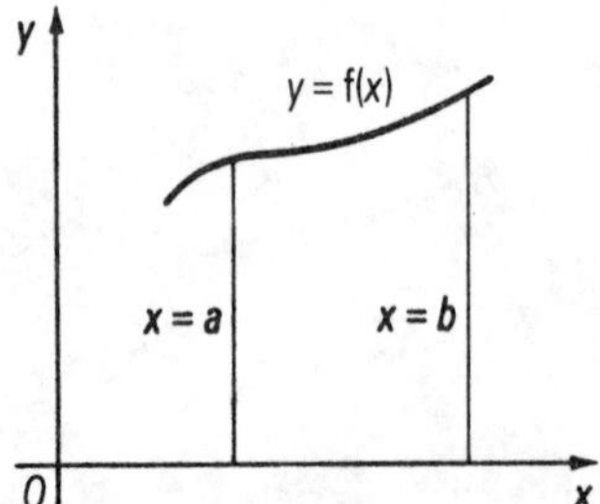

Figure 33.1

If a region R is bounded by a curve $y=\mathrm{f}(x)$, the x-axis and the lines $x=a$, $x=b$, the coordinates of the centre of mass are given by

$$\bar{x}\int_a^b y\,dx=\int_a^b xy\,dx, \qquad \bar{y}\int_a^b y\,dx=\tfrac{1}{2}\int_a^b y^2\,dx$$

If this region is rotated about the x-axis, the coordinates of the centre of mass are given by

$$\bar{x}\int_a^b y^2 dx = \int_a^b xy^2 dx,\ \bar{y}=0$$

Similarly, if a solid of revolution is formed by rotating a similar region about the y-axis, the coordinates of the centre of mass are given by

$$\bar{x}=0 \text{ and } \bar{y}\int_c^d x^2 dy = \int_c^d yx^2 dy.$$

These results assume that the density is uniform.

Centroid

The centre of mass of a body of uniform density is at the **centroid** of that body.

Centre of gravity

If we have two particles, masses m, $2m$, at points A, B respectively, then by taking moments we find that their weights are equivalent to the weight of a single particle mass $3m$ acting at a point G dividing AB in the ratio 2:1. This point G we call the centre of gravity (Figure 33.2). If these particles are at points with

Figure 33.2

displacements x_1, x_2, then the displacement of G is $\frac{1}{3}(x_1+2x_2)$. Generalizing, we find the centre of gravity of particles mass m_1, m_2, m_3, ... displacements x_1, x_2 ... is

$$\frac{m_1x_1+m_2x_2+m_3x_3+\ldots}{m_1+m_2+m_3+\ldots}, \text{ i.e. } \frac{\Sigma m_ix_i}{\Sigma m_i}.$$

If we have several particles in a plane, the centre of gravity $(\bar{x},\bar{y})$ has coordinates

$$\bar{x}=\frac{\Sigma m_ix_i}{\Sigma m_i}, \ \bar{y}=\frac{\Sigma m_iy_i}{\Sigma m_i}$$

Centre of mass

A body only has 'weight' if it is in a gravitational field, and we find it useful to generalize the idea of a centre of gravity by defining a centre of mass to have coordinates

$$\bar{x}=\frac{\Sigma m_ix_i}{\Sigma m_i}, \ \bar{y}=\frac{\Sigma m_iy_i}{\Sigma m_i} \tag{1}$$

if we have a system of small bodies that we can regard as particles. If there is a uniform gravitational field, then the centre of mass coincides with the centre of gravity. The equations in (1) can be summarized in vector notation

$$\bar{x}\mathbf{i}+\bar{y}\mathbf{j}=\frac{\Sigma m_ix_i}{\Sigma m_i}\mathbf{i}+\frac{\Sigma m_iy_i}{\Sigma m_i}\mathbf{j}$$

Centroid

We know of a point G in a triangle called the centroid, and that this point, the point of intersection of the medians, is the centre of mass of a uniform lamina covering the triangle. The centroid of any plane figure is the centre of mass of a uniform lamina covering that figure; of a body in three dimensions it is the centre of mass of a uniform solid filling that body. It is a further generalization of centre of mass, and can be defined so that it is not dependent on the idea of mass. At present we can regard centre of gravity, centre of mass and centroid as referring to the same point.

Example. Find the centre of mass of particles mass m, $2m$, $3m$, $4m$ at points with position vectors $(\mathbf{i}+\mathbf{j})$, $(2\mathbf{i}-3\mathbf{j})$, $(-\mathbf{i}+\mathbf{j})$ and $(-2\mathbf{i}-3\mathbf{j})$, respectively.

Always draw a diagram to see that your answer is reasonable.

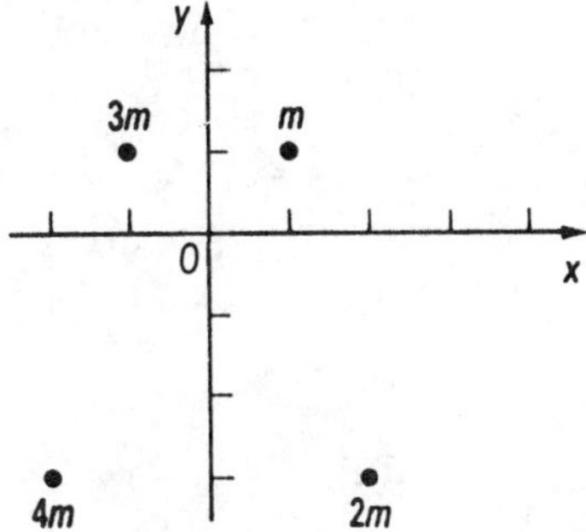

Figure 33.3

$$\text{Now}\quad 10m(\bar{x}\mathbf{i}+\bar{y}\mathbf{j})=m(\mathbf{i}+\mathbf{j})+2m(2\mathbf{i}-3\mathbf{j})+3m(-\mathbf{i}+\mathbf{j})+4m(-2\mathbf{i}-3\mathbf{j})$$

$$=-6m\mathbf{i}-14m\mathbf{j}$$

$$\bar{x}\mathbf{i}+\bar{y}\mathbf{j}=-0.6\mathbf{i}-1.4\mathbf{j}$$

The coordinates of the centre of mass are $(-0.6, -1.4)$. From Figure 33.3, we see that this is reasonable, as the heaviest particle is in the fourth quadrant.

Centre of mass of a rod

A rod can be regarded as a number of small particles mass $m\delta x$ distributed along the length of the rod, where m is the mass per unit length, not necessarily uniform. To find the centre of mass we generalize equation (1) (page 368) and write

Figure 33.4

$$\bar{x}\int_0^l m\mathrm{d}x=\int_0^l xm\mathrm{d}x$$

where $\int_0^l m\mathrm{d}x$ is the total mass of the rod. If the mass-distribution at a point distance x from one end A is kx^2,

$$\bar{x}\int_0^l kx^2\mathrm{d}x=\int_0^l x\times kx^2\mathrm{d}x$$

$$\tfrac{1}{3}l^3k\bar{x}=\tfrac{1}{4}kl^4$$

$$\bar{x}=\tfrac{3}{4}l$$

The centre of mass is $\frac{3}{4}l$ from A.

We can extend this idea into two dimensions, by dividing laminae into suitable 'rectangular strips' and regarding each strip as a particle, with mass that of the strip, placed at the 'midpoint' of the strip.

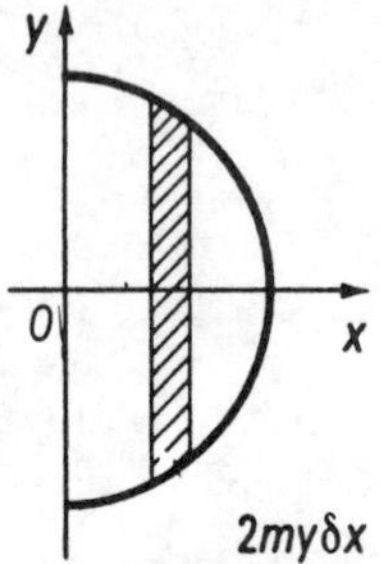

Figure 33.5

By symmetry, the centre of mass lies on Ox (Figure 33.5). To find $\bar{x}$, we know the mass of the semicircular lamina is $\frac{1}{2}\pi a^2 m$, where m is the mass per unit area, so dividing the lamina into strips mass $m(2y\delta x)$,

$$\tfrac{1}{2}\pi a^2 m\bar{x}=\int_0^a x(2my)\mathrm{d}x$$

i.e. $$\tfrac{1}{2}\pi a^2\bar{x}=2\int_0^a xy\mathrm{d}x$$

But the semicircle is part of the circle $x^2+y^2=a^2$, i.e. $y=\sqrt{(a^2-x^2)}$, so

$$\tfrac{1}{2}\pi a^2\bar{x}=2\int_0^a x(a-x)^{1/2}\mathrm{d}x$$

$$=[-\tfrac{2}{3}(a^2-x^2)^{3/2}]_o^a$$

$$=\tfrac{2}{3}a^3$$

$$\bar{x}=\frac{4}{3\pi}a$$

The coordinates of the centre of mass are $((4/3\pi)a,0)$.

Use of symmetry

In the example above we used the symmetry of the lamina to help find the position of the centre of mass, and this often helps reduce the calculations required. We should form the habit of noticing any axes of symmetry that a body possesses.

A solid formed by rotating a region about an axis has that axis of rotation as an axis of symmetry, and this enables us to solve a problem in three dimensions with only one calculation.

Example 1. A finite region R bounded by the coordinate axes, the curve $y=e^x$ and the line $x=1$. The region is rotated completely about the x-axis. Find the centre of mass of the solid so formed when filled by matter of uniform density.

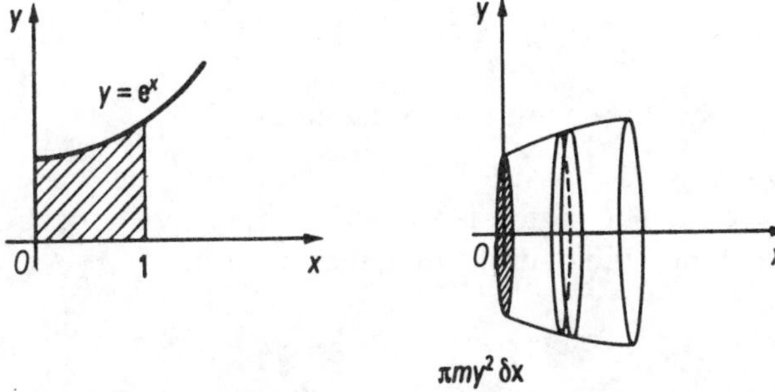

Figure 33.6

If the region R is divided into rectangular 'strips', when these strips are rotated they form 'cylinders', mass $m\pi y^2\delta x$, where m is the mass per unit volume of the solid. Because of the symmetry of the body, these cylinders are equivalent, in this context, to particles mass $\pi y^2\delta x$ along the axis of symmetry, so the x-coordinate of the centre of mass $\bar{x}$, is given by

$$\bar{x}\int m\pi y^2 dx=\int m\pi x y^2 dx$$

But $y=e^x$ is the equation of the curved boundary of R, so

$$\int_0^1 y^2 dx = \int_0^1 e^{2x} dx = \tfrac{1}{2}(e^2-1),$$

and

$$\int_0^1 xy^2 dx = \int_0^1 xe^{2x} dx$$

$$= \left[\tfrac{1}{2}xe^{2x} - \tfrac{1}{4}e^{2x}\right]_0^1$$

$$= \tfrac{1}{4}(e^2+1)$$

$$\tfrac{1}{2}(e^2-1)\bar{x} = \tfrac{1}{4}(e^2+1)$$

$$\bar{x} = \frac{e^2+1}{2(e^2-1)}$$

$$\simeq 0.7$$

We expect a value a little larger than 0.5, so this is reasonable.

Example 2. A finite region R is bounded by one arc of the curve $y=\sin x$ and the x-axis, for $0 \leqslant x \leqslant \pi$. The region is rotated completely about the x-axis. Find the centre of mass of the solid of uniform density so formed.

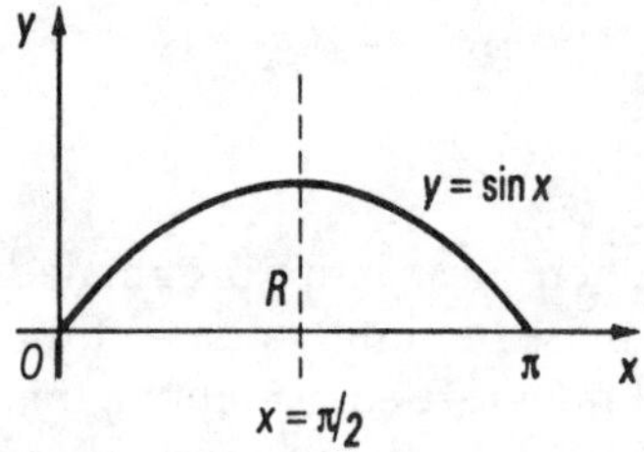

Figure 33.7

The solid of revolution is symmetrical about the x-axis, and so $y=0$. However, the region R is symmetrical about the line $x=\pi/2$, which is perpendicular to the axis of rotation, so that the resulting solid is also symmetrical about $x=\pi/2$, and the centre of mass must lie on the line $x=\pi/2$. The coordinates of the centre of mass are $(\pi/2, 0)$.

Exercise 33.1

Find the centre of mass of each of the following systems of particles:

1 $2m$, $3m$, $5m$ at points with position vectors $\mathbf{i}$, $3\mathbf{i}$, $5\mathbf{i}$, respectively.

2 $2m$, $3m$, $5m$ at points with position vectors $(\mathbf{i}-\mathbf{j})$, $(3\mathbf{i}+2\mathbf{j})$, $(2\mathbf{i}-5\mathbf{j})$, respectively.

3 $3m$, $7m$, $10m$ at points with position vectors $\mathbf{j}$, $(-2\mathbf{i}-5\mathbf{j})$, $(\mathbf{i}+2\mathbf{j})$, respectively.

4 m, $2m$, $2m$ at points with position vectors $\mathbf{i}$, $-\mathbf{j}$, $(2\mathbf{i}-\mathbf{j})$, respectively.

5 m, $2m$, $3m$ and $4m$ at points position vectors $\mathbf{i}$, $-3\mathbf{j}$, $(2\mathbf{i}+\mathbf{j}+\mathbf{k})$, $(-\mathbf{i}-\mathbf{j}+\mathbf{k})$, respectively.

6 Sketch each of the regions defined below, and find the coordinates of its centre of mass.
(a) The region bounded by $y=\sin x$, and the x-axis from 0 to π.
(b) The region bounded by the curve $y=\cos x$ and the x-axis from $-\pi/2$ to $\pi/2$.
(c) The region bounded by $y^2=x$ and the line $x=4$.
(d) The region bounded by $y=x^2$ and the line $y=4$.
(e) The region bounded $y=x^{1/2}$, the x-axis and the lines $x=1$, $x=4$.
7 Sketch each of the regions described below. The region is rotated about the x-axis, to form a solid of uniform density. Use the symmetry of each body to find the coordinate of its centre of mass.
(a) The region bounded by $y=x(2-x)$ and the x-axis between $x=0$ and $x=2$.
(b) The region bounded by $y=x^2(2-x)^2$ and the x-axis between $x=0$ and $x=2$.
(c) The region bounded by $y=e^{-x^2}$ the x-axis and the lines $x=1$, $x=-1$.
(d) he region bounded by $y=\cos x$ and the x-axis between $\pi/2$ and $3\pi/2$.
(e) The region bounded by $y=\sin^2 x$ and the x-axis between 0 and π.
8 Sketch each of the regions described below. The region is rotated about the x-axis, to form a solid of uniform density. Find the coordinates of the centre of mass.
(a) $y=x^2$, the x-axis and the line $x=2$.
(b) $y=1/x^2$, the x-axis and the lines $x=1$, $x=2$.
9 Sketch each of the regions defined below. The region is rotated about the y-axis and forms a solid of uniform density. Find the coordinates of the centre of mass.
(a) $y=x^2$, the y-axis and the line $y=2$.
(b) $y=x^{1/2}$, the y-axis and the line $y=2$.

Probability 34

Definition 377

Mutually exclusive events 377

Independent events 377

Dependent events 377

Addition law 378

Application of Venn diagrams 379

Conditional probability 379

Product law 380

Use of tree diagrams 381

Binomial distribution 383

Geometric distribution 384

Notes

The probability of an event A, is defined as

$$\frac{\text{the number of } \textbf{equiprobable favourable} \text{ outcomes}}{\text{total number of } \textbf{equiprobable} \text{ outcomes}}$$

If A and B denote two events

$$P(A \text{ or } B \text{ or both}) = P(A) + P(B) - P(\text{both } A \text{ and } B)$$

This can be written

$$P(A \cup B) = P(A) + P(B) - P(A \cap B)$$

Dependent events

$P(B|A)$ denotes the probability of event B, **given that event A has already happened.**

$$P(B|A) = \frac{P(A \cap B)}{P(A)}$$

Remember that *tree diagrams* are often useful.

Binomial distribution

If the probability of success in one trial is p, the probability of r successes out of n trials is

$$\frac{n!}{r!(n-r)!} p^r (1-p)^{n-r}$$

Geometric distribution

If an experiment finishes as soon as a success is recorded, the probability of a success at the rth attempt is $(1-p)^{r-1}p$.

Definition

The probability of an event A written $P(A)$ is defined as the ratio

$$\frac{\text{number of equiprobable favourable outcomes}}{\text{total number of equiprobable outcomes}}$$

e.g. P (card drawn at random from a pack of 52 cards is a king) is 4/52, since there are four kings; P (a fair die shows a number divisible by 3) is 2/6, since there are two numbers, 3 and 6, divisible by three. Note *equiprobable* favourable events. It is incorrect to say that because there are three possible outcomes when throwing a pair of coins, TT, TH and HH, that the probability of both coins showing heads is 1/3; the three possible outcomes are not equiprobable. The correct probability of two heads is 1/4.

Mutually exclusive events

If two events are such that one excludes the other, the events are said to be mutually exclusive, e.g. a coin cannot show heads and tails, a match cannot be both lost and won.

Independent events

If two events are such that neither has any effect on the other, they are called independent events. Unless events are clearly dependent on each other, such as the outcome of drawing a second card from a pack when the first card drawn has not been replaced, assume that the events are independent unless told otherwise. In practice it might be argued that they are not independent, because if one athlete sets a fast pace to break the record, then that may help the other athlete, but ignore connections like this unless told otherwise.

Dependent events

Two events are dependent if knowledge that one event has occurred affects the probability that the other will occur. If a spade has been drawn from a standard pack of 52 cards, the probability that the next card drawn is a spade is 12/51, because there are only 12 spades left out of 51 cards.

The probability of an event A given that an event B has already happened, is written $P(A|B)$. If two events are independent, so that the probability of the second event is not affected by the first, $P(A|B)=P(A)$, and $P(B|A)=P(B)$

Example. A card is drawn at random from a standard pack of 52 cards, and then replaced. The probability that the next card is a spade is 13/52, 1/4, and is not affected by whether the first card was a spade or not. The draws are independent. If the first card is not replaced, however, then the probability that the second card is a spade is affected by whether or not the first is a spade, and these events are dependent.

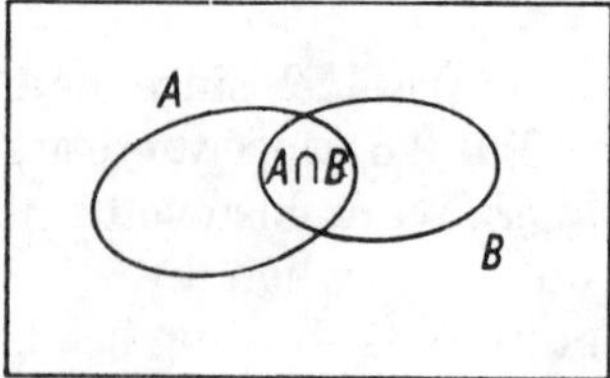

Figure 34.1

When we are calculating $\mathrm{P}(B|A)$, we know that A has already occurred, so that A represents the set of all possible outcomes. The event B only occurs if any of the outcomes in $A\cap B$ occur, so that

$$\mathrm{P}(B|A)=\frac{n\{A\cap B\}}{n\{A\}}=\frac{\mathrm{P}(A\cap B)}{\mathrm{P}(A)}$$

Addition law

If events A and B are mutually exclusive, the probability of both A and B is $\mathrm{P}(A)+\mathrm{P}(B)$. More generally, if $\mathrm{P}(A\cup B)$ is the probability of A and B,

$$\mathrm{P}(A\cup B)=\mathrm{P}(A)+\mathrm{P}(B)-\mathrm{P}(A\cap B).$$

This is illustrated by the Venn diagram in Figure 34.2.

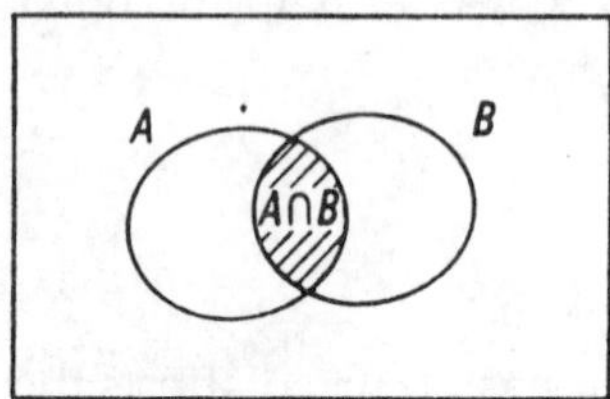

Figure 34.2

Example. Find the probability that a card drawn at random from a pack of 52 cards is either a two or a spade.

P(two)	=4/52
P(spade)	=13/52
P(two of spades)	=1/52
P(two or a spade)	=4/52×13/52−1/52=16/52

Alternatively, we can see that there are 16 different favourable cards, the thirteen spades, and the three cards, two of hearts, diamonds and clubs, out of a total of 52 different cards.

Application of Venn diagrams

Many problems can be solved using Venn diagrams, as in this example.

Example. Two events A and B are such that $P(A)=0.2$, $P(A\cap B)=0.15$ and $P(A'\cap B)=0.25$. Find $P(A\cap B')$ and $P(A|B)$.

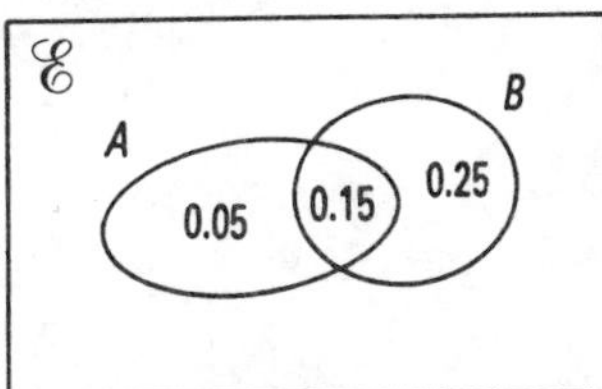

Figure 34.3

Since the probability of any event is proportional to the number of elements in a certain set, we can fill in the Venn diagram as above, starting with $A\cap B=0.15$, the value of 0.05 being $0.2-0.15$. This is $P(A\cap B')$, so

$$P(A\cap B')=0.05$$

To find $P(A|B)$, we have to choose events A from the set B, and we see that

$$P(A|B)=\frac{P(A\cap B)}{P(B)}$$

$$=\frac{0.15}{0.4}=0.375$$

Conditional probability

Sometimes these problems can be solved using a Venn diagram, sometimes by just using the formula

$$P(A|B)=\frac{P(A\cap B)}{P(B)},$$

sometimes it helps if we tabulate the equiprobable outcomes, and use our definition of probability

$$P(A)=\frac{\text{number of equiprobable favourable outcomes}}{\text{total number of equiprobable outcomes}}$$

Example. Three fair coins are spun. Find the probability that two of them show Heads, given that at least one shows Heads.

The equiprobable outcomes are

TTT, TTH, THT, HTT, HHT, HTH, THH, HHH

and we have to select from the last seven of these, since we are given that at least one shows Heads. Of these

HHT, HTH, THH

are 'favourable', so that

$$\text{P(two show Heads}|\text{one shows Heads)}=3/7$$

Notice that P(two show Heads)=3/8
P(one shows Heads)=7/8
so that $\text{P(two show Heads}|\text{at least one shows Heads)}=\frac{3/8}{7/8}=\frac{3}{7}$

Product law

If events A and B are independent, then the probability that both events happen, written $P(A\cap B)$, is given by

$$P(A\cap B)=P(A)\times P(B)$$

Example. The probability that Jack catches the bus one morning is 1/3; the probability that Jill catches the bus is 1/4.

Find the probability that (a) both catch the bus, (b) both miss the bus, (c) just one misses the bus.

(a) P(Jack catches the bus) =1/3
P(Jill catches the bus) =1/4
P(both catch the bus) =1/3×1/4=1/12.

(b) Either Jack catches the bus or he does not, so the probability that he does not catch the bus is 1−1/3, i.e. 2/3; similarly the probability that Jill does not catch the bus is 1−1/4, i.e. 3/4, so the probability that both miss the bus is 2/3×3/4, i.e. 1/2.

(c) If just one misses the bus, then either Jack catches the bus but Jill does not, 1/3×3/4, i.e. 1/4, or Jack does not catch the bus but Jill does, probability 2/3×1/4, i.e. 1/6.

∴ P(just one misses the bus)=1/4+1/6=5/12

Wherever possible, check probabilities, and here we see that

P(both catch the bus) =1/12
P(just one catches the bus) =5/12
P(both miss the bus) =1/2

These are all the possible outcomes, and 1/12+5/12+1/2=1.

Use of tree diagrams

A model of the climate in a certain region may be made by classifying each day as wet or fine, and saying that if it is fine one day, the probability that it is fine the next will be 3/4; that if it is wet one day the probability that it will be wet the next is 2/3. If it is fine on Monday of one week, can we find the probability that it will be fine on Wednesday and Thursday?

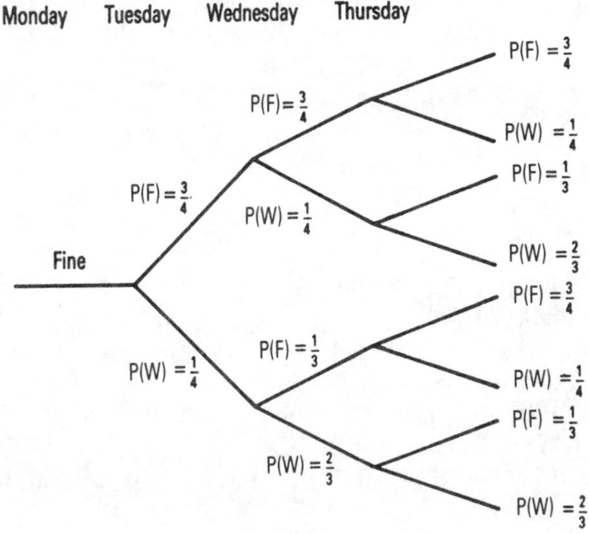

Figure 34.4

Draw a tree diagram (Figure 34.4) and complete the probability of events. Then if it is fine on Wednesday, we can have FF or WF. Thus

$$\begin{aligned}\text{P(fine on Wednesday)} &= \text{P(FF)}+\text{P(WF)}\\ &= 3/4\times3/4+1/4\times1/3\\ &= 31/48\end{aligned}$$

Similarly,

$$\begin{aligned}\text{P(wet on Wednesday)} &= \text{P(WW)}+\text{P(FW)}\\ &= 1/4\times2/3+3/4\times1/4\\ &= 17/48\end{aligned}$$

and we notice that

$$31/48+17/48 = 1$$

To find the probability that it is fine on Thursday, we have

$$\begin{aligned}\text{P(fine on Thursday)} &= 3/4\times\text{P(fine on Wednesday)}\\ &\quad +1/3\times\text{P(wet on Wednesday)}\\ &= 3/4\times 31/48+1/3\times 17/48\\ &= 347/576\end{aligned}$$

and

$$\begin{aligned}\text{P(wet on Thursday)} &= 1/4\times\text{P(fine on Wednesday)}\\ &\quad +2/3\times\text{P(wet on Wednesday)}\\ &= 1/4\times 31/48+2/3\times 17/48\\ &= 229/576\end{aligned}$$

Notice again that

$$347/576+229/576=1$$

Exercise 34.1

1 Events A and B are such that $P(A)=0.7$, $P(B)=0.5$, and $P(A\cap B)=0.3$. Find (a) $P(A\cup B)$, (b) $P(A|B)$, (c) $P(B|A)$.

2 Events A and B are such that $P(A)=0.7$, $P(B)=0.4$, and $P(A\cup B)=0.9$. Find (a) $P(A\cap B)$, (b) $P(A|B)$, (c) $P(B|A)$.

3 Events A and B are such that $P(A)=0.7$, $P(B)=0.4$, and $P(A\cap B)=0.28$. Find (a) $P(A|B)$, (b) $P(A|B')$, (c) $P(B|A)$.

4 Events A and B are such that $P(A)=a$, $P(B)=b$. Prove that $P(A\cap B)=ab$ if and only if $P(A|B)=P(A|B')$.

5 Events A and B are such that $P(A'\cap B)=0.15$, $P(A\cap B')=0.2$, and $P(A|B)=0.4$. Find (a) $P(A\cap B)$, (b) $P(A\cup B)$, (c) $P(B|A)$.

6 The probability that a card drawn at random from a pack is 1/4. Find the probability that, when four draws are made,
(a) three are spades,
(b) three are spades, given that at least one is a spade,
(c) three are spades, given that at least two are spades,
(d) three are spades, given that at least three are spades.

7 With the data of Q.6, find the probability that, when four draws are made,
(a) two are spades, given that at least one is a spade,
(b) one is a spade, given that at least one is a spade.

8 The probability that the bus is late any one day is 0.2. Find the probability that, in a week of five days,
(a) the bus is late on two days,
(b) it is late on two days, given that it is late on at least one day,
(c) it is late on two days, given that it is late on at least two days.

9 In a certain examination, 80% of the candidates pass English and 75% pass French, whereas 15% fail both examinations. Find the probability that a candidate selected at random
(a) passes both examinations,

(b) passes both examinations, given that he passes English,
(c) passes both examinations, given that he passes French.

10 In a certain village, 50% of the inhabitants have cars, 60% have bicycles and 30% have neither. Find the probability that a person selected at random
(a) has both a car and a bicycle, given that he has a car,
(b) has both, given that he has a bicycle.

11 Red and yellow dice are rolled and the numbers on their faces are recorded. Find the probability that these numbers
(a) total 2, (b) total 7, (c) total more than 7.
Given that the red die shows a 4, find the probability of each of the events above.

12 Two numbers, not necessarily different, are chosen at random from the numbers 1, 2, 3, ... 10. Find the probability that these numbers
(a) are both even, (b) are the same, (c) are different.
Given that the first number is 3, find now the probability of each of the above events.

13 The probability that Arthur solves a particular problem is 1/2; that Bert solves that problem is 2/5; that Chris solves the problem is 3/4. Given that these probabilities are independent, find the probability that
(a) all three solve the problem,
(b) only one solves the problem,
(c) the problem is not solved by any of them.

14 From a standard pack of cards all the spades and all the aces are removed. Find the probability that
(a) a card drawn at random is the queen of diamonds,
(b) when two cards are drawn together at random, both are queens,
(c) when two cards are drawn together at random, neither is a queen.

15 If a boy oversleeps one morning, the probability that he oversleeps the next day is 0.1; if he wakes on time one morning, the probability that he wakes on time the next is 0.3. If he wakes on time on Monday, find the probability that he
(a) wakes on time on Wednesday,
(b) oversleeps on Wednesday,
(c) oversleeps on Thursday,
(d) wakes on time on Friday.

Binomial distribution

To find the probability of one failure (F) out of four trials, favourable outcomes can be written

FSSS; SFSS; SSFS and SSSF

Thus if the probability of success is p, the probability of failure is $(1-p)$, and the probability of the outcome FSSS is $(1-p)p^3$; since there are four equiprobable favourable outcomes, each with a probability $(1-p)p^3$, the probability of one failure out of four trials is $4(1-p)p^3$. Generally, if we have an experiment in which we want r successes out of n trials, there will be $\binom{n}{r}$ ways in which these r successes can occur, each with a probability of $p^r(1-p)^{n-r}$, so that the probability of r successes out of n trials is $\binom{n}{r}p^r(1-p)^{n-r}$. This is an example of a binomial distribution.

Example. When practising, the probability that a tennis player serves an 'Ace' is 0.2. Find the probability that he serves an 'Ace' twice in five attempts.

The probability p that he serves an 'Ace' is 0.2, so the probability that he does not serve an 'Ace' is 0.8. If A denotes that he serves an 'Ace' and X that he does not serve an 'Ace', then AAXXX would be an acceptable order, so would AXAXX and AXXAX. There are $\frac{5!}{2!3!}$ i.e. $\binom{5}{2}$, 10 such orders. The probability of each is $(0.2)^2(0.8)^3$, so that the probability that he serves two 'Aces' out of five attempts is $10(0.2)^2(0.8)^3$, i.e. 0.2048.

Geometric distribution

Some experiments end as soon as one success (or failure) has been attained. A cricketer's innings finishes as soon as he is 'out', many games begin by throwing a 'six', and most students stop when they have found one solution to a problem, instead of trying to find a better solution. If we suppose that an experiment finishes after a success, then possible outcomes are

S, FS, FFS, FFFS, ...

every experiment finishing as soon as a success is recorded. Denoting the probability of success by p, the probability of the experiment finishing after five failures and one success is $(1-p)^5p$, after r failures and one success by $(1-p)^rp$. This is an example of geometric distribution.

Example. The probability that a certain person passes the driving test is 0.7. Find the probability of that person passing (a) at the second attempt, (b) at the tenth attempt.

Since the probability of passing is 0.7, the probability of failing is 0.3, so the probability of passing (S) at the second time is $P(F)\times P(S)=0.3\times 0.7=0.21$.

The probability of passing at the tenth attempt is the probability of nine failures then success, i.e. $(0.3)^9(0.7)$, about 1.4×10^{-5}.

Exercise 34.2

1 The probability of success in a certain trial is 0.4. Find the probability that in 5 trials, there are
(a) 5 successes, (b) 4 successes, (c) 3 successes, (d) 2 successes, (e) 1 success, (f) no successes.

2 The probability that a certain biassed coin shows 'Heads' is 0.8. Find the probability that in 5 throws,
(a) there are 3 'Heads',
(b) there are 4 'Heads',
(c) there are more 'Heads' than 'Tails'.

3 In a certain district, the weather is classified as either 'dry' or 'wet', and the weather any one day is independent of the weather on any other day. The probability that any one day is 'wet' is 0.3. Find the probability that in a week of 7 days,
(a) there are 5 'wet' days,
(b) there are at least 5 'wet' days,
(c) there are less than 5 'wet' days.

4 A certain 'one-armed bandit' costs 5p a time, but pays out £1 if more than 8 balls out of 10 roll into a specified slot. If the probability of any one ball rolling into that slot is 0.6, find the probability that
(a) all 10 balls roll there,
(b) no balls roll there,
(c) only 9 of the 10 balls roll there,
(d) only 1 of the 10 balls rolls there.
Deduce the probability of a player winning with one attempt.

5 Some of the tins of one brand of baked beans contain sausages, but these tins are indistinguishable from those that do not contain sausages. The probability that any one tin opened at random contains a sausage is 0.3. Find the probability that out of 10 tins
(a) none contain sausages,
(b) all 10 contain sausages,
(c) exactly two contain sausages,
(d) exactly two do not contain sausages.

6 The probability of success in a certain trial is 0.6. Find the probability that the first success is
(a) at the first attempt,
(b) at the second attempt,
(c) at the third attempt,
(d) before the fourth attempt.

7 The probability that a golfer holes a putt is 0.3. Find the probability that, when practising, she holes her first putt
(a) at the first attempt,
(b) at the second attempt,
(c) at the third attempt.

8 How many attempts will the golfer in Q.7 need to have a probability of 0.9 of having holed her putt?

9 A schoolmaster has bought a large consignment of tins of cat food and dog food at a sale. Although the tins have all lost their labels, he is assured that three-quarters of them contain cat food. To feed his cat, he has to open tins successively until he comes to one containing cat food. Find the probability that

(a) the second tin he opens contains cat food,
(b) the fourth tin he opens contains cat food,
(c) he opens five or more tins before finding one with cat food.

10 Two friends A and B play a game, throwing a fair die alternately, the first to throw a '5' winning. A throws first. Find the probability that he wins.

11 The school chess champion plays two opponents A and B in turn until one of them beats him. The probability that the champion beats A is 0.9; that the champion beats B is 0.8. If the first game is against A, find the probability that it is A who beats the champion.

Statistics 35

Some definitions 389

Frequency 389

Summary 391

Working zero 392

Measures of spread, dispersion 393

Grouped data 395

Continuous variable 396

Cumulative frequency curve 398

Median and quartiles 399

Upper boundary 399

Notes

For a set of scores $x_1, x_2, x_3 \ldots$
the **frequency** f_i records how often each score x_i occurs.
The **mode** is the score with the highest frequency.
The **median** is the middle score when they are arranged in order of size. (If the number of scores is even, the median is generally taken to be half the sum of the two 'middle' scores.)
The **mean** $\bar{x}$ (or m) is given by

$$\bar{x}=\frac{1}{n}(x_1+x_2+\ldots x_n) \text{ if there are } n \text{ scores}$$

which can be written

$$\bar{x}=\frac{\Sigma f_i x_i}{\Sigma f_i}$$

Measures of spread

The **range** is the difference between the greatest and the least scores.
The **inter-quartile range** is the difference between the upper and lower quartiles.
The **standard deviation** s is defined by

$$s^2=\frac{\Sigma f_i(x_i-\bar{x})^2}{\Sigma f_i}$$

but is usually calculated from the equivalent form

$$s^2=\frac{\Sigma f_i x_i^2}{\Sigma f_i}-\bar{x}^2$$

The quantity s^2 is called the **variance**.

Some definitions

What is the mass of a 'large' loaf of bread? To answer this question, we would weigh some loaves ('sampling'). We would be most unlikely to find that they were all of exactly the same mass, though we might well decide they were 'about 800 grams', and this we might think an 'average' mass. Suppose the masses, in grams, are

800 802 798 803 798

To find an 'average', we can sum these five masses, and divide by 5, giving 800.2; this is the **mean**. We can arrange them in order of size, i.e.

798 798 800 802 803

and select the middle number, 800; this is called the **median**. Or we can notice that 798 occurs twice, whereas no other score occurs more than once, and so we can take the commonest, 800; this is called the **mode**. There are many other 'averages' that users of statistics find helpful; the *Financial Times* Indices of Stock Prices are based on geometric means, e.g. here the geometric mean of the five scores is $(798\times798\times800\times802\times803)^{1/5}$, i.e. 800.1974. One advantage of this is that it is not much affected by a considerable change in just one of the scores. We choose whatever 'average' is most suitable for our purposes. The median is not distorted by a few extreme values, the mode is very easily observed and sometimes we just want 'the commonest' score; the mean, though, for a variety of reasons, is the 'average' that statisticians generally use.

The figures that we have obtained by sampling are called the **scores**. We should of course choose loaves at random, without any kind of bias (it would be misleading to choose those that looked largest, or the last loaf in each batch, etc.) and so these are '**random samples**'. The mass of each loaf we measure to an appropriate degree of accuracy, to the nearest gram in this case. With this degree of accuracy, possible 'scores' might be 797, 798, 799, 800, etc., but not values in between. These are called '**discrete variables**'. The height of a child grows from say 1 metre to 1.5 metres; at some time in between it takes any value between those extremes, and is a **continuous variable**, yet as soon as we measure the height 'correct to the nearest ...' it becomes a **discrete variable**. In some cases there is little difference between continuous variables and discrete variables, and we shall see later that we often use one to describe (or 'model') the other, sometimes needing to make appropriate allowances.

Frequency

With only five scores, it was easy to add these together and divide by five to find the mean. In practice, we should not expect to obtain an 'average' that accurately described all the loaves from a sample of only five. If we take 20 loaves, their masses might be

795 803 801 804 803 799 799 797 801 802
802 800 803 799 798 798 800 801 802 799

We notice that the score 803 occurs three times; the frequency of 803 is 3.

We find it useful to draw up frequency tables, indicating each time a score occurs by a tally mark / (Table 35.1). To help count, if we have more than four tally marks in the same interval, we place the fifth across ~~////~~.

Table 35.1

Score (x)	Tally marks	Frequency (f)
795	/	1
796		0
797	/	1
798	//	2
799	////	4
800	//	2
801	///	3
802	///	3
803	///	3
804	/	1
	Total	20

To find the total mass of the loaves, it is easier to multiply each score x by the corresponding frequency f, and sum the products fx (Table 35.2), written Σfx.

Table 35.2

Score (x)	Frequency (f)	Product (fx)
795	1	795
796	0	0
797	1	797
798	2	1596
799	4	3196
800	2	1600
801	3	2403
802	3	2406
803	3	2409
804	1	804
	Total	16 006

The mean is 16 006÷20, i.e. 800.3. This is written

$$m \equiv \bar{x} = \frac{1}{n}\Sigma fx = 800.3$$

using either m or $\bar{x}$ to denote the mean, and n the number of scores.

Summary

The mean of the n scores $x_1, x_2, x_3 \ldots x_n$, written x_i, $i=1,2,3 \ldots n$,

is $(x_1+x_2+x_3 \ldots x_n) \div n$, i.e. $\frac{1}{n}\sum_{i=1}^{n} x_i$

When f_i is the frequency of x_i, the mean is $\frac{\Sigma f_i x_i}{\Sigma f_i}$

The median is the middle score when they are arranged in order; when there are two 'middle' scores, the median is the mean of these two 'middle' scores. Sometimes, e.g. 1, 2, 2, 2, 2, 2, 2, 2, 2, there is no number that can really be called the median.

The mode is the commonest score, i.e. the score with the highest frequency.

Exercise 35.1

1 Find the mean, median and mode of each of the following set of scores:

(a) 2, 3, 3, 3, 5,
(b) 4, 0, 2, 9, 0,
(c) 0, 1, 4, 5, 9, 9,
(d) 5, 0, 1, 2, 0, 7,
(e) −3, −5, 1, 0, 7.

2 Find the mean of −1, 0, 1, 4, 5. Deduce the mean of

(a) 9, 10, 11, 14, 15,
(b) −4, 0, 4, 16, 20,
(c) −0.9, 0.1, 1.1, 4.1, 5.1.

3 Find x if the mean of 1, 4, 6, x, 9 is 6.4.

4 Find x if the mode of 1, 6, 4, 6, 1, 5, x is 6.

5 Find x if the median of 1, 7, x, 6, 3, 7 is 5.

6 Find the mean of the following scores:

4	5	5	4	6	7	3	7	2	3
4	4	6	4	7	7	6	3	8	7
4	5	6	7	7	8	3	4	4	5
5	5	6	7	8	4	2	2	8	6
3	4	5	6	5	5	4	4	6	7

7 Find the mean of the following scores with corresponding frequencies:

Score (x)	1	2	3	4	5	6	7	8
Frequency (f)	3	5	9	13	17	23	29	1

8 Find the mean of the following scores with corresponding frequencies:

Score (x)	181	182	183	184	185	186	187	188
Frequency	2	5	13	25	41	7	5	2

Working zero

We notice that the mass of each loaf is 'about 800 grams', and if we subtract 800 from each score we shall have 20 scores with the same spread as the original scores, and with the mean just 800 less. These smaller scores will be easier to total than the original. The number 800 is called the 'working zero'; sometimes it is called a **working mean** (which it certainly is not!) or an '**estimated mean**' (which again it certainly is not!).

Table 35.3

Score x	$x-w$	f	$f(x-w)$
795	−5	1	−5
796	−4	0	0
797	−3	1	−3
798	−2	2	−4
799	−1	4	−4
800	0	2	0
801	1	3	3
802	2	3	6
803	3	3	9
804	4	1	4
		Total	6

The calculation can be set out now as in Table 35.3. The mean of the scores $(x-w)$ is $6\div20$, i.e. 0.3; the mean of the scores x is $800+0.3$, i.e. 800.3, as we have already calculated. The calculation of a mean can now usually be done on an electronic calculator, either using frequencies of the scores or by addition.

Example 1. Find the mean, median and mode of each of the following sets of scores: (a) 1, 3, 1, 5, 7, (b) 1, 3, 3, 3, 3, (c) 1, 3, 1, 3, 5, 2.

(a) The mean is $(1+3+1+5+7)\div5$, i.e. 3.4
The median is the middle score when arranged in order, 1,1,3,5,7, so the median is 3.
The mode is the commonest, i.e. 1.

(b) The mean is $(1+3+3+3+3)\div5$, i.e. 2.6.
The mode is 3; there is no number that can meaningfully be called the 'middle' one, so no median.

(c) The mean is $(1+3+1+3+5+2)\div6$, i.e. 2.5.
The median is the mean of the two middle scores, when arranged in increasing order: 1 1 2 3 3 5, i.e. $\frac{1}{2}(2+3)$, 2.5.
Both 1 and 3 occur twice, the highest frequency, so there are two modes, and the scores are called bimodal.

Example 2. Find the mean of the scores 1, 3, 4, 6, 7. Deduce the mean of each of the following sets of scores: (a) 100, 300, 400, 600, 700, (b) 1.1, 3.1, 4.1, 6.1, 7.1.

The mean of 1,3,4,6,7 is $(1+3+4+6+7)\div 5$, i.e. 4.2.

The scores in the set (a) are each 100 times the scores in the first set, so the mean of the scores in (a) is 420.

The scores in set (b) are each 0.1 more than the scores in the first set, so their mean is $4.2+0.1$, i.e. 4.3.

Measures of spread, dispersion

The difference between the greatest and least mass of the loaves sampled was $803-798$, i.e. 5 g. This is called the range of the scores, and is one easy measure of spread.

Table 35.4

Score (x)	$x-\bar{x}$	$\lvert x-\bar{x}\rvert$	$(x-\bar{x})^2$
798	−2.2	2.2	4.84
798	−2.2	2.2	4.84
800	−0.2	0.2	0.04
802	1.8	1.8	3.24
803	2.8	2.8	7.84
Total	0	9.2	20.8

Looking at the scores x and their relation to the mean $\bar{x}$, we have Table 35.4. The sum of the entries in the $x-\bar{x}$ column is zero, and this will always be zero, from the nature of the mean. To prevent the positive and negative deviations cancelling, we can average their moduli (column 3), giving a statistic of $\frac{1}{5}(9.2)=1.84$; this is occasionally used as a measure of spread, and called the mean deviation from the mean, deviation being positive. Or we can consider the mean deviation from the median, and again this is sometimes used, but the commonest measure of spread is the standard deviation s, obtained from column 4. The variance, s^2, is defined by

$$s^2=\frac{1}{n}\Sigma(x-\bar{x})^2$$

and the standard deviation s is the square root of the variance. Here,

$$s^2=\tfrac{1}{5}(20.8),\ \text{so } s\approx 2.0396.$$

This can be obtained directly from most electronic calculators, using the key generally marked σ_n.

If we are using a frequency distribution, the definition of s^2 is

$$s^2=\frac{1}{n}\Sigma f_i(x_i-\bar{x})^2,\ \text{where } n=\Sigma f_i$$

We find that the variance s^2 is often an easier statistic to use than the standard deviation s, which contains a square root. For example, we can expand the brackets we are summing, thus

$ns^2=\Sigma f(x-\bar{x})^2$, omitting the suffix i, as there is no ambiguity
$=\Sigma fx^2-\Sigma 2fx\bar{x}+\Sigma f\bar{x}^2$
$=\Sigma fx^2-2\bar{x}\Sigma fx+\bar{x}^2\Sigma f$

Now $\Sigma f=n$, and $\Sigma fx=\bar{x}n$, from the definition of the mean

so $ns^2=\Sigma fx^2-2n\bar{x}^2+n\bar{x}^2$
$=\Sigma fx^2-n\bar{x}^2$

and $s^2=\frac{1}{n}\Sigma fx^2-\bar{x}^2$

This form is much easier to use for calculations than the form given in the definition. We can check that the standard deviation of 798, 798, 800, 802 and 803 is

$$\sqrt{[\tfrac{1}{5}(798^2+798^2+800^2+802^2+803^2)-800.2^2]}, \text{ i.e. } 2.0396$$

In the same way that we can find many different 'averages', i.e. measures of size, so can find many different measures of spread which users of statistics find helpful. We shall consider only those tested in present A-level syllabuses.

Example. Find the mean and variance of these scores with the corresponding frequencies.

x	11	12	13	14	15	16
f	8	18	21	27	16	10

These numbers should now be entered correctly into a calculator and the mean variance read from the display; it is often useful to read n, where $n\equiv\Sigma f=100$, to check that the frequencies have been entered correctly. The calculations are displayed in Table 35.5, in case a calculator is not available, and to show the calculations being made.

Table 35.5

Score x	Frequency f	fx	x^2	fx^2
11	8	88	121	968
12	18	216	144	2592
13	21	273	169	3549
14	27	378	196	5292
15	16	240	225	3600
16	10	160	256	2560
Totals	$\Sigma f=100$	$\Sigma fx=1355$		$\Sigma fx^2=18\,561$

The mean $\bar{x}=\Sigma fx/\Sigma f=1355\div100=13.55$

The variance $s^2=\frac{1}{n}\Sigma fx^2-\bar{x}^2=\frac{1}{100}\times18\,561-13.55^2$
$=2.0075$

The standard deviation $s=\sqrt{2.0075}, \approx 1.417$.

The range of the scores above is 16−11, i.e. 5. As a very rough test of the accuracy of our calculations of the standard deviation, for very many distributions the standard deviation is about one-quarter to one-sixth of the range, so a value of s about 1 is reasonable.

From the definition of standard deviation, sets of scores like 1, 2, 4, 7, 10 and 11, 12, 14, 17, 20 and 51, 52, 54, 57, 60, which have the same 'spread', should have the same measure of that spread. We can verify that these three sets of scores do have the same standard deviation. By contrast, 1, 2, 4, 7, 10 and 10, 20, 40, 70 and 100 are in the ratio 1:10, so we should expect any measures of spread also to be in the ratio 1:10. Again, we can verify that this is so. These properties are often useful when scaling or using a working zero.

Exercise 35.2

1 Find the mean and standard deviation of each of the following sets of scores:
(a) 1, 2, 3, 4, 5,
(b) 1, 3, 5, 7, 9,
(c) 10, 12, 14, 16, 18,
(d) 10, 20, 30, 40, 50,
(e) 13.1, 13.2, 13.3, 13.4, 13.5.

2 Find the mean and standard deviation of each of the following sets of scores and associated frequencies:

(a)	x	1	2	3	4	5	6
	f	7	17	23	29	15	9
(b)	x	2	4	6	8	10	12
	f	6	18	22	30	14	10

Grouped data

For reliable results, we often have to take fairly large samples; we should be foolish to think that we could estimate a likely mass of a large loaf from just five samples. If we weighed 100 loaves, their masses might range from 785 g to 815 g; we should find the calculations tedious with up to 31 different values for x, so we might group them in intervals 785– 790– 795– 800– 805– 810–815
which means that the scores 785, 786, 787, 788 and 789 are all recorded in the interval 785– , the interval including 785 and stopping just before the next score shown, here 790. Calculations made from the grouped data may not be quite as accurate as if we use the original scores, and there are correction factors devised by statisticians to try to reduce that inaccuracy, but they do not concern us at this stage.

When using grouped data, we suppose that all the scores in one interval have the value of the middle value of that interval, the mid-interval value (m.i.v.). It is often helpful to use a working zero.

Example. Find the mean and standard deviation of the mass of each of 100 loaves, recorded as follows:

Mass (in grams)	785–	790–	795–	800–	805–	810–815
No. of loaves	5	17	24	27	17	10

The values grouped in the first interval are 785, 786, 787, 788 and 789, so the mid-interval value is 787 (Table 35.6). We take 797 as the working zero w.

Table 35.6

Mid-interval value x	$x-w$	f	$f(x-w)$	$(x-w)^2$	$f(x-w)^2$
787	−10	5	−50	100	500
792	−5	17	−85	25	425
797	0	24	0	0	0
802	5	27	135	25	675
807	10	17	170	100	1700
812	15	10	150	225	2250
Total		$\Sigma f=100$	$\Sigma f(x-w)=320$		$\Sigma f(x-w)^2=5550$

Since $\bar{x}-w=\frac{1}{n}\Sigma f(x-w)$, $\bar{x}=797+\frac{320}{100}$

$$=800.2$$

The spread of the original scores x is the same as the spread of the scores $(x-w)$, so

$$\begin{aligned} s^2 &= \frac{1}{n}\Sigma f(x-w)^2-(\bar{x}-w)^2 \\ &= \frac{5550}{100}-3.2^2 \\ &= 45.26 \end{aligned}$$

the standard deviation $s\approx 6.728$. Notice again that the standard deviation is between one-quarter and one-sixth of the range.

Continuous variable

If we had had a continuous variable, so that all scores were possible in the interval 785 up to but not including 790, the mid-interval value would have been 787.5; if we had been working to a greater degree of accuracy than to the nearest gram, all scores say to 0.01 g, all scores from 785 up to and including 789.99 would be included in the first interval, and the m.i.v. would be strictly 787.495, which we would probably take as 787.5.

Example. One hundred Army recruits were set to change a wheel on a vehicle, and their times recorded to the nearest second. The results were grouped as follows:

Time (min)	4–	5–	6–	7–	8–	9–10
Frequency	16	36	20	15	8	5

As the times were recorded 'to the nearest second', the first interval contains all times up to 4 minutes 59.5 seconds, and so we can take the mid-interval values as 4.5 minutes, 5.5, 6.5, etc. Here we are using a continuous variable to approximate to a discrete variable.

Table 35.7

Time x	$x-w$	f	$f(x-w)$	$(x-w)^2$	$f(x-w)^2$
4.5	−2	16	−32	4	64
5.5	−1	36	−36	1	36
6.5	0	20	0	0	0
7.5	1	15	15	1	15
8.5	2	8	16	4	32
9.5	3	5	15	9	45
Total		$\Sigma f=100$	$\Sigma f(x-w)=-22$		$\Sigma f(x-w)^2=192$

Take $w=6.5$. Then $\Sigma(\bar{x}-w)=-22\div100$, $\bar{x}=6.28$

and $$s^2=\frac{192}{100}-(-0.22)^2$$
$$=1.8716$$

$s=1.368$. The mean time taken is 6.28 minutes, with standard deviation 1.368 minutes.

Exercise 35.3

1 A commuter records the time, correct to the nearest minute, that her train was late on each of 50 journeys, with the following results:

Minutes late	0–4	5–9	10–14	15–19	20–24	25–29
Frequency	12	13	9	8	5	3

Find the mean and standard deviation of the number of minutes her train was late.

2 Another commuter made a similar survey, grouping the data as shown:

Minutes late	0–	5–	10–	15–	20–	25–30
Frequency	14	10	9	7	6	6

Find the mean and standard deviation of the number of minutes his train was late.

3 A supermarket buyer recorded the mass of a grape, correct to the nearest gram, in a sample of 500 grapes, with the following results:

Mass of 1 grape (grams)	2–4	5–7	8–10	11–13	14–16
No. of grapes	8	140	153	134	65

Find the mean and standard deviation of the size, in grams, of a grape in this sample.

4 The length of a stride of each of 50 children was measured and recorded as follows:

Length (cm)	70–74	75–79	80–84	85–89	90–94
No. of children	7	18	17	7	1

Find the mean and standard deviation of the length in centimetres of this sample.

Cumulative frequency curve

Look again at the data for the Example on page 000. Sixteen recruits took less than 5 minutes to change a tyre, 52 recruits (i.e. 16+36) took less than 6 minutes, 72 recruits (16+36+20) took less than 7 minutes, 87 took less than 8 minutes, 95 took less than 9 minutes and all 100 took less than 10 minutes. We can obtain these figures by looking at the table as given, but it often helps to tabulate as shown in Table 35.8.

Table 35.8

Time x (min)	Frequency	x	Cumulative frequency
4–	16	5	16
5–	36	6	52
6–	20	7	72
7–	15	8	87
8–	8	9	95
9–10	5	10	100

These results can be displayed as in Figure 35.1. The curve is called a cumulative frequency curve (or ogive). From Figure 35.1 we see that no recruit took less than 4 minutes to change a tyre, 16 recruits less than 5 minutes, etc.

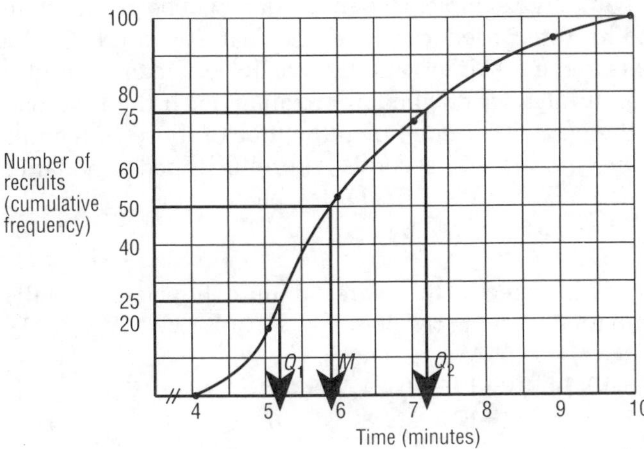

Figure 35.1

Reading from the '*y*-axis', we see that 50 recruits took less than 5.9 minutes. This is an estimate of the median. As the data is grouped, we can only make an estimate, but with a fairly large sample, here 100, it will probably be quite accurate. Cumulative frequency curves are a useful introduction to cumulative density functions, or distribution functions, but may be inaccurate for samples of less than about 100.

Median and quartiles

For a continuous distribution, we can define the median M as the value such that half of the distribution is less than M. The quartiles will be similarly defined, the lower quartile Q_1 such that one-quarter of the distribution is less than Q_1, the upper quartile Q_2 such that three-quarters of the distribution is less than Q_2. Here, M=5.9, Q_1=5.2 and Q_2=7.2.

The difference between the quartiles, Q_2-Q_1, gives a measure of spread, and is called the inter-quartile range, here 2 minutes. The semi-inter-quartile range, obviously half the inter-quartile range, is also sometimes used as a measure of spread.

Percentiles are defined in a similar manner. The 40th percentile is the value P such that 40% of the distribution is less than P. Here, 40% of the distribution takes less than 5.6 minutes.

Upper boundary

Care must be taken to determine the upper boundary of each class interval. Since cumulative frequency curves may not be very accurate for small samples, they should only be used with large samples, when the data will be grouped. In this example, the time had been recorded 'correct to the nearest second', so the time taken by the 16 recruits in the first intervals was strictly 'less than 4 minutes 59.5 seconds', for which 5 minutes was a good approximation. If the time had been recorded 'correct to the nearest minute', then the time of those 16 recruits would have been 'less than 4 minutes 30 seconds', and our upper boundaries would have been 4.5 minutes, 5.5 minutes, 6.5 minutes, etc.

Exercise 35.4

1 An office manager recorded, correct to the nearest minute, how late were the trains used by his staff, with the following results:

Minutes late	0–4	5–9	10–14	15–19	20–24	25–29
Frequency	25	25	19	17	8	6

Draw a cumulative frequency curve. From the curve estimate
(a) the median,
(b) the upper and lower quartiles,
(c) the inter-quartile range
of the number of minutes the trains were late.

2 Another firm made a similar survey with these results:

Minutes late	0–	5–	10–	15–	20–	25–30
Frequency	55	45	40	34	16	10

Draw a cumulative frequency curve to display this data. From the curve estimate
(a) the median,
(b) the upper and lower quartiles,
(c) the semi-inter-quartile range
of the number of minutes the trains were late.
(d) The railway company promises a cash payment if the trains are more than a certain number of minutes late. If 6% of the travellers receive the payment, how many minutes late must a train be to qualify for that payment?

Answers

Exercise 1.1 (page 6)

1 (a) $\{-6, -3, 3, 6\}$, (b) $\{-5, -4, -2, -1\}$, (c) $\{3, 2, 0, -1\}$, (d) $\{-\frac{1}{2}, -1, 1, \frac{1}{2}\}$, (e) $\{\frac{1}{4}, 1, 1, \frac{1}{4}\}$, (f) $\{4, 1, 1, 4\}$, (g) $\{-3, 0, 0, -3\}$, (h) $\{\frac{1}{4}, \frac{1}{2}, 2, 4\}$, (i) $\{0, 1, 1, 0\}$, (j) $\{-1, 0, 0, -1\}$.
2 (a), (b), (c), (d), (h).
3 (a) f: $x \to \frac{1}{3}x$, (b) f: $x \to x+3$, (c) f: $x \to 1-x$, (d) f: $x \to 1/x$, (h) f: $x \to \log_2 x$.
4 $x{:}\to(x-1)^{\frac{1}{2}}$.
5 $\{y: -1 \leqslant y \leqslant 1\}$; $\{y: 0 \leqslant y \leqslant \frac{1}{2}\}$.

Exercise 1.2 (page 8)

1 (a) 8, 12, (b) $\frac{2}{3}$, 2, (c) 2, $3\frac{1}{3}$.
3 (a) 49, 14, (b) 2.
4 (a) x^2+2, (b) $(x+2)^2$.
5 1.

Exercise 1.3 (page 10)

1 Even (a), (e); odd (b), (c); neither (d).
2 All except (a); (b), 180, (c) 720, (d) 90, (e) 360.

Exercise 1.4 (page 10)

1 (a) Many-to-one, (b) $\{x: 0 < x \leqslant 200\}$, $\{24, 36, 45, 54\}$.
2 (a) Yes, (b) No; one corresponds to 'un' and 'une'.
3 (a), (b), (c), (e).
4 Any subset of each domain will serve as an acceptable domain. Other domains may also be acceptable, e.g. (a) $\{x: x \geqslant 1\}$, (b) $\{x: x \geqslant -2\}$ or $\{x: x \leqslant -2\}$, (c) $\{x: -45 \leqslant x \leqslant 45\}$, etc., (d) $\{x: 0 \leqslant x \leqslant 90\}$, etc., (e) $\mathbb{R}^+$ (or $\mathbb{R}^-$).
5 (a) h: $x \to 3(x+2)$, H: $x \to 3x+2$, (b) h: $x \to (x+1)^2$, H: $x \to x^2+1$, (c) h: $x \to \sin(x^2)°$, H: $x \to (\sin x°)^2$.
6 (a) $x \to \frac{1}{3}x-2$, $x \to \frac{1}{3}(x-2)$, (b) $x \to x^{1/2}-1$; $x \to (x-1)^{1/2}$, (c) $x \to (\arcsin x)^{1/2}$, $x \to \arcsin(x^{1/2})$.
7 $x \to 9x^2+1$.
8 f: $x \to x^2$, g: $x \to 1/x$, h: $x \to x+2$.
9 $-\frac{1}{4}$, 1.

10
(a) $1 \leqslant x \leqslant 25$, $\frac{1}{7} \leqslant x \leqslant \frac{1}{3}$,
(b) fg: $x \to \dfrac{1}{(x+2)^2}$, gf: $x \to \dfrac{1}{x^2+2}$,
(c) $\frac{1}{9} \leqslant x \leqslant \frac{1}{49}$, $\frac{1}{25} \leqslant x \leqslant 1$,
(d) $x \to +\sqrt{x}$; $x \to \dfrac{1}{x} - 2$.

Exercise 1.5 (page 11)

1 (a) No: f is many-to-one when $x < -1$ or $x > 1$, (b) Odd.
2 $\{x: 1 \leqslant x\}$; $\ln x$.
3 (a) Even, (b) odd, (c) even, (d) odd, (e) even, (f) odd, (g) odd, (h) odd, (i) even, (j) even.
4 3, −2.
5 $\{x: 1 \leqslant x\}$.
6 (a) fgh, (b) gfh, (c) hgf.
7 (a) $\ln (x-1)$, (b) $\{x: 1 < x\}$.
8

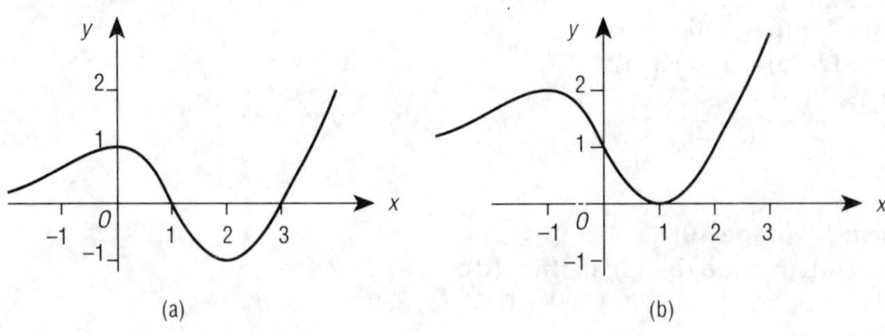

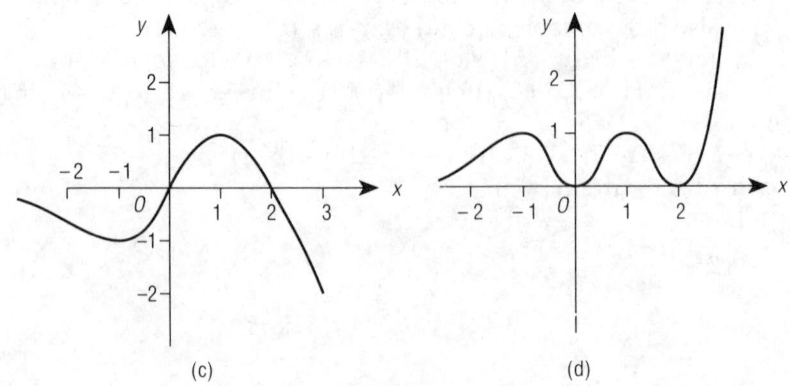

8 continued

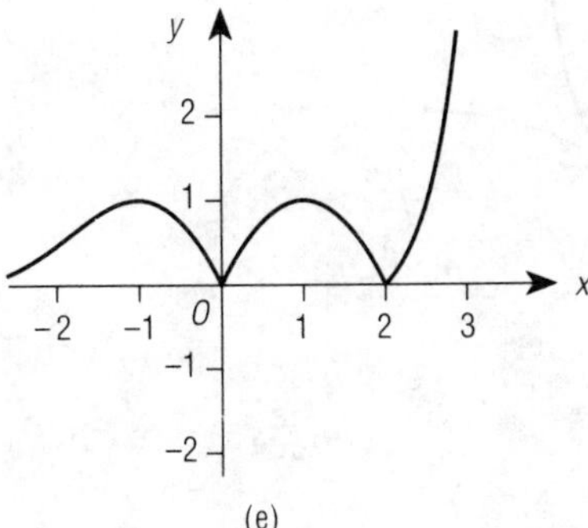

(e)

9

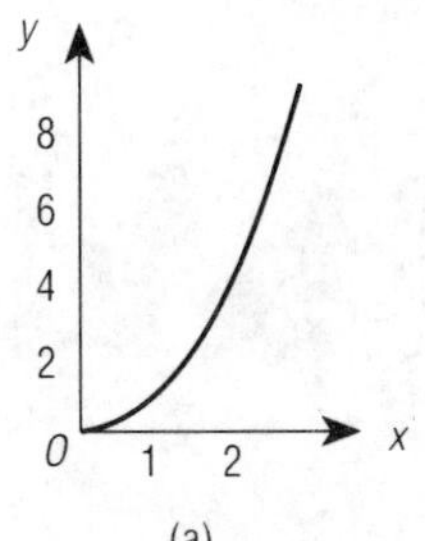

(a)

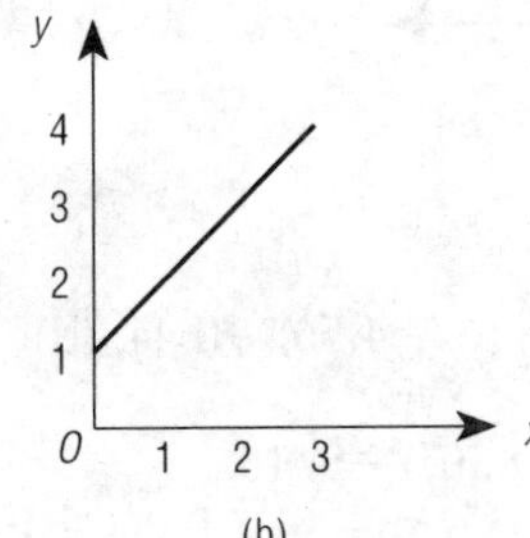

(b)

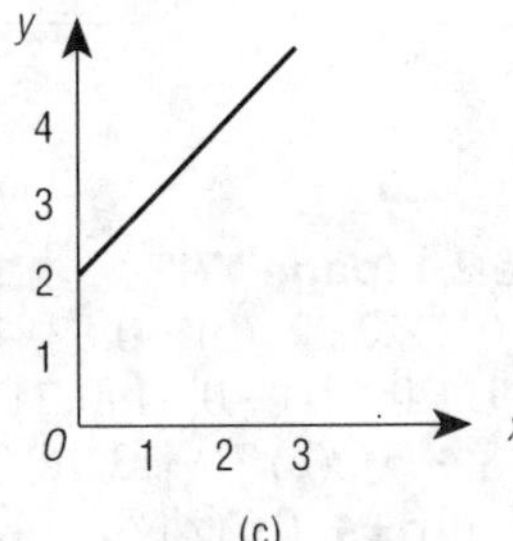

(c)

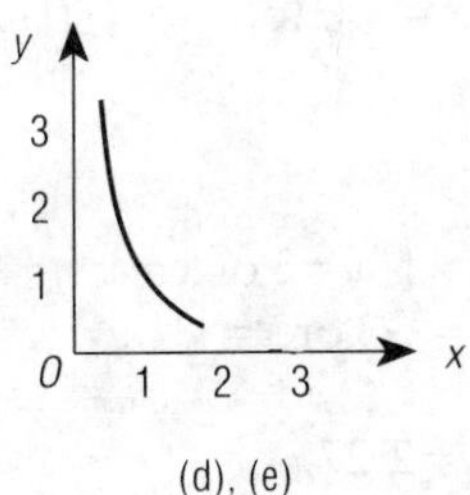

(d), (e)

10

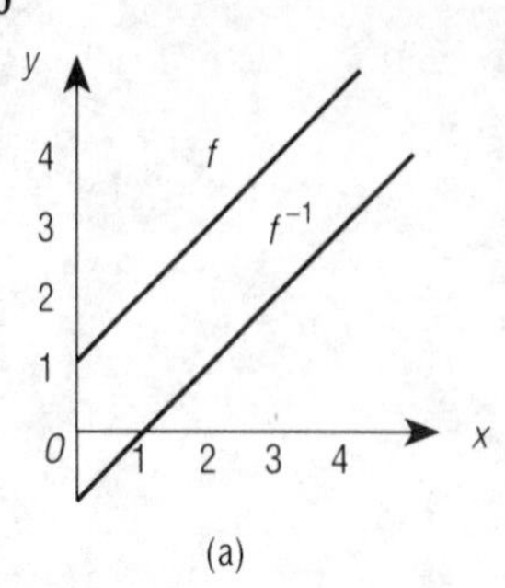

(a)

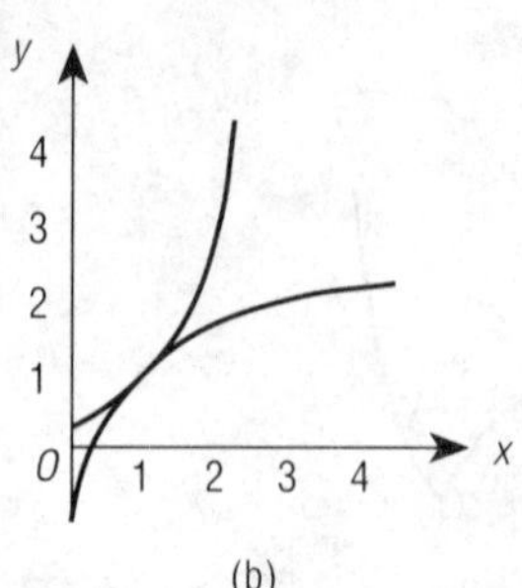

(b)

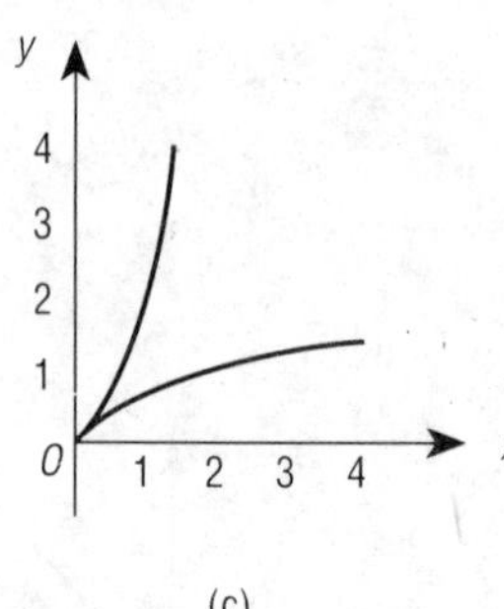

(c)

Exercise 2.1 (page 17)

1 (a) $-0.22, 2.22$, (b) $-0.83, 4.83$, (c) $-4.56, -0.44$, (d) $-2.12, 0.79$, (e) $-4.59, 1.09$, (f) $-0.84, 0.24$.
2 (a) $-3, -5\frac{1}{2}$, (b) $7, -13$, (c) $2, -8$, (d) $-5, 10$.
3 (a) $(x+5)^2+4$, (b) $(x+5)^2-4$, (c) $(x-5)^2-46$, (d) $2(x+\frac{5}{2})^2+\frac{55}{2}$, (e) $2(x+\frac{5}{2})^2+\frac{25}{2}$, (f) $8-(1+x)^2$, (g) $50-(5+x)^2$, (h) $\frac{75}{2}-2(\frac{5}{2}+x)^2$.
4 (a) 4, when $x=-5$, (b) -4 when $x=-5$, (c) -46 when $x=5$, (d) $\frac{55}{2}$ when $x=-\frac{5}{2}$, (e) $\frac{25}{2}$ when $x=-\frac{5}{2}$, (f) 8 when $x=-1$, (g) 50 when $x=-5$, (h) $\frac{75}{2}$ when $x=-\frac{5}{2}$.
5 (a) $x=-5$, (b) $x=-5$, (c) $x=5$, (d) $x=-\frac{5}{2}$, (e) $x=-\frac{5}{2}$, (f) $x=-1$, (g) $x=-5$, (h) $x=-\frac{5}{2}$.

Exercise 2.2 (page 18)

1 (a) $x=1, y=2$ or $x=2, y=-1$, (b) $x=1, y=2$ or $x=4, y=-7$, (c) $x=1, y=2$ or $x=\frac{2}{3}, y=3$, (d) $x=2, y=-3$ or $x=\frac{18}{5}, y=\frac{1}{5}$, (e) $x=4, y=-5$ or $x=-1, y=5$.
2 (a) $x=2.09, y=-1.27$ or $x=0.91, y=2.27$, (b) $x=2.81, y=-0.63$ or $x=1.47, y=2.05$, (c) $x=1.45, y=4.82$ or $x=-1.20, y=-5.82$.
4 $x=2, y=1$ or $x=8, y=-11$.
5 $-3\sqrt{2}\leqslant k\leqslant 3\sqrt{2}$.

Exercise 2.3 (page 20)

1 (a) $x^2-5x+5=0$, (b) $x^2-3x+1=0$, (c) $x^2-5x+5=0$.

2 $2x^2-7x+4=0$.
3 (a) $9x^2+29x+25=0$, (b) $9x^2+11x+5=0$, (c) $25x^2+29x+9=0$.
4 (a) $13x^2+4x+3=0$, (b) $x^2+4x+5=0$.
5 16, 8.

Exercise 2.4 (page 20)

1 (a) $k<1$, (b) $k<\frac{1}{3}$, (c) $k<-2$ or $k>2$, (d) $k>-\frac{5}{4}$.
2 (a) 4 (when $x=0$), (b) 4 (when $x=1$), (c) 5 (when $x=1$), (d) 7 (when $x=2$).
3 (a) 4 (when $x=0$), (b) 3 (when $x=-1$), (c) 3 (when $x=-1$), (d) -1 (when $x=-2$).
4 (a) $x=1$, $y=2$ or $x=2$, $y=-1$, (b) $x=1$, $y=2$ or $x=4$, $y=-7$, (c) $x=1$, $y=2$ or $x=\frac{2}{3}$, $y=3$.
6 Circle, centre origin, radius 1; not cut by the straight line.
7 $-2\sqrt{2}\leqslant k\leqslant 2\sqrt{2}$.
8 $x^2+2x-2=0$.
9 $x^2-3x-6=0$.
10 $2x^2-4x-3=0$.
11 $2x^2+4x-5=0$.
12 $x^2-29x+29=0$.
13 1; 2.
14 $k<0$ or $k>1$.
15 True for all values of k.
16 -1 or $\frac{1}{4}$.
17 $x\leqslant 3$, $y\geqslant -1$.
18 $x=\frac{1}{2}$, $y=3$.
19 ± 9, 20.
20 $x^2-47x+1=0$.

Exercise 3.1 (page 26)

1 (a) $(x-2)(x-3)$, (b) $(x-4)(x+3)$, (c) $(x-1)(x-2)(x-3)$, (d) $(x-1)(x+1)(x-2)(x+2)$, (e) $x^2(x-1)(x-2)$.
2 (a) $(x-1)$, (b) $x(x-1)(x-3)$, (c) $(x-1)$, (d) $(x-1)$, (e) $(x+1)$.
3 (a) $(x-1)$, (b) $(x+1)$, (c) $(x-2)$, (d) $(x-3)$, (e) $(x+5)$.

Exercise 3.2 (page 27)

1 (a) 8, (b) 4, (c) 0.125, (d) 0.0625, (e) 0.5.
2 (a) 5, (b) 0.008, (c) 0.04, (d) 0.2, (e) 0.2.
3 (a) $x^{1/2}$, (b) $x^{1/3}$, (c) $x^{2/3}$, (d) x^{-2}, (e) $x^{-1/2}$.
4 $x=4$ or 9.
5 $x=1$ or 64.

Exercise 3.3 (page 29)

1 (a) 2.322, (b) 5.322, (c) 11.97, (d) 0.631, (e) 1.631, (f) 2.631, (g) 3.262.

Exercise 3.4 (page 30)

1 (a) $\frac{1}{2}(\sqrt{3}-1)$, (b) $2+\sqrt{2}$, (c) $\frac{1}{4}(5+3\sqrt{5})$.

2 (a) $\frac{1}{5}(2-i)$, (b) $\frac{1}{5}(3+4i)$, (c) $-i$, (d) $\dfrac{11-2i}{25}$, (e) $\dfrac{-38+41i}{25}$.

3 (a) 5, (b) 3 or 7, (c) 6.

Exercise 3.5 (page 31)

1 (a) 2, (b) 4, (c) -2, (d) -4, (e) 0.

2 (a) 3, (b) 5, (c) -1, (d) -2, (e) 0.

3 (a) 3, (b) 3, (c) 5, (d) 2, (e) 0.

4 (a) $\log y=\log a+n\log x$, (b) $\log x+\log y=\log a$, (c) $n\log x+\log y=\log a$, (d) $\log a+\log y=x\log b$, (e) $y\log a=\log b+\log x$, (f) $y\log a=\log k+x\log b$.

5 40 000, -1.5.

6 2.1, 3.1.

7 57, 3.5.

Exercise 3.6 (page 32)

1 $(x-1)(x-2)(x-7)$.

2 $3x^2-26x+40$; $(x-2)(3x-20)$; $(x-2)$ is a repeated factor.

3 7.

4 12,4.

5 Other linear factors are $(x-1)(3x-2)(2x+3)$.

6 (a) 8, (b) 4, (c) $\frac{1}{4096}$, (d) $\frac{1}{16}$, (e) $\frac{1}{2}$.

7 (a) $x^{1/4}$, (b) x^{-3}, (c) $x^{2/3}$, (d) $x^{3/2}$, (e) x^2.

8 (a) $\frac{4}{5}x^{5/4}+C$, (b) $\frac{3}{4}x^{4/3}+C$, (c) $2x^{1/2}+C$, (d) $\frac{3}{2}x^{2/3}+C$, (e) $\frac{3}{5}x^{5/3}+C$.

9 $\frac{2}{3}(x+1)^{3/2}+\frac{2}{3}x^{3/2}+C$.

10 (a) 3, (b) $\frac{1}{3}$.

11 (a) $3^{1/27}$, (b) $2^{1/8}$.

12 $\log_{10}x\log_5 10$; 0.4307.

13 2; 1.893.

14 16, -1.

15 -1, -6.

16 -9, 0.

17 (a) 4, (b) $\frac{1}{4}$, (c) 3.2, (d) 625, (e) 68, (f) $\frac{5}{256}$

18 (a) $\frac{2}{5}x^{5/2}+\frac{2}{3}x^{3/2}+C$, (b) $\frac{2}{3}x^{3/2}+2x^{1/2}+C$, (c) $\ln x-\dfrac{1}{x}+C$, (d) $x+\ln x+C$.

19 (a) $\frac{3}{2}$, (b) $\frac{1}{6}$, (c) $\frac{3}{4}$, (d) $\frac{4}{3}$.

20 All.

21 (c).

22 5.

23 2.

Exercise 5.1 (page 47)

1 Arithmetic series (d), geometric series (c).

2 Arithmetic series (a), (b), (e).

3 $-3, 105$.
4 $6\frac{1}{2}, 325$.
5 -1.
6 $\pm\frac{1}{4}, \pm 192$.
7 10, 22.
8 201st term is 1002.
9 5th term is 1250.
10 7.

Exercise 5.2 (page 50)

1 (a) $8+12x+6x^2+x^3$, (b) $1+6x+12x^2+8x^3$, (c) $8-36x+54x^2-27x^3$, (d) $1-12x+54x^2-108x^3+81x^4$, (e) $16-96x+216x^2-216x^3+81x^4$, (f) $16+96x+216x^2+216x^3+81x^4$.
2 (a) $1+2x+4x^2+8x^3$; $-\frac{1}{2}<x<\frac{1}{2}$, (b) $1+4x+12x^2+32x^3$; $-\frac{1}{2}<x<\frac{1}{2}$, (c) $1+x+\frac{3}{2}x^2+\frac{5}{2}x^3$; $-\frac{1}{2}\leqslant x<\frac{1}{2}$, (d) $1-x-\frac{1}{2}x^2-\frac{1}{2}x^3$; $-\frac{1}{2}\leqslant x\leqslant\frac{1}{2}$, (e) $1+2x^2+4x^4+8x^6$; $-1\sqrt{2}<x<1/\sqrt{2}$, (f) $\frac{1}{2}+\frac{1}{4}x+\frac{1}{8}x^2+\frac{1}{16}x^3$; $-2<x<2$.
3 (a) $1-x^2+x^4$, $-1\leqslant x\leqslant 1$, (b) $1-2x^2+3x^4$, $-1<x<1$, (c) $1-3x^2+6x^4$, $-1<x<1$, (d) $1+2x^2+4x^4$, $-\frac{1}{\sqrt{2}}\leqslant x\leqslant\frac{1}{\sqrt{2}}$, (e) $x+3x^3+9x^5$, $-\frac{1}{\sqrt{3}}\leqslant x\leqslant\frac{1}{\sqrt{3}}$, (f) $x^2+x^4+x^6$, $-1\leqslant x\leqslant -\frac{1}{\sqrt{3}}$.
4 (a) $\frac{1}{x}+\frac{1}{x^2}+\frac{1}{x^3}+\frac{1}{x^4}$, (b) $\frac{1}{x^2}-\frac{2}{x^4}+\frac{4}{x^6}-\frac{8}{x^8}$, (c) $\frac{1}{x^2}-\frac{2}{x^3}+\frac{3}{x^4}-\frac{4}{x^5}$, (d) $\frac{1}{x^4}+\frac{4}{x^6}+\frac{12}{x^8}+\frac{32}{x^{10}}$.
5 $1-2x-2x^2-4x^3$; $3, -\frac{1}{3}$.

Exercise 5.3 (page 51)

1 (a) $-x-\frac{x^2}{2}-\frac{x^3}{3}-\frac{x^4}{4}$, (b) $-2x-2x^2-\frac{8}{3}x^3-4x^4$, (c) $3x-\frac{9}{2}x^2+9x^3-\frac{81}{4}x^4$, (d) $3x^2-\frac{9}{2}x^4+9x^6-\frac{81}{4}x^8$, (e) $-4x^2-8x^4-\frac{64}{3}x^6-64x^8$, (f) $1+2x+2x^2+\frac{4}{3}x^3$, (g) $e\left(1+x+\frac{x^2}{2!}+\frac{x^3}{3!}\right)$, (h) $e\left(1+x^2+\frac{x^4}{2!}+\frac{x^6}{3!}\right)$, (i) $2x-\frac{8x^3}{3!}+\frac{32x^5}{5!}-\frac{128x^7}{7!}$, (j) $1-\frac{x^4}{2!}+\frac{x^6}{3!}-\frac{x^8}{4!}$.
2 $(1-2x)(1-x)$; $-3x-\frac{5}{2}x^2-3x^3-\frac{17}{4}x^4$; -0.328.
3 $5x-\frac{5}{2}x^2+\frac{35}{3}x^3-\frac{65}{4}x^4$; $\ln\left(\frac{1.3}{0.8}\right)=0.4855$.
4 $\sin x\cos x \approx x-\frac{4x^3}{3!}+\frac{16x^5}{5!}-\frac{64x^7}{7!}$.
5 (a) $1+\frac{x^2}{2!}+\frac{x^4}{4!}+\frac{x^6}{6!}$, (b) $x+\frac{x^3}{3!}+\frac{x^5}{5!}+\frac{x^7}{7!}$.

Exercise 5.4 (page 52)

3 £50 000.
5 55 log 2.
6 8.

7 3479.
8 $2S/n-x$.
9 $\frac{1}{3}$; 9.
10 8.
11 2, 610.
12 4, 26 terms.
13 $(\frac{1}{2})^7$; 8.
14 -12.
15 5, 6.
16 $-\frac{3}{4}x-\frac{139}{64}x^2$.
17 $\frac{1}{2}$, $\frac{7}{16}$, $-\frac{35}{64}$.
18 $1-2x-6x^2$.
19 2, 3.
20 33 952; 2.541.
21 $\frac{1}{2}$, $\frac{1}{4}$.
23 $\ln 2-\frac{1}{2}x-\frac{1}{8}x^2-\frac{1}{24}x^3$; $\ln 2-\frac{3}{2}x-\frac{5}{8}x^2-\frac{3}{8}x^3$.
24 1, $\frac{1}{2}$.
25 -1, 1/12.

Exercise 6.1 (page 57)

1 (a) Put $x=0, -1, -2$.
3 (a) 3 or -3, (b) 2 or -3, (c) 6, (d) 0.
4 (a) Not true for any values of x, (b) Is an identity.

Exercise 6.2 (page 63)

1 (a) 1, -1, (b) -1, 2, (c) 1, -4, (d) $-\frac{1}{3}$, $-\frac{1}{3}$, $\frac{1}{3}$, (e) 1, -1, (f) $-\frac{1}{2}$, 2, $-\frac{3}{2}$, (g) 1, -1, -1, (h) $\frac{1}{2}$, $\frac{1}{2}$.
2 (a) $\frac{-7}{x-2}+\frac{9}{x-3}$, (b) $\frac{1}{x-2}-\frac{x}{x^2+3}$, (c) $\frac{7}{(x-2)}-\frac{7}{(x-3)}+\frac{9}{(x-3)^2}$, (d) $\frac{-7}{5(x-2)}-\frac{1}{10(x+3)}+\frac{3}{2(x-3)}$, (e) $2-\frac{11}{(x-2)}+\frac{21}{(x-3)}$, (f) $2(x+5)-\frac{16}{x-2}+\frac{54}{x-3}$.

Exercise 6.3 (page 64)

1 $1-3x+7x^2$.
2 $1+4x+13x^2$.
3 $1+5x+19x^2$.
4 $1+x+7x^2$.
5 $1-x$.
6 $1+x+3x^2$.
7 $x-x^2$.
8 $x-3x^2$.
9 $\frac{1}{2}x-\frac{3}{4}x^2$.
10 $\frac{1}{10}x-\frac{7}{100}x^2$.
11 $1+9x+67x^2$.
12 $1+(a+b)x+(a^2+ab+b^2)x^2$.

13 $\ln\left|\frac{x}{x+1}\right|+C.$

14 $\frac{1}{2}\ln\left|\frac{x^2}{x^2+1}\right|+C.$

15 $\ln\left|\frac{x-2}{x-1}\right|+C.$

16 $\frac{1}{4}\ln\left|\frac{x-5}{x-1}\right|+C.$

17 $\frac{1}{3}\ln\left|\frac{x-3}{2x-3}\right|+C.$

18 $\frac{1}{2}\ln|x-1|-\frac{1}{4}\ln(x^2+1)-\frac{1}{2}\arctan x+C.$

19 $\frac{1}{4}\ln\left|\frac{2x-3}{2x-1}\right|+C.$

20 $\frac{1}{5}\ln\left|\frac{2x-1}{x+2}\right|+C.$

Exercise 6.4 (page 65)

1 (a) $\frac{\frac{1}{3}}{x-1}-\frac{\frac{1}{3}}{x+2}$, (b) $\frac{\frac{1}{3}}{x-1}+\frac{\frac{2}{3}}{x+2}$, (c) $\frac{\frac{5}{3}}{x-2}-\frac{\frac{2}{3}}{x+1}$, (d) $\frac{\frac{1}{3}}{x}+\frac{\frac{2}{3}}{x+3}$, (e) $\frac{\frac{3}{4}}{x-1}-\frac{\frac{3}{4}}{x+3}$,
(f) $\frac{\frac{2}{5}}{x-2}+\frac{\frac{3}{5}}{x+3}$, (g) $\frac{1}{x-1}-\frac{x+1}{x^2+1}$, (h) $\frac{\frac{2}{5}}{x-2}-\frac{\frac{2}{5}x-\frac{1}{5}}{x^2+1}$, (i) $\frac{4}{x-2}-\frac{3}{x-1}-\frac{1}{(x-1)^2}$,
(j) $\frac{1}{x}-\frac{1}{x-1}+\frac{1}{(x-1)^2}$, (k) $\frac{1}{x-1}-\frac{9}{x+3}+\frac{20}{x+5}$, (l) $\frac{\frac{9}{4}}{x+3}+\frac{\frac{1}{2}}{(x+1)^2}-\frac{\frac{5}{4}}{x+1}$.

2 (a) $1+3x+7x^2$, (b) $x+3x^2$, (c) $-1-2x-3x^2$, (d) $-1-3x^2$.

3 (a) $\frac{1}{4}\ln\left|\frac{2x-1}{2x+1}\right|+C$, (b) $\frac{1}{2}\ln\left|\frac{x^2}{x^2+1}\right|+C$, (c) $\frac{1}{2}\ln\left|\frac{x^2-1}{x^2}\right|+C$, (d) $\ln|x-1|-\frac{1}{x-1}+C$.

Exercise 7.1 (page 71)

1 (a) $x>4$, (b) $x\geqslant-3$, (c) $x>\frac{12}{5}$, (d) $x<0$ or $x>1$, (e) $-3<x<0$, (f) $x\leqslant1$ or $x\geqslant2$,
(g) $x\leqslant-5$ or $x\geqslant1$, (h) $x<-2$ or $x>8$, (i) All values of x, (j) $x<0$ or $1<x<5$.

2 (a) $0<x<6$, (b) $x>0$, (c) $x\geqslant2$, (d) $0\leqslant x\leqslant1$, (e) $x>0$.

3 (a) $x>2$, (b) $-1<x<0$ or $x>6$, (c) $x>1$, (d) $x>1$, (e) $x>1$ or $-\frac{7}{2}<x<-2$.

Exercise 7.2 (page 73)

1 (a) $x<-1$ or $x>1$, (b) $-1\leqslant x\leqslant1$, (c) $x\leqslant-\frac{1}{2}$ or $x\geqslant\frac{1}{2}$, (d) $-\frac{3}{2}<x<\frac{3}{2}$, (e) $x>0$,
(f) All values of x, (g) No values of x, (h) $x\leqslant-\frac{1}{3}$, (i) $x<0$, (j) $x<\frac{1}{2}$, (k) $x<-3$ or $x>\frac{1}{3}$,
(l) $-\frac{1}{4}\leqslant x\leqslant\frac{3}{2}$.

Exercise 7.3 (page 77)

1

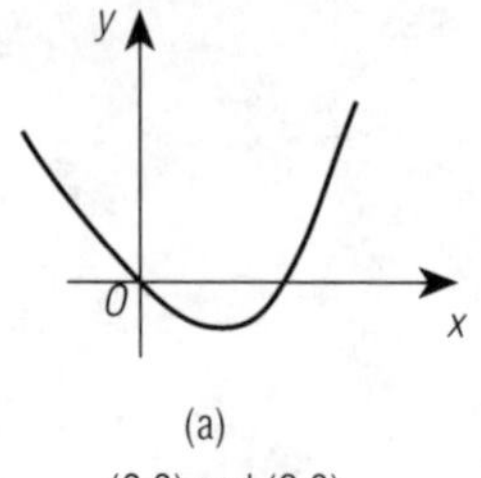

(a)
(0,0) and (2,0)

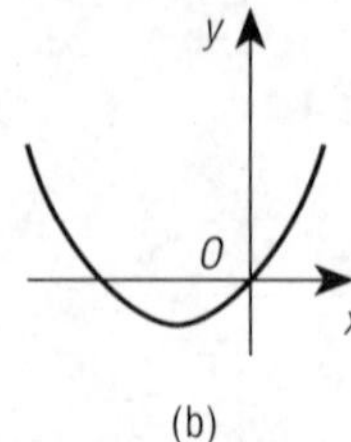

(b)
(−2,0) and (0,0)

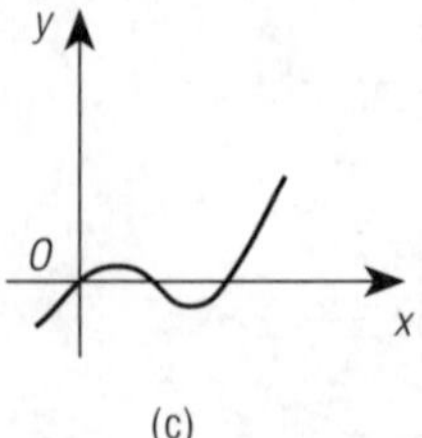

(c)
(0,0), (1,0) and (2,0)

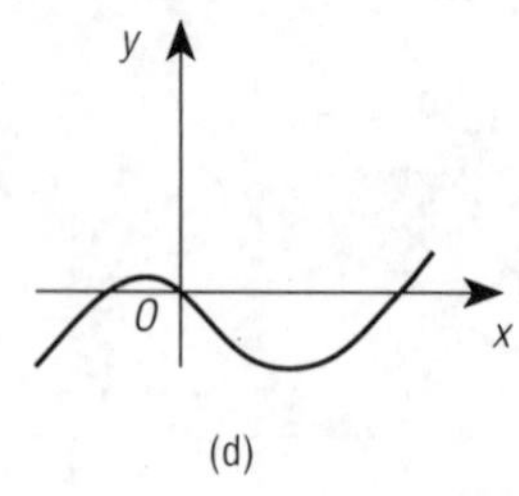

(d)
(−1,0), (0,0) and (3,0)

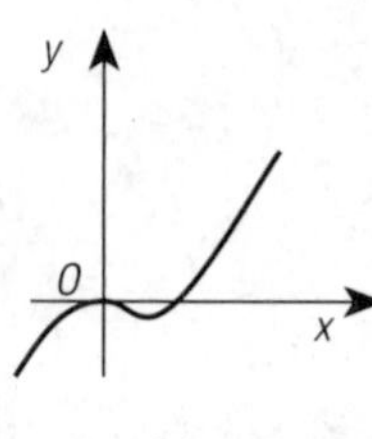

(e)
(0,0) and (1,0)

2

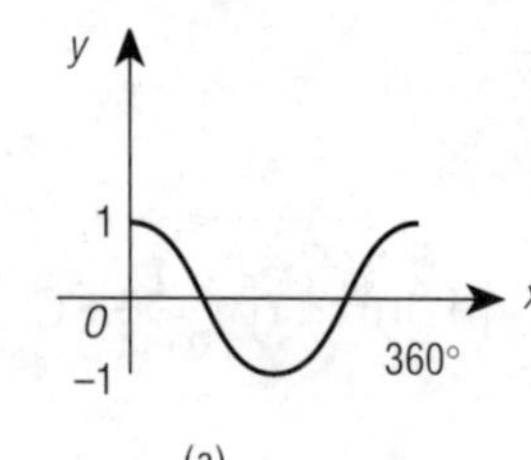

(a)

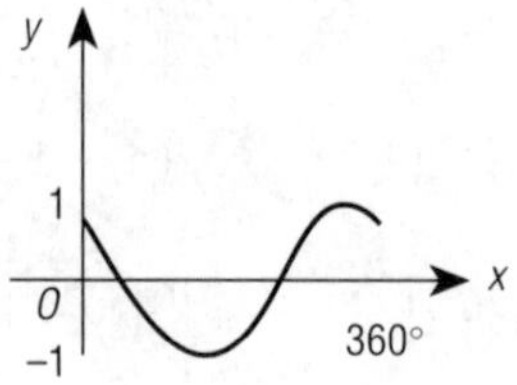

(b)

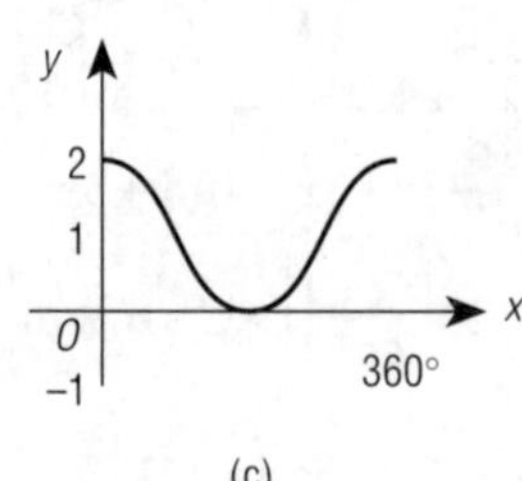

(c)

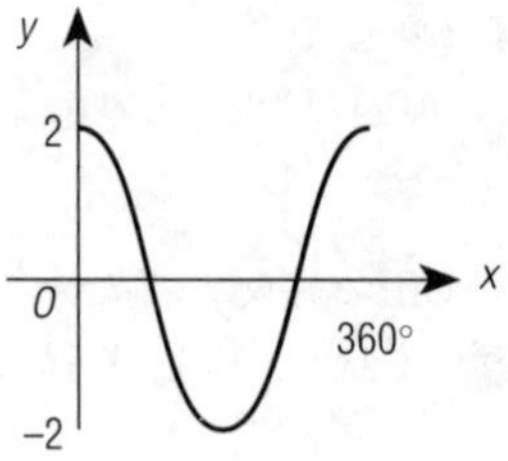

(d)

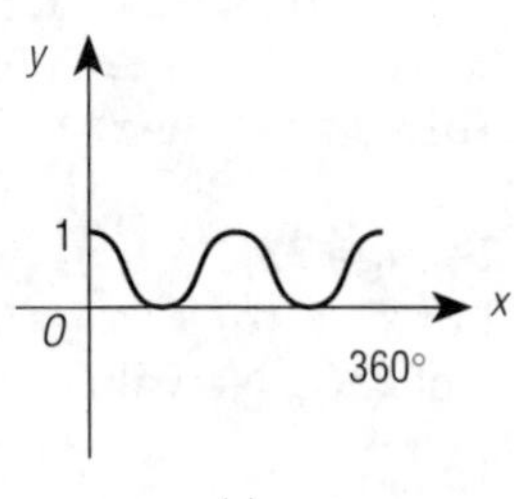

(e)

3

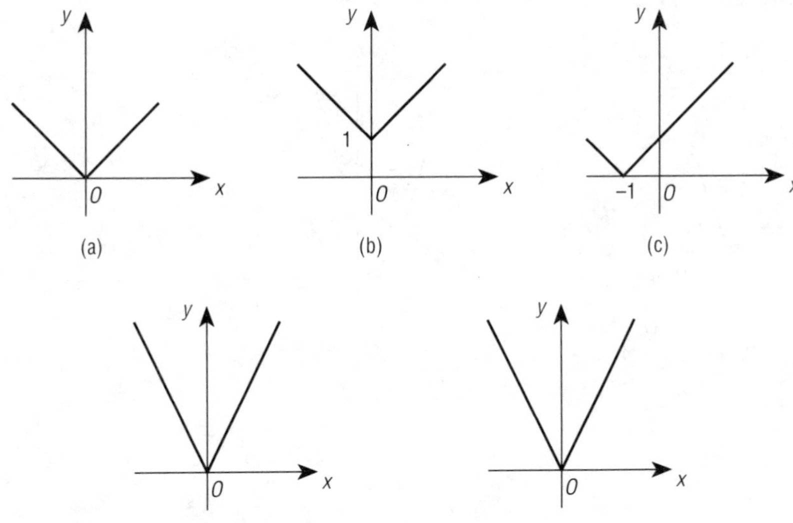

(d) (e)

4

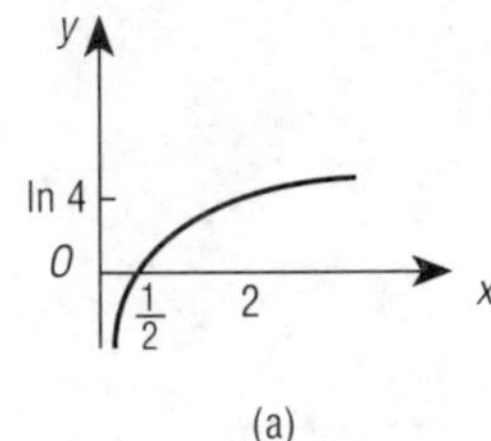

(a)

(b)

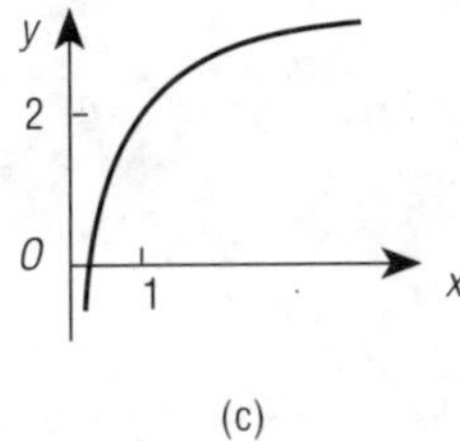

(c)

5

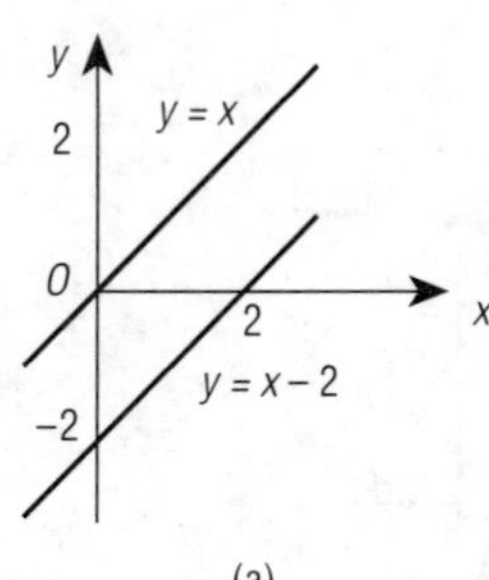

(a)

(b)

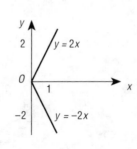

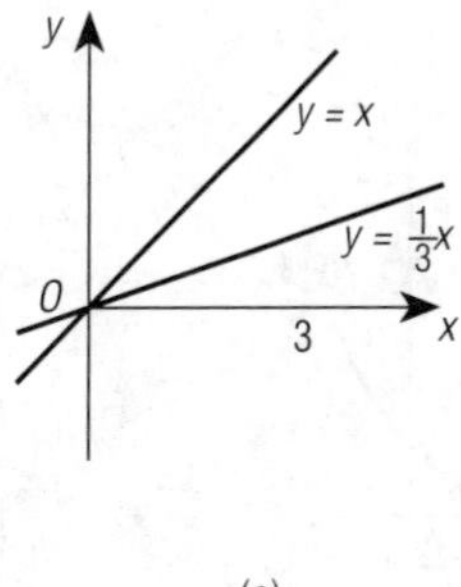

(c)

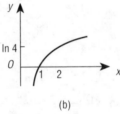

5 continued

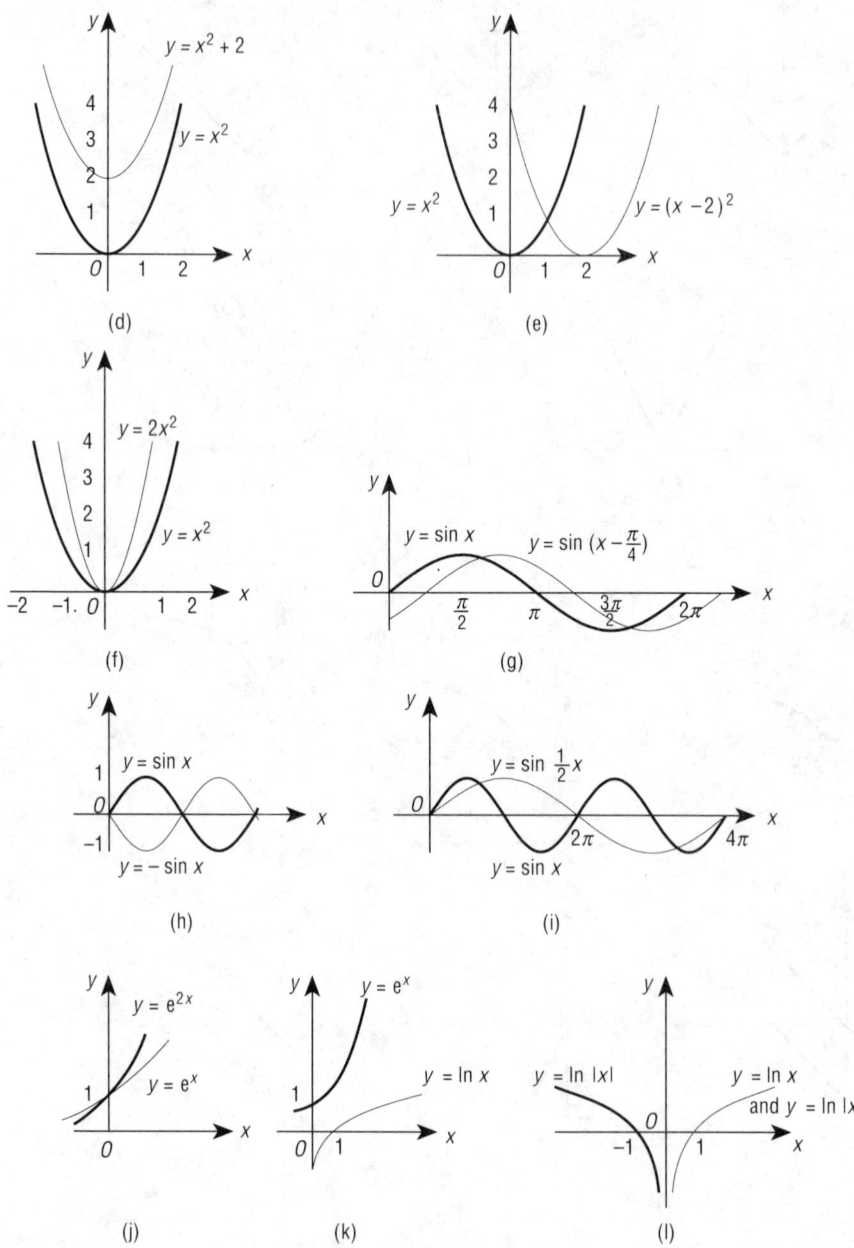

y = x^2 + 2
y = x^2
y = (x − 2)^2
y = 2x^2
y = sin x
y = sin (x − π/4)
y = − sin x
y = sin ½x
y = e^{2x}
y = e^x
y = ln x
y = ln |x|
y = ln x and y = ln |x|
(d)
(e)
(f)
(g)
(h)
(i)
(j)
(k)
(l)

Exercise 7.4 (page 80)

1 (a) (i) $x \neq 3$; all y, (ii) Not obvious, (iii) $(0, \frac{2}{3})$, $(2, 0)$, (iv) $x=3$, $y=1$.
(b) (i) $x \neq 1$; all y, (ii) Not obvious, (iii) $(0,0)$, (v) $y=0$.
(c) (i) $x \neq 0$; $y \leqslant \frac{1}{4}$, (iii) $(1,0)$, (iv) $x=0$, $y=0$.
(d) (i) all x; all y, (ii) Not obvious, (iii) $(0,0)$, $(3, 0)$, (v) $y=-3x^2$.
(e) (i) $x \neq 2$ and $x \neq 3$; $y \leqslant -9$ or $y \geqslant -1$, (iii) $(0, -\frac{5}{6})$, $(\frac{5}{3}, 0)$, (iv) $x=2$, $x=3$, $y=0$.
(f) (i) $x \neq 1$ or $x \neq 3$; all y, (iii) $(\frac{5}{3}, 0)$, $(0, -\frac{5}{3})$, (iv) $x=1$, $x=3$, $y=0$.

2

(a)

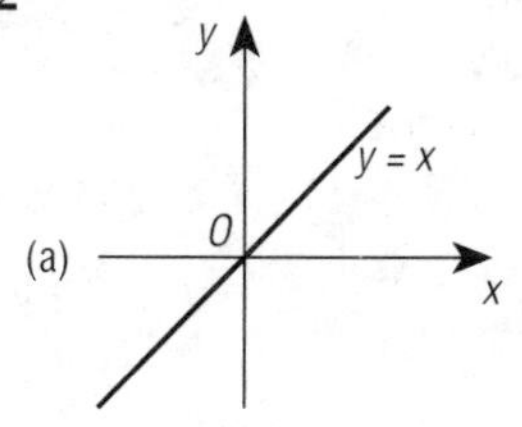

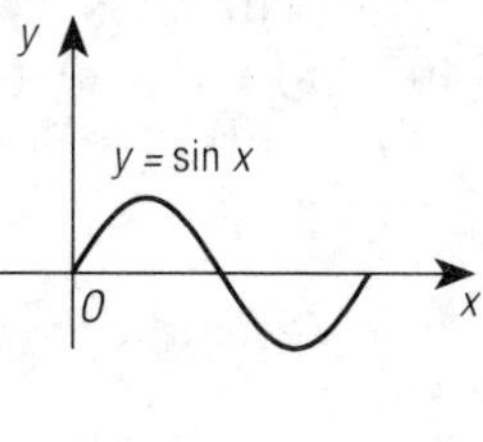

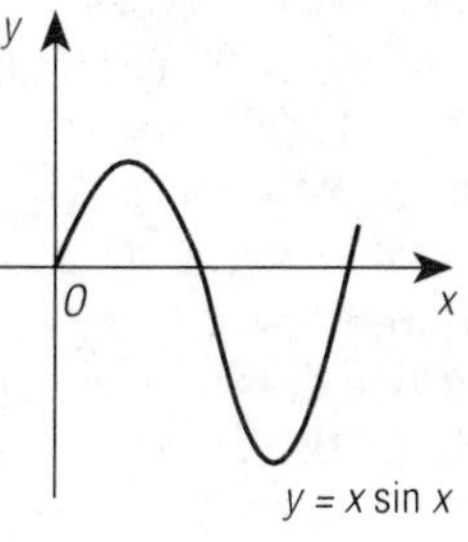

(b)

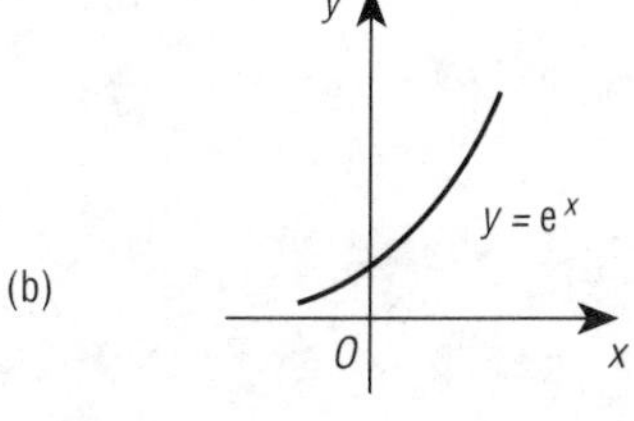

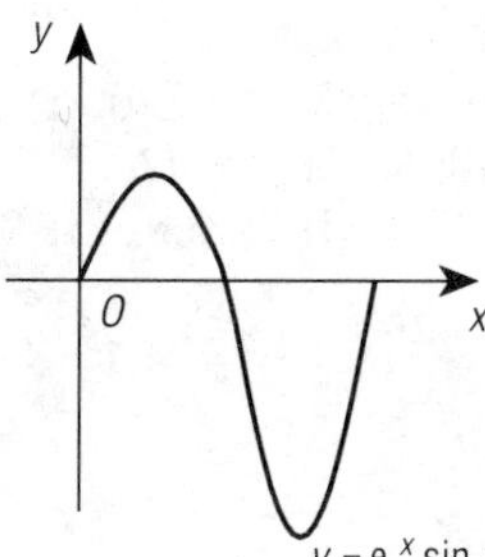

(c)

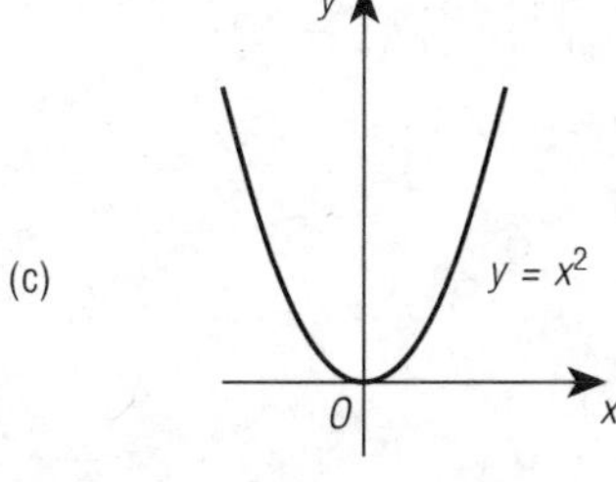

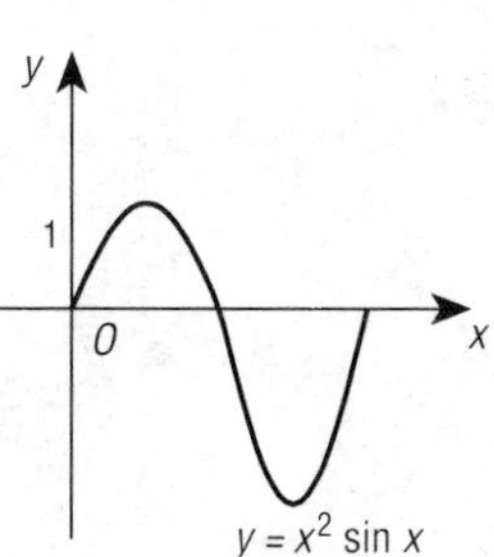

(d)

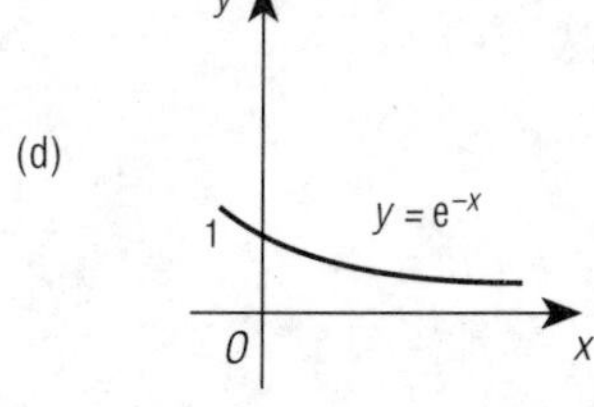

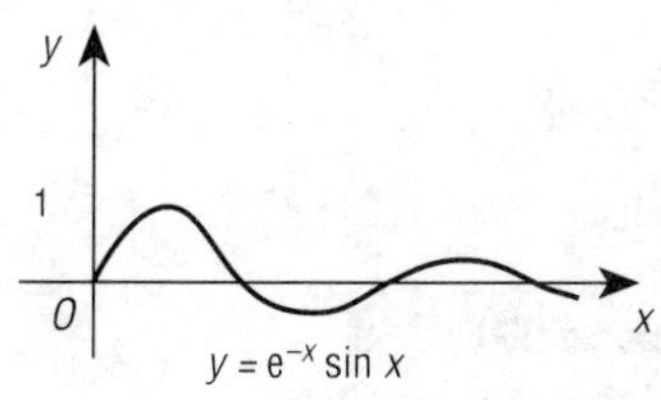

Exercise 7.5 (page 80)

1 (a) $x<-2$, (b) $x\leqslant 4$, (c) $x<2$ or $x>3$, (d) $-\frac{3}{2}\leqslant x<-1$ or $x\geqslant 1$, (e) $-1<x<0$ or $x>6$.
2 (a) $0<x<3$, (b) $0<x\leqslant 1$ or $x\geqslant 3$, (c) $-1<x<0$ or $x>3$, (d) $x<-4$ or $-1<x<2$.
3 (a) $2<x<3$, (b) $x\geqslant 3$.
4 (a) $x<-2$ or $x>2$, (b) $x<0$, (c) $x<-6$ or $x>2$, (d) $x<-\frac{2}{3}$ or $x>8$,
(e) $x<-3$ or $x>\frac{1}{3}$.
5 Curves cut the coordinate axes at
(a) $(-4,0)$, $(2,0)$ $(0,-8)$, (b) $(-3,0)$, $(0,0)$ $(1,0)$, (c) $(0,0)$, $(1,0)$,
(d) $(-1,0)$, $(0,0)$, $(1,0)$, (e) $(1,0)$, $(2,0)$, $(3,0)$ and $(0,6)$, (f) $(0,0)$, $(1,0)$.
6 (a) $-1\leqslant y\leqslant 1$, (b) $-1\leqslant y\leqslant 1$, (c) $0\leqslant y\leqslant 1$, (d) $0\leqslant y\leqslant 2$, (e) $-2\leqslant y\leqslant 2$.
7 (a) $(0,1)$; as $x\mapsto -\infty$, $y\mapsto\infty$; as $x\mapsto\infty$, $y\mapsto 0$,
(b) $(0,1)$; as $x\mapsto -\infty$, $y\mapsto 0$, as $x\mapsto\infty$, $y\mapsto\infty$,
(c) $(1,0)$; as $x\mapsto -\infty$, $y\mapsto\infty$, as $x\mapsto\infty$, $y\mapsto\infty$ (curve is $y=2\ln|x|$),
(d) $(1,0)$; only exists when $x>0$; as $x\mapsto\infty$, $y\mapsto\infty$.
8 (a) $(0,0)$, $(\pi,0)$, $(2\pi,0)$, . . . y oscillates, increasing amplitude, (b) $(1,0)$,
(c) $(0,0)$, $(\pi,0)$, $(2\pi,0)$, . . . y oscillates, decreasing amplitude.

Exercise 8.1 (page 87)

1 (a) 2, (b) 6, (c) 24, (d) 120, (e) 720, (f) 5040.
2 (a) 6, (b) 12, (c) 20, (d) 30, (e) 42.
3 (a) 12, (b) 60, (c) 180, (d) 2520, (e) 10 080, (f) 22 680.
4 120.
5 12.
6 2.
7 10 080.
8 1260.
9 (a) 6, (b) 10, (c) 15, (d) $\frac{1}{2}n(n-1)$.
10 220.

Exercise 8.2 (page 88)

1 60.
2 302 400.
3 2520.
4 420.
5 70.
6 70.
7 630.
8 15.
9 359.
10 22 100; 286.
11 5040; 72.
12 $(2n-1)!$; $\frac{1}{2}n!(n-1)!$

Exercise 9.1 (page 97)

1 Closed, not associative. No.

2 Closed over $\mathbb{R}^+$ but not over $\mathbb{Z}$. Commutative but not associative.
3 Same table as cyclic group when reordered $\{1, i, -1, -i\}$.
4 $1^{-1}=1, 3^{-1}=3, 5^{-1}=5, 7^{-1}=7$. Klein group.
5 (a) not closed, (b) no unit element, (c) not associative.
7 Klein group

	f_1	f_2	f_3	f_4
f_1	f_1	f_2	f_3	f_4
f_2	f_2	f_1	f_4	f_3
f_3	f_3	f_4	f_1	f_2
f_4	f_4	f_3	f_2	f_1

8 Klein group.
9 Klein group.

Exercise 10.1 (page 102)
1 (a) 5, (b) 5, (c) 5, (d) 13, (e) $\sqrt{5}$, (f) 2.6.
2 (a) (4,3), (b) (−1,−2), (c) (−4,−6), (d) (−1,−3).
3 (a) (3,6) and (5,9), (b) (1,0) and (3,−3), (c) (0,1) and (2,5).
4 (a) (2,2), (b) (4,0), (c) (3,6), (d) (5,7), (e) (6,−1).
5 (a) (4,4), (b) (0,3).

Exercise 10.2 (page 105)
1 (a) $y=x+2$, (b) $y=2x+1$, (c) $y=3x-1$, (d) $x+y=5$, (e) $2x+y=10$.
2 (a) $y=2x-1$, (b) $2y=x-5$, (c) $x+y=1$, (d) $y=-5$, (e) $2y+x+2=0$.
3 (a) $2x+5y=10$, (b) $2x+3y=1$, (c) $x-2y+2=0$.
4 (a) $y=x+1$, (b) $y=3x-7$, (c) $y=-x+5$, (d) $2y=x-3$.
5 (a) $\frac{1}{3}$, (b) $\frac{1}{7}$, (c) $\frac{1}{3}$, (d) $\frac{1}{7}$.

Exercise 10.3 (page 107)
1 (a) $x^2+y^2-2x-4y-4=0$, (b) $x^2+y^2+4x-8y-5=0$, (c) $x^2+y^2+4x+2y-11=0$.
2 (a) (3,4); 5, (b) (1,−2); 1, (c) $(\frac{7}{8},1)$; $\frac{1}{8}\sqrt{145}$.
3 (a) $x^2+y^2-12x-13y+36=0$, (b) $x^2+y^2-3x-5y+6=0$.
4 $4y-3x=25$.
5 $3x+4y=31$.

Exercise 10.4 (page 107)
1 (a) 5, (b) 13.
2 (a) (4, −1), (b) $(-\frac{1}{2}, 1)$.
3 (6, 5).
4 (10, 13).
5 (a) (3, 1), (b) (0,0).
6 (a) $x+3y=10$, (b) $y=2x-3$, (c) $3x+2y=6$, (d) $y=x-3$, (e) $3y=2x-8$, (f) $3x+2y=1$.
7 (a) $\frac{1}{7}$, (b) 1.
8 $(x+3)^2+(y-2)^2=16$.

9 (3,−1); 5.
10 $2x^2+2y^2-10x-14y+19=0$.
11 $-3x+4y=25$.
12 $y=1$.
13 (4, −3); (12, −9).
14 $x^2+y^2-3x-y=0$.
15 $x^2+y^2-2x-2y+1=0$; $x^2+y^2-10x-10y+25=0$.
16 −4 or $-\frac{56}{11}$.
17 $y=mx$, where $m=\frac{1}{4}(3\pm\sqrt{3})$.

Exercise 11.1 (page 113)

1 (a) $y^2=16x$, (b) $y^2=-8x$, (c) $x^2=4y$, (d) $x^2=-12y$, (e) $y^2=12x+12$, (f) $y^2=12(x-1)$, (g) $y^2=-16(x-1)$, (h) $x^2=24(y+2)$, (i) $x^2=-8(y-6)$, (j) $(y-2)^2=8x$.
2 (a) $y=0$, (1,0), (b) $y=0$ (4,0), (c) $y=1$, (4,1), (d) $x=2$, (2,0), (e) $x=2$, (2,1).
3 (a) $2y=4x+1$, (b) $2y=4x+3$, (c) $8y=16x+1$.
4 (a) $y=x+2$, (b) $y=2x+1$, (c) $2y=x+8$.

Exercise 11.2 (page 117)

1 (a) (±4, ±4); $x+y=\pm4$, (b) (±4, ±4), $x-y=\pm4$, (c) $(\pm\frac{1}{2}\sqrt{2}, \pm\frac{1}{2}\sqrt{2})$, $x+y=\pm\frac{1}{2}\sqrt{2}$.
2 (a) $x=1$, $y=2$, (b) $x=2$, $y=-4$, (c) $x=2$, $y=3$.
3 (a) $(x-2)(y-1)=1$, (b) $(x-2)(y-1)=2$.
4 (a) $x+4y=8$, $4x-y=15$, (b) $2x+y=16$, $x-2y=-12$, (c) $x+4y=-4$, $8x-2y=15$.
5 (a) $(\frac{1}{2}, 8)$.

Exercise 11.3 (page 117)

1 $y^2=16x$.
2 $(x-4)^2+(y-3)^2=(x+2)^2$.
3 $\frac{3}{4}$.
4 $y=x+2$; $x+y=6$.
5 $am^2=ln$.
10 $n^2=4lmc^2$.

Exercise 12.1 (page 127)

1 $(\pm\sqrt{5},0)$, $\frac{1}{3}\sqrt{5}$; $(0, \pm\sqrt{5})$, $\frac{1}{3}\sqrt{5}$.
2 $4x+3y=11$, $3x-4y=2$; $4x-3y=11$, $3x+4y=2$.
3 $y=4x\pm\sqrt{61}$.
4 $y=1$, $x=-2$; (1,1), (−5, 1), $x=\frac{10}{3}$, $x=-\frac{22}{3}$.
5 $(\pm\frac{64}{17}, \mp\frac{225}{17})$; $y+x=\pm\frac{161}{17}$.
6 $(\pm\sqrt{13},0)$;$x=\pm\frac{4}{\sqrt{13}}$; $3x+2y=0$$(\pm\sqrt{13},0)$; $x=\pm\frac{9}{\sqrt{13}}$ and $2x+3y=0$.
7 $2x-y=1$, $x+2y=3$.
8 $y=3x\pm\sqrt{11}$.
9 $x=1$, $y=-2$; $(1\pm\frac{4}{5}\sqrt{41}, -2)$, $y+2=\pm\frac{5}{4}(x-1)$.
10 $(\pm\frac{25}{3}, \pm\frac{16}{3})$; $x+y=\pm\frac{41}{3}$.

Exercise 13.1 (page 136)

1 (a) $(5\cos\theta, 5\sin\theta)$, (b) $\frac{1}{2}\cos\theta, \frac{1}{2}\sin\theta)$, (c) $(t^2, 2t)$, (d) $(-t^2, 6t)$, (e) (t, t^2), (f) $(3t, 3/t)$, (g) $(5t/2, 5/2t)$, (h) $(-ct, c/t)$, (i) $\left(\frac{2}{3}t, -\frac{2}{3t}\right)$, (j) $(1+ct, 2+c/t)$.
2 (a) $x^2+y^2=4$, (b) $x^2+y^2=9$, (c) $xy=4$, (d) $(x-1)(y-1)=1$, (e) $4y=x^2$.
3 (a) $3x-4y=25$, $4x+3y=0$, (b) $y=x+3$, $x+y=9$, (c) $y=4x-16$, $x+4y=72$, (d) $4y=4-x$, $2y=8x-15$, (e) $x+4y+16=0$, $y=4x+30$.
4 $y=\pm(x+1)$.
5 $2y=x+4$, $2y=-4x-1$.

Exercise 13.2 (page 139)

1 (a) $(4\cos\theta, 5\sin\theta)$, (b) $(5\cos\theta, 2\sin\theta)$, (c) $(\frac{1}{2}t^2, \frac{1}{5}t^5)$, (d) (t^5, t^2), (e) $(\frac{1}{\sqrt{2}}\cos\theta, \frac{1}{\sqrt{3}}\sin\theta)$.
2 (a) $x^2/4+y^2/9=1$, (b) $4x^2+y^2=1$, (c) $8y^2=9x^3$, (d) $8y=x^3$, (e) $y=(x-1)^3$.
3 $2x+3\sqrt{3}y=12$; $3\sqrt{3}x-2y=\frac{5}{2}\sqrt{3}$.
4 $2y=3x-1$, $2x+3y=5$.
5 $x\sin t+y\cos t=a\sin t\cos t$.

Exercise 13.3 (page 140)

1 $(p+q)y=2(x+apq)$.
4 $(0, 2c/t)$, $(2ct, 0)$.
8 $\frac{1}{2}x\cos\theta+\frac{1}{3}y\sin\theta=1$; (2,0) and (1.6, 1.8).
10 $\pm\sqrt{3}$.
11 $y=x\sqrt{2}-2\sqrt{2}$; $-1/\sqrt{2}$.

Exercise 14.1 (page 146)

5 (a) $r^2\cos 2\theta=a^2$, (b) $r^2\sin 2\theta=2c^2$, (c) $r+4\cos\theta=0$.
6 (a) $xy=\frac{1}{2}$, (b) $x^2-y^2=1$, (c) $(x^2+y^2)^2=2a^2xy$.

Exercise 14.2 (page 148)

1 (a) πa^2, (b) $\frac{1}{4}\pi a^2$, (c) $\frac{1}{2}a^2$, (d) $\frac{1}{2}a^2$, (e) $\frac{4}{3}\pi^3a^2$.

Exercise 14.3 (page 148)

2 $(x-a)^2(x^2+y^2)=b^2x^2$.
3 $\frac{1}{2}a^2$.
4 $\pi-\frac{3}{2}\sqrt{3}$.
5 πab.

Exercise 15.2 (page 155)

1 (a) 23.6°, 156.4°, (b) 53.1°, 306.9°, (c) 26.6°, 206.6°, (d) 216.9°, 323.1°, (e) 113.6°, 246.4°, (f) 111.8°, 291.8°, (g) 64.2°, 115.8°, (h) 95.7°, 264.3°, (i) 21.8°, 201.8°, (j) 48.6°, 131.4°.
2 (a) 15°, 75°, (b) ±37.8°, (c) −45°, 15°, 75°, (d) 34.2°, 85.8°, (e) 19.2°, 70.8°, (f) −46.6°, (g) ±60°, (h) −90°, 30°, (i) −31.3°, 41.3°, (j) 30°.
3 (a) 53.1°, $(360n+53.1)°$ or $[180(2n+1)-53.1]°$, (b) 154.2°, $(360n\pm154.2)°$,

(c) 63.4°, $(180n+63.4)°$, (d) $-56.3°$, $(180n-56.3)°$, (e) 45.6°, $(360n\pm45.6)°$, (f) $-23.6°$, $(360n-23.6)°$ or $[180(2n+1)23.6]°$.

4 (a) $\frac{\pi}{4}$, (b) $\frac{7\pi}{6}$, (c) $-\frac{1}{2}\pi$, (d) $\frac{2\pi}{3}$.

5 (a) 0.698, (b) 3.49, (c) -0.175, (d) -1.75.

6 (a) $\frac{\pi}{2}$, $2n\pi+\frac{\pi}{2}$, (b) $\frac{\pi}{3}$, $2n\pi\pm\frac{\pi}{3}$, (c) $\frac{\pi}{4}$, $n\pi+\frac{\pi}{4}$.

7 (a) 0.305, (b) 2.21, (c) -1.11.

8 (a) $\pi/6$; $5\pi/6$, $-7\pi/6$, $-11\pi/6$, (b) $\pi/4$; $-7\pi/4$, $-\pi/4$, $7\pi/4$, (c) $\pi/4$; $-3\pi/4$, $5\pi/4$, $-7\pi/4$, (d) $\pi/4$, $-\pi/4$; $-7\pi/4$, $-5\pi/4$, $3\pi/4$; $-3\pi/4$, $5\pi/4$, $7\pi/4$, (e) $\pi/6$, $5\pi/6$; $-11\pi/6$, $-\pi/6$, $11\pi/6$; $-7\pi/6$, $-5\pi/6$, $7\pi/6$.

9 (a) $\pi/4$, (b) $\pi/3$, (c) $\pi/6$, (d) $\pi/12$, $5\pi/12$, $3\pi/4$, (e) $3\pi/16$, $7\pi/16$.

10 (a) 0.56, 1.01, (b) 1.25, 1.89, (c) 0.69, 2.26.

Exercise 15.3 (page 159)

1 (a) 4.00 cm, 7.66 cm, 88°, (b) 5.22 cm, 5.39 cm, 46°, (c) 5.50 cm, 11.6 cm, 26°, (d) 8.16 cm, 23.2°, 26.8°, (e) 7.10 cm, 56.6°, 91.4°, (f) 15.6 cm, 37.1°, 94.6°, (g) 32°, 122°, 8.32 cm or 148°, 6°, 1.03 cm, (h) 13.2°, 90.3°, 76.5°, (i) 28.4°, 78.9°, 72.7°, (j) 63.2°, 65.8°, 3.17 cm or 116.9°, 12.1°, 0.73 cm.

2 5.46 km.

3 50.5°, 129.5°.

4 (a) 10.8 cm, (b) 12.5 cm.

5 237 m.

6 3.58 cm, 36.4°, 98.6°.

7 46.6°, 57.9°, 75.5°.

8 1530 m, 730 m, 16.8°.

Exercise 16.1 (page 167)

8 (a) $2\sin 3x\cos 2x$, (b) $2\cos 4x\cos x$, (c) $2\cos\frac{7}{2}x\sin\frac{3}{2}x$, (d) $2\sin 6x\sin x$.

9 (a) $\sin 8x+\sin 2x$, (b) $\cos 5x+\cos 3x$, (c) $\frac{1}{2}(\sin 9x-\sin x)$, (d) $-\frac{1}{2}(\cos 3x-\cos x)$.

10 $8c^4-8c^2+1$, where $c\equiv\cos\theta$.

11 (a) 0, 180°, 360°, (b) $60n°$ or $120n°$, $n=0,1,2,3$, (c) $45n°$, $n=0,1,2,\ldots 8$, (d) 0, 49.8°, 130.2°, 229.8°, 310.2°.

Exercise 16.2 (page 169)

1 (a) $-41.6°$ or 115.4°, (b) $-24.3°$ or 114.3°, (c) $-107.6°$ or 40.2°, (d) 118° or 180°, (e) $-122.3°$ or $-20.8°$ or 57.7° or 159.2°.

2 (a) ±5, (b) ±5, (c) $\pm\sqrt{2}$, (d) $\pm\sqrt{5}$, (e) $\pm\sqrt{13}$.

3 (a) 5 when $x=53.1°$; -5 when $x=233.1°$,
(b) 5 when $x=126.9°$; -5 when $x=306.9°$,
(c) $\sqrt{2}$ when $x=135°$; $-\sqrt{2}$ when $x=315°$,
(d) $\sqrt{2}$ when $x=67.5°$ or 247.5°; $-\sqrt{2}$ when $x=157.5°$ or 337.5°,
(e) $\sqrt{5}$ when $x=76.7°$ or 256.7°; $-\sqrt{5}$ when $x=166.7°$ or 346.7°.

4 $\frac{1}{\sqrt{5}}$ when $x=[63.4+180n]°$.

5 (a) -0.96, (b) -0.8432, (c) $\frac{1}{10}\sqrt{2}$, (d) -0.8.

Exercise 17.1 (page 174)

1 (a) $\pm 5i$, (b) $\pm\frac{3}{2}i$, (c) $1\pm 2i$, (d) $\frac{1}{2}(3\pm 5i)$, (e) $7+2i$, $-7+2i$, (f) $9i$ or $-5i$.
2 (a) $2+i$, (b) $3-4i$, (c) $2+i$, (d) $\frac{1}{5}(2+i)$, (e) $\frac{1}{10}(3+i)$.
3 (a) $4-i$, (b) $9-7i$, (c) $-3+11i$, (d) $\frac{1}{130}(43+19i)$, (e) $\frac{1}{13}(-2+11i)$.
4 (a) 4, -3, (b) 26, 30.
5 $3-i$.
6 $3+2i$, 13, 6.

Exercise 17.2 (page 177)

1 (a) 3, 0, (b) 2, $\frac{\pi}{2}$, (c) 1, π, (d) 2, $-\frac{1}{2}\pi$, (e) 5, α where $\cos\alpha:\sin\alpha:1=3:4:5$.
2 (a) 1, $\frac{\pi}{3}$, (b) 2, $-\frac{\pi}{6}$, (c) 4, $\frac{5\pi}{6}$, (d) 1, $-\frac{2\pi}{3}$, (e) 2, $-\frac{5\pi}{6}$.
3 (a) $10(\cos\frac{1}{2}\theta+i\sin\frac{1}{2}\theta)$, (b) $\frac{2}{5}\left(\cos\frac{\pi}{6}+i\sin\frac{\pi}{6}\right)$, (c) $30\left(\cos\frac{\pi}{4}+i\sin\frac{\pi}{4}\right)$,
(d) $4\left(\cos\frac{2\pi}{3}+i\sin\frac{2\pi}{3}\right)$, (e) $125(\cos\frac{1}{2}\pi+i\sin\frac{1}{2}\pi)$, (f) $\frac{10}{9}(\cos\pi+i\sin\pi)$.
4 $\sqrt{3}(\cos\pi/6+i\sin\pi/6)$: (a) $3(\cos\pi/3+i\sin\pi/3)=\frac{3}{2}(1+i\sqrt{3})$,
(b) $3\sqrt{3}(\cos\pi/2+i\sin\pi/2)=3\sqrt{3}i$, (c) $\frac{1}{3}(\cos\pi/3-i\sin\pi/3)=\frac{1}{6}(\sqrt{3}-i)$, (d) 6.
5 (a) $2\cos\frac{1}{2}\theta(\cos\frac{1}{2}\theta+i\sin\frac{1}{2}\theta)$, (b) $4\cos^2\frac{1}{2}\theta(\cos\theta+i\sin\theta)$,
(c) $\frac{1}{2\cos\frac{1}{2}\theta}[\cos(-\frac{1}{2}\theta)+i\sin(-\frac{1}{2}\theta)]$, (d) $16\cos^4\frac{1}{2}\theta(\cos 2\theta+i\sin 2\theta)$.

Exercise 17.3 (page 180)

1 Circle centre (0, 0), radius 2; centre (2, 3), radius 2.
5 (1, 1).
7 $2i$, $\sqrt{3}-i$.
8 $-1+i$, $2+i$.
10 $\sqrt{2}-i\sqrt{2}$, $-\sqrt{2}\pm i\sqrt{2}$.
11 Circle $|z|=2$, described in clockwise sense; circle $|z|=\frac{1}{2}$, described in clockwise sense.
14 $32c^6-48c^4+18c^2-1$, where $c=\cos\theta$.

Exercise 18.1 (page 190)

1 (a) Enlargement factor 3, (b) enlargement factor $\frac{1}{2}$, (c) reflection in y-axis, (d) rotation thro' $-90°$ and enlargement factor 2, (e) rotation thro' $+90°$, (f) rotation thro' $+90°$ and enlargement factor $\frac{1}{2}$.
2 (a) $\begin{pmatrix}6\\8\end{pmatrix}$, $\begin{pmatrix}-8\\6\end{pmatrix}$, (b) rotation thro' $+53.1°$,
(c) $\begin{pmatrix}-0.28 & -0.96\\ 0.96 & -0.28\end{pmatrix}$, $\begin{pmatrix}-2.8\\9.6\end{pmatrix}$, $\begin{pmatrix}-9.6\\-2.8\end{pmatrix}$ rotation thro' 106.2°,
(d) $\begin{pmatrix}0.6 & 0.8\\ -0.8 & 0.6\end{pmatrix}$ rotation thro' --53.1°, (e) $\begin{pmatrix}0.8 & -0.6\\ 0.6 & 0.8\end{pmatrix}$, rotation thro' +90°.

3 (b) 5, 53.1°, (c) rotation thro′ +26.6°, enlargement factor $\sqrt{5}$.
5 (a) $y=2x$, (b) $x=0$, (c) $y=2x$.
6 (a) $y=-x$, $y=-\frac{1}{2}x$, (b) $y=-3x$.

Exercise 18.2 (page 193)

1 (a) −72, −36, −4, −4, (b) −72, 36, −4, 4.

2 $\begin{pmatrix} -72 & 56 & -8 \\ 36 & -28 & 5 \\ -4 & 4 & -1 \end{pmatrix}$.

3 $\begin{pmatrix} -9 & 7 & -1 \\ \frac{9}{2} & -\frac{7}{2} & \frac{5}{8} \\ -\frac{1}{2} & \frac{1}{2} & -\frac{1}{8} \end{pmatrix}$.

4 8.

5 (a) Singular, (b) $\begin{pmatrix} -3 & -2 & 3 \\ 2 & 4 & -3 \\ 2 & -1 & -1 \end{pmatrix}$.

6 Maps plane $x+y=0$ onto the origin.
7 (a) $3x=4y$, (b) $4x-3y=0$,
(c) every point on $3y=x$ maps onto itself; the line $y=-3x$ maps onto itself.
8 5.

9 $\frac{1}{7}\begin{pmatrix} 5 & 2 & -1 \\ -3 & 3 & 2 \\ -3 & -4 & 2 \end{pmatrix}$; 2, 1, −3.

Exercise 19.1 (page 205)

1 (a) 3**i**+**j**, (b) **i**+5**j**, (c) 6**i**+9**j**, (d) −7**i**−14**j**, (e) −7**j**.
2 (a) $\sqrt{10}$, 18.4°, (b) $\sqrt{26}$, 78.7°, (c) $3\sqrt{13}$, 56.3°, (d) $7\sqrt{5}$, −116.6°, (e) 7, −90°.
3 (a) 3**i**+4**j**−2**k**, (b) **i**+2**j**, (c) 2**i**+2**j**−2**k**, (d) **j**+**k**, (e) **i**−2**k**.
4 (a) $\sqrt{29}$, 56.1°, (b) $\sqrt{5}$, 63.4°, (c) $2\sqrt{3}$, 54.7°, (d) $\sqrt{2}$, 90°, (e) $\sqrt{5}$, 63.4°.
5 Yes.
9 $\sqrt{18}$, $\sqrt{38}$, $\sqrt{6}$; greater.
10 (a) 17, (b) 17, (c) 170, (d) 50, (e) 78.
11 (a) 7, (b) $\sqrt{19}$, (c) 105.
12 (a) Yes, (b) no, (c) yes.
13 10.
14 $\frac{15}{4}$.
16 (a) 3**i**+3**j**, (b) **i**+2**j**, (c) −**j**, (d) 3**i**+3**k**, (e) 3**i**+4**j**.
17 (a) 5**i**+7**j**, (b) −5**i**+12**j**, (c) 3**i**+8**j**, (d) −3**i**+11**j**.
18 (a) −8**i**−**j**, (b) 3**j**, (c) 2**i**+4**j**, (d) −10**i**−2**j**.
19 (a) 4**i**+3**j**+9**k**, (b) −**j**+5**k**, (c) 5**i**+4**j**+10**k**, (d) −**i**−2**j**+4**k**.
21 $\mathbf{a}=\frac{1}{2}(\mathbf{b}+\mathbf{c})$.
22 $\mathbf{p}=\frac{1}{3}(2\mathbf{a}+\mathbf{b})$, $\mathbf{q}=\frac{1}{3}(\mathbf{a}+2\mathbf{b})$.
23 $\mathbf{d}=\mathbf{b}+\mathbf{c}-\mathbf{a}$.
24 $\mathbf{e}=2(\mathbf{d}-\mathbf{a})+\mathbf{c}$.
25 $m : m+n$.

Exercise 19.2 (page 209)

1 (a) $\mathbf{r}=3\mathbf{i}+\mathbf{j}+t(\mathbf{i}-\mathbf{j})$; $\mathbf{r}=\begin{pmatrix}3\\1\end{pmatrix}+t\begin{pmatrix}1\\-1\end{pmatrix}$.

(b) $\mathbf{r}=4\mathbf{i}-\mathbf{j}+t(-\mathbf{i}-\mathbf{j})$; $\mathbf{r}=\begin{pmatrix}4\\-1\end{pmatrix}+t\begin{pmatrix}-1\\-1\end{pmatrix}$.

(c) $\mathbf{r}=\mathbf{i}+2\mathbf{j}+3\mathbf{k}+t(\mathbf{i}+\mathbf{j}+\mathbf{k})$; $\mathbf{r}=\begin{pmatrix}1\\2\\3\end{pmatrix}+t\begin{pmatrix}1\\1\\1\end{pmatrix}$.

(d) $\mathbf{r}=t(\mathbf{i}+2\mathbf{j}+3\mathbf{k})$; $\mathbf{r}=t\begin{pmatrix}1\\2\\3\end{pmatrix}$.

(e) $\mathbf{r}=3\mathbf{i}+t\mathbf{j}$; $\mathbf{r}=\begin{pmatrix}3\\0\end{pmatrix}+t\begin{pmatrix}0\\1\end{pmatrix}$.

(f) $\mathbf{r}=3\mathbf{i}+2\mathbf{j}+t\mathbf{k}$; $\mathbf{r}=\begin{pmatrix}3\\2\\0\end{pmatrix}+t\begin{pmatrix}0\\0\\1\end{pmatrix}$.

(g) $\mathbf{r}=\mathbf{i}+t(\mathbf{j}+\mathbf{k})$; $\mathbf{r}=\begin{pmatrix}1\\0\\0\end{pmatrix}+t\begin{pmatrix}0\\1\\1\end{pmatrix}$.

(h) $\mathbf{r}=\mathbf{i}+\mathbf{j}+t\mathbf{k}$; $\mathbf{r}=\begin{pmatrix}1\\1\\0\end{pmatrix}+t\begin{pmatrix}0\\0\\1\end{pmatrix}$.

(i) $\mathbf{r}=t(\mathbf{i}+\mathbf{j}+\mathbf{k})$; $\mathbf{r}=t\begin{pmatrix}1\\1\\1\end{pmatrix}$.

(j) $\mathbf{r}=t(\mathbf{i}+\mathbf{j})$; $\mathbf{r}=t\begin{pmatrix}1\\1\end{pmatrix}$.

2 (a) $\mathbf{r}=3\mathbf{i}+\mathbf{j}+t(\mathbf{i}-2\mathbf{j})$; $\mathbf{r}=\begin{pmatrix}3\\1\end{pmatrix}+t\begin{pmatrix}1\\-2\end{pmatrix}$.

(b) $\mathbf{r}=\mathbf{i}+\mathbf{j}+t(2\mathbf{i})$; $\mathbf{r}=\begin{pmatrix}1\\1\end{pmatrix}+t\begin{pmatrix}2\\0\end{pmatrix}$.

(c) $\mathbf{r}=\mathbf{i}+\mathbf{j}+\mathbf{k}+t(4\mathbf{k})$; $\mathbf{r}=\begin{pmatrix}1\\1\\1\end{pmatrix}+t\begin{pmatrix}0\\0\\4\end{pmatrix}$.

(d) $\mathbf{r}=2\mathbf{i}+3\mathbf{j}+\mathbf{k}+t(2\mathbf{j})$; $\mathbf{r}=\begin{pmatrix}2\\3\\1\end{pmatrix}+t\begin{pmatrix}0\\2\\0\end{pmatrix}$.

(e) $\mathbf{r}=3\mathbf{i}+2\mathbf{j}+\mathbf{k}+t(\mathbf{i}+\mathbf{j})$; $\mathbf{r}=\begin{pmatrix}3\\2\\1\end{pmatrix}+t\begin{pmatrix}1\\1\\0\end{pmatrix}$.

3 (d) and (i).

4 (b).

5 (e).

Exercise 19.3 (page 212)

1 (a) -1, (b) 0, (c) -5, (d) 2, (e) 2.

2 (a) $\frac{-1}{\sqrt{26}}$, (b) $\frac{-5}{\sqrt{26}}$, (c) 0, (d) $\frac{-1}{5\sqrt{2}}$, (e) $\frac{1}{\sqrt{2}}$.

3 (a) 1, (b) -2, (c) 1, (d) 3, (e) 2.

4 (a) $\frac{1}{\sqrt{15}}$, (b) $\frac{1}{\sqrt{10}}$, (c) $-\sqrt{\frac{2}{3}}$, (d) $\sqrt{\frac{3}{5}}$, (e) $\frac{-5}{\sqrt{26}}$.

5 (a) $\pm\frac{1}{5}(3\mathbf{i}+4\mathbf{j})$, (b) $\pm\frac{1}{\sqrt{2}}(\mathbf{i}-\mathbf{j})$.

6 (a) $\mathbf{j}$, (b) $\mathbf{k}$, (c) $\pm\frac{1}{\sqrt{17}}(2\mathbf{i}+2\mathbf{j}-3\mathbf{k})$, (d) $\frac{1}{\sqrt{35}}(\mathbf{i}-5\mathbf{j}+3\mathbf{k})$, (e) $\frac{1}{\sqrt{26}}(\mathbf{i}-4\mathbf{j}+3\mathbf{k})$.

7 (a) $\mathbf{r}.(3\mathbf{i}+5\mathbf{j})=1$; $3x+5y=1$, (b) $\mathbf{r}.(\mathbf{i}+2\mathbf{j})=-7$; $x+2y=-7$,
(c) $\mathbf{r}.(-3\mathbf{i}-2\mathbf{j})=-23$; $3x+2y=23$.

Exercise 19.4 (page 214)

1 (b) $\begin{pmatrix}8\\9\end{pmatrix}$, (c) $\begin{pmatrix}5\frac{1}{2}\\8\end{pmatrix}$, $\begin{pmatrix}7\\6\frac{1}{2}\end{pmatrix}$, (d) $\begin{pmatrix}1\frac{1}{2}\\-1\frac{1}{2}\end{pmatrix}$.

2 (a) $\begin{pmatrix}-4\\-5\end{pmatrix}$, (b) $\begin{pmatrix}2\\3\end{pmatrix}$.

3 (a) $\begin{pmatrix}3\frac{1}{2}\\4\frac{1}{2}\end{pmatrix}$, (b) $\begin{pmatrix}2\\1\end{pmatrix}$, (c) $\begin{pmatrix}2\\2\end{pmatrix}$, (d) $\begin{pmatrix}2\\2\end{pmatrix}$.

4 $\sqrt{6}$, $3\sqrt{6}$, $3\sqrt{2}$.

5 $\begin{pmatrix}4\\7\\6\end{pmatrix}$, $\begin{pmatrix}0\\1\\1\end{pmatrix}$, $\begin{pmatrix}6\\10\\7\end{pmatrix}$.

6 (a) $\mathbf{r}=\begin{pmatrix}2\\1\end{pmatrix}+t\begin{pmatrix}-1\\-1\end{pmatrix}$, (b) $\mathbf{r}=\begin{pmatrix}2\\1\end{pmatrix}+t\begin{pmatrix}-6\\1\end{pmatrix}$, (c) $\mathbf{r}=\begin{pmatrix}2\\1\end{pmatrix}+t\begin{pmatrix}0\\1\end{pmatrix}$.

7 A and C.

8 $\mathbf{r}=\begin{pmatrix}1\\3\end{pmatrix}+t\begin{pmatrix}2\\4\end{pmatrix}$, $y=2x+1$;

$\mathbf{r}=\begin{pmatrix}3\\7\end{pmatrix}+t\begin{pmatrix}2\\-8\end{pmatrix}$, $y+4x=19$;

$\mathbf{r}=\begin{pmatrix}5\\-1\end{pmatrix}+t\begin{pmatrix}4\\-4\end{pmatrix}$, $x+y=4$.

9 $\mathbf{r}=\begin{pmatrix}3\\1\\2\end{pmatrix}+t\begin{pmatrix}-1\\2\\-3\end{pmatrix}$.

10 $\mathbf{r}=\begin{pmatrix}2\\1\\0\end{pmatrix}+t\begin{pmatrix}2\\-1\\-1\end{pmatrix}$, $\frac{x-2}{2}=\frac{y-1}{-1}=\frac{z}{-1}$;

$\mathbf{r}=\begin{pmatrix}4\\0\\-1\end{pmatrix}+t\begin{pmatrix}1\\-1\\2\end{pmatrix}$, $\frac{x-4}{1}=\frac{y}{-1}=\frac{z+1}{2}$;

$\mathbf{r}=\begin{pmatrix}2\\1\\0\end{pmatrix}+t\begin{pmatrix}3\\-2\\1\end{pmatrix}$, $\frac{x-2}{3}=\frac{y-1}{-2}=\frac{z}{1}$.

11 4, −9, 4.
13 $1/\sqrt{10}$.
14 $-\frac{6}{5\sqrt{13}}$, $-\frac{1}{5\sqrt{2}}$, $\frac{5}{\sqrt{26}}$.
15 $0.8\mathbf{i}+0.6\mathbf{j}$.
16 $\pm\frac{1}{\sqrt{2}}(\mathbf{i}-\mathbf{k})$.
18 $-\frac{\sqrt{3}}{2\sqrt{7}}$.
19 $-\frac{1}{5\sqrt{2}}$.
20 $\pm\frac{1}{\sqrt{5}}(\mathbf{i}+2\mathbf{j})$; e.g. $\mathbf{k}$.
21 (a) $x-2y+3z=4$, (b) $2x-3y=12$, (c) $x=3$.
22 (a) $\mathbf{i}+2\mathbf{j}+2\mathbf{k}$, (b) $4\mathbf{i}+\mathbf{j}+\mathbf{k}$, (c) $\mathbf{i}+\mathbf{j}+3\mathbf{k}$.
23 (a) $\mathbf{i}+2\mathbf{j}+2\mathbf{k}$, (b) $\mathbf{r}=3\mathbf{i}-2\mathbf{j}-\mathbf{k}+t(\mathbf{i}+2\mathbf{j}+2\mathbf{k})$, (c) (4, 0, 1), (d) 3, (e) $5\mathbf{i}+2\mathbf{j}+3\mathbf{k}$.
24 (a) 3, $-2\mathbf{i}+\mathbf{j}+8\mathbf{k}$, (b) $\sqrt{5}$, $5\mathbf{i}-4\mathbf{j}+\mathbf{k}$, (c) $\sqrt{14}$, $9\mathbf{i}$.
25 $-\frac{1}{3\sqrt{3}}$.
26 (a) Several possible forms, one of which is $\mathbf{r}=2\mathbf{i}+\mathbf{j}+s(-\mathbf{i}+\mathbf{k})+t(\mathbf{i}-2\mathbf{j}-\mathbf{k})$, (b) $\mathbf{r}.(3\mathbf{i}+2\mathbf{j}+\mathbf{k})=6$.
27 $\mathbf{r}=4\mathbf{i}-3\mathbf{j}-2\mathbf{k}+s(6\mathbf{i}-4\mathbf{j}-4\mathbf{k})+t(\mathbf{i}-2\mathbf{j}-\mathbf{k})$; $\mathbf{r}.(2\mathbf{i}-\mathbf{j}+4\mathbf{k})=3$.
28 $3x+2y-z=5$; $\mathbf{r}=\mathbf{i}+2\mathbf{j}+2\mathbf{k}+s(\mathbf{j}+2\mathbf{k})+t(\mathbf{i}+3\mathbf{k})$.
29 $4x+3y+2z=3$.
30 The plane is $\mathbf{r}.(3\mathbf{i}+5\mathbf{j}+\mathbf{k})=2$.
31 (a) $\mathbf{a}-\mathbf{b}+\mathbf{c}$, (b) $\mathbf{c}+\mathbf{b}-\mathbf{a}$.
32 $3\mathbf{i}+2\mathbf{j}$; $\sqrt{0.6}$.
34 $(\mathbf{r}-\mathbf{i}-\mathbf{j}).(\mathbf{r}-3\mathbf{i}+5\mathbf{j})=0$; $(\mathbf{r}-3\mathbf{i}+4\mathbf{j}-\mathbf{k}).(\mathbf{r}-\mathbf{i}+2\mathbf{j}-3\mathbf{k})=0$.
35 $\frac{5}{2}\sqrt{5}$, $\frac{1}{2}\sqrt{38}$.
36 (a) $5\mathbf{i}-\mathbf{k}$, (b) (5, 0, −1), same plane and same line.
37 $\frac{8}{7\sqrt{6}}$.
38 $\frac{4}{\sqrt{406}}$.

Exercise 20.1 (page 223)

1 (a) $3+8x+15x^2$, (b) $\frac{3}{2}x^{-1/2}+2x^{-1/3}+6x^{-1/4}$, (c) $2x+6x^2+12x^3$, (d) $x^{-1/2}+6x^{1/2}+20x^{3/2}$, (e) $-x^{-2}+3$, (f) $-x^{-3/2}+2x^{-1/2}+6x^{1/2}$, (g) $3x^2+10x^{3/2}+16x^{5/3}$, (h) $5x^{1/4}+36x^{5/4}$, (i) $-6x^{-3}-4x^{-2}-3x^{-4}$, (j) $-x^{-3/2}+\frac{3}{2}x^{-1/2}+6x^{1/2}$.

Exercise 20.2 (page 227)

1 (a) $-3\sin 3x$, (b) $\frac{1}{2}\sec^2 \frac{1}{2}x$, (c) $2\cos(2x+\pi/2)$, (d) $2x\cos(x^2)$, (e) $-\sin(x-\pi/6)$.
2 (a) $x\cos x+\sin x$, (b) $2\cos\frac{1}{2}x-x\sin\frac{1}{2}x$, (c) $2x\tan x+x^2\sec^2 x$,
(d) $2\cos 2x\cos x-\sin 2x\sin x$, (e) $-\dfrac{2\sin x\sin 2x+\cos 2x\cos x}{\sin^2 x}$.

Exercise 20.3 (page 228)

1 (a) $1/x$, (b) $3/(3x+1)$, (c) $-\tan x$, (d) $\cot(x+\pi/3)$, (e) $2x/(x^2+1)$, (f) $3e^{3x}$,
(g) $3e^{3x+1}$, (h) $-\sin x\, e^{\cos x}$, (i) $2x\, e^{x^2}$, (j) $2e^{2x}$.
2 (a) $1+\ln x$, (b) $2x/(2x+1)+\ln(2x+1)$, (c) $1+\ln(1+x)$, (d) $e^x(1+x)$, (e) $(x^2+2x)e^x$,
(f) $(4x+2)e^{2x}$, (g) $(1/x+\ln x)e^x$, (h) $\ln\sin x+x\cot x$, (i) $(\cos x-\sin^2 x)e^{\cos x}$,
(j) $(1-x\sin x)\,e^{\cos x}$.

Exercise 20.4 (page 232)

1 (a) $-1/\sqrt{(1-x^2)}$, (b) $-y/(x+2y)$, (c) $-y/(x+e^y)$.
2 (a) $3t^2$, (b) $-\tan t$, (c) -1.

Exercise 20.5 (page 232)

1 (a) $\dfrac{x}{\sqrt{(1+x^2)}}$, (b) $\dfrac{-2}{(1+2x)^2}$, (c) $4\cos 4x$, (d) $\dfrac{1}{x}$, (e) $3e^{3x+2}$.
2 (a) $\dfrac{-3}{(3x+2)^2}$, (b) $2\sin x\cos x$, (c) $-\tan x$, (d) $\cos x\, e^{\sin x}$, (e) $\dfrac{\cos x}{2\sqrt{(1+\sin x)}}$.
3 (a) $\frac{2}{3}$, (b) $-\frac{2}{9}\sqrt{3}$, (c) 1.
4 $\sin 3x+3x\cos 3x$.
5 $2x\cos 2x-2x^2\sin 2x$.
6 $x^3\sec^2 x+3x^2\tan x$.
7 $e^{2x}(1+2x)$.
8 $2x(1+x)e^{2x+1}$.
9 $1+\ln x$.
10 $\dfrac{x(5x+4)}{2(x+1)^{1/2}}$.
11 $\dfrac{x\cos x-\sin x}{x^2}$.
12 $-\dfrac{x\sin x+2\cos x}{x^3}$.
13 $\dfrac{\cos x-\sin x}{e^x}$.
14 $\dfrac{1-2\ln x}{x^3}$.
15 $-\dfrac{2\sin x\sin 2x+\cos x\cos 2x}{\sin^2 x}$.
16 (a) $\dfrac{-\sin y}{1+x\cos y}$, (b) $\dfrac{\cos x-y}{x+3y^2}$, (c) $\dfrac{2x-ye^x}{2y+e^x}$.
17 -1.

20 (a) $\frac{3}{2}t$, (b) $\dfrac{-\sin t}{2\cos 2t}$, (c) -1.

21 $\left(\dfrac{1-t^2}{1+t^2}\right)^3$.

22 $\dfrac{-2\sin 2x}{1+\cos 2x}$.

23 (a) $\dfrac{2}{x}$, (b) $\dfrac{2}{x}\ln x$.

24 $1-\dfrac{x\arcsin x}{\sqrt{(1-x^2)}}$.

25 $\dfrac{-\sin t}{1+\cos t}$; $x+y=2+\dfrac{\pi}{2}$.

26 (a) $\dfrac{4x}{(x^2+1)^2}$, (b) $1+\dfrac{1}{(x+1)^2}$.

27 $\dfrac{1-x^2}{x(1+x^2)}$.

28 $e^{-x}(1-x^2)$.

Exercise 21.1 (page 243)

1 (a) (0, 0), point of inflexion, (b) $(-1, 0)$ and (1, 0), minima; (0,1) maximum, (c) $(-\frac{1}{4}, -\frac{1}{256})$, minimum; (0, 0), point of inflexion, (d $\left(-\dfrac{2}{3}, \dfrac{-2\sqrt{3}}{9}\right)$, minimum.

2 (a) min. value 3 when $x=1$,
(b) max. value 0 when $x=0$, min. value $-\frac{4}{27}$ when $x=\frac{2}{3}$,
(c) max. value $\dfrac{2\sqrt{3}}{9}$ when $\cos x=\frac{1}{3}\sqrt{3}$,
(d) max. value $e^{-1/2}$ when $x=1$; min. value $-e^{-1/2}$ when $x=-1$.

3 (a) 100, (b) 5, (c) $4\sqrt{3}$.

4 25 cm^2.

5 3.75%; 3.8%.

6 4%.

7 $(1, \frac{1}{2})$, max; $(-1, -\frac{1}{2})$, min.

8 (0, 1), max; $(-1, 0)$, min.

9 $\frac{1}{3}$; $(2e-3)/e^2$.

10 Radius of circle centre (0, 0) touching $3x+4y=5$ is 1.

11 (a) 1%, (b) 6.4%.

14 $\left(\dfrac{\pi}{6}, \frac{1}{3}\sqrt{3}\right)$, max; $\left(\dfrac{5\pi}{6}, -\frac{1}{3}\sqrt{3}\right)$, min.

16 3.5 metres.

Exercise 22.1 (page 248)

1 (a) x^6+x^7+C, (b) $\frac{1}{2}x^4+\frac{1}{3}x^3+x+C$, (c) $\frac{4}{3}x^{3/2}+\frac{1}{2}x+C$, (d) $\frac{1}{4}x^4+\frac{1}{3}x^3+\frac{1}{2}x^2+x+C$, (e) $\frac{1}{5}x^5+\frac{1}{6}x^6+C$, (f) $-\dfrac{1}{x}-\dfrac{1}{2x^2}-\dfrac{1}{3x^3}+C$, (g) $-1/x+\frac{1}{2}x^2+\frac{1}{3}x^3+C$,

(h) $\frac{2}{5}x^{5/2}+\frac{4}{3}x^{3/2}+2x^{1/2}+C$, (i) $\dfrac{x^{m+1}}{m+1}+\dfrac{a\,x^{n+1}}{n+1}+C$, (j) $\dfrac{a\,x^{m+n-1}}{m+n+1}+C$.

2 (a) $-\frac{1}{3}\cos 3x+C$, (b) $4\sin\frac{1}{4}x+C$, (c) $\frac{1}{4}\tan 4x+C$, (d) $\sin 2x+C$, (e) $x+\frac{1}{2}\sin 2x+C$.

Exercise 22.2 (page 249)

1 (a) $\frac{1}{2}x-\frac{1}{4}\sin 2x+C$, (b) $\frac{1}{2}x+\frac{1}{2}\sin x+C$, (c) $-\frac{1}{4}\cos 2x+C$,
(d) $-\frac{1}{6}\cos 3x-\frac{1}{2}\cos x+C$, (e) $-\frac{1}{8}\cos 4x-\frac{1}{4}\cos 2x+C$, (f) $-\frac{1}{12}\sin 6x+\frac{1}{4}\sin 2x+C$,
(g) $\frac{1}{12}\sin 6x+\frac{1}{8}\sin 4x+C$, (h) $-\frac{1}{6}\cos^6 x+C$, (i) $-\frac{1}{8}\cos 4x+C$,
(j) $\frac{3}{8}x+\frac{1}{4}\sin 2x+\frac{1}{8}\sin 4x+C$.

Exercise 22.3 (page 251)

1 (a) $\ln(x^2+3)+C$, (b) $\ln(3x^2+2)+C$, (c) $\ln(1+\sin 2x)+C$, (d) $\ln(e^x+x+1)+C$,
(e) $\ln(1+x+x^2)+C$, (f) $\ln(x+\tan x)+C$.

2 (a) $\ln\left|\dfrac{A(x-1)}{x}\right|$, (b) $\frac{1}{3}\ln\left|\dfrac{A(x-2)}{x+1}\right|$, (c) $\frac{1}{2}\ln\left|\dfrac{A(x+1)}{x-1}\right|$,
(d) $\frac{1}{3}\ln|A(x-1)(x+2)^2|$, (e) $\ln\left|\dfrac{A(x+2)^2}{x+1}\right|$, (f) $\frac{1}{2}\ln|A(x^2-1)|$.

3 (a) $\frac{1}{2}\arctan\frac{1}{2}x+C$, (b) $\frac{1}{3}\arctan\frac{1}{3}x+C$, (c) $\arcsin\frac{1}{2}x+C$, (d) $\arcsin\frac{1}{3}x+C$,
(e) $\frac{1}{5}\arctan\frac{1}{5}x+C$, (f) $\frac{1}{2}\arcsin 2x+C$.

Exercise 22.4 (page 254)

1 (a) $\frac{1}{3}(x^2+2)^{3/2}+C$, (b) $\frac{3}{4}(3x^2+1)^{4/3}+C$, (c) $\frac{1}{6}(x+2)^6+C$, (d) $\frac{1}{16}(2x+1)^8+C$,
(e) $\frac{1}{5}\sin^5 x+C$, (f) $-\frac{1}{6}\cos^6 x+C$, (g) $\frac{1}{4}\sec^4 x+C$, (h) $\frac{1}{4}(e^x+1)^4+C$.

2 (a) $x\sin x+\cos x+C$, (b) $-\frac{1}{2}x\cos 2x+\frac{1}{4}\sin 2x+C$, (c) $x\,e^x-e^x+C$
(d) $\frac{1}{6}x(x+1)^6-\frac{1}{7}(x+1)^7+C$, (e) $-(x+1)\cos x+\sin x+C$, (f) $e^x[x^2-2x+2]+C$,
(g) $-x^2\cos x+2x\sin x+2\cos x+C$, (h) $\frac{1}{2}[e^x(\sin x-\cos x)]+C$.

Exercise 22.5 (page 259)

1 (a) $\frac{1}{4}$, (b) 12, (c) $\frac{22}{3}$, (d) $-\frac{1}{3}$, (e) 1, (f) 1, (g) $e-1$, (h) $2\ln 2-1$, (i) $\frac{7}{12}$, (j) $\frac{72}{65}$.

2 (a) $\frac{16}{3}$, (b) $\frac{45}{4}$, (c) 1, (d) $e-1$, (e) e^2+1.

3 (a) (0,0) and (1,1); $\frac{1}{2}$, (b) (−2,4) and (2,4); $\frac{64}{3}$, (c) $(-\frac{3}{4}\pi, \frac{1}{\sqrt{2}})$ and $(\frac{1}{4}\pi, \frac{1}{\sqrt{2}})$; $2\sqrt{2}$,
(d) (0,0) and (2,0); 8/3, (e) (1,4) and (4,1); $7\frac{1}{2}-8\ln 2$.

Exercise 22.6 (page 261)

1 (a) $\frac{1}{5}\pi$, (b) $\frac{1}{2}\pi$, (c) $\frac{1}{7}\pi$, (d) $\frac{7}{12}\pi$.

2 (a) $\frac{1}{6}\pi$, (b) π, (c) $\frac{1}{2}\pi^2$.

3 (a) $\frac{1}{3}\pi$, (b) $\frac{1}{2}\pi$, (c) $\frac{1}{5}\pi$, (d) $\frac{7}{3}\pi$.

Exercise 22.7 (page 262)

1 (a) $\frac{2}{3}$, (b) $\frac{4}{3}$, (c) $\frac{20}{3}$, (d) $\frac{3}{4}$.

2 $\frac{1}{2}$, $\frac{2}{3}$, $2/\pi$.

Exercise 22.8 (page 263)

1 $\frac{1}{2}x+\frac{1}{4}\sin 2x+C$.

2 $\frac{1}{4}\sin 2x+\frac{1}{8}\sin 4x+C$.

3 $-\frac{1}{10}\cos 5x-\frac{1}{2}\cos x+C$.
4 $\frac{1}{8}\sin 4x-\frac{1}{12}\sin 6x+C$.
5 $\frac{\pi}{2}$.
6 $\frac{1}{2}\pi$.
7 $\frac{2}{3}-\frac{1}{4}\sqrt{3}$.
8 $\frac{1}{3}$.
9 0.
10 $\frac{3}{16}\pi$.
11 $\ln(x+2)+C$.
12 $x-2\ln(x+2)+C$.
13 $\frac{1}{2}x^2-2x+4\ln(x+2)+C$.
14 $\ln(2-\cos x)+C$.
15 $\frac{1}{2}\ln(1+e^{2x})+C$.
16 $\frac{1}{3}\ln 2$.
17 $\frac{1}{3}\ln(\frac{8}{5})$.
18 $\ln 2$.
19 $\ln\frac{1}{2}(\sqrt{3}-1)$.
20 $\frac{1}{2}\ln(\frac{8}{5})$.
21 $\arcsin\left(\frac{x}{2}\right)+C$.
22 $\frac{1}{2}\arctan\left(\frac{x-1}{2}\right)+C$.
23 $\frac{1}{2}\arctan 2x+C$.
24 $\frac{1}{2}\arcsin 2x+C$.
25 $\frac{1}{15}\arctan\left(\frac{3x}{5}\right)+C$.
26 $\frac{\pi}{6}$.
27 $\frac{\pi}{12}$.
28 $\frac{\pi}{6}$.
29 $\frac{\pi}{6}$.
30 $\frac{\pi}{20}$.
31 $\arctan(x+2)+C$.
32 $\frac{1}{2}\ln\left(\frac{x+1}{x+3}\right)+C$.
33 $\frac{116}{15}$.
34 $\frac{\pi}{4}$.
35 $\frac{\pi}{2}$.

36 $-x \cos x+\sin x+C$.
37 xe^x-e^x+C.
38 $e^x(x^2-2x+2)+C$.
39 $\frac{1}{3}x^3(\ln x-\frac{1}{3})+C$.
40 $x \arctan x-\frac{1}{2}\ln(1+x^2)+C$.
41 $\frac{4}{3}; \frac{16}{15}\pi$.
42 $\frac{4}{3}, \frac{56}{15}\pi$.
43 $2; \dfrac{\pi^2}{2}$.
44 $\frac{5}{24}\pi a^3$.
45 $\dfrac{\pi}{2}\left(e^4-1\right)$.
46 $\frac{1}{4}$.
47 30.
48 $\dfrac{2}{\pi}$.
49 0.
50 $\frac{1}{2}$.
51 (a) $-2(4-x)^{1/2}+C$, (b) $-\ln(4-x)+C$, (c) $\arcsin\left(\dfrac{x}{2}\right)+C$, (d) $\frac{1}{2}\arctan\left(\dfrac{x}{2}\right)+C$.
52 $\arctan(e^x)+C$.
53 $x \arcsin x+(1-x^2)^{\frac{1}{2}}+C$.
54 $1+\frac{1}{2}\ln 2-\frac{9}{2}\ln(\frac{4}{3})$.
55 $2(\sqrt{2}-1); \pi \ln 2; \frac{4}{3}\pi(2-\sqrt{2})$.
58 $\frac{1}{2}\ln\dfrac{x^2(1+x)}{(1-x)}+C$.
59 $\dfrac{4}{3\pi}$.
60 $\dfrac{2}{\pi}; \dfrac{\pi}{4}$.

Exercise 23.1 (page 272)

1 $y=x^3+x^4-1$.
2 $y=-\cos x+e^x$.
3 $y=\frac{1}{3}x^3-e^{-x}+1$.
4 $y=\frac{1}{2}\sin 2x-\frac{1}{2}$.
5 $y=2e^{5x}$.
6 $y=2e^{3x}$.
7 $y=5e^{-4x}$.
8 $y=e^{(2-x)}$.
9 $\dfrac{1}{y}+\ln x-1=0$.
10 $\cos y=x-1$.
11 $\arctan y=\dfrac{\pi}{4}+\ln \sec x$.

12 $y=\dfrac{1-2\cos^2 x}{1+2\cos^2 x}$.

13 $\dfrac{1}{y}=2-\ln x-x^2$.

14 $y=Ae^x-1-x$.

15 $y=\tan\left(x-\dfrac{\pi}{4}\right)-x$.

16 $y^2=2x^2(\ln x+\frac{1}{2})$.

17 $y^2=\frac{1}{2}(x^2-x^{-2})$.

Exercise 23.2 (page 276)

1 $y=e^{2x}+e^{-2x}$.
2 $y=2\cos 2x$.
3 $y=e^{3x}-e^{-3x}$.
4 $y=2\sin 3x$.
5 $y=\sin x+3\cos x$.
6 $y=2e^{2x}-e^{-x}$.
7 $y=3\sin\frac{1}{2}x$.
8 $y=\frac{3}{2}[e^{1/2(x-1)}+e^{-1/2(x-1)}]$.
9 $y=5[\cos(\frac{2}{5}x)+\frac{1}{2}\sin(\frac{2}{5}x)]$.
10 $y=5e^{2x/5}$.
11 $y=2+\cos 2x$.
12 $y=3e^{2x}+3e^{-2x}-2$.
13 $y=xe^x$.
14 $y^4=1+2x^2$.
15 $\dfrac{1}{y^2}=x^2-2x+2$.
16 $\ln y=\frac{1}{4}x^2-1$.
17 $3y+x^3+3x^4=19$.
18 $y=Ae^{-4x}+B$.
19 $y=2x+B+Ae^{-4x}$.
20 $y(1+Ax^2)=2$.
21 $y=\dfrac{2}{(1-Ae^{\frac{1}{2}x^2})}$.
22 $y(A\cos x-1)=1$.

Exercise 24.1 (page 284)

1 (a) 1.32, (b) $1\frac{1}{3}$; $1\frac{1}{3}$.
2 (a) 1.954, (b) 2.001, (c) 2.
3 (a) 0.524 6, (b) 0.523 6; 3.147 5, 3.141 5.
4 (a) 0.785 0, (b) 0.785 4; $\pi/4$, 3.140, 3.141 593.
5 (a) 81, (b) $81\frac{1}{3}$.

Exercise 24.2 (page 286)

1 (a) $x-\frac{1}{2}x^2+\frac{1}{3}x^3$, (b) $\ln 2+\frac{1}{2}x-\frac{1}{8}x^2+\frac{1}{24}x^3$, (c) $1-2x+3x^2$, (d) $x-\frac{1}{6}x^3+\frac{1}{120}x^5$, (e) $1-2x^2+\frac{2}{3}x^4$, (f) $2x-\dfrac{8x^3}{3}+\dfrac{32x^5}{5}$, (g) $x+x^2+\dfrac{x^3}{2}$.

Exercise 24.3 (page 290)

1 0.21.
2 0.202.
3 2.11.
4 6, 0.14, −2, 6; 2.18.
5 1.4958.

Exercise 24.4 (page 290)

1 0.693 8; 0.693 15; 0.693 15.
2 1.291 0; 1.881.
3 54.5; 54.3.
6 $1+x+\frac{1}{2}x^2-\frac{1}{8}x^4$.
7 $x+x^2+\frac{1}{3}x^3$.
9 0.414.
10 0.167.
11 2.201.
12 1.972.
13 1.21.
14 4.56.
15 0.339 8; $F'(2)=6>1$; $x_{r+1}=(6x_r-2)^{1/3}$.
16 $F(x)=\frac{1}{10}(x^3+1)$ gives $x\approx 0.10$; $F(x)=(10x-1)^{1/3}$ gives $x\approx 3.11$ and $x\approx -3.21$.
17 1.17.
18 $x_{r+1}=\ln(6/x_r)$; 1.43.

Exercise 25.1 (page 297)

1 14 m s^{-1}; 60 m.
2 10 m s^{-1}; $\frac{1}{9}$ m s^{-2}.
3 3.6 km.
4 6.5 s.
5 7.5 minutes.

Exercise 25.2 (page 302)

1 48 m s^{-1}; 64 m, 35 m.
2 11.25 m s^{-1}; 187.5 m.
3 2 m s^{-1}.
4 1.26 m s^{-1}; 0.74 m.
5 3 m s^{-1}; 4 m s^{-1}.
6 0.58 m, 6 m.
7 12.6 m s^{-1}; 2 m.
9 31.25 m s^{-1}, 75 m s^{-1}; 937.5 W, 3 kW.

10 200 N.
12 1500 N; 25.3 kW; 15.5 kW; 9.1 kW.
13 710 m.

Exercise 26.1 (page 308)

1 (a) $(2\mathbf{i}+2\mathbf{j})$ m s^{-1}, (b) $2\sqrt{2}$ m s^{-1}.
2 (a) $(2\mathbf{i}+2\mathbf{j})$ m s^{-1}, $2\sqrt{2}$ m s^{-1}, (b) $(6\mathbf{i}+6\mathbf{j})$ m s^{-1}, $6\sqrt{2}$ m s^{-1}, (c) $(2\mathbf{i}+\mathbf{j})$ m s^{-1}, $\sqrt{5}$ m s^{-1}.
3 (a) $4\mathbf{i}$ N, (b) 0, (c) $12(t\mathbf{i}+\mathbf{j})$ N.
4 (a) $(4\mathbf{i}+\mathbf{j})$ N, (b) $(\frac{1}{2}\mathbf{i}+24\mathbf{j})$ N, (c) $(4.5\mathbf{i}+24\mathbf{j})$ N.
5 (a) $-2t\mathbf{i}+(2-3t^2)\mathbf{j}$, (b) $(2-3t^2)\mathbf{i}+2t\mathbf{j}$.

Exercise 26.2 (page 311)

1 (a) $5\mathbf{i}+2\mathbf{j}$, (b) $\sqrt{178}$, (c) $-5\mathbf{i}-2\mathbf{j}$, (d) 2, 1, (e) 3: −2.
2 (a) 62.5 J, (b) 125 J, (c) 125 J.
3 $(-20\mathbf{i}+36)$ Ns.

Exercise 26.3 (page 311)

1 $2t\mathbf{i}+3t^2\mathbf{j}$; $2\mathbf{i}+6t\mathbf{j}$; $\sqrt{160}$; $8\mathbf{i}+240\mathbf{j}$.
3 $-e^{-t}\mathbf{i}+2t\mathbf{j}$; $e^{-t}\mathbf{i}+2\mathbf{j}$; $2(e^{-t}\mathbf{i}+2\mathbf{j})$.
4 $4\mathbf{i}-4\mathbf{j}+10\mathbf{k}$
5 $\mathbf{v}=t^2\mathbf{i}-4t^3\mathbf{j}$; $\mathbf{s}=\frac{1}{3}t^3\mathbf{i}-t^4\mathbf{j}$.
6 $-\mathbf{i}+k\mathbf{j}+t(\mathbf{i}-2\mathbf{j})$; $k=2$.
7 $\sqrt{(5t^2-16t+13)}$; $t=\frac{8}{5}$.
8 $6\mathbf{i}-2\mathbf{j}$; $12\mathbf{i}$; $-10\mathbf{i}-5\mathbf{j}$.
9 10, 3.
10 $m(t^2\mathbf{i}+t\mathbf{j}+\mathbf{k})$; $\frac{1}{2}m(t^4+t^2+1)$; $m(2t\mathbf{i}+\mathbf{j})$; $mt(2t^2+1)$.
12 $\frac{17}{\sqrt{410}}$.
13 $12(\mathbf{i}+\mathbf{j})$ m s^{-1}, $24(\mathbf{i}+\mathbf{j})$ Ns, 288 J.
14 $5\mathbf{i}+2\mathbf{j}$.
15 $3\mathbf{i}+4\mathbf{j}-3\mathbf{k}$.
16 $4\mathbf{i}+6\mathbf{j}$.
17 $\frac{1}{11}$.
18 100 J.
19 $\frac{1}{2}(7\mathbf{i}-\mathbf{j})$ m s^{-2}; $\frac{5}{2}(7\mathbf{i}-\mathbf{j})$ m s^{-1}, 225 J, 250 W.
20 75 J.
21 $\frac{1}{1+t^2}$.
22 $(8\mathbf{i}+16\mathbf{j})$ Ns, 80 J, 304 W.

Exercise 27.1 (page 319)

1 $3u$.
2 (a) $0.8\mathbf{i}$, $2.6\mathbf{i}$, (b) $-\frac{4}{3}\mathbf{i}$, $\frac{5}{3}\mathbf{i}$, (c) $-\frac{7}{3}\mathbf{i}$, $\frac{2}{3}\mathbf{i}$.
3 $\frac{1}{3}$.

4 $3mu^2$; $\frac{9}{4}mu^2$.
5 $\frac{1}{3}$; 0.
6 $\frac{1}{2}$; $\frac{2}{3}$.
7 $\sqrt{\frac{2}{3}}$.
8 $mu(1+e)$.
9 $1.2\mathbf{i}$, $2.4\mathbf{i}$; 2.8 Ns; 2.52 J.

Exercise 28.1 (page 325)

1 (a) 1.25 s, (b) 7.8 m, (c) 2.5 s, (d) 54 m.
2 14.1 m s^{-1}, 15 m s^{-1}.
3 6.6 m.
4 24.5 m s^{-1}, 26.3 m s^{-1}.
5 2 km.

Exercise 28.2 (page 330)

1 125 m; 26.6° or 63.4°; 12.5 m, 50 m.
2 $\frac{2uv}{g}$.
5 80° or −58°; 58° or −71°; 3:1.
6 $\frac{\pi}{12}$ or $\frac{5\pi}{12}$.

Exercise 29.1 (page 338)

1 (a) 80 N, (b) 2400 N.
2 (a) 10 rad s^{-1}, (b) 20 rad s^{-1}, (c) 5 rad s^{-1}.
3 2630 N.
4 (a) 2.5 N, (b) 0.4 N, (c) 2.53 N.
5 83°, 240 N, 9.1 rad s^{-1}.
6 (a) 875 N, (b) 3500 N.
7 9°.
8 0.53; 4.1 rad s^{-1}.

Exercise 29.2 (page 341)

1 (a) 21 N, 15 N, (b) 18 N, (c) 16.5 N, 19.5 N.
2 5 mg.
3 100°.
4 41°.

Exercise 29.3 (page 341)

1 $4\pi^2 m^2 Ml$; $\arccos\left(\frac{g}{4\pi^2 m^2 l}\right)$.
2 $\frac{1}{9}mg$; $\frac{3}{2}\sqrt{ga}$.
3 0.2 m.
4 $\frac{1}{3}l$.
5 $\frac{1}{3}$.

Exercise 30.1 (page 347)

1 $80\,\text{N m}^{-1}$; $1.6\times10^3\,\text{N m}^{-1}$.
2 160 N, 400 N.
3 1 N.
4 0.5 N.
5 c; $\frac{1}{2}c$; $2c$.
6 0.2 J, 0.6 J, 0.7 J.
7 $m\ddot{x}=mg-\dfrac{4mgx}{a}$, i.e. $\ddot{x}+\dfrac{4g}{a}\left(x-\frac{1}{4}a\right)=0$; s.h.m. about $x=\frac{1}{4}a$; $\pi\sqrt{\dfrac{a}{g}}$.
8 $d\sqrt{\left(\dfrac{\lambda}{a(M+m)}\right)}$; $m\left(g+\dfrac{d\lambda}{a(M+m)}\right)$.

Exercise 31.1 (page 354)

1 (a) 1 N, (b) 10 N, (c) 12 N, $1\,\text{m s}^{-2}$, (d) 12 N, $2\,\text{m s}^{-2}$.
2 (a) $-150\mathbf{i}$, (b) $-180\mathbf{j}$ N, $\frac{2}{3}\mathbf{j}\,\text{m s}^{-2}$, (c) $-(108\mathbf{i}+144\mathbf{j})$ N, $\frac{1}{30}(42\mathbf{i}+56\mathbf{j})\,\text{m s}^{-2}$.
3 (a) $-1050\mathbf{i}$ N, (b) $1050\mathbf{i}$ N.
4 (a) 2 N, (b) 6 N, (c) 14 N, (d) 14 N, (e) 14 N.
5 (a) 100 N, (b) 50 N, (c) 100 N, (d) 82.4 N; $F=0$, 0, 50 N, 24.3 N;
F:$R=0$, 0, 1:2, 24.3:82.4, $\mu\geqslant0.5$.

Exercise 31.2 (page 354)

1 After 1 s; $5.8\,\text{m s}^{-1}$.
3 $\dfrac{u}{g(\sin\alpha+\mu\cos\alpha)}$; $\dfrac{u^2}{2g(\sin\alpha+\mu\cos\alpha)}$; $\dfrac{u}{g\sqrt{(\sin^2\alpha-\mu^2\cos^2\alpha)}}$.

Exercise 32.1 (page 361)

1 (a) 15 N, 36.9°, (b) 15.6 N, 39.8°, (c) 18.3 N, 25.3°, (d) 10.8 N, 46.1°, (e) 27.3 N, 30.3°.
2 (a) 9.8 N, 41.6°, (b) 9.98 N, 56.6°, (c) 4.6 N, 36.1°, (d) 3.8 N, 48.9°, (e) 4.54 N, 97.6°.

Exercise 32.2 (page 362)

1 (a) 8, (b) 5, (c) -1.
2 (a) 7, (b) 6, (c) -12.
3 (a) $10a$, (b) 0, (c) $4a$, (d) $6a$.

Exercise 32.3 (page 364)

1 7.4 N.
2 5.2 N.
3 8.9 N.
4 364 N, 0.3.
5 (a) 880 N, 264 N, (b) $40(1+20x)\cos 70°$.
6 43 N.
7 70 N.
8 12 N, 1 m.

Exercise 33.1 (page 372)

1 3.6**i**.
2 2.1**i**−2.1**j**.
3 −0.2**i**−0.6**j**.
4 **i**−0.8**j**.
5 0.3**i**−0.7**j**+0.7**k**.
6 (a) $\left(\frac{\pi}{2}, \frac{\pi}{8}\right)$, (b) $\left(0, \frac{\pi}{8}\right)$, (c) (2.4, 0), (d) (0, 2.4), (e) $\left(\frac{93}{35}\right)$, $\left(\frac{45}{56}\right)$.
7 (a) (1, 0), (b) (1, 0), (c) (0, 0), (d) (π, 0), (e) $\left(\frac{\pi}{2}, 0\right)$.
8 (a) ($\frac{5}{3}$, 0), (b) ($\frac{9}{7}$, 0).
9 (a) (0, $\frac{4}{3}$), (b) (0, $\frac{5}{3}$).

Exercise 34.1 (page 382)

1 (a) $\frac{9}{10}$, (b) $\frac{3}{5}$, (c) $\frac{3}{7}$.
2 (a) $\frac{2}{10}$, (b) $\frac{1}{2}$, (c) $\frac{2}{7}$.
3 (a) $\frac{7}{10}$, (b) $\frac{7}{10}$, (c) $\frac{4}{10}$.
4 If $n\{\mathscr{E}\}=k$, $n\{A\}=ka$, etc. Draw Venn diagram.
5 (a) 0.1, (b) 0.45, (c) $\frac{1}{3}$.
6 (a) 3/64, (b) 12/175, (c) 12/67, (d) 12/13.
7 (a) 54/175, (b) 108/175.
8 (a) 0.2048, (b) 0.4872, (c) 0.2778.
9 (a) 7/10, (b) 7/8, (c) 14/15.
10 (a) 4/5, (b) 2/3.
11 $\frac{1}{36}$, $\frac{1}{6}$, $\frac{5}{12}$; 0, $\frac{1}{6}$, $\frac{1}{2}$.
12 $\frac{1}{4}$, $\frac{1}{10}$, $\frac{9}{10}$; 0, $\frac{1}{10}$, $\frac{9}{10}$.
13 0.15, 0.35, 0.075
14 $\frac{1}{36}$, $\frac{1}{210}$, $\frac{88}{105}$
15 0.72, 0.28, 0.532, 0.6192.

Exercise 34.2 (page 384)

1 (a) 0.010 24, (b) 0.0768, (c) 0.2304, (d) 0.3456, (e) 0.2592, (f) 0.077 76.
2 (a) 0.2048, (b) 0.4096, (c) 0.942 08.
3 (a) 0.0250, (b) 0.0288, (c) 0.9712.
4 (a) 6×10^{-3}, (b) 10^{-4}, (c) 4×10^{-2}, (d) 1.6×10^{-3}, (e) 0.046.
5 (a) 0.028, (b) 5.9×10^{-6}, (c) 0.23, (d) 1.4×10^{-3}.
6 (a) 0.6, (b) 0.24 , (c) 0.096, (d) 0.936.
7 (a) 0.3, (b) 0.21, (c) 0.147.
8 7.
9 (a) 3/16, (b) 27/256, (c) $(\frac{1}{4})^5$.
10 6/11.
11 5/14.

Exercise 35.1 (page 391)

1 (a) 3.2, 3, 3, (b) 3, 2, 0, (c) $4\frac{2}{3}$, $4\frac{1}{2}$, 9, (d) 2.5, 1.5, 0, (e) 0, 0, no mode.

2 1.8, (a) 11.8, (b) 7.2, (c) 1.9.
3 12.
4 6.
5 4.
6 5.18.
7 5.26.
8 184.49.

Exercise 35.2 (page 395)
1 (a) 3, $\sqrt{2}$, (b) 5, $2\sqrt{2}$, (c) 14, $2\sqrt{2}$, (d) 30, $10\sqrt{2}$, (e) 13.3, $\frac{1}{10}\sqrt{2}$.
2 (a) 3.55, 1.36, (b) 7.16, 2.716.

Exercise 35.3 (page 397)
1 11 minutes, 7.55 minutes.
2 12.4 minutes, 8.69 minutes.
3 9.648 grams, 3.13 grams.
4 79.7 cm, 4.82 cm.

Exercise 35.4 (page 400)
1 (a) 9.5 minutes, (b) 16 minutes, 4.5 minutes, (c) 11.5 minutes.
2 (a) 10 minutes, (b) 16.5 minutes, 4.5 minutes, (c) 6 minutes, (d) 24 minutes.

Index

Abelian group 93
Acceleration 295, 336
Amplitude 175
Angle between two lines 105
  between two planes 217
Angular speed 336
Approximations 49
Area of sector 147
Argand diagram 175
Argument 172
Arrangements 85
Associative 92
Asymptote 115, 126
Auxiliary angle 162

Binomial distribution 376, 383
  expansion 48
  theorem 38

Cardioid 147
Centre of gravity 366, 368
Centre of mass 366, 368, 369
Centroid 367, 368
Circle, centre 106
  parametric form 131
  radius 106
  tangent 106, 131
Closed set 91
Coefficient of restitution 318
Commutative 91
Complex numbers 173
  conjugates 173
  products of 176
  quotients of 176
Convergence 45, 47
Cosine formula 158, 163
Cumulative frequency curve 398

Dependent events 377
De Moivre's theorem 177
Derivatives 222, 223, 225, 227, 228
Determinants 184, 186, 191
Differential equations
  boundary conditions 274, 276
  initial conditions 274, 275, 276
  second-order 273
  separable variables 270
Dimensions 347
Dispersion 393
Displacement 295, 300, 307
Distance between two points 101

Elasticity, modulus of 344
Element
  identity 92
  inverse 92
Ellipse
  directrix 122
  focus 122
  normal to 124, 137
  parametric form 137
  symmetry of 123
  tangent to 123, 124, 137
Energy, kinetic 310
Equilibrium 362

Factors 25
Force
  components of 309, 358, 360
  moment about an axis 359, 361
  resolved parts 358
Frequency 389
Friction, laws of 351
Function
  composite 7, 225
  definition 3
  domain of a 3
  even 8, 9
  odd 8, 9
  periodic 9
  quadratic 16
  trigonometric 6, 152

Geometric
  distribution 376, 384
Geometric (*contd*)
  mean 46, 389
  series 45
Group
  Abelian 93
  cyclic 94, 97
  definition of a 93
  generators 94
  isomorphic 94
  Klein 95, 97
  order of a 93
  permutation 95
  symmetric 95

Harmonic motion, simple 346
Hooke's law 345
Hyperbola
  asymptotes 126
  directrix 125
  foci 125
  normal to a 126
  rectangular 114, 134
  symmetry 114
  tangents to a 126

Identities 57, 166
Impacts, direct 316, 326
Impulse 316
Increments, small 242
Indices 26
Induction 37
Inequalities 68, 70
Inflexion, points of 236, 238
Integrals, table of standard
  forms 246
Integration
  by parts 252
  by substitution 251
Inverse functions 4, 5
Iterative methods, convergence
  of 289, 291

Kinetic energy, loss in impacts 319

Limiting velocity 299
Lines, straight
  angle between two 105
  equation of 103, 104, 144, 207, 211
Loci 177
Logarithms
  change of base 28
  definition 27
  natural 28

Maclaurin's theorem 280, 285
Magnitude of a vector 199
Matrix
  adjoint 192
  inverse 187, 193
  transpose 186
Maximum 236, 238, 241
Mean
  arithmetic 46, 388
  geometric 46, 389
Mean value 247, 261
Median 388, 389, 399
Midpoint 101, 205
Minimum 236, 238, 241
Mode 388, 389
Modulus of elasticity 345
Momentum 310, 316
Mutually exclusive events 377

Newton–Raphson formula 281, 286
Newton's experimental law 316, 318

Parabola
  axis of symmetry 111
  directrix 111
  focus 111
  normal 113, 133
  tangent 112, 132
Parameters, differentiating 132, 135, 139, 230
Partial fractions 58
Plane, equation of 197, 212, 213
Polar equations of curves 144
Power 301, 310
Principal values 6
Products, to differentiate 224
Progression 44
Projectiles
  on inclined plane 322, 323
  range 322, 323, 326
  flight 323

Quartiles 399

Radian 151, 156
Range
  of a distribution 393
  under a function 3
  of a projectile 322, 323, 326
Rectangular hyperbola
  asymptotes 115
  axes 115
  normal 116, 135
  parametric form 134
  symmetry of 114
  tangent to a 116, 135
Remainder 24
Restitution, coefficient of 318
Roots of an equation 18

Scalar products 196, 210, 309
Section theorem 196, 203
Sector, area of a 147
Selections 86
Separable variables 270
Sequence 44
Series
  arithmetic 44
Series (*contd*)
  binomial 48
  convergent 45, 47
  exponential 51
  geometric 45
  logarithmic 50
  trigonometric 51
Simpson's rule 280, 282
Sine formula 157
Small increments 242
Spiral 146
Speed 295
Spread, measures of 393
Spring constant 344
Standard deviation 393
Stationary points 236
Straight line, equation of 103, 104, 144, 207, 211
Symmetry
  axis of 111
  use of, in solving problems 78, 79, 371

Tangents, equation of 106, 112, 116, 123, 124, 126, 131, 132, 135, 137
Taylor's theorem 280
Trapezium rule 280, 282
Tree diagrams 381
Turning points 236, 243

Variance 393
Vectors
  components 198
  magnitude 199
Velocity
  definition 295, 307
  relative 308
Venn diagrams 173, 379

Work 310, 344